To the student:

Math — you'll need it.

The authors

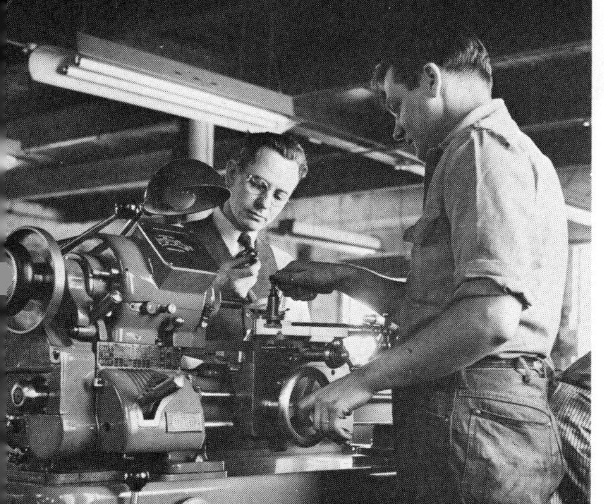

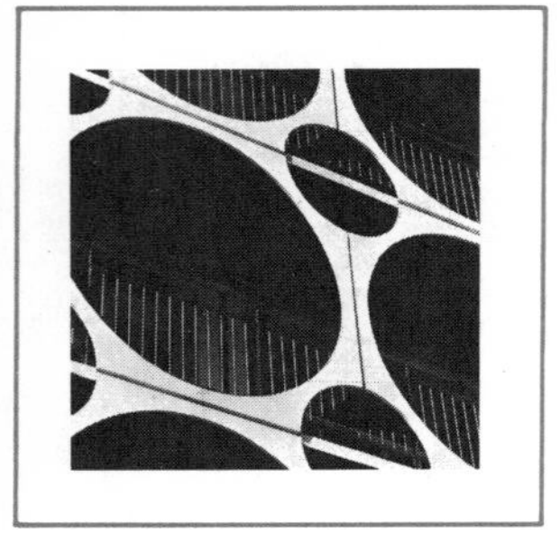

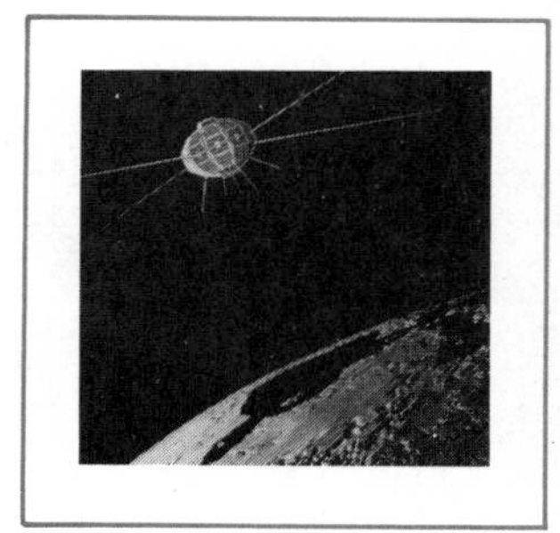

CHINESE NUMERALS

一 二 三 四 五 六 七 八 九 十

BABYLONIAN NUMERALS

ABACUS: Add 232 to 176

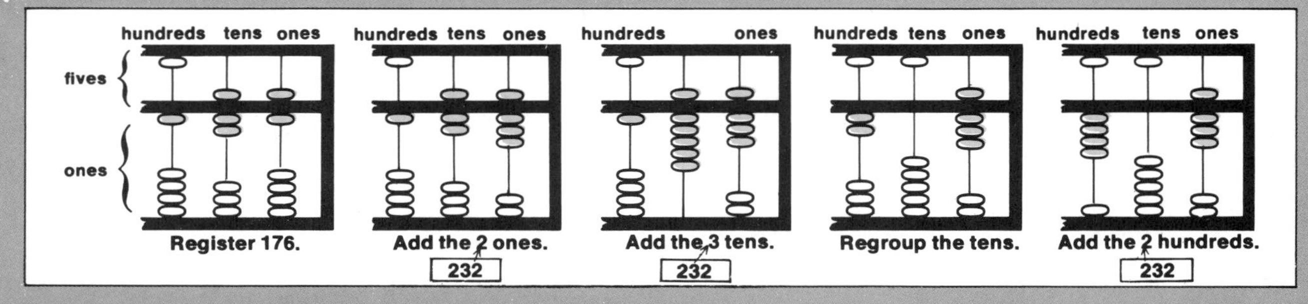

hundreds tens ones
fives
ones
Register 176.
Add the 2 ones.
232
Add the 3 tens.
232
Regroup the tens.
Add the 2 hundreds.
232

MEDIEVAL COUNTING TABLE: Add 232 to 176

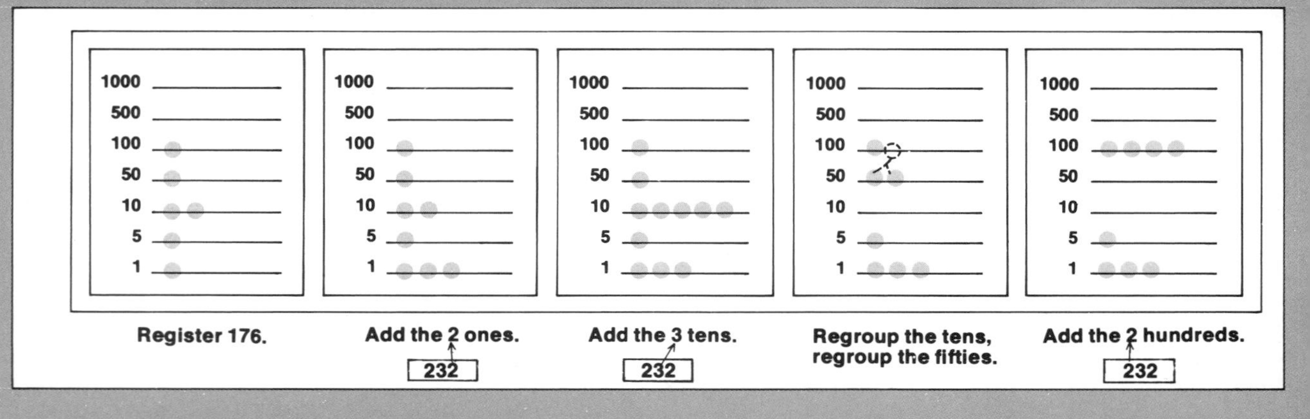

1000
500
100
50
10
5
1
Register 176.
Add the 2 ones.
232
Add the 3 tens.
232
Regroup the tens, regroup the fifties.
Add the 2 hundreds.
232

Unit 1
The Whole Numbers

The numbers we use casually every day had their beginning with ancient peoples. From simple counting to the invention of symbols representing numbers was a development that took a very long time. It ranks as one of the great advances in history.

Many experiments were tried with number systems through the ages. One was the creation of a different digit for each of the numbers from one to sixty. This system made a good memory necessary!

Two inventions that made computations possible with larger numbers were the *abacus* and the *counting table*. (Each set of illustrations shows how two hundred thirty-two is added to one hundred seventy-six. Try to follow them through.)

But then some genius simplified it all by using the digit 0. After that, any number—no matter how large—could be expressed with only the digits 1, 2, 3, 4, 5, 6, 7, 8, 9, and 0. With just the set of whole numbers, all computations could be made on paper without an abacus or counting table.

Later, we will see how new problems were solved by the invention of new number systems.

$$\begin{array}{r} 176 \\ 232 \\ \hline 408 \end{array}$$

The set of whole numbers is

$W = \{0, 1, 2, 3, \ldots\}$

1(a) 1118 (e) 132 379
(c) 17 250 (g) 954 901

3(d) 42 120 (j) 676
(f) 44 190 (k) 34 568
(h) 482 020 (l) 286 578
(i) 75 112

4(f) 703 (k) 38
(i) 3214 (l) 146
(j) 57

Get-Set Exercise with Whole Numbers

1. Add to find the sum.

(*a*)	(*c*)	(*e*)	(*g*)
368	3851	52 684	173 623
457	4073	37 512	354 891
293	9326	42 183	426 387

(*b*)	(*d*)	(*f*)	(*h*)
28	356	13 583	19
94	4	9 429	738
76	1237	85	5 619
154	429	617	12 883
29	8732	3 029	4 598

2. Subtract to find the difference. Check by addition.

(*a*)	(*c*)	(*e*)	(*g*)
65	831	9326	932
42	516	7213	565

(*b*)	(*d*)	(*f*)	(*h*)
4297	57 162	298	1000
3638	29 084	179	832

3. Multiply to find the product.

(*a*)	(*d*)	(*g*)	(*j*)
56	3510	568	26
8	12	70	26

(*b*)	(*e*)	(*h*)	(*k*)
396	380	4382	596
4	50	110	58

(*c*)	(*f*)	(*i*)	(*l*)
1285	1473	1832	3294
7	30	41	87

4. Divide to find the quotient.

(*a*) 4)84	(*d*) 6)1020	(*g*) 8)6120	(*j*) 23)1311
(*b*) 7)427	(*e*) 10)5820	(*h*) 9)3456	(*k*) 62)2356
(*c*) 5)385	(*f*) 12)8436	(*i*) 15)48 210	(*l*) 47)6862

5. List the numbers from smallest to largest and find their sum.

(*a*) 42, 638, 57, 29, 598, 5820, 1837

(*b*) 236, 5918, 761, 8291, 845, 174

(*c*) 1984, 1356, 3850, 964, 89, 17 321

(*d*) 83 692, 118 496, 9315, 54 829, 236 598

6. How much greater is the larger number?

(*a*) 97, 38 (*c*) 5291, 384 (*e*) 968, 1835

(*b*) 139, 278 (*d*) 1100, 10 000 (*f*) 99 000, 1 000 000

7. Find the product of each pair of numbers.

(*a*) 365, 12 (*e*) 6397, 85 (*i*) 5031, 63

(*b*) 123, 18 (*f*) 425, 203 (*j*) 398, 1200

(*c*) 42, 596 (*g*) 1297, 32 (*k*) 1057, 69

(*d*) 300, 45 (*h*) 29, 581 (*l*) 125, 4392

8. What is the remainder when the larger number is divided by the smaller number?

(*a*) 8, 86 (*e*) 105, 12 (*i*) 4792, 46

(*b*) 47, 7 (*f*) 483, 20 (*j*) 15 931, 82

(*c*) 5, 121 (*g*) 80, 962 (*k*) 68, 35 629

(*d*) 309, 6 (*h*) 25, 375 (*l*) 519, 105

9. In each case, multiply the given numbers.

(*a*) 4, 5, 6 (*d*) 15, 20, 25 (*g*) 12, 16, 5

(*b*) 10, 3, 8 (*e*) 100, 26, 8 (*h*) 2, 3, 4, 5, 6

(*c*) 9, 32, 5 (*f*) 43, 25, 40 (*i*) 7, 8, 9, 10

10. Evaluate.

(*a*) 52^2 (*b*) 120^2 (*c*) 8^3 (*d*) 2^4

5(a) 9021 **(c)** 25 564

7(a) 4380 **(g)** 41 504
(b) 2214 **(h)** 16 849
(c) 25 032 **(i)** 316 953
(d) 13 500 **(j)** 477 600
(e) 543 745 **(k)** 72 933
(f) 86 275 **(l)** 549 000

8(a) 6 **(e)** 9 **(i)** 8
(b) 5 **(f)** 3 **(j)** 23
(c) 1 **(g)** 2 **(k)** 65
(d) 3 **(h)** 0 **(l)** 99

9(a) 120 **(g)** 960
(c) 1440 **(h)** 720
(e) 20 800 **(i)** 5040

10(a) 2704 **(c)** 512

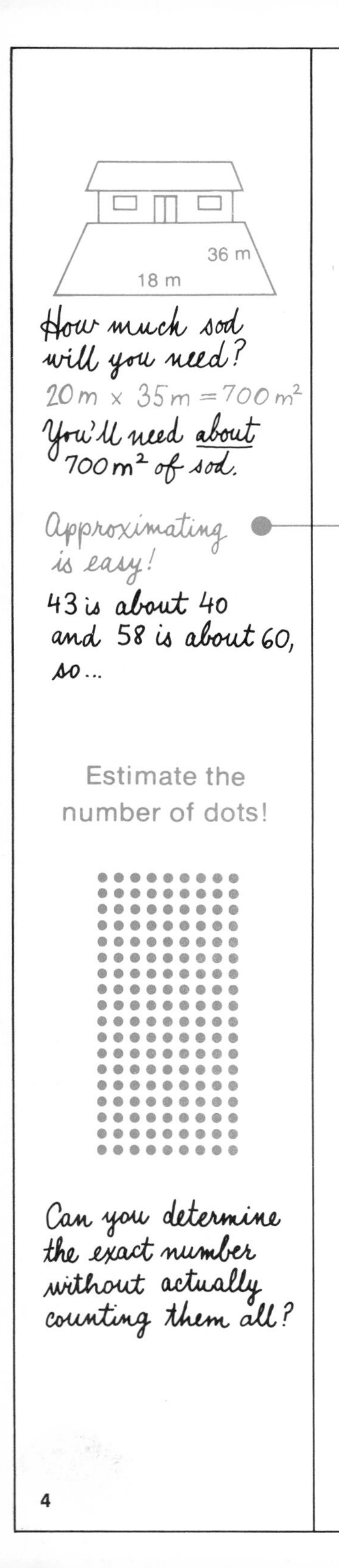

36 m
18 m
How much sod will you need?
20 m × 35 m = 700 m²
You'll need about 700 m² of sod.
Approximating is easy!
43 is about 40 and 58 is about 60, so...
Estimate the number of dots!
Can you determine the exact number without actually counting them all?

1.1 Approximations in *W*

"I'll have at least \$50 saved by the end of the summer."

"32 students. About $2\frac{1}{2}$ hot dogs each. Let's see, 30×3 . . . I'll need about 90 hot dogs for the party."

You may not be entirely accurate when you make approximations, but you certainly save time! In mathematics, approximations are quite useful in checking the reasonableness of answers.

1. Estimate the following products.

   (*a*) 43×58 (*b*) 89×29 (*c*) 119×41

2. Estimate the following quotients.

   (*a*) $808 \div 21$ (*b*) $468 \div 9$ (*c*) $7.98 \div 4.06$

Exercise 1.1

Discussion

1. Which is the best approximation?

   (*a*) 11×83
   - (*i*) 10×80
   - (*ii*) 10×90
   - (*iii*) 10×85
   - (*iv*) 15×90

   (*b*) $59 \div 19$
   - (*i*) $60 \div 15$
   - (*ii*) $50 \div 20$
   - (*iii*) $60 \div 20$
   - (*iv*) $60 \div 10$

   (*c*) 61×29
   - (*i*) 60×25
   - (*ii*) 50×30
   - (*iii*) 60×20
   - (*iv*) 60×30

   (*d*) $138 \div 14$
   - (*i*) $150 \div 10$
   - (*ii*) $100 \div 15$
   - (*iii*) $140 \div 14$
   - (*iv*) $140 \div 10$

2. Which answer is the best approximation?

   (*a*) 693×28
   - (*i*) 18 000
   - (*ii*) 21 000
   - (*iii*) 2100
   - (*iv*) 14 000

   (*b*) $624 \div 19$
   - (*i*) 30
   - (*ii*) 300
   - (*iii*) 40
   - (*iv*) 35

   (*c*) 43×898
   - (*i*) 32 000
   - (*ii*) 45 000
   - (*iii*) 36 000
   - (*iv*) 34 000

   (*d*) $8976 \div 289$
   - (*i*) 40
   - (*ii*) 36
   - (*iii*) 3
   - (*iv*) 30

3. Are these situations reasonable or not?
   (*a*) a house mortgage payment of \$2000/month
   (*b*) a 400 h work week
   (*c*) municipal taxes of \$300.28
   (*d*) a highway speed limit of 100 km/h
   (*e*) a town speed limit of 3 km/h
   (*f*) an engine capacity of 6 ℓ
   (*g*) interest on a savings account of 77.5%
   (*h*) an hourly wage of \$0.25

Written Solutions

4. Find approximate products.

(*a*) 43 × 81	(*c*) 309 × 11	(*e*) 2197 × 52
(*b*) 198 × 19	(*d*) 1205 × 41	(*f*) 1510 × 98

5. Find an approximation to each quotient.

(*a*) 62 ÷ 11	(*c*) 1806 ÷ 9	(*e*) 2958 ÷ 61
(*b*) 193 ÷ 21	(*d*) 518 ÷ 27	(*f*) 2012 ÷ 49

1.2 Simplifying Number Phrases

1. Consider the following ways of simplifying 14 − 6 × 2.

(*a*)
$$\begin{aligned} & 14 - 6 \times 2 \\ &= 8 \times 2 \\ &= 16 \end{aligned}$$

(*b*)
$$\begin{aligned} & 14 - 6 \times 2 \\ &= 14 - 12 \\ &= 2 \end{aligned}$$

One expression with 2 values would cause confusion. The confusion arises because the expressions were evaluated in different ways. Therefore, there is an *order of operations.*

Brackets
"Of"
Division, Multiplication } in order, as you come to them
Addition, Subtraction } in order, as you come to them

2. The first letter of each word in the list can be put together to make a *key word.* What is the key word?

Now apply the key word to parts (*a*) and (*b*) in Question 1 above and to the examples following.

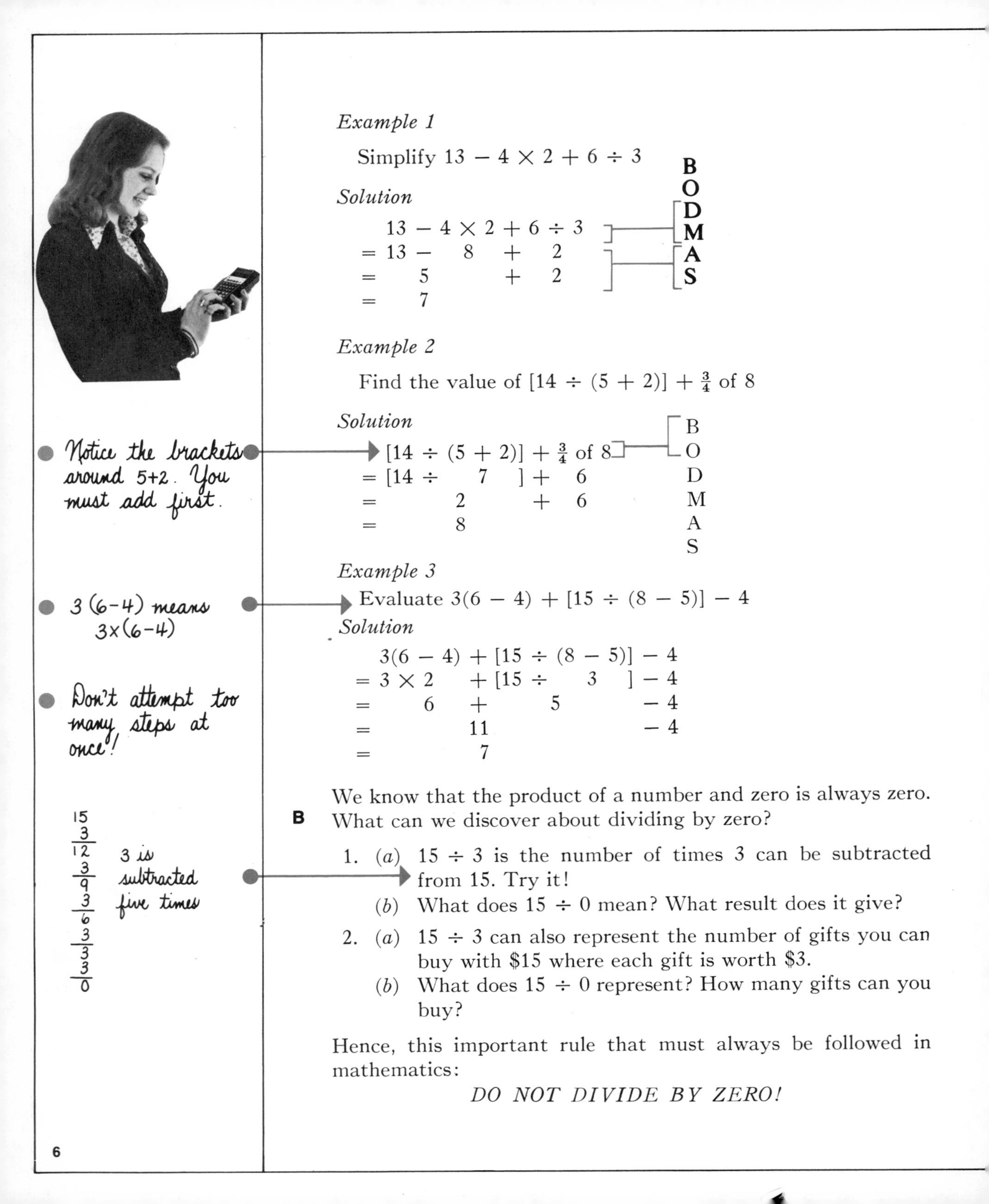

Example 1

Simplify $13 - 4 \times 2 + 6 \div 3$

Solution

$$\begin{aligned} & 13 - 4 \times 2 + 6 \div 3 \\ = {} & 13 - 8 + 2 \\ = {} & 5 + 2 \\ = {} & 7 \end{aligned}$$

B
O
D
M
A
S

Example 2

Find the value of $[14 \div (5 + 2)] + \frac{3}{4}$ of 8

Solution

Notice the brackets around 5+2. You must add first.

$$\begin{aligned} & [14 \div (5 + 2)] + \tfrac{3}{4} \text{ of } 8 \\ = {} & [14 \div 7] + 6 \\ = {} & 2 + 6 \\ = {} & 8 \end{aligned}$$

B
O
D
M
A
S

Example 3

3 (6−4) means 3×(6−4)

Evaluate $3(6 - 4) + [15 \div (8 - 5)] - 4$

Solution

$$\begin{aligned} & 3(6 - 4) + [15 \div (8 - 5)] - 4 \\ = {} & 3 \times 2 + [15 \div 3] - 4 \\ = {} & 6 + 5 - 4 \\ = {} & 11 - 4 \\ = {} & 7 \end{aligned}$$

Don't attempt too many steps at once!

B We know that the product of a number and zero is always zero. What can we discover about dividing by zero?

$$\begin{array}{r} 15 \\ \underline{3} \\ 12 \\ \underline{3} \\ 9 \\ \underline{3} \\ 6 \\ \underline{3} \\ 3 \\ \underline{3} \\ 0 \end{array}$$

3 is subtracted five times

1. (*a*) $15 \div 3$ is the number of times 3 can be subtracted from 15. Try it!
   (*b*) What does $15 \div 0$ mean? What result does it give?
2. (*a*) $15 \div 3$ can also represent the number of gifts you can buy with \$15 where each gift is worth \$3.
   (*b*) What does $15 \div 0$ represent? How many gifts can you buy?

Hence, this important rule that must always be followed in mathematics:

DO NOT DIVIDE BY ZERO!

Exercise 1.2

Discussion

1. Which operation should be performed first? State the resulting value of the expression.

   (*a*) $26 - 10 \times 2$
   (*b*) $14 + 6 \div 3$
   (*c*) $15 - 8 + 4$
   (*d*) $16 \div 8 \times 2$

2. State the order in which you would simplify each of the following expressions.

   (*a*) $5 + 8 \div 2 - 3$
   (*b*) $4 - (16 - 5) \div 11$
   (*c*) $3 \times (6 - 2) + 4 - 5$
   (*d*) $\frac{3}{4}$ of $4 \times 5 \div (6 - 3)$

3. What does $5(8 + 3)$ mean? State the value.

4. The following represent the steps in simplifying an expression. Put them in order.

   (*a*) $[18 - 12] \times 2$
   (*b*) 6×2
   (*c*) $[18 - (4 + 8)] \times 2$
   (*d*) 12

Written Solutions

5. Perform the operations indicated.

   (*a*) $2 \times 4 \times 3$
   (*b*) $6 - 2 \times 1$
   (*c*) $15 - 12 \div 3$
   (*d*) $7 + 8 \times 2$
   (*e*) $8 - 4 \div 2$
   (*f*) $(8 - 4) \div 2$
   (*g*) $16 \times (7 - 4)$
   (*h*) $12 \div (1 + 5)$

6. Simplify.

   (*a*) $29 - 16 \div 4 + 8$
   (*b*) $13 \times 2 - 12 \div 6$
   (*c*) $16 \div 4 - 28 \div 7$
   (*d*) $\frac{3}{8}$ of $(29 - 5)$
   (*e*) $5 \times 6 \div (12 - 10)$
   (*f*) $32 \div 4 \times 2 - 16 \div 8$
   (*g*) $11 - \frac{4}{5}$ of $10 + 6$
   (*h*) $16 \times 3 \div (10 + 2)$

7. Find the value of each of the following.

   (*a*) $48 \div 16 \times 3 - 1$
   (*b*) $11 + 2 \times 2 - 5$
   (*c*) $36 \div (15 + 3 - 9)$
   (*d*) $16 \div (13 - 5) + 10$
   (*e*) $4 \times 16 \div 2 - 10 + 4$
   (*f*) $(29 - 8 \div 4) \div (\frac{3}{4}$ of $12)$

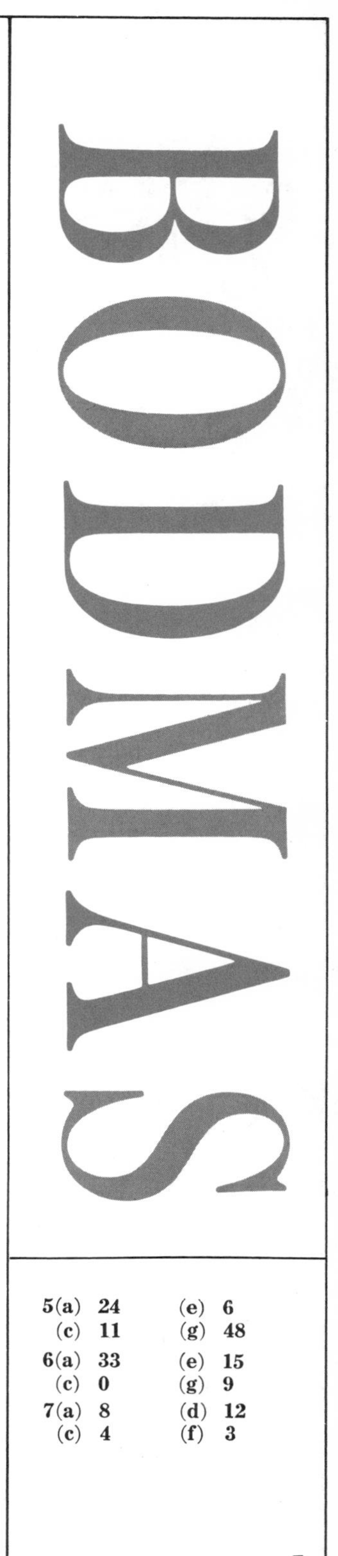

5(a) 24 **(c)** 11 **(e)** 6 **(g)** 48
6(a) 33 **(c)** 0 **(e)** 15 **(g)** 9
7(a) 8 **(c)** 4 **(d)** 12 **(f)** 3

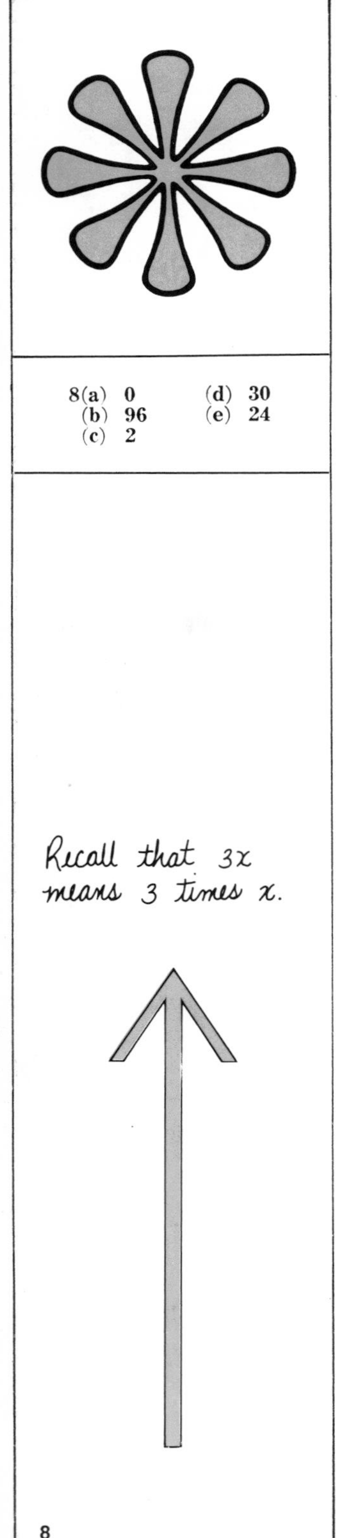

8(a) 0 (b) 96 (c) 2 (d) 30 (e) 24

8. Evaluate.
   (*a*) $17 + 34 \div 2 - (4 \times 7 + 6)$
   (*b*) $[15 \times 5 - 32 \div 8] + [6 \times 7 - (4 \times 3 + 5)]$
   (*c*) $\dfrac{4 \times 12 \div (3 \times 2 - 4)}{9 + (24 \div 8)}$
   (*d*) $360 \div [(16 - 12) \times 5] + (18 \div 3) \times 2$
   (*e*) $[27 - 3 \times 9 + 6(4 - 2)] \div 3 + 20$

9. Why is it not possible to evaluate the expression $5[6 + 18 \div 2 - 11] \div [14 - 21 \times 2 \div 3]$?

1.3 Evaluation by Substitution

A

1. So far, we have considered only numerical expressions. What name do we give to expressions like these?

   $3x, \quad 5a - 6, \quad 10m^2n, \quad 17s - 4t, \quad 5x^2 + 3y^4$

2. Name the *variables* in each expression. What do variables stand for?

B

Recall that 3x means 3 times x.

In an *algebraic expression*, each variable is a placeholder for some unspecified number of a set. In the expression $3x + 2$, if the variable represents one whole number from W, then W is called the replacement set, or *domain* of the variable.

1. What is the value of the algebraic expression $3x + 2$ when x is assigned a value of 4? of 2? of 11?

2. Find the value of each of the following when $x = 3$.

(*a*) $7x$	(*d*) $x \div 3$	(*g*) $16x + 1$
(*b*) $2x - 1$	(*e*) $2x + 5$	(*h*) $7(x + 1)$
(*c*) $3x + 5$	(*f*) $4x - 9$	(*i*) $5(x - 3)$

C

The process of finding the value of an algebraic expression when each variable is given a specific value is called *evaluation*. This involves substituting for each variable and simplifying the resulting expression using BODMAS. Study the following examples.

Example 1

Find the value of $5a + 3b$ when $a = 2$, $b = 3$.

Solution

$$\begin{aligned} & 5a + 3b \\ &= 5(a) + 3(b) \\ &= 5(2) + 3(3) \end{aligned} \quad \Big\} \text{Substitution}$$

$$\begin{aligned} &= 10 + 9 \\ &= 19 \end{aligned} \quad \Big\} \text{Simplification}$$

$a = 2$
$b = 3$

Example 2

If $k = 2$, $m = 1$, and $n = 4$, find the value of $13mn + 5k$.

Solution

$$\begin{aligned} & 13mn + 5k \\ &= 13(m)(n) + 5(k) \\ &= 13(1)(4) + 5(2) \\ &= 52 + 10 \\ &= 62 \end{aligned}$$

$m = 1$
$n = 4$
$k = 2$

Steps in Evaluation
1. Copy the expression
2. Rewrite with brackets
3. Substitute
4. Evaluate, using BODMAS

Note that the *same* value is always substituted for a variable wherever the variable appears in the expression.

Example 3

Evaluate $\dfrac{3xy - 2z}{2y}$ if $x = 4$, $y = 2$, and $z = 10$.

Solution

$$\begin{aligned} & \frac{3xy - 2z}{2y} \\ &= \frac{3(x)(y) - 2(z)}{2(y)} \\ &= \frac{3(4)(2) - 2(10)}{2(2)} \\ &= \frac{24 - 20}{4} \\ &= \frac{4}{4} \\ &= 1 \end{aligned}$$

$x = 4$
$y = 2$
$z = 10$

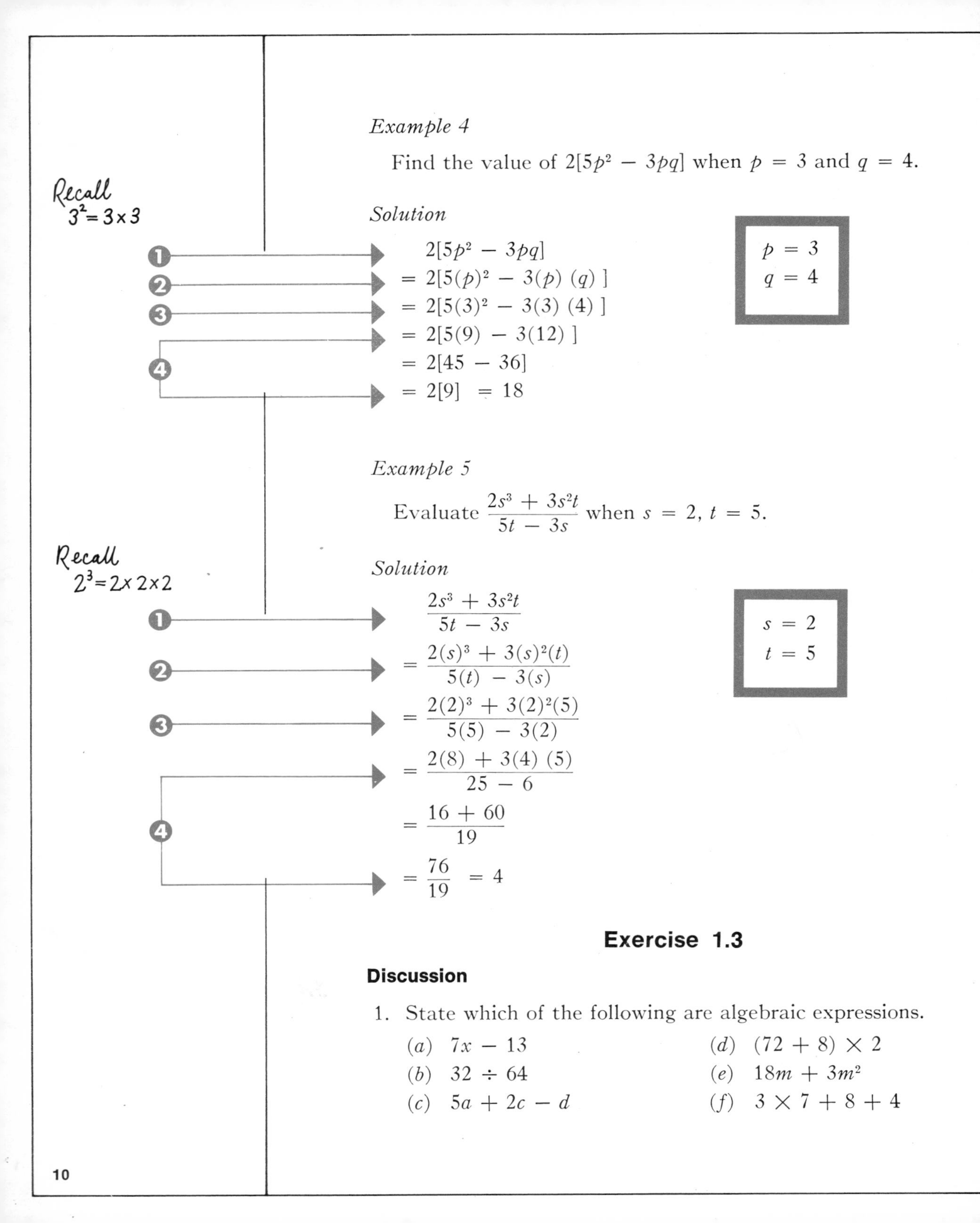

Example 4

Find the value of $2[5p^2 - 3pq]$ when $p = 3$ and $q = 4$.

Recall
$3^2 = 3 \times 3$

Solution

$p = 3$
$q = 4$

1. $2[5p^2 - 3pq]$
2. $= 2[5(p)^2 - 3(p)\,(q)\,]$
3. $= 2[5(3)^2 - 3(3)\,(4)\,]$
4. $= 2[5(9) - 3(12)\,]$
   $= 2[45 - 36]$
   $= 2[9] = 18$

Example 5

Evaluate $\dfrac{2s^3 + 3s^2t}{5t - 3s}$ when $s = 2$, $t = 5$.

Recall
$2^3 = 2 \times 2 \times 2$

Solution

$s = 2$
$t = 5$

1. $\dfrac{2s^3 + 3s^2t}{5t - 3s}$
2. $= \dfrac{2(s)^3 + 3(s)^2(t)}{5(t) - 3(s)}$
3. $= \dfrac{2(2)^3 + 3(2)^2(5)}{5(5) - 3(2)}$
4. $= \dfrac{2(8) + 3(4)\,(5)}{25 - 6}$
   $= \dfrac{16 + 60}{19}$
   $= \dfrac{76}{19} = 4$

Exercise 1.3

Discussion

1. State which of the following are algebraic expressions.
   (*a*) $7x - 13$
   (*b*) $32 \div 64$
   (*c*) $5a + 2c - d$
   (*d*) $(72 + 8) \times 2$
   (*e*) $18m + 3m^2$
   (*f*) $3 \times 7 + 8 + 4$

2. The terms "variable" and "domain" need not apply only to algebraic expressions. In the sentence "He plays soccer for Central Tech," the variable is "he" and its domain is "all the boys who go to Central Tech." In each of the following sentences, state the variable and its domain.

   (*a*) She is the tallest girl in her drafting class.
   (*b*) He is the oldest boy in form 9C.
   (*c*) It was judged the best painting in the art show.
   (*d*) Of all the students who took the electronics course, she obtained the highest mark.
   (*e*) He's the most talkative person I know!
   (*f*) It was one of the best dances ever held at Fairview.

3. Determine which of the following are true when $a = 2$, and $b = 3$.

   (*a*) $a + b = 5$
   (*b*) $2a + b = 17$
   (*c*) $5a - b = 7$
   (*d*) $2(a + b) = 12$
   (*e*) $12a - 3b = 11$
   (*f*) $6a - 4b = 0$

4. Evaluate when $x = 1$ and $y = 2$.

   (*a*) $x + y$
   (*b*) $6x + 2y$
   (*c*) $7xy$
   (*d*) $4x + 7y$
   (*e*) $5x - 2y$
   (*f*) $48xy$
   (*g*) $2(x + y)$
   (*h*) $7y - 12x$
   (*i*) $x(y + 4)$

5. State the value of each of the following.

   (*a*) $2xy$ when $x = 3, y = 4$
   (*b*) $a^2 + b^2 + c^2$ when $a = 2, b = 1, c = 3$
   (*c*) $8x - 4y$ when $x = 1, y = 2$
   (*d*) $5s - 6t$ when $s = 6, t = 5$
   (*e*) $42cd$ when $c = 18, d = 0$

Written Solutions

6. Evaluate if $a = 2, b = 3$.

   (*a*) $a + b$
   (*b*) $b - a$
   (*c*) ab
   (*d*) $3a \div b$
   (*e*) $4a$
   (*f*) $3ab$
   (*g*) $a + 4b$
   (*h*) $2a + 3b$
   (*i*) $3a - 2b$

6(a) 5
(c) 6
(e) 8
(g) 14
(i) 0

7. Evaluate if $a = 4$, $b = 5$.

(a) a^2 (d) ab^2 (g) $a^2 + b^2$
(b) $3a^2$ (e) a^2b (h) $8a^2 - 2b^2$
(c) $5a^2$ (f) a^2b^2 (i) $\frac{2a + 7b + 1}{11}$

8. Find the value of each of the following when $x = 2$, $y = 5$.

(a) $13x - 2y$ (c) y^3 (e) $2y^2$
(b) $2x + y^2$ (d) $5y^2 - 10x^2$ (f) $(2y)^2$

9. Evaluate the following algebraic expressions if $a = 2$, $b = 3$, $c = 1$, $d = 0$.

(a) $3(a + 2b - c)$ (d) $5a(16b - 4c)$
(b) $5a - 2(b + c)$ (e) $6(2ac - b) + 4$
(c) $6(2b - 3a)$ (f) $3d(5abc - 10) \div b$

10. Evaluate if $p = 0$, $q = 2$, $r = 1$, $s = 4$.

(a) $3s^2 \div (4r)$ (d) $16p + 7q^2r$
(b) $5(qr)^2$ (e) $rq^4 - 2q^2 + 10$
(c) $5q^2r^2$ (f) $s^2 - q^3 - 8r + p$

11. Evaluate $2a^2 - 3b + c^3$ when

(a) $a = 4$, $b = 2$, $c = 5$ (c) $a = 3$, $b = 2$, $c = 1$
(b) $a = 9$, $b = 1$, $c = 0$ (d) $a = 6$, $b = 0$, $c = 4$

12. Evaluate.

(a) $\frac{3ad + 4b}{2c}$ when $a = 2$, $b = 3$, $c = 1$, $d = 0$

(b) $\frac{15w + 6p}{x + y}$ when $w = 1$, $p = 0$, $x = 2$, $y = 3$

(c) $\frac{mn(7k - 4)}{3n}$ when $m = 2$, $n = 3$, $k = 1$

(d) $\frac{6b - a(c - d)}{4(2b - 3a)}$ when $a = 2$, $b = 3$, $c = 1$, $d = 0$

13. Evaluate each of the following if $p = 0$, $q = 2$, $r = 1$, $s = 4$.

(a) $\frac{(3q^2 - 10r)^3}{s^2 \div 2s}$ (c) $2pq \div (17q^2 - s^3)$
(b) $(2q^2)^3 \div s^3$ (d) $(4s^2 - 3q + p^4) \div (3p^2 + q - 2r)$

7(a)	**16**	**(g)**	**41**
(c)	**80**	**(i)**	**4**
(e)	**80**		
8(a)	**16**	**(d)**	**85**
(b)	**29**	**(e)**	**50**
(c)	**125**	**(f)**	**100**
9(a)	**21**	**(d)**	**440**
(b)	**2**	**(e)**	**10**
(c)	**0**	**(f)**	**0**
10(a)	**12**	**(d)**	**28**
(b)	**20**	**(e)**	**18**
(c)	**20**	**(f)**	**0**
11(a)	**151**	**(c)**	**13**
(b)	**159**	**(d)**	**136**
12(a)	**6**	**(c)**	**2**
(b)	**3**	**(d)**	**impossible**
13(a)	**4**	**(c)**	**0**
(b)	**8**	**(d)**	**impossible**

Can You Follow Directions?

1. You are allowed 3 min to complete this test. Read everything before doing anything.
2. Take an ordinary sheet of notepaper, and write your name in the upper right-hand corner.
3. In the left margin, number each question beginning with 4.
4. Find the sum of 316 and 792.
5. Subtract 437 from your answer to Question 4.
6. Double this new result and increase it by 4268.
7. In a normal speaking voice, state your full name, age, and address.
8. Stand up and touch your toes five times.
9. Now that you are fully relaxed, divide your answer to Question 6 by 30.
10. If your answer to Question 9 is 187, proceed to Question 11; if not, stand at attention and recite the alphabet aloud, as quickly as you can.
11. Now that you have finished reading this entire test, do only Questions 1 and 2.

Puzzles and Problems

1. Given only 30 ml and 50 ml containers and a pail of water, how would you measure out exactly 40 ml of water?
2. Mark Tyme's wrist watch loses 8 min/h. If it gives the correct time at 01:00, what is the correct time when the watch reads 18:00 the same day?
3. If a hen and a half lay an egg and a half in a day and a half, how many eggs do 6 hens lay in 6 days?

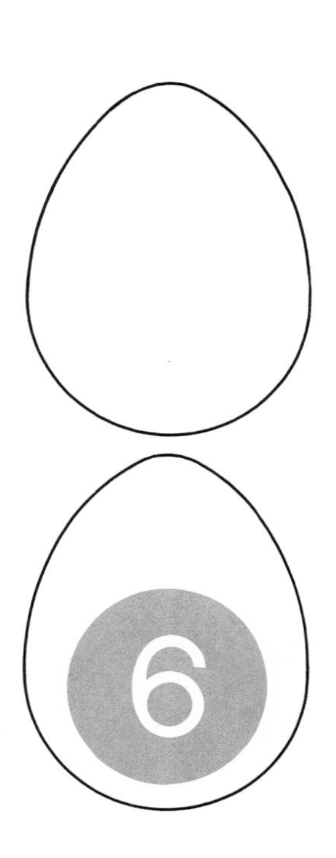

3x+2

Unit 2

Mathematical Equations

People are animals with inquiring minds. It is human nature to want to know the "what?, why?, and wherefore?" of things. This trait is especially evident in mathematics when we are dealing with *equations*. Equations are used to solve problems that ask us to find unknown quantities.

An equation is a mathematical sentence containing an "=" sign. If $A = B$, we mean that A and B are names for the same thing. Thus $1 + 4 = 5$ because '$1 + 4$' and '5' name the same number. In this unit we shall study equations and the various steps used in solving them.

2.1 Solving Equations by Inspection

Recall the meaning of variable, domain, and substitution.

A $x - 5 = 3$, $4a + 3 = 7$, and $2(y - 5) = 12$ are examples of equations. In this section, our problem is to determine the value (or values) of the *variable*, chosen from the *domain*, for which the equation expresses a *true statement*.

$\in$ means "belongs to"

1. What value substituted for x will produce true statements in each of the following? ($x \in W$)
   (*a*) $x - 5 = 3$
   (*b*) $7 + x = 12$
   (*c*) $x \div 4 = 2$
   (*d*) $3x = 0$

B The equation $x - 3 = 7$, $x \in W$, is true only if x has the value 10. We say that the *solution set* of the equation is $\{10\}$. Finding the solution set of an equation is called *solving* the equation.

1. Solve the following. The domain of all variables is W.
   (*a*) $17 - y = 12$
   (*b*) $26 + 13 = p$
   (*c*) $2k + 1 = 3$
   (*d*) $7 - 3r = 7$
   (*e*) $8x = 6 + 2$
   (*f*) $4m = 3$

Careful in 1(f)!

2. Is 5 a member of the solution set of $4x + 3 = 23$?

3. Is 2 a member of the solution set of $31 - 4m = 26$?

4. Does 0 belong to the solution set of $3x + 2x = 5x$?

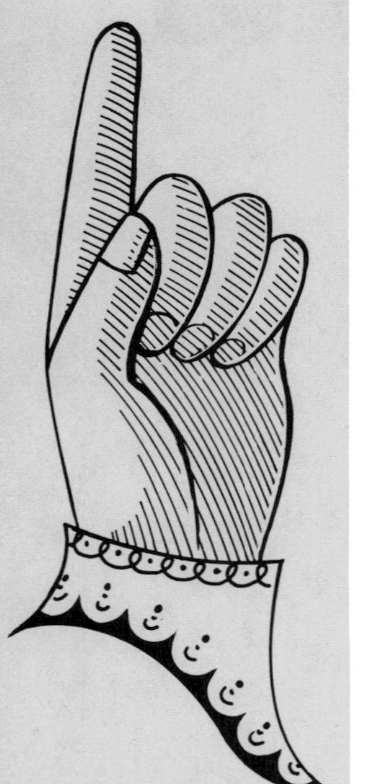

C When the equations become somewhat more difficult, it often helps to have a method of presenting a written solution. Study the following examples carefully.

Example 1

Solve the equation $3x + 2 = 11$, $x \in N$.

Solution

$$\begin{aligned} \because\quad 3x + 2 &= 11 \\ \text{and}\quad 9 + 2 &= 11 \\ \text{then}\quad 3x &= 9 \\ \therefore\quad x &= 3 \end{aligned}$$

$\therefore$ the solution set is $\{3\}$.

Example 2

List and graph the solution set of $(4m - 8) \div 3 = 4,\ m \in W$.

Solution

$$\begin{array}{ll} \because & (4m - 8) \div 3 = 4 \\ \text{and} & 12 \div 3 = 4 \\ \text{then} & 4m - 8 = 12 \\ \because & 20 - 8 = 12 \\ \text{then} & 4m = 20 \\ \therefore & m = 5 \end{array}$$

$\therefore$ the solution set is $\{5\}$.

W-line
0 1 2 3 4 5 6 7

Example 3

List the solution set of $x^2 + y = 8,\ x, y \in W$.

Solution

$$\begin{array}{ll} \because 0^2 + 8 = 8, & \therefore x = 0,\ y = 8 \\ \because 1^2 + 7 = 8, & \therefore x = 1,\ y = 7 \\ \because 2^2 + 4 = 8, & \therefore x = 2,\ y = 4 \end{array}$$

$\therefore$ the solution set is $\{(0, 8), (1, 7), (2, 4)\}$

value of x value of y

Example 4

List and graph the solution set of $2 + x = x + 2,\ x \in N$.

Solution

Here the left side of the equation always has the same value as the right side, regardless of the value substituted for x. Thus, the equation represents a true statement for *all* values of x. Such an equation is called an *identity*. The solution set is $\{1, 2, 3, \ldots\}$, the set of natural numbers.

N-line
1 2 3 4 5 6 7 8 9

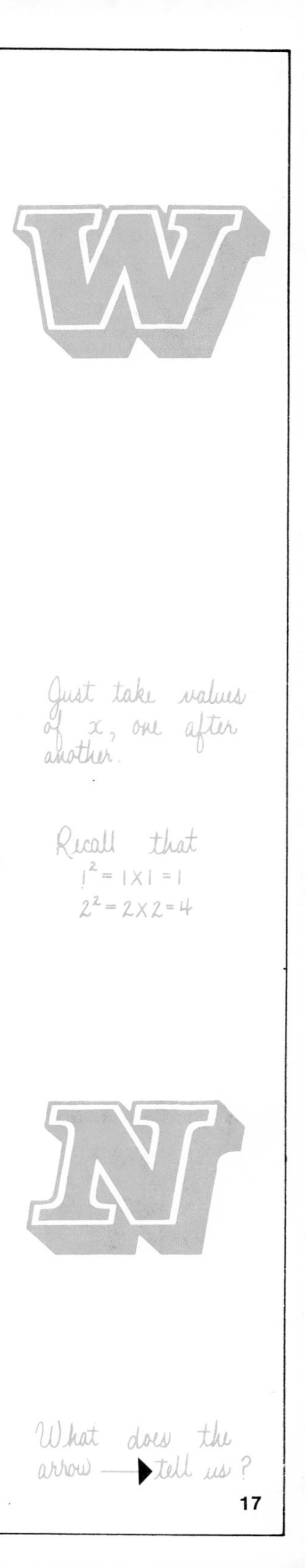

W
Just take values of x, one after another.
Recall that
$1^2 = 1 \times 1 = 1$
$2^2 = 2 \times 2 = 4$
N
What does the arrow tell us?

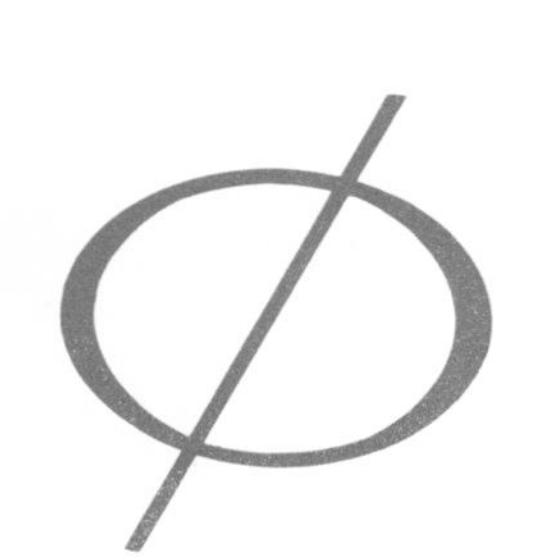

Example 5

Solve $3x + 4 = 15, \quad x \in W$.

Solution

$$\begin{aligned} \because \quad 3x + 4 &= 15 \\ \text{and} \quad 11 + 4 &= 15 \\ \text{then} \quad 3x &= 11 \end{aligned}$$

However, no number in W multiplied by 3 is 11.

$\therefore$ the solution set is ϕ.

ϕ is the "empty set." You know—like the set of all kids with 3 eyes!

A number that "satisfies" an equation belongs to the solution set of the equation.

Example 6

By substitution, check to see if 5 satisfies the equation
$$29 - 3x = 14.$$

Solution

Consider $29 - 3x = 14$, when $x = 5$.

Check

LS means "left side"
RS means "right side"

LS	RS
$29 - 3x$	14
$= 29 - 3(5)$	
$= 29 - 15$	
$= 14$	

$\therefore$ 5 satisfies the equation $29 - 3x = 14$.

Exercise 2.1

Discussion

1. In each of the equations below, substitute the given value for the variables, and determine whether the resulting statement is true or false.
   (*a*) $x - 3 = 8,\ x = 11$
   (*b*) $7 + n = 9,\ n = 3$
   (*c*) $3q = 22 + 2,\ q = 8$
   (*d*) $4k \div 3 = 12,\ k = 9$
   (*e*) $m^2 + 2 = 10,\ m = 3$
   (*f*) $3(t + 4) = 3t + 12,\ t = 1$
2. Does 7 belong to the solution set of $4p + 2 = 18,\ p \in N$?
3. Is 0 a member of the solution set of $16 - 3r^2 = 20 - 4$?

4. State the solution set of each of the following. All variables have domain W.
   (a) $x + 2 = 4$
   (b) $t - 7 = 12$
   (c) $2m = 16$
   (d) $p \div 3 = 9$
   (e) $4k = 36$
   (f) $3x = 14$

5. Solve.
   (a) $2a + 1 = 7,\ a \in N$
   (b) $m^3 = 8,\ m \in N$
   (c) $x + 3 = 3 + x,\ x \in W$
   (d) $b^2 = 25,\ b \in N$
   (e) $x + y = 4,\ x, y \in N$
   (f) $2m + n = 7,\ m, n \in W$

6. In your own words, state what is meant by an "identity."

7. State which part of Question 5 is an identity.

Remember?
$W = \{0, 1, 2, 3, \ldots\}$

$N = \{1, 2, 3, \ldots\}$

Written Solutions

8. By substitution, check to see if the value given for the variable in each of the following satisfies the equation.
   (a) $2x - 3 = 8,\ x = 6$
   (b) $x \div 4 = 7,\ x = 28$
   (c) $17 - 5x = 7,\ x = 3$
   (d) $x \div 4 + 2 = 5,\ x = 12$
   (e) $4x - 2 = 3x + 3,\ x = 5$
   (f) $2(x + 6) = 3x,\ x = 6$

Remember!
LS | RS

9. Solve. All variables have domain W.
   (a) $3y + 5 = 11$
   (b) $\frac{7 + x}{5} = 2$
   (c) $h^3 + 1 = 9$ *
   (d) $7r - 2 = 19$
   (e) $\frac{2s}{3} = 1$
   (f) $(5t + 3) \div 4 = 2$
   (g) $5k + 7 = 3 + 4$
   (h) $5y + 7 = 22$
   (i) $3x - 4 = 11$
   (j) $2a - 7 = 3$

*

Recall that
$h^3 = h \times h \times h$

10. List and graph the solution set of each of the following. All variables have domain W.
   (a) $x^2 - 12 = 4$
   (b) $3(x + 2) = 3x + 6$
   (c) $4a + 3 = 4a + 2$
   (d) $2y^2 + 5 = 23$
   (e) $w + 5 = 2w$
   (f) $3d + d = 4d$
   (g) $3x^2 + 9 = 12$
   (h) $2a^2 - 4 = 14$

11. List equations from Questions 9 and 10 that are identities.

9(a) $y = 2$ **(g)** $k = 0$
(c) $h = 2$ **(i)** $x = 5$
(e) No solution

10(a) $\{4\}$ **(e)** $\{5\}$
(b) W **(f)** W
(c) ϕ **(g)** $\{1\}$
(d) $\{3\}$ **(h)** $\{3\}$

12. Make up two identities different from those in Question 11.

13. Make up 3 equations whose solution set is ϕ.

14. Solve.
    (*a*) $x + y = 2, \ x, y \in N$
    (*b*) $m + 3n = 5, \ m, n \in W$
    (*c*) $2m + n = 0, \ m, n \in W$
    (*d*) $3m + n = 12, \ m \in N, n \in W$
    (*e*) $6 - a = b, a, b \in W$
    (*f*) $2a - 5 = b, a, b \in N$

Find 4 pairs in (d).

Careful in (f)!

Let's see ...
If $x = 1$,
LS $= 1 + 1 = 2$
RS $= 16 - 2 = 14$
$\therefore$ 1 does not satisfy.

Now if $x = 2$,
LS $= 2 + 1 = 3$
RS $= 16 - 6 = 10$
⋮

Golly!
This could take a long time!

2.2 Solving Equations by Adding and Subtracting

An equation such as $x + 3 = 5$ is not too difficult for you to solve by trial. Something like $3x - 7 = 8$ becomes more difficult and $x + 1 = 16 - 2x$ even more so. Try to solve it! *

There are other methods that will help you when solving complicated equations.

A You know that 2 satisfies the equation $x = 2$. But 2 also satisfies the equation $x + 3 = 5$. We say that these are *equivalent* equations because they have the same solution set, $\{2\}$.

Compare the equations

$$x = 2 \quad \text{and} \quad x + 3 = 5.$$

Do you see that the second equation results from adding 3 to each side of the first?

1. Form another equation by adding 8 to each side of $x = 2$. Does 2 satisfy this new equation?

2. By adding the same number to each side, form equivalent equations of the form $y = ▤$.

   (*a*) $y - 2 = 5$ (*b*) $y - 3 = 2$ (*c*) $y - 1 = 6$

This method of adding the same number to each side of an equation can be used to solve an equation.

Example 1

Solve $a - 7 = 2, a \in W$.

Solution

$$\because \quad a - 7 = 2$$
$$\text{then } a - 7 + 7 = 2 + 7 \quad (1)$$
$$\therefore \quad a = 9 \quad (2)$$

That sure simplifies the LS!

3. In Example 1,

   (*a*) What number was added to *each* side in step (1)?

   (*b*) How did we get a in step (2)?

   (*c*) Why was 7 added to each side?

4. What number would you add to the following expressions to give the result a?

   (*a*) $a - 1$ (*b*) $a - 5$ (*c*) $a - 17$

5. Solve by adding the same number to *each side* of the equation.

   (*a*) $x - 1 = 5$ (*b*) $x - 5 = 11$ (*c*) $x - 7 = 0$

B Adding seems to help solve certain equations, but suppose you had the equation

$$w + 9 = 15.$$

1. Can you add a whole number to the left side to give the result w?

2. What operation will change $w + 9$ to w? *

Can we subtract the same number from each side of an equation and not change the solution set? Let's see.

Starting with $x + 1 = 3$, by subtracting 1 from each side we get $x = 2$. Both equations are satisfied by 2. It appears that we can use subtraction to help us as well.

* Try flowcharting the equation!

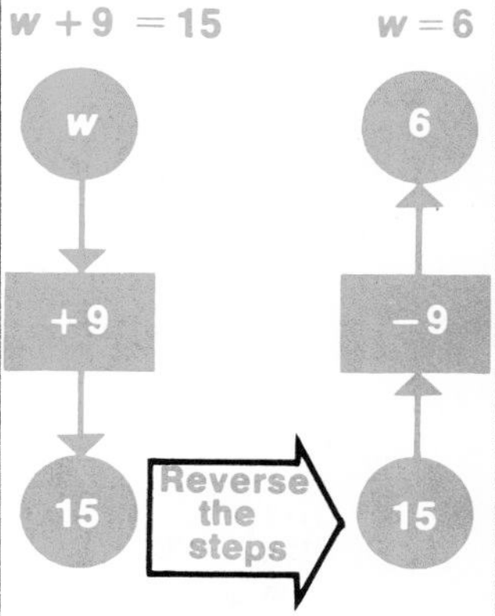

That's why we subtract 9!

$x = 2$ and $x + 1 = 3$ are equivalent equations.

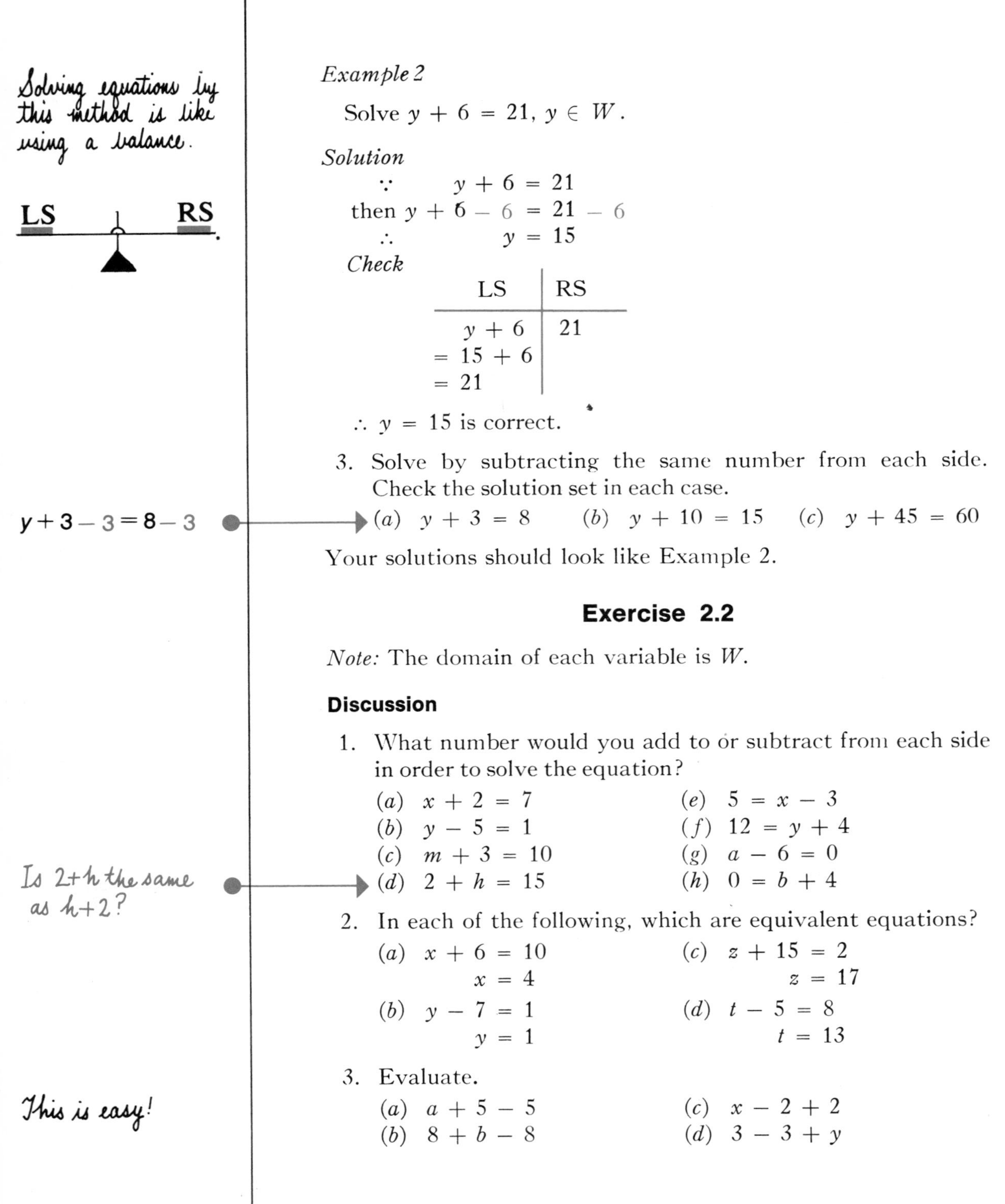

Solving equations by this method is like using a balance.

LS RS

Example 2

Solve $y + 6 = 21,\ y \in W$.

Solution

$$\because \quad y + 6 = 21$$
$$\text{then } y + 6 - 6 = 21 - 6$$
$$\therefore \quad y = 15$$

Check

LS	RS
$y + 6$	21
$= 15 + 6$	
$= 21$	

$\therefore\ y = 15$ is correct.

3. Solve by subtracting the same number from each side. Check the solution set in each case.

$y + 3 - 3 = 8 - 3$

(*a*) $y + 3 = 8$ (*b*) $y + 10 = 15$ (*c*) $y + 45 = 60$

Your solutions should look like Example 2.

Exercise 2.2

Note: The domain of each variable is W.

Discussion

1. What number would you add to or subtract from each side in order to solve the equation?

(*a*) $x + 2 = 7$
(*b*) $y - 5 = 1$
(*c*) $m + 3 = 10$
(*d*) $2 + h = 15$
(*e*) $5 = x - 3$
(*f*) $12 = y + 4$
(*g*) $a - 6 = 0$
(*h*) $0 = b + 4$

Is $2+h$ the same as $h+2$?

2. In each of the following, which are equivalent equations?

(*a*) $x + 6 = 10$, $x = 4$
(*b*) $y - 7 = 1$, $y = 1$
(*c*) $z + 15 = 2$, $z = 17$
(*d*) $t - 5 = 8$, $t = 13$

3. Evaluate.

This is easy!

(*a*) $a + 5 - 5$
(*b*) $8 + b - 8$
(*c*) $x - 2 + 2$
(*d*) $3 - 3 + y$

Written Solutions

4. Solve.

(*a*) $x - 1 = 7$ (*d*) $x - 25 = 40$
(*b*) $x - 15 = 4$ (*e*) $x - 250 = 1000$
(*c*) $x - 3 = 8$ (*f*) $x - 48 = 73$

5. Solve.

(*a*) $y + 7 = 10$ (*d*) $y + 18 = 33$
(*b*) $y + 5 = 20$ (*e*) $y + 27 = 38$
(*c*) $y + 50 = 100$ (*f*) $y + 253 = 407$

6. Solve and check.

(*a*) $b - 15 = 1$ (*d*) $5 = x - 2$
(*b*) $t + 6 = 10$ (*e*) $3 = y + 1$
(*c*) $r - 6 = 0$ (*f*) $12 + t = 15$

7. Simplify each side, where possible, and then solve.

(*a*) $x + 2 \times 3 = 10$ (*d*) $(18 + 3) \div 7 + x = 5$
(*b*) $3 - 2 + h = 5(6 - 3)$ (*e*) $6 + y - 4 = 10 - 7$
(*c*) $25 \div 5 - 2 = x + 1$ (*f*) $3(16 - 4) - 10 = 20 + x$

8. Now try this one! Solve $y^2 + 3 = 4 \times 7$.

4(a) $x = 8$ **(c)** $x = 11$ **(e)** $x = 1250$
5(a) $y = 3$ **(c)** $y = 50$ **(e)** $y = 11$
7(a) $x = 4$ **(b)** $h = 14$ **(d)** $x = 2$
8. $y = 5$

BODMAS!

2.3 Solving Equations by Dividing

Would adding or subtracting help you solve equations like

$$3x = 15 \quad \text{or} \quad 3x - 15 = 12?$$

You know that

$$x + 5 = 13 \quad (1) \qquad \text{and} \qquad x = 8 \quad (2)$$

are equivalent equations because you can subtract 5 from each side of (1) to give (2).

Here are 2 more pairs of equivalent equations.

(*a*) $2x = 12$, $x = 6$ (*b*) $5x = 15$, $x = 3$

We find the second equation from the first as follows.

(*a*) $\because 2x = 12$, then $\frac{2x}{2} = \frac{12}{2}$, $\therefore x = 6$

(*b*) $\because 5x = 15$, then $\frac{5x}{5} = \frac{15}{5}$, $\therefore x = 3$

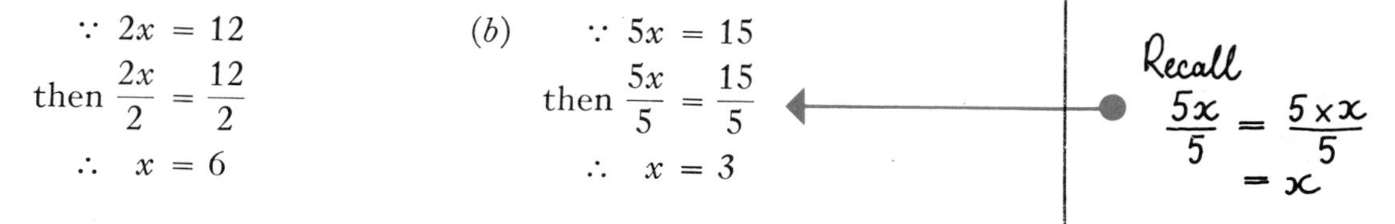

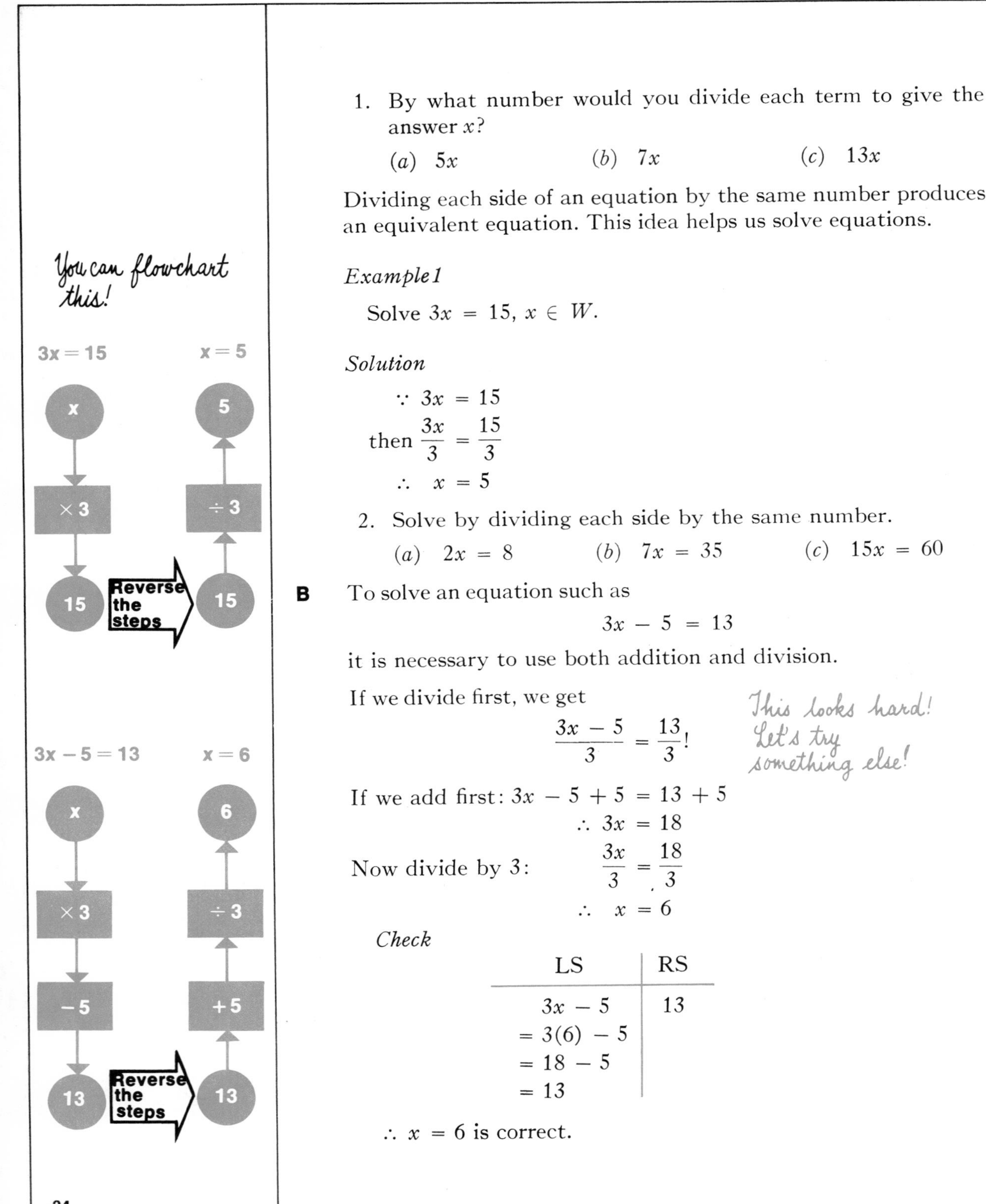

1. By what number would you divide each term to give the answer x?

   (*a*) $5x$ (*b*) $7x$ (*c*) $13x$

Dividing each side of an equation by the same number produces an equivalent equation. This idea helps us solve equations.

Example 1

Solve $3x = 15$, $x \in W$.

Solution

$$\because\ 3x = 15$$

$$\text{then } \frac{3x}{3} = \frac{15}{3}$$

$$\therefore\ x = 5$$

2. Solve by dividing each side by the same number.

   (*a*) $2x = 8$ (*b*) $7x = 35$ (*c*) $15x = 60$

B To solve an equation such as

$$3x - 5 = 13$$

it is necessary to use both addition and division.

If we divide first, we get

$$\frac{3x - 5}{3} = \frac{13}{3}!$$

This looks hard! Let's try something else!

If we add first: $3x - 5 + 5 = 13 + 5$

$$\therefore\ 3x = 18$$

Now divide by 3: $\dfrac{3x}{3} = \dfrac{18}{3}$

$$\therefore\ x = 6$$

Check

LS	RS
$3x - 5$	13
$= 3(6) - 5$	
$= 18 - 5$	
$= 13$	

$\therefore\ x = 6$ is correct.

1. State the first 2 steps in the solution of each equation.
   (*a*) $2x - 5 = 7$ (*b*) $4y + 6 = 18$ (*c*) $6 = 4 + 2z$

Example 2

Solve $11 + 5x - 3 = 43, x \in W$.

Solution

$$\begin{aligned}
\because\quad 11 + 5x - 3 &= 43 \\
8 + 5x &= 43 \\
\text{then}\quad 8 + 5x - 8 &= 43 - 8 \\
\therefore\quad 5x &= 35 \\
\text{then}\quad \frac{5x}{5} &= \frac{35}{5} \\
\therefore\quad x &= 7
\end{aligned}$$

Check

LS	RS
$8 + 5x$	43
$= 8 + 5(7)$	
$= 8 + 35$	
$= 43$	

$\therefore x = 7$ is correct.

Learn these steps in solving equations.

1. Simplify each side.
2. Add or subtract the same number on each side.
3. Divide each side by the same number.

Remember to simplify each side of an equation before adding, subtracting, or dividing by a new number.

Example 3

Solve $15 + 4x - 3(4 - 1) = 3 + 16 \div 8 + 7, x \in W$.

This looks tough!

Solution

$$\begin{aligned}
\because\quad 15 + 4x - 3(4 - 1) &= 3 + 16 \div 8 + 7 \\
\text{then}\quad 15 + 4x - 3(3) &= 3 + 2 + 7 \\
\text{and}\quad 15 + 4x - 9 &= 12 \\
\therefore\quad 4x + 6 &= 12 \\
\text{then}\quad 4x + 6 - 6 &= 12 - 6 \\
\therefore\quad 4x &= 6 \\
\text{then}\quad \frac{4x}{4} &= \frac{6}{4} \\
\therefore\quad x &= \tfrac{3}{2}
\end{aligned}$$

1. Simplify, using BODMAS.
2. Subtract 6 from each side.
3. Divide each side by 4.

$\because \frac{3}{2}$ is not a whole number

$\therefore$ the solution set is $\{\ \}$.

$\{\ \} = \emptyset$, the empty set.

Remember: The domain is W!

Is $28 = 4m$ equivalent to $4m = 28$?

Exercise 2.3

Note: The domain of each variable is W.

Discussion

1. What would you do first to solve each of the following equations? State the resulting equation.

   (*a*) $x + 5 = 8$
   (*b*) $3x - 2 = 7$
   (*c*) $7x = 21$
   (*d*) $1 + 3x = 7$
   (*e*) $13 = 2x + 5$
   (*f*) $10 = 6x - 50$

2. Solve the following equations.

   (*a*) $5x = 30$
   (*b*) $4y = 28$
   (*c*) $z + 6 = 10$
   (*d*) $r - 3 = 8$
   (*e*) $14 = 7s$
   (*f*) $21 = 5t$

Written Solutions

3. Solve the following equations.

   (*a*) $3x = 12$
   (*b*) $6y = 42$
   (*c*) $10z = 80$
   (*d*) $28 = 4m$
   (*e*) $36 = 9y$
   (*f*) $25n = 150$
   (*g*) $7r = 32$
   (*h*) $63 = 9s$

4. Solve the following equations. Flowcharts will help you check your answers.

   (*a*) $a + 16 = 25$
   (*b*) $b - 23 = 48$
   (*c*) $105 = c + 70$
   (*d*) $43 = d - 10$
   (*e*) $2r + 5 = 11$
   (*f*) $3s - 6 = 21$
   (*g*) $5t - 1 = 19$
   (*h*) $6 + 7t = 20$

5. Solve and check.

   (*a*) $12x + 3 = 27$
   (*b*) $8x - 6 = 58$
   (*c*) $5 + 4y = 21$
   (*d*) $11y - 66 = 0$
   (*e*) $28 = 4m - 8$
   (*f*) $42 = 3m + 21$
   (*g*) $116 = 100 + 8r$
   (*h*) $0 = 5r - 40$

3(a) $x = 4$ (e) $y = 4$
(c) $z = 8$ (g) No solution
4(a) $a = 9$ (e) $r = 3$
(c) $c = 35$ (g) $t = 4$
5(a) $x = 2$ (e) $m = 9$
(c) $y = 4$ (g) $r = 2$

6. Simplify the following expressions.

(*a*)	$3 + 2(6 - 4)$	(*e*)	$20 + 2x + 6 \times 2$
(*b*)	$18 \div (4 + 5) + 2x$	(*f*)	$45 + 2 \times 6 + 5x$
(*c*)	$3t + 10 \times 4 - 3$	(*g*)	$7a - (12 + 3)$
(*d*)	$14 + 4y - 8$	(*h*)	$34 + 2a + 5 \times 9$

7. Solve the following equations.

(*a*)	$6t + 3 \times 4 = 30$	(*e*)	$28 - 3 = 2m - 7$
(*b*)	$5t - 8 \div 4 = 18$	(*f*)	$7 - 4 \div 2 = 3m - 4$
(*c*)	$4 + 8r = 34 - 2 \times 3$	(*g*)	$12x - 54 = 16 \times 3$
(*d*)	$3 + 7r + 2 = 13(5 - 3)$	(*h*)	$14 + 20y - 2 = 2 \times 4^2$

8. Solve and check.

(*a*) $5a - 4 \times 2 = 7$
(*b*) $14 + 3x - 8 = 21$
(*c*) $3(8 - 2) + 9x = 5 \times 3^2$
(*d*) $10 - 5 \times 2 = 15x$
(*e*) $4 + 2 \times 12 = 9x + 10$
(*f*) $12 + 8x - 5 \times 2 = 6(2 + 3^2)$
(*g*) $5t^2 = 45$
(*h*) $4y^2 - 15 = 85$

9. The sides of a triangle are equal in length and the perimeter is 21 cm. Find the length of each side.

10. The cost in dollars of producing a school magazine is given by the equation

$$\text{Cost} = 1575 + 3n$$

where n is the number of magazines printed.

(*a*) Find the cost when 750 magazines are printed.
(*b*) If the total cost was \$4200, how many copies were printed and what was the cost per copy?

11. The value in cents of q quarters and d dimes is given by the formula

$$V = 25q + 10d$$

If a total value of \$15.05 includes 58 dimes, find the number of quarters.

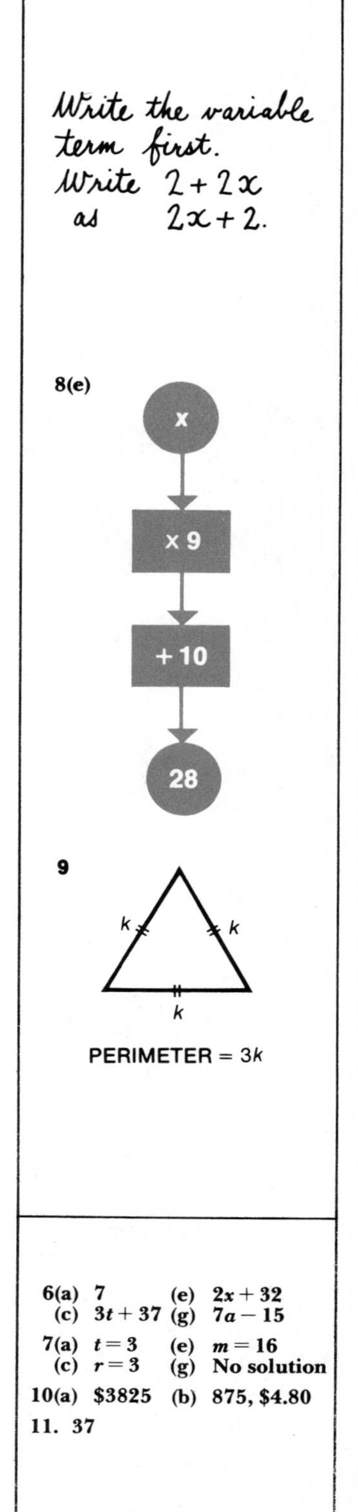

Unit 3
Inequations and Word Problems

"John is taller than Jim."

"Mary is smaller than Lisa."

Although in math we seem to concentrate on equality in the form of equations, in real life expressions involving *inequality* occur more frequently. Comparisons of height, mass, age, school marks, weekly allowance, and so on, use phrases such as "greater than," "less than," "more," or "fewer" far more often than the phrase "is the same as."

In studying inequations in this unit, we will find that many ideas we learned when solving equations will apply here as well.

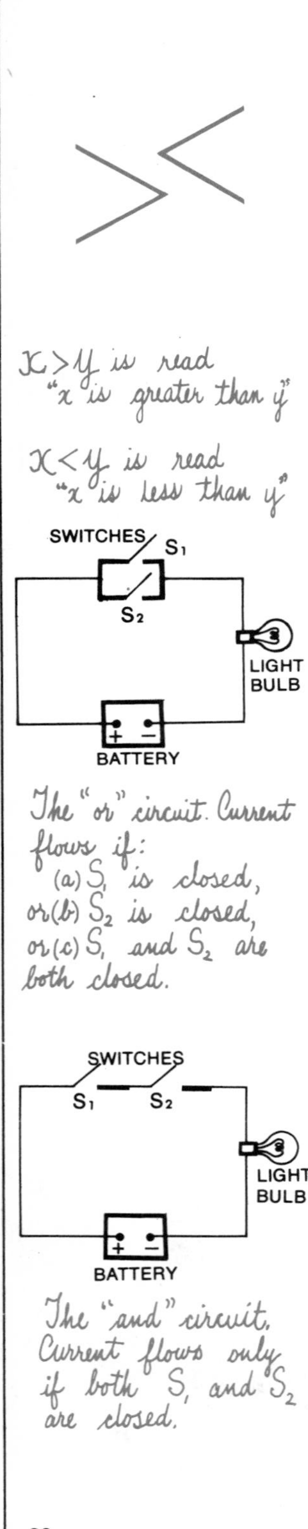

x > y is read "x is greater than y"
x < y is read "x is less than y"
SWITCHES
S₁
S₂
LIGHT BULB
BATTERY
The "or" circuit. Current flows if:
(a) S₁ is closed,
or (b) S₂ is closed,
or (c) S₁ and S₂ are both closed.
SWITCHES
S₁
S₂
LIGHT BULB
BATTERY
The "and" circuit. Current flows only if both S₁ and S₂ are closed.

3.1 Inequations

A If we compare the heights of two boys, Wilberforce and Buttersworth, there are only three possible outcomes:

(1) The two boys are the same height.
(2) Wilberforce is taller than Buttersworth.
(3) Wilberforce is shorter than Buttersworth.

Similarly, in comparing two whole numbers, x and y, there are only three possible results:

(1) $x = y$ (2) $x > y$ (3) $x < y$

The symbols $>$ and $<$ are *inequality signs*, and the sentences $x > y$ and $x < y$ are *inequations*. Note that in a true statement the arrow always points to the smaller number. In comparing 5 and 9, for instance, we could write $5 < 9$ or $9 > 5$ to give true statements.

1. Use the symbols $>$ or $<$ to express true statements in comparing the following numbers.
   (*a*) 6, 18 (*b*) 4, 1 (*c*) 10, 21 (*d*) 5, 9, 3

B Recall that $>$ and $<$ are not the only signs of inequality.

1. What is meant by each of the following inequality signs?

$$\geq, \ \leq, \ \ngtr, \ \neq, \ \nleq, \ \nless, \ \ngeq$$

The symbol $\geq$ is read "is greater than or equal to." That is, the inequation $3 \geq 2$ can be written $3 > 2$ *or* $3 = 2$. Hence, if *either* $3 > 2$ *or* $3 = 2$ is true, then $3 \geq 2$ is considered true.

2. Which of the following express true statements?
   (*a*) $13 \ngtr 4$ (*d*) $17 < 2 \times 3$ (*g*) $125 \div 5 \ngeq 3 \times 4$
   (*b*) $9 \nleq 5$ (*e*) $4 + 9 \neq 12$ (*h*) $11 + 5 \nless 7 + 3$
   (*c*) $2 \geq 2$ (*f*) $15 \div 3 \leq 5$ (*i*) $12 \div 3 \geq 15 - 14$

Another word that has a different meaning in mathematics than in ordinary usage is the word "and." A better interpretation for "and" in mathematics is "common to."

For instance, the sentence $x > 5, x \in N$ is read

"x is greater than 5 *and* x belongs to N."

The solution set is then $\{6, 7, 8, \ldots\}$. This is the set of elements *common to* $\{6, 7, 8, \ldots\}$ *and* $\{1, 2, 3, \ldots\}$.

Quite often, 2 sentences may be combined. For example,

$6 > x > 3$ means $6 > x$ *and* $x > 3$
$7 \leq p < 10$ means $7 \leq p$ *and* $p < 10$

Find the solution set for each of these.

Study carefully the following examples.

Example 1

List and graph the solution set of $3x < 12$, $x \in W$.

Solution

$\because 3 \times 0 < 12$
and $3 \times 1 < 12$
and $3 \times 2 < 12$
and $3 \times 3 < 12$ are all true,
$\therefore$ the solution set is $\{0, 1, 2, 3\}$.*

W-line: 0 1 2 3 4 5 6

* An inequation has a solution set—just like an equation.

Example 2

Solve $5t + 3 > 17$, $t \in N$.

Solution

$\because 5t + 3 > 17$
and $14 + 3 = 17$, $15 + 3 > 17$, $16 + 3 > 17$, $17 + 3 > 17, \ldots$
$\therefore 5t > 14$

$\therefore$ the solution set is $\{3, 4, 5, \ldots\}$.

Example 3

Find the solution set for $p < 2$ *or* $p \geq 4$, $p \in W$.

Solution

Consider the sentences $p < 2$ and $p \geq 4$ separately.

$p < 2$
$\therefore$ the solution set is $\{0, 1\}$.

$p \geq 4$
$\therefore$ the solution set is $\{4, 5, 6, \ldots\}$.

The solution set contains elements
either from $\{0, 1\}$ *or* from $\{4, 5, 6, \ldots\}$.

The solution set of $p < 2$ *or* $p \geq 4$ is $\{0, 1, 4, 5, 6, \ldots\}$.

Verrrry interesting!

Example 4

List the solution set of $m \geq 5$ *and* $m < 8$, $m \in N$.

Solution

Again, consider the sentences separately.

$m \geq 5$

$\therefore$ the solution set is $\{5, 6, 7, \ldots\}$.

$m < 8$

$\therefore$ the solution set is $\{1, 2, 3, 4, 5, 6, 7\}$.

The solution set contains elements *common to* $\{5, 6, 7, \ldots\}$ *and* $\{1, 2, 3, 4, 5, 6, 7\}$.

$\therefore$ the solution set of $m \geq 5$ *and* $m < 8$ is $\{5, 6, 7\}$.

Example 5

Solve $4 \leq y + 1 < 7$, $y \in W$.

Solution

Consider

$4 \leq y + 1$

$\therefore 3 \leq y$

$\therefore y \geq 3$

$\therefore$ the solution set is $\{3, 4, 5, \ldots\}$.

$y + 1 < 7$

$\therefore \quad y < 6$

$\therefore$ the solution set is $\{0, 1, 2, 3, 4, 5\}$.

$\therefore$ the solution set of $4 \leq y + 1 < 7$ is $\{3, 4, 5\}$.

Exercise 3.1

Discussion

1. State three inequations that express true statements and three that express false statements.

2. Notice that $4 < 6$ means exactly the same thing as $4 \ngeq 6$. That is, the symbol $<$ is equivalent to the symbol $\ngeq$. What symbol is equivalent in meaning to these symbols?

   (*a*) $>$ (*b*) $\geq$ (*c*) $\leq$

3. State the solution set for each of the following (all variables have domain W).

   (*a*) $y > 9$
   (*b*) $t + 2 < 6$
   (*c*) $q - 2 > 5$
   (*d*) $m \nleq 0$
   (*e*) $\frac{c}{3} < 2$
   (*f*) $5 + b < 3$

Written Solutions

4. List and graph the solution set of each of the following.
   (*a*) $m + 3 < 6, \quad m \in W$
   (*b*) $16 - 2n \geq 5, \quad n \in N$
   (*c*) $n > 2$ or $n < 1, \quad n \in W$
   (*d*) $x + 3 \geq x + 7, \quad x \in W$
   (*e*) $2 \leq r^2 < 13, \quad r \in N$
   (*f*) $x + 2 < x + 4, \quad x \in W$
   (*g*) $12 < p - 3 \leq 14, \quad p \in W$

5. Determine if the graph represents the solution set of the given inequation. If it does not, redraw the graph.
   (*a*) $k^2 \leq 10$ — 0 1 2 3 4 5 6 7 8 9 10 W-line
   (*b*) $x + 2 > 3$ — 1 2 3 4 5 6 7 8 9 N-line
   (*c*) $m - 4 \leq 3$ — 0 1 2 3 4 5 6 7 8 9 10 W-line
   (*d*) $6b + 2 \leq 8$ — 0 1 2 3 4 5 6 W-line
   (*e*) $3w + 2 \leq 12$ — 0 1 2 3 4 5 6 7 W-line
   (*f*) $t < 4$ and $t > 7$ — 1 2 3 4 5 6 7 8 9 10 N-line
   (*g*) $1 < 2r \leq 9$ — 0 1 2 3 4 5 6 W-line
   (*h*) $8 \leq p - 3 < 13$ — 10 11 12 13 14 15 16 N-line
   (*i*) $1 < 2b + 3 \leq 10$ — 0 1 2 3 4 5 6 7 W-line

6. Find the solution sets. All variables have domain W.
   (*a*) $2x < 5$
   (*b*) $3s > 10$
   (*c*) $m^2 \ngtr 4$
   (*d*) $2x + 10 > 2x + 9$
   (*e*) $4t + 7 < 8$
   (*f*) $3y + 2 \leq 11$
   (*g*) $2 \leq x < 4$
   (*h*) $x \geq 8$ or $x < 4$
   (*i*) $4 \leq 3 + n^2 \leq 7$
   (*j*) $1 < 2k - 1 \leq 5$

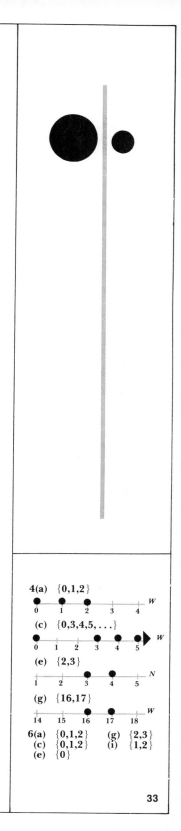

4(a) $\{0,1,2\}$ — 0 1 2 3 4 W
(c) $\{0,3,4,5,\ldots\}$ — 0 1 2 3 4 5 W
(e) $\{2,3\}$ — 1 2 3 4 5 N
(g) $\{16,17\}$ — 14 15 16 17 18 W

6(a) $\{0,1,2\}$ **(c)** $\{0,1,2\}$ **(e)** $\{0\}$ **(g)** $\{2,3\}$ **(i)** $\{1,2\}$

3.2 Methods for Solving Inequations

By inspection, the solution set for the inequation $3x > 12$, $x \in W$ is $\{5, 6, 7, \ldots\}$. If this sentence were $3x = 12$, we would have solved by dividing each side by 3. Let's try it!

$$\because 3x > 12$$
$$\therefore \frac{3x}{3} > \frac{12}{3}$$
$$\therefore x > 4$$

and $\{5, 6, 7 \ldots\}$ is the solution set.

1. Solve by inspection. $x \in W$.

   (a) $x + 5 > 7$ (b) $x - 3 \leq 2$ (c) $15 < 2x + 6$

Now let's apply the rules for solving equations to the same inequations.

Did you get the same answers by inspection?

(a) $\because x + 5 > 7$
then $x + 5 - 5 > 7 - 5$
$\therefore x > 2$

$\therefore$ SS $= \{3, 4, 5, \ldots\}$

Graph:

(b) $\because x - 3 \leq 2$
then $x - 3 + 3 \leq 2 + 3$
$\therefore x \leq 5$

$\therefore$ SS $= \{0, 1, 2, 3, 4, 5\}$

Graph:

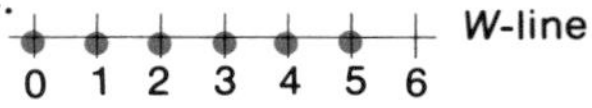

SS

SS means "solution set."

(c) $\because 15 < 2x + 6$
then $2x + 6 > 15$
and $2x + 6 - 6 > 15 - 6$
$\therefore 2x > 9$
and $\frac{2x}{2} < \frac{9}{2}$
$\therefore x > 4\frac{1}{2}$

Remember $x \in W$

$\therefore$ SS $= \{5, 6, 7, \ldots\}$

Do you agree again?

Graph:

We form equivalent inequations by adding, subtracting, or dividing each side of an inequation by the same whole number. The methods used to solve inequations are essentially the same as those used to solve equations.

Exercise 3.2

Note: All variables represent whole numbers.

Discussion

1. What steps would you take in solving the following inequations?

   (*a*) $5x < 10$
   (*b*) $x + 6 \geq 13$
   (*c*) $x - 5 < 1$
   (*d*) $2x + 7 \leq 9$
   (*e*) $1 \geq x - 9$
   (*f*) $2x < 6$ *and* $2x > 0$
   (*g*) $6 < 2x < 20$
   (*h*) $3x < 12$ *or* $3x > 21$

Remember: Perform the same operation on each side of an inequation!

2. Restate as a simpler equivalent inequation. What did you do to each side?

   (*a*) $3x \leq 9$
   (*b*) $7y > 35$
   (*c*) $8x \geq 56$
   (*d*) $9y < 72$
   (*e*) $x + 8 \geq 10$
   (*f*) $y - 5 < 3$
   (*g*) $5 + 3x \leq 15$
   (*h*) $10 \geq y + 6$
   (*i*) $-2 < y - 5$

3. List the solution set for each inequation.

   (*a*) $5r < 30$
   (*b*) $8r \geq 16$
   (*c*) $s + 3 \leq 7$
   (*d*) $s - 5 > 1$
   (*e*) $6t \leq 38$
   (*f*) $15 < 7t$
   (*g*) $3 < x \leq 7$
   (*h*) $k + 10 \geq 10$
   (*i*) $5 < y - 6$

4. Restate with the variable on the left side.

   (*a*) $4 < 6x$
   (*b*) $1 > x - 4$
   (*c*) $13 < 8 + y$
   (*d*) $23 \geq 5y - 6$

5. Separate into 2 inequations.

   (*a*) $6 \leq 3y < 24$
   (*b*) $14 > 7y \geq 0$

Written Solutions

6. Solve, and graph the solution set.

   (*a*) $4x > 20$
   (*b*) $13y \leq 52$
   (*c*) $7z \geq 28$
   (*d*) $14x < 42$
   (*e*) $20y \geq 80$
   (*f*) $9z > 23$

6(a) 4 5 6 7 8 9 W
(b) 0 1 2 3 4 5 W
(f) 1 2 3 4 5 6 W

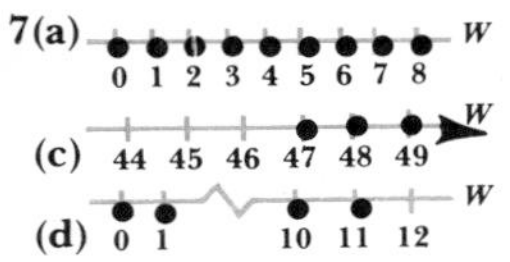

7(a) 0 1 2 3 4 5 6 7 8 W
(c) 44 45 46 47 48 49 W
(d) 0 1 10 11 12 W
8(a) $\{5, 6, 7, \ldots\}$
(c) $\{3, 4, 5, \ldots\}$
(e) $\{0, 1, 2, 3, 4, 5\}$
9(a) 3 4 5 6 7 8 9 W
(c) 5 6 7 8 9 10 11 12 W
10(a) 0 1 2 3 4 5 6 W
(b) 0 1 2 3 4 5 6 W
(c) 0 1 2 3 4 5 6 W
(d) 0 1 2 3 4 5 6 W

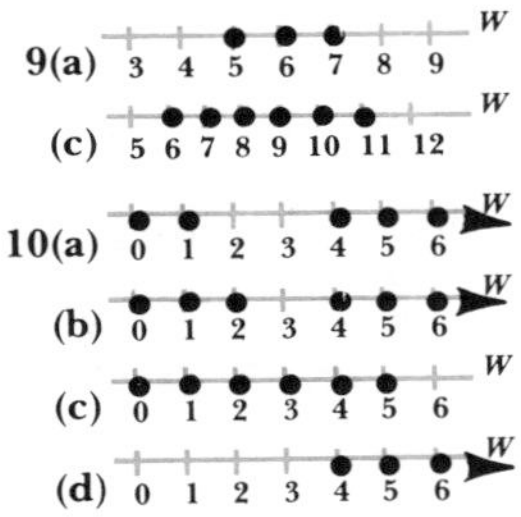

7. Solve, and graph the solution set.

(*a*) $x - 6 \leq 1$
(*b*) $y + 4 > 9$
(*c*) $z - 19 \geq 27$
(*d*) $1 \geq y - 10$
(*e*) $14 < x + 4$
(*f*) $0 > z - 18$

8. Solve and check. For example, if $\{3, 4, 5, \ldots\}$ is the solution set, check that 2 does not satisfy the inequation but 3 does.

(*a*) $3t + 5 > 17$
(*b*) $6w - 4 \leq 32$
(*c*) $20 + 5k \geq 35$
(*d*) $12 < 3x - 23$
(*e*) $45 \geq 6 + 7x$
(*f*) $0 > 12x - 60$

9. Graph the solution set.

(*a*) $5 \leq x < 8$
(*b*) $4 < 2x \leq 10$
(*c*) $7 \leq x + 1 < 12$
(*d*) $45 > 5x > 20$

10. Graph the solution set.

(*a*) $3t + 1 > 10$ *or* $3t + 1 \leq 4$
(*b*) $5t - 2 \leq 8$ *or* $5t - 2 > 13$
(*c*) $t^2 \leq 25$
(*d*) $t^2 > 9$

11. The cost of food for 5 campers for a weekend is between \$20 and \$30. Write the range of the cost for each camper as an inequation.

12. The school's Kiddy Kare baby-sitting service has rates of 60¢/h for a 13-year-old sitter. Older sitters receive 15¢/h more for each year over 13. If Kevin, who is 15, works t hours and earns between \$24 and \$30, find the range of t.

product?
more than?
quotient?
sum?
less than?
difference?

3.3 Word Problems

A The first step in solving a word problem is to translate the English sentence into a mathematical sentence. To do this, you must know the mathematical equivalent of such phrases as *the difference between*, *increased by*, *the product of*, and so on.

1. List two different words or phrases in English that can be used to represent the mathematical operation of

(*a*) addition
(*b*) subtraction

2. List two different words or phrases in English that can be used to represent the mathematical operation of
   (*a*) multiplication   (*b*) division

B The unknown number in an English sentence may be named by means of a variable in the mathematical sentence. For example, in the illustration below, x names the unknown number in each case.

	English phrase	*Mathematical equivalent*
(*a*)	7 more than the number	$x + 7$
(*b*)	the sum of 2 and the number, divided by 15	$(2 + x) \div 15$ *or* $\frac{(2 + x)}{15}$
(*c*)	the product of 12, and 3 more than the number	$12(x + 3)$

You may use any letter. I use j because my name is Janis.

1. Represent each of the following English phrases by a mathematical phrase. In each case, represent the unspecified number by m.
   (*a*) 3 times the number, plus 1
   (*b*) 6 less than the number
   (*c*) the number divided by 5
   (*d*) 2 multiplied by the number, less 4

Mary or Morton must have chosen this letter!

2. Describe in words the following algebraic expressions.
   (*a*) $4x + 3$ (*c*) $2x \div 4$
   (*b*) $7 - x$ (*d*) $8(5x - 1)$

C The steps in solving word problems algebraically are shown in the following examples.

Example 1

The sum of 8 and a number is 20. Find the number.

Solution

Let the number be represented by p.

$\because \quad 8 + p = 20$ *

then $8 + p - 8 = 20 - 8$

$\therefore \quad p = 12$

$\therefore$ the number is 12.

* $8 + p$ and 20 are the same number.

Example 2

When 3 is subtracted from the product of 4 and a number, the result is 17. Find the number.

Solution

Let the number be represented by t.

$$\begin{aligned} \because \quad & 4t - 3 = 17 \\ \text{then } & 4t - 3 + 3 = 17 + 3 \\ \text{and } & 4t = 20 \\ \therefore \quad & t = 5 \end{aligned}$$

$\therefore$ the number is 5.

Example 3

The sum of a whole number and 4 is less than or equal to 7. Find all such numbers.

Solution

Let the number be represented by p.

$$\begin{aligned} \because \quad & p + 4 \leq 7 \\ \text{then } & p + 4 - 4 \leq 7 - 4 \\ \therefore \quad & p \leq 3 \end{aligned}$$

$\therefore$ the number could be 0, 1, 2, or 3.

Wow! A lot of different words for +, −, ×, ÷.

Exercise 3.3

Discussion

1. Below is a list of English phrases or words that describe the mathematical operations of addition, subtraction, multiplication, and division. State which operation is described by each word or phrase.

sum	divide
minus	add
smaller than	decrease
increase	multiply
product	more than
plus	times
quotient	greater than
difference	subtract
diminished by	less than

2. Consider these phrases.
   (*a*) the number, divided by 6 plus 3
   (*b*) the number divided by 6, plus 3

   Do each of the phrases mean the same thing? Why?

3. Show that each of the following phrases can have at least two meanings. Use commas to show the different meanings.
   (*a*) 4 times the number decreased by 7
   (*b*) 6 more than the number multiplied by 12
   (*c*) the product of 8 and the number less 3

4. Describe in words each of the following algebraic expressions in at least two different ways.
   (*a*) $b + 2$ (*c*) $2y - 3$ (*e*) $x - 7$
   (*b*) $3k$ (*d*) $7 - x$ (*f*) $2m + 1$

5. Using x as a variable to represent the number, state each of the following phrases as an algebraic expression.
   (*a*) the number diminished by 3
   (*b*) the sum of the number and 9
   (*c*) the number divided by 5
   (*d*) the product of 13 and the number
   (*e*) 7 less than the number
   (*f*) $\frac{3}{4}$ of the number
   (*g*) 16 added to the number
   (*h*) 4 increased by twice the number
   (*i*) the number decreased by 12
   (*j*) the difference between 5 and the number
   (*k*) 27 multiplied by the number
   (*l*) 3 times the number, less 1
   (*m*) 6 subtracted from the number
   (*n*) 6 subtract the number

I see 2 ways to do (j)!

Written Solutions

Use a "let" statement to introduce a variable to represent the number. Write the following as algebraic expressions.

6. 7 times the number, less 2
7. 16 plus the product of 4 and the number
8. the sum of 10 and the number, divided by 3

Like "Let the number be n."

19. **7**
23. **0, 1, 2, 3, 4, or 5**
25. **83.51**
27. **30 cm**
28. **168 g**
29. **90 min**

Look back at the examples in part C of this section.

9. $\frac{1}{2}$ the number, increased by 8
10. the product of 9, and the number plus 3
11. the product of 9 and the number, plus 3
12. the difference between the number and 4, divided by 18
13. 31 diminished by the product of 11 and the number
14. the difference between 19 and the square of the number
15. the number, increased by 2 times itself
16. the number increased by 2, times itself

Find the number by an algebraic solution.

17. The sum of the number and 7 is 10.
18. 15 decreased by the number is equal to 4.
19. The product of 8 and the number, increased by 2, gives 58.
20. The sum of 3 and twice the number is 5.
21. 19 diminished by 3 times the number is 4.
22. The sum of the number and 7 is less than 12.
23. The product of 4 and the number is not greater than 20.

Solve algebraically.

24. In 8 more years, Polly Gone will be 21 years old. What is Polly's present age?
25. Thirteen members in a club raised \$45.63 in a fund-raising drive. If each member raised the same amount, then how much did each member raise?
26. A platform 5 cm thick is supported by concrete blocks of equal thickness as shown, and the top of the platform is 1 m off the floor. How thick is each concrete block?
27. A metre-stick is just 10 cm longer than the distance along the edge of 3 floor tiles. How long is each tile?
28. If the mass of 7 bolts is 176 g more than 1 kg of washers, find the mass of each bolt.
29. An astronaut orbiting earth finds that he completes 14 orbits in 1 day less 3 h. How many minutes does it take him to complete 1 orbit?

Activities — What's A Million?

1. How high is a stack of 1 000 000 one dollar bills?
2. In the James Bond movie "Goldfinger," one million dollars' worth of gold was loaded into the trunk of a Lincoln Continental. Prove that the Lincoln's springs would have broken. (The price of gold was $1.23/g at that time.)
3. To prove that a person cannot write 1 000 000 zeros in 24 h of continuous writing, proceed as follows.
   (*a*) Determine the number of zeros you can write in 15 s. Write as fast as you can.
   (*b*) Determine the number of zeros you could write in 1 min and 1 h if you wrote at the same rate.
   (*c*) Calculate the number of hours required to write 1 000 000 zeros at your 15 s rate.
4. Determine the thickness of one of your hairs. (The shop teacher can lend you an instrument to do this). Find the width of 1 000 000 hairs placed side by side.
5. One million ants are marching in single file. How long is the marching file of ants? (Assume there is no space between them.)
6. In a "March of Dimes," contributors placed dimes in a strip along Main Street. $100 000 was collected in the strip. How long was the strip?
7. Estimate the time it would take you to count from 1 to 1 000 000.
8. The earth travels around the sun at approximately 32 km/s. How many kilometres has the earth travelled in the last 1000 years?
9. A bullet from a high-speed rifle travels at about 1500 m/s. The distance from the earth to the sun is about 150 000 000 km. How long would it take a bullet to reach the sun if the bullet were unaffected by the gravity of the sun or earth?
10. Find the number of times your heart beats in a year.

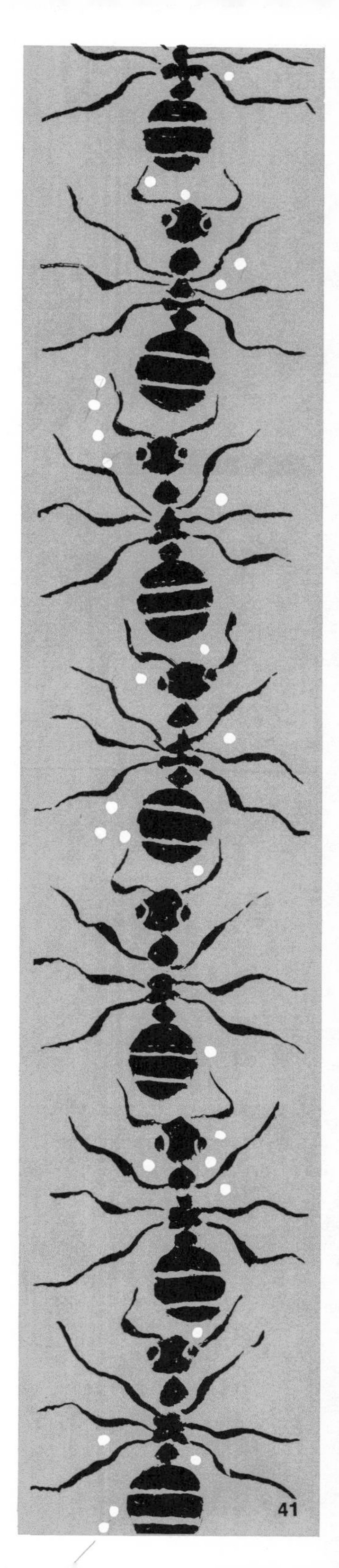

Unit 4
Addition and Subtraction of Integers

4.1 Adding Integers

A

1. Sometimes we need numbers on the other side of zero. Here are 2 examples. Think of some others.

   (*a*) The temperature drops away down on a frosty January morning. We might say,

   "It's twenty degrees below zero this morning."

   – 20°C

   (*b*) Two business partners are talking. One asks, "Are we making any money this month?" Her partner, who keeps the books, replies,

   "Sorry, Elayne. We're two thousand dollars in debt."

   –$2000

Which sums are "in the red" or "in the black"?

2. Read each dollar graph.

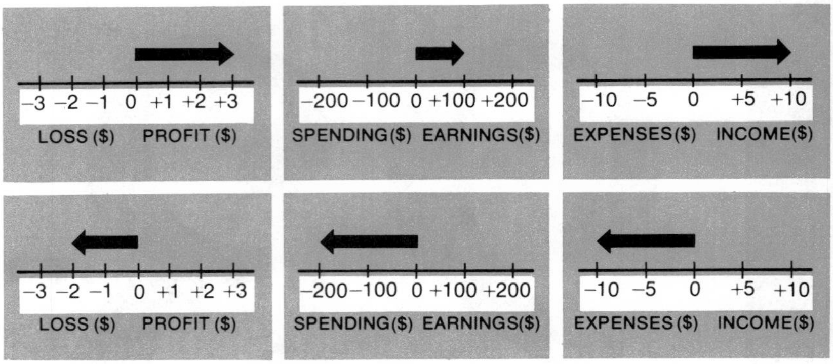

→ −3 −2 −1 0 +1 +2 +3 LOSS ($) PROFIT ($)	→ −200 −100 0 +100 +200 SPENDING($) EARNINGS($)	→ −10 −5 0 +5 +10 EXPENSES($) INCOME($)
← −3 −2 −1 0 +1 +2 +3 LOSS ($) PROFIT ($)	← −200 −100 0 +100 +200 SPENDING($) EARNINGS($)	← −10 −5 0 +5 +10 EXPENSES($) INCOME($)

3. Match the items in column A with those in column B.

A		B	
(*a*)	salary \$150	(*i*)	+150
(*b*)	profit \$2000	(*ii*)	−150
(*c*)	expenses \$2000	(*iii*)	+2000
(*d*)	spending \$7	(*iv*)	−2000
(*e*)	loss \$150	(*v*)	+7
(*f*)	income \$7	(*vi*)	−7

B 1. Everybody can add 4 + 5.

What is the total?

Christmas Card Sales

First week	\$4
Second week	\$5
Total	\$?

How much are you "in the hole"?

But suppose you earn \$4 one week and have \$5 expenses as well!

\$4 income + \$5 expenses = ?

Addition usually means an increase, as 4 + 5 = 9. But for now, when you see +, think *followed by*.

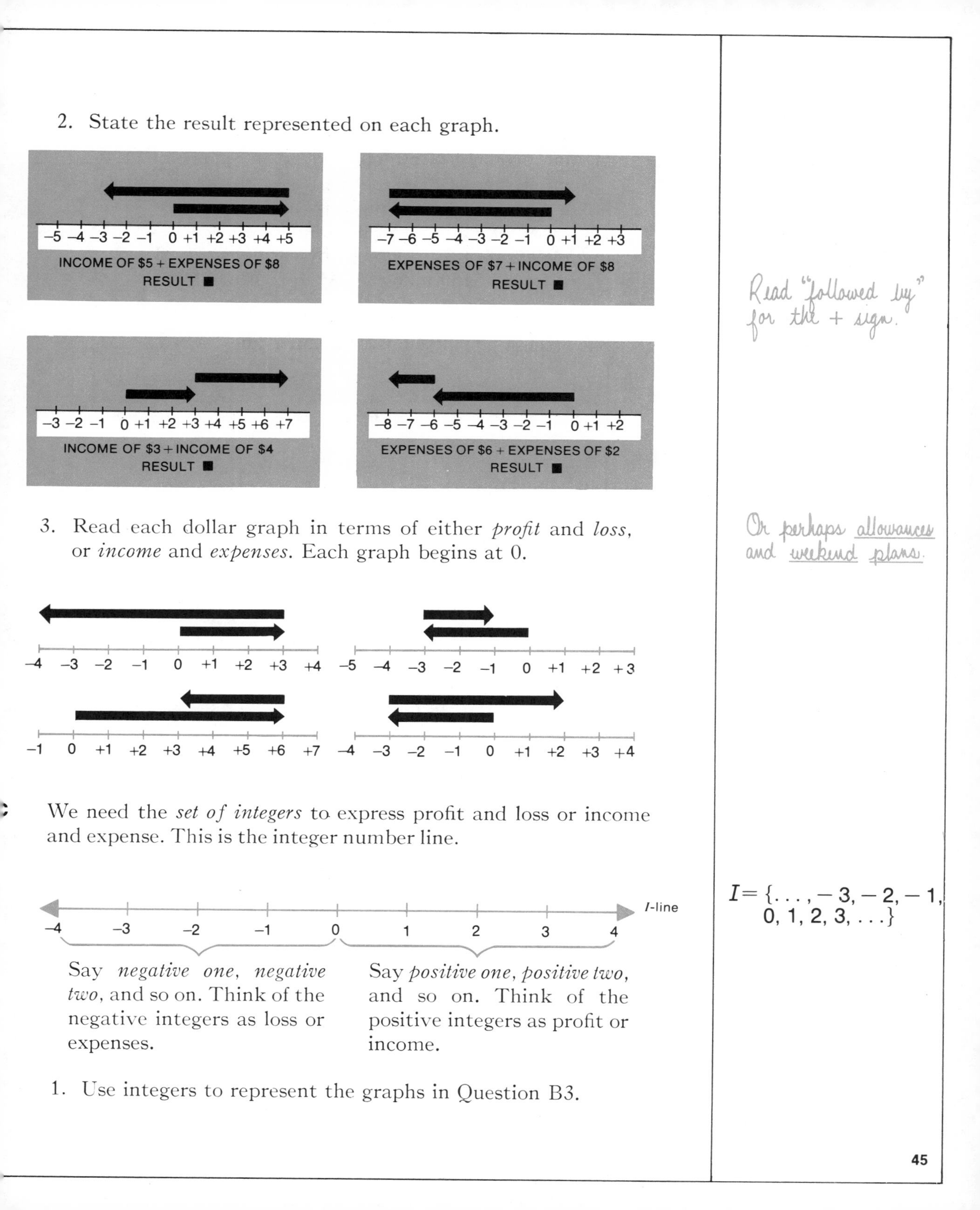

2. State the result represented on each graph.

−5 −4 −3 −2 −1 0 +1 +2 +3 +4 +5

INCOME OF $5 + EXPENSES OF $8
RESULT ■

−7 −6 −5 −4 −3 −2 −1 0 +1 +2 +3

EXPENSES OF $7 + INCOME OF $8
RESULT ■

−3 −2 −1 0 +1 +2 +3 +4 +5 +6 +7

INCOME OF $3 + INCOME OF $4
RESULT ■

−8 −7 −6 −5 −4 −3 −2 −1 0 +1 +2

EXPENSES OF $6 + EXPENSES OF $2
RESULT ■

Read "followed by" for the + sign.

3. Read each dollar graph in terms of either *profit* and *loss*, or *income* and *expenses*. Each graph begins at 0.

Or perhaps allowances and weekend plans.

−4 −3 −2 −1 0 +1 +2 +3 +4

−5 −4 −3 −2 −1 0 +1 +2 +3

−1 0 +1 +2 +3 +4 +5 +6 +7

−4 −3 −2 −1 0 +1 +2 +3 +4

C We need the *set of integers* to express profit and loss or income and expense. This is the integer number line.

−4 −3 −2 −1 0 1 2 3 4 *I*-line

$I = \{\ldots, -3, -2, -1, 0, 1, 2, 3, \ldots\}$

Say *negative one*, *negative two*, and so on. Think of the negative integers as loss or expenses.

Say *positive one*, *positive two*, and so on. Think of the positive integers as profit or income.

1. Use integers to represent the graphs in Question B3.

2. Use integers to rewrite these statements.
   (*a*) an income of $150 followed by an income of $150
   (*b*) an income of $100 followed by expenses of $40
   (*c*) a profit of $100 followed by a loss of $125
   (*d*) a loss of $4 followed by a loss of $6.50
   (*e*) expenses of $13 followed by earnings of $20
   (*f*) a loss of $150 followed by a profit of $140

3. Show the following sums using an *I*-line.

(*a*) $3 + 5$	(*d*) $-3 + (-5)$	(*g*) $5 + (-1)$
(*b*) $2 + 4$	(*e*) $4 + 1$	(*h*) $4 + (-4)$
(*c*) $-1 + (-3)$	(*f*) $-2 + (-4)$	(*i*) $3 + (-5)$

NOTE:
You don't need brackets for the first number in a sum.

4. Find the sum.

(*a*) $5 + 6$	(*e*) $5 + (-3)$	(*i*) $-8 + 7$
(*b*) $-4 + (-5)$	(*f*) $4 + (-4)$	(*j*) $6 + (-10)$
(*c*) $-2 + (-3)$	(*g*) $-6 + 2$	(*k*) $5 + (-15)$
(*d*) $8 + (-4)$	(*h*) $-5 + 3$	(*l*) $-4 + 9$

D

1. Find the sums for (*a*) and (*b*); (*c*) and (*d*); (*e*) and (*f*); (*g*) and (*h*). Then answer Question 2.

(*a*) $(4 + 2) + 16$	(*b*) $4 + (2 + 16)$
(*c*) $[(-3) + (-8)] + 15$	(*d*) $-3 + [(-8) + 15]$
(*e*) $[(-2) + (-6)] + (-15)$	(*f*) $-2 + [(-6) + (-15)]$
(*g*) $[(-4) + 7] + (-2)$	(*h*) $-4 + [7 + (-2)]$

2. Does it matter in what order you add integers?

Here's a useful tip!

You can use this idea to make addition easier. Group together the positive integers and the negative integers, like this.

$$
\begin{aligned}
& -6 + 4 + (-8) + 16 \\
&= \underbrace{-6 + (-8)} + \underbrace{4 + 16} \\
&= \quad -14 \quad + \quad 20 \\
&= 6
\end{aligned}
$$

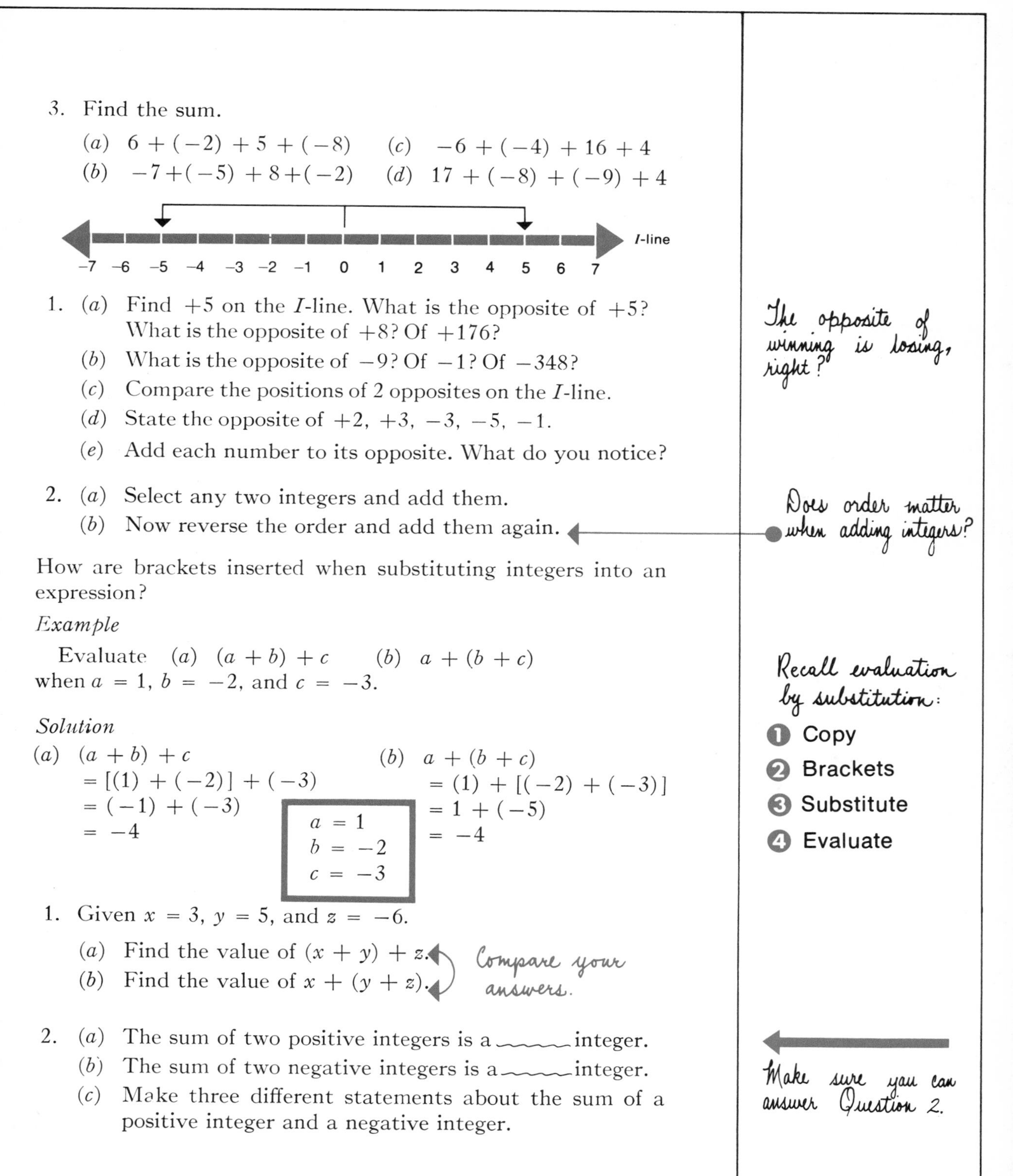

3. Find the sum.

   (a) $6 + (-2) + 5 + (-8)$ (c) $-6 + (-4) + 16 + 4$

   (b) $-7 + (-5) + 8 + (-2)$ (d) $17 + (-8) + (-9) + 4$

1. (a) Find $+5$ on the I-line. What is the opposite of $+5$? What is the opposite of $+8$? Of $+176$?
   (b) What is the opposite of -9? Of -1? Of -348?
   (c) Compare the positions of 2 opposites on the I-line.
   (d) State the opposite of $+2$, $+3$, -3, -5, -1.
   (e) Add each number to its opposite. What do you notice?

The opposite of winning is losing, right?

2. (a) Select any two integers and add them.
   (b) Now reverse the order and add them again.

Does order matter when adding integers?

How are brackets inserted when substituting integers into an expression?

Example

Evaluate (a) $(a + b) + c$ (b) $a + (b + c)$ when $a = 1$, $b = -2$, and $c = -3$.

Recall evaluation by substitution:

1. Copy
2. Brackets
3. Substitute
4. Evaluate

Solution

(a) $(a + b) + c$
$= [(1) + (-2)] + (-3)$
$= (-1) + (-3)$
$= -4$

(b) $a + (b + c)$
$= (1) + [(-2) + (-3)]$
$= 1 + (-5)$
$= -4$

$a = 1$
$b = -2$
$c = -3$

1. Given $x = 3$, $y = 5$, and $z = -6$.
   (a) Find the value of $(x + y) + z$.
   (b) Find the value of $x + (y + z)$.

Compare your answers.

2. (a) The sum of two positive integers is a ______ integer.
   (b) The sum of two negative integers is a ______ integer.
   (c) Make three different statements about the sum of a positive integer and a negative integer.

Make sure you can answer Question 2.

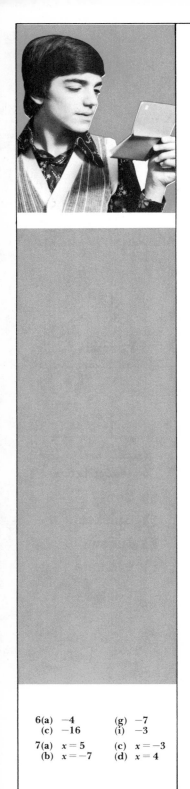

Exercise 4.1

Discussion

1. Represent the following using integers.
   (*a*) An increase of 10°C in temperature.
   (*b*) The loss of 50¢.
   (*c*) A rise in the river water level of 4 m.
   (*d*) A bank deposit of $10 as related to your bank balance.
   (*e*) A bank deposit of $10 as related to the cash in your wallet.

2. Read and find the sum.

(*a*) $5 + 6$	(*e*) $5 + (-3)$	(*i*) $-8 + 7$
(*b*) $-4 + (-5)$	(*f*) $4 + (-4)$	(*j*) $6 + (-10)$
(*c*) $-2 + (-3)$	(*g*) $-6 + 2$	(*k*) $5 + (-15)$
(*d*) $8 + (-4)$	(*h*) $-5 + 3$	(*l*) $-4 + 9$

3. Add.

−2	−6	4	6	−2	−4	6	−5
4	−2	−5	−2	−3	5	−7	−2
				5	−3	1	−1

4. State the sum.
   (*a*) -2 and 2 (*b*) 4 and -4

5. (*a*) What is the easiest way to find $(-6) + 5 + 1$?
   (*b*) Does the order of adding integers matter?

Written Solutions

6. Find the sum.

(*a*) $4 + (-3) + (-5)$	(*f*) $3 + (-5) + 6 + (-4)$
(*b*) $-2 + 4 + (-3)$	(*g*) $-12 + 15 + (-7) + (-3)$
(*c*) $-6 + (-8) + (-2)$	(*h*) $-4 + (-3) + 5 + (-1)$
(*d*) $-3 + (-2) + (-8)$	(*i*) $10 + (-7) + (-8) + 2$
(*e*) $6 + 4 + (-5)$	(*j*) $-48 + 73 + (-101)$

7. Solve.

(*a*) $-2 + x = 3$	(*c*) $5 + x = 2$
(*b*) $6 + x = -1$	(*d*) $-5 + x = -1$

6(a) −4 **(c)** −16 **(g)** −7 **(i)** −3
7(a) $x = 5$ **(b)** $x = -7$ **(c)** $x = -3$ **(d)** $x = 4$

8. Represent each of the following events using a sum of integers and state the result.

   (*a*) Income is \$5 and expenses are \$1.50 and \$2.00.
   (*b*) The temperature is 5°C and falls 8°C.
   (*c*) The river water level is 1 m below normal and rises 2 m.
   (*d*) Represent Janine's financial position if Laura owes Janine 25¢, and Janine owes Marya 30¢.
   (*e*) The temperature is −21°C and rises 13°C.
   (*f*) Write the opposites of 6, −2, 7, 0, and −5.
   (*g*) Add: 3 to the opposite of 4
   −6 to the opposite of 2
   −1 to the opposite of −3
   2 to the opposite of −5

9. Evaluate the following expressions.

   (*a*) $r + s + t$, when $r = -5$, $s = 6$, and $t = -7$.
   (*b*) $(a + b) + (c + d)$, when $a = b = -2$ and $c = d = -3$.
   (*c*) $x + (y + z)$, when $x = 4$, $y = -3$, and $z = 1$.
   (*d*) $k + (l + m) + 6$, when $k = -2$, $l = 14$, and $m = -18$.

8(b) $5 + (-8) = -3$
∴ The temperature is −3°C.
(d) $25 + (-30) = -5$
∴ Janine is 5¢ in debt.

9(a) −6 **(c)** 2
(b) −10 **(d)** 0

4.2 Subtracting Integers

1. *Subtract* the integers in column A but *add* the integers in column B.

	A	B
(*a*)	8 − 5	8 + (−5)
(*b*)	9 − 2	9 + (−2)
(*c*)	6 − 3	6 + (−3)
(*d*)	11 − 7	11 + (−7)
(*e*)	9 − 9	9 + (−9)

2. Compare your answers in columns A and B. Study the columns further and then try to complete this statement.

> To subtract an integer, we ~~~~~

3. Find the missing answers in column C.

C	D
(*a*) $3 - 5 = \square$	(*a*) $3 + (-5) = -2$
(*b*) $3 - 4 = \square$	(*b*) $3 + (-4) = -1$
(*c*) $3 - 3 = 0$	(*c*) $3 + (-3) = 0$
(*d*) $3 - 2 = 1$	(*d*) $3 + (-2) = 1$
(*e*) $3 - 1 = 2$	(*e*) $3 + (-1) = 2$
(*f*) $3 - 0 = 3$	(*f*) $3 + 0 = 3$
(*g*) $3 - (-1) = \square$	(*g*) $3 + 1 = 4$
(*h*) $3 - (-2) = \square$	(*h*) $3 + 2 = 5$

4. Compare the equations in C and D. Can you complete the statement now?

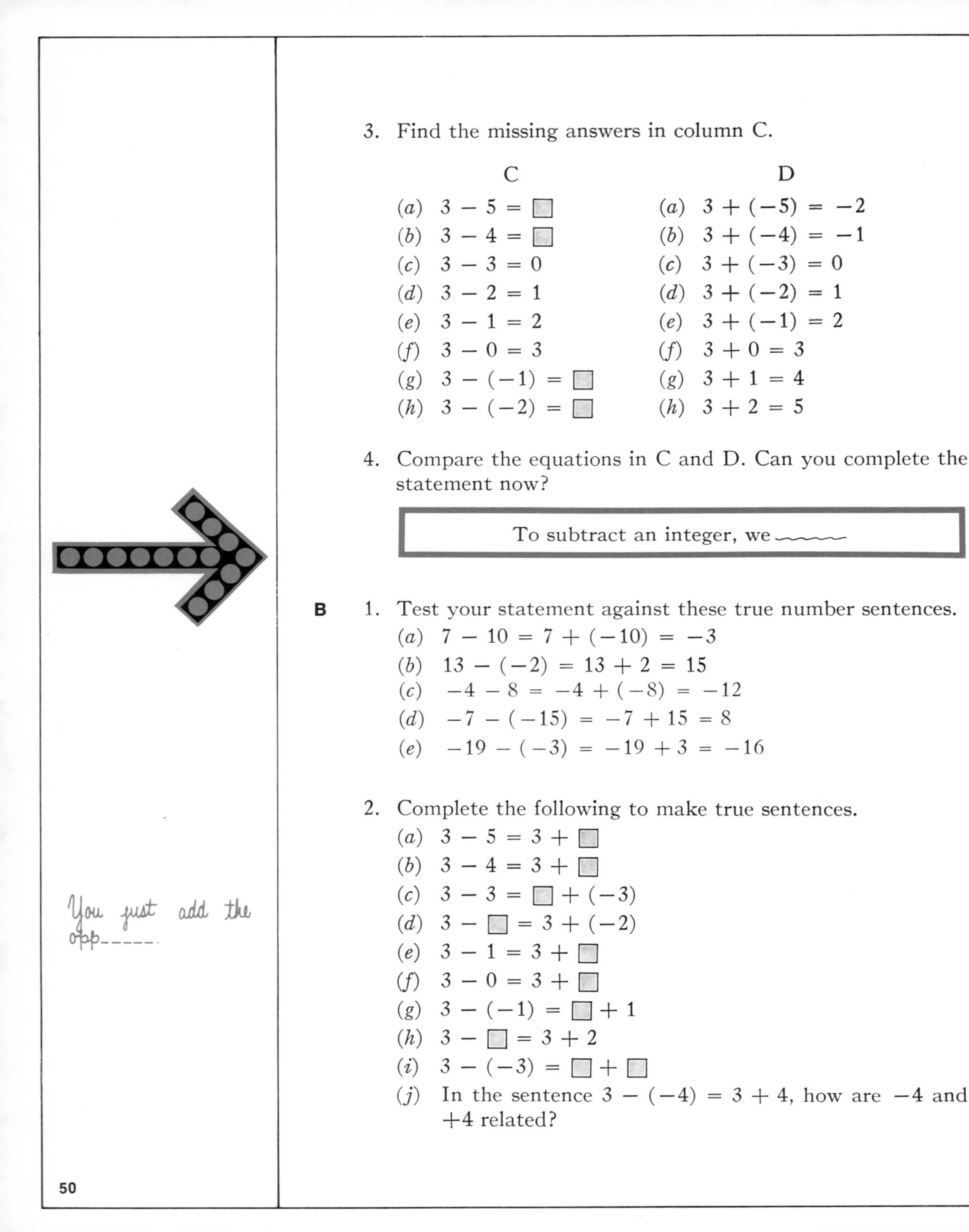

To subtract an integer, we ~~~~~

B 1. Test your statement against these true number sentences.

(*a*) $7 - 10 = 7 + (-10) = -3$

(*b*) $13 - (-2) = 13 + 2 = 15$

(*c*) $-4 - 8 = -4 + (-8) = -12$

(*d*) $-7 - (-15) = -7 + 15 = 8$

(*e*) $-19 - (-3) = -19 + 3 = -16$

2. Complete the following to make true sentences.

(*a*) $3 - 5 = 3 + \square$

(*b*) $3 - 4 = 3 + \square$

(*c*) $3 - 3 = \square + (-3)$

(*d*) $3 - \square = 3 + (-2)$

(*e*) $3 - 1 = 3 + \square$

(*f*) $3 - 0 = 3 + \square$

(*g*) $3 - (-1) = \square + 1$

(*h*) $3 - \square = 3 + 2$

(*i*) $3 - (-3) = \square + \square$

(*j*) In the sentence $3 - (-4) = 3 + 4$, how are -4 and $+4$ related?

You just add the opp-----

3. Find the difference.

5	8	0	−1	6	−7	4	−5	0	−22
11	−2	6	0	−13	8	−2	−3	−5	−7

4. Subtract.

(*a*) 9 from 4 (*c*) −14 from 5 (*e*) −5 from −3
(*b*) 7 from 2 (*d*) −3 from −5 (*f*) 6 from −2

5. Find the difference.

(*a*) $23 - (-7)$ (*d*) $31 - 11$ (*g*) $-11 - 5$
(*b*) $13 - (-40)$ (*e*) $19 - 40$ (*h*) $-16 - (-2)$
(*c*) $13 - 4$ (*f*) $-3 - 4$ (*i*) $-8 - (-21)$

C Study the example to see how to substitute integers into algebraic expressions.

Example

Evaluate (*a*) $2a - b + c$ (*b*) $2a - (b - c)$
when $a = 3$, $b = -4$, and $c = -5$.

Solution

(*a*) $2a - b + c$
$= 2(a) - (b) + (c)$
$= 2(3) - (-4) + (-5)$
$= 6 + 4 + (-5)$
$= 10 + (-5)$
$= 5$

(*b*) $2a - (b - c)$
$= 2(a) - [(b) - (c)]$
$= 2(3) - [(-4) - (-5)]$
$= 6 - [-4 + 5]$
$= 6 - 1$
$= 5$

$a = 3$
$b = -4$
$c = -5$

Exercise 4.2

Discussion

1. (*a*) Subtract 6 from 4. Explain your result by referring to a thermometer.
   (*b*) In subtracting −5 from 2 you write $2 - (-5)$. What do you write next? State in your own words what you do to subtract an integer.

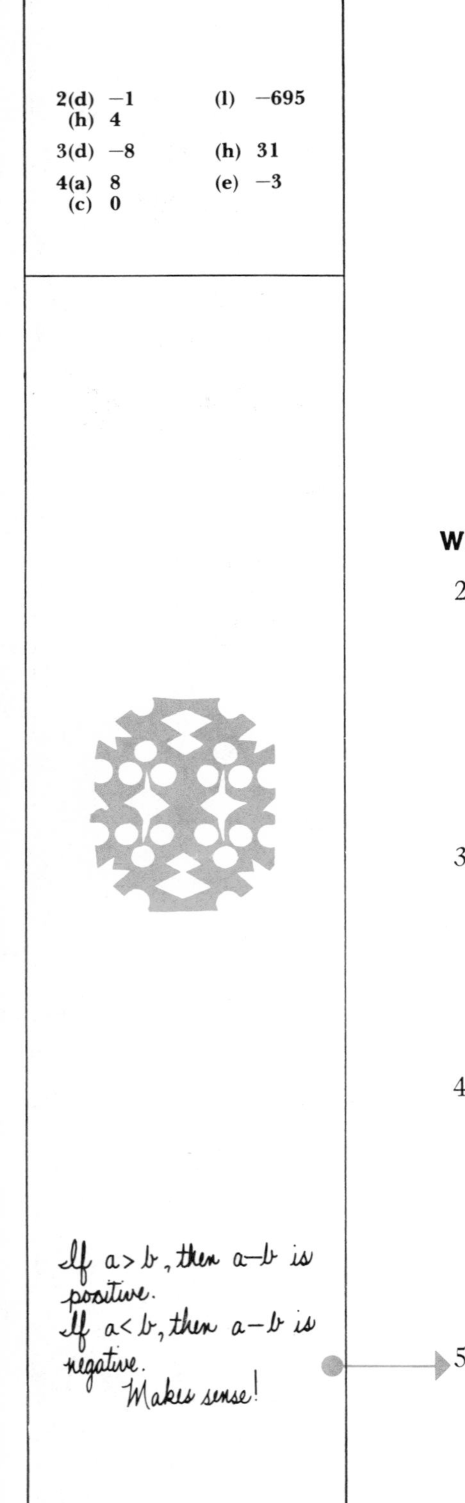
2(d) −1
(h) 4
(l) −695
3(d) −8
(h) 31
4(a) 8
(c) 0
(e) −3
If a > b, then a − b is positive.
If a < b, then a − b is negative.
Makes sense!

(*c*) Subtract 5 from 0, 2 from 0, −3 from 0, and −7 from 0. What do you notice?

(*d*) Is the following statement true?

$$-5 - (-3) \neq -3 - (-5)$$

Can you change the order of integers when you subtract?

(*e*) Subtract.

8	2	−3	−1	0	3	−2	5
5	−1	−2	−6	2	8	4	−1

7	5	−6	−9	−4	24	43	−16
−3	0	13	12	−17	30	−71	−95

Written Solutions

2. Find the difference.

(*a*) $6 - 2$
(*b*) $-4 - 2$
(*c*) $8 - (-1)$
(*d*) $-3 - (-2)$
(*e*) $-4 - (-7)$
(*f*) $3 - (-6)$
(*g*) $5 - 8$
(*h*) $0 - (-4)$
(*i*) $16 - 72$
(*j*) $-19 - 47$
(*k*) $569 - (-748)$
(*l*) $-1648 - (-953)$

3. Subtract.

(*a*)	(*c*)	(*e*)	(*g*)
34	−40	−18	−30
20	10	−5	−50

(*b*)	(*d*)	(*f*)	(*h*)
8	−2	74	−48
10	6	−99	−79

4. Find the value of the following.

(*a*) $a - b + c$ when $a = 6, b = 2, c = 4$
(*b*) $x - y - z$ when $x = -3, y = 4, z = -1$
(*c*) $p - (q - r)$ when $p = -2, q = 3, r = 5$
(*d*) $(r - s) + t$ when $r = -2, s = 4, t = -3$
(*e*) $(a - b) - (c - d)$
when $a = b = -1, c = 1, d = -2$

5. By subtraction determine which is the larger of the following numbers.

(*a*) −2, −1 (*b*) 5, −1 (*c*) −15, −20

6. In each of the following, represent the event by a difference of integers and state the result.
   (*a*) You have \$20 and lose a \$5 bill.
   (*b*) The temperature is -5°C and it drops by 15°C.
   (*c*) In 1 week, Art Broken earns \$10 and spends \$12.
   (*d*) Dee Posit has \$56 in the bank and writes a cheque for \$62.
   (*e*) Willie Stopp's mass is 60 kg and he gains 15 kg.

7. Simplify.
   (*a*) $-3 - 3 - 3 - 3$
   (*b*) $2 + 2 + 2$
   (*c*) $+(-3) + (-3) + (-3) + (-3)$
   (*d*) $-(-2) - (-2) - (-2)$

8. Express each as a sum and simplify.
   (*a*) $2 + 7 - 19$
   (*b*) $-4 + 7 - (-3)$
   (*c*) $5 - 9 - (-14) - 3$
   (*d*) $-2 + (-8) - 7 - (-25)$
   (*e*) $13 - (-4) + (-10) - 7$
   (*f*) $-1 + (-2) - 3 - (-4) + 5$
   (*g*) $92 - (-23) - 126 + (-18)$
   (*h*) $-819 - (-420) + 83 - 26 - (-178)$

9. Simplify.
   (*a*) $-2 + (3 - 4) - 5$
   (*b*) $3 - [1 - (-5)] + (-2 + 4)$
   (*c*) $-7 + [-3 - (-8)] + 10$
   (*d*) $[4 + (-2)] + [-6 + 2]$
   (*e*) $[-3 - 1] + [5 - 7]$
   (*f*) $[4 - (-3)] - [(-20) + 49]$

10. Find the value of the following.
   (*a*) $a - b + c$ if $a = 2, b = 3, c = -1$
   (*b*) $m + n + p$ if $m = -4, n = -2, p = 0$
   (*c*) $q - r - s + t$ if $q = -3, r = -5, s = -6, t = 11$
   (*d*) $x - y + 2z$ if $x = -7, y = -2, z = 5$
   (*e*) $p - q + 3r$ if $p = -3, q = -4, r = 2$
   (*f*) $2a - b + 7$ if $a = 5, b = -3$
   (*g*) $-k - m - n$ if $k = -4, m = 9, n = -1$

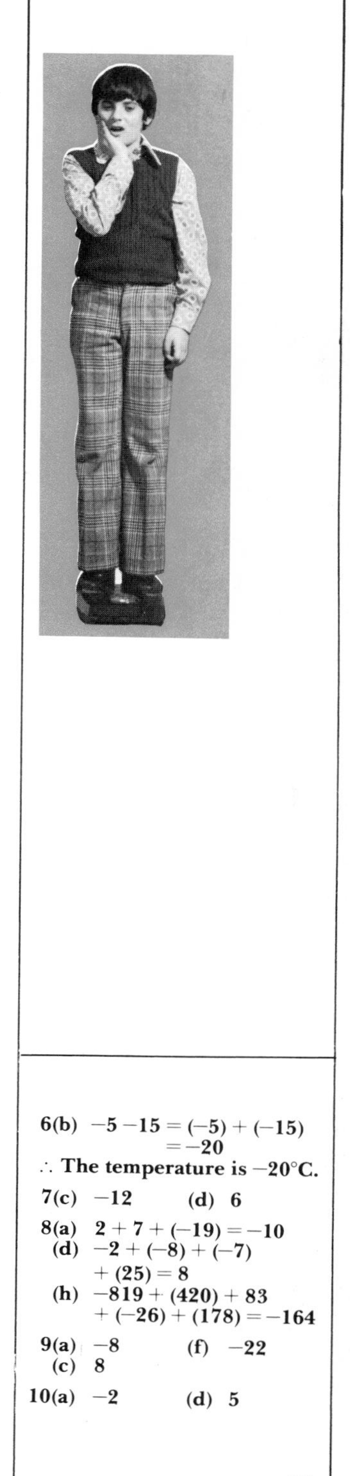

6(b) $-5 - 15 = (-5) + (-15) = -20$

∴ The temperature is -20°C.

7(c) -12 **(d)** 6

8(a) $2 + 7 + (-19) = -10$

(d) $-2 + (-8) + (-7) + (25) = 8$

(h) $-819 + (420) + 83 + (-26) + (178) = -164$

9(a) -8 **(f)** -22

(c) 8

10(a) -2 **(d)** 5

4.3 Summary of Addition and Subtraction of Integers

A *Addition of Integers*

(*a*) $(+2) + (+3) = +5$

> The sum of 2 positive integers is a positive integer.

(*b*) $(-2) + (-3) = -5$

> The sum of 2 negative integers is a negative integer.

(*c*) $(+2) + (-3) = -1$, $(-2) + (+3) = +1$

> The sum of a positive integer and a negative integer may be either a positive integer or a negative integer.

Hint: When adding many integers together, add all the positive integers, then all the negative integers, and combine the results.

(*d*)
$$\begin{aligned} & -2 + 6 + 5 + (-6) + (-4) \\ &= \underbrace{(-2) + (-6) + (-4)}_{} + \underbrace{6 + 5}_{} \\ &= \quad -12 \quad + \quad 11 \\ &= -1 \end{aligned}$$

B *Subtraction of Integers*

(*a*)
$$\begin{aligned} & (+2) - (+3) \\ &= (+2) + (-3) \\ &= -1 \end{aligned}$$

(*b*)
$$\begin{aligned} & (+2) - (-3) \\ &= (+2) + (+3) \\ &= +5 \end{aligned}$$

> To subtract an integer, add its opposite.

Hint: In simplifying, change all subtractions to additions of opposites.

(*c*)
$$\begin{aligned} & 6 - (-2) + 5 + (-6) - 3 \\ &= 6 + 2 + 5 + (-6) + (-3) \\ &= 13 + (-9) \\ &= 4 \end{aligned}$$

Exercise 4.3

Discussion

1. Add.

3	5	6	−2	−6	−4	−8	4	10	−4
2	−3	−8	5	3	−2	−10	7	−5	−1

2. Subtract.

7	5	4	5	−3	−5	−4	−6	4	6
3	9	−1	−8	2	10	−1	−8	9	−3

Written Solutions

3. Add or subtract as indicated.

   (*a*) $35 + 43$ (*d*) $-25 + 18$ (*g*) $63 + (-49)$
   (*b*) $26 - 58$ (*e*) $-14 - 53$ (*h*) $-87 + (-54)$
   (*c*) $-13 + 42$ (*f*) $28 - (-18)$ (*i*) $-14 - (-15)$

4. Evaluate each expression.

   (*a*) $46 - 15 + 29$ (*d*) $-15 + (-68) + (-17)$
   (*b*) $12 - 18 - 20$ (*e*) $28 - (-42) - 50$
   (*c*) $42 + (-16) - 5$ (*f*) $-21 + 15 - (-13)$

5. Evaluate when $a = -2$, $b = 5$, $c = -4$, and $d = 6$.

   (*a*) $a - (b + c)$ (*d*) $d - (a - c) + b$
   (*b*) $a + b - (c + d)$ (*e*) $c - a + b - d$
   (*c*) $b - a + (d - c)$ (*f*) $-(a - b) + (c - d)$

6. Express each group of numbers as a sum, and then evaluate.

   (*a*) −42, 43, −44 (*c*) 250, −372, −137, 463
   (*b*) 28, −73, −28, 73 (*d*) −287, 529, −156, −817, 647

7. Express the difference between the following pairs of numbers in 2 ways, and then evaluate.

   (*a*) 5, 8 (*c*) 58, −29 (*e*) −147, 260
   (*b*) −3, 9 (*d*) −46, −57 (*f*) −529, −637

8. Evaluate.

   (*a*) $3 - [(-5) + (-6)]$ (*d*) $-(45 - 35) + [-6 - (-10)]$
   (*b*) $(2 - 5) - (5 - 2)$ (*e*) $5[6 - (-2)] - 4(-3 + 8)$
   (*c*) $14 - 3[5 + (-4)]$ (*f*) $16 - 28 - 2[6 + (-5)]$

3(a) 78 **(c)** 29 **(e)** −67 **(g)** 14 **(i)** 1

4(a) 60 **(c)** 21 **(d)** −100 **(f)** 7

That is:
5(a) −3 **(c)** 17 **(e)** −3

6(b) 0 **(c)** 204

7(a) 3, −3 **(c)** 87, −87 **(e)** 407, −407

8(a) 14 **(c)** 11 **(e)** 20 **(g)** 12

The difference between 2 and 3 is either 2−3 or 3−2.

BODMAS!

Unit 5
Multiplication and Division of Integers

Integers were created about 300 years ago to meet the needs of mathematics and science. In the last unit, we learned how to add and subtract integers. Now we will extend our work to include the operations of multiplication and division in the set of integers.

There are 3 possibilities in multiplying or dividing 2 integers:

Both integers may be positive.

One may be positive and the other negative.

Both may be negative.

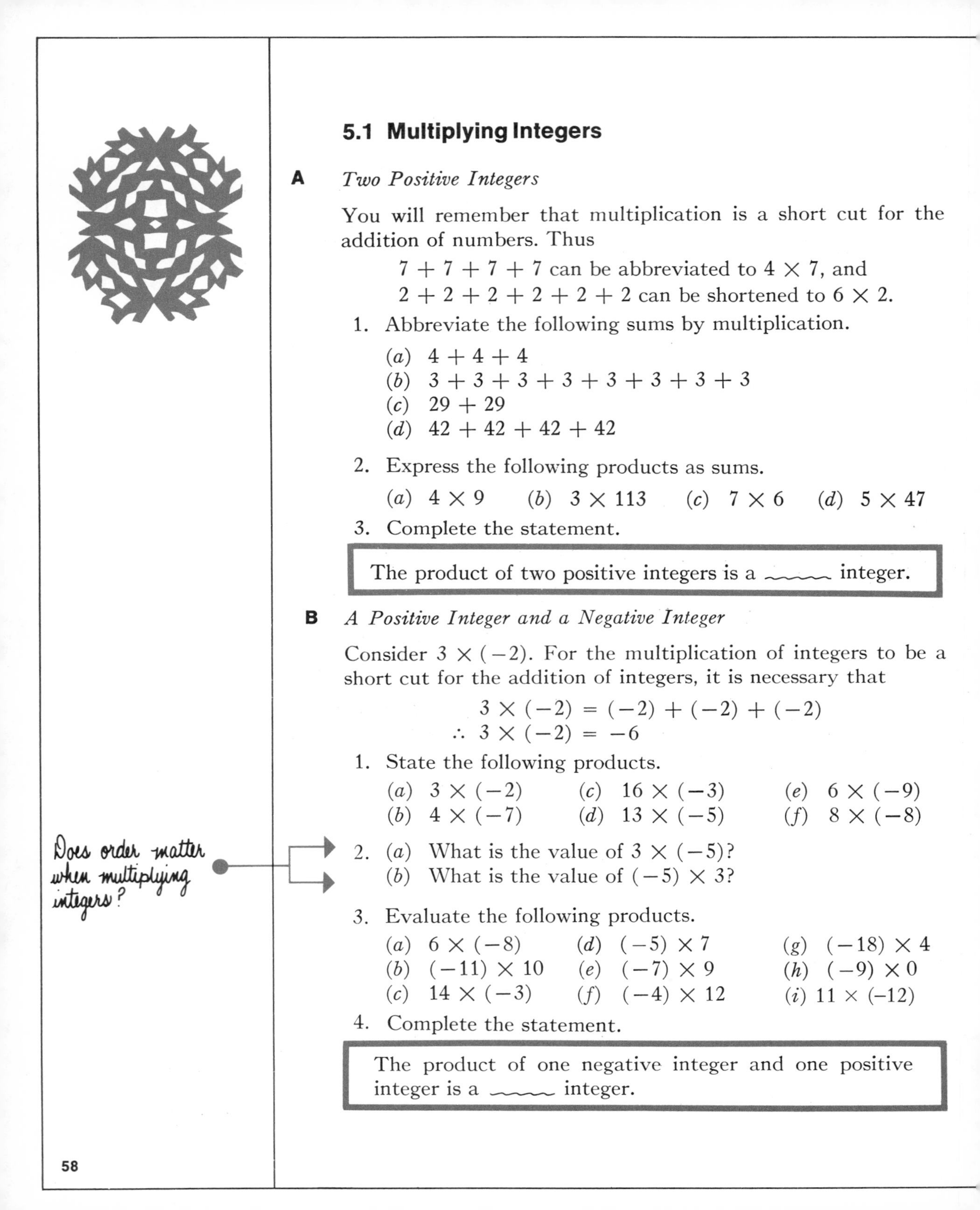

5.1 Multiplying Integers

A *Two Positive Integers*

You will remember that multiplication is a short cut for the addition of numbers. Thus

$7 + 7 + 7 + 7$ can be abbreviated to 4×7, and
$2 + 2 + 2 + 2 + 2 + 2$ can be shortened to 6×2.

1. Abbreviate the following sums by multiplication.
   (*a*) $4 + 4 + 4$
   (*b*) $3 + 3 + 3 + 3 + 3 + 3 + 3 + 3$
   (*c*) $29 + 29$
   (*d*) $42 + 42 + 42 + 42$

2. Express the following products as sums.
   (*a*) 4×9 (*b*) 3×113 (*c*) 7×6 (*d*) 5×47

3. Complete the statement.

> The product of two positive integers is a ~~~~ integer.

B *A Positive Integer and a Negative Integer*

Consider $3 \times (-2)$. For the multiplication of integers to be a short cut for the addition of integers, it is necessary that

$$3 \times (-2) = (-2) + (-2) + (-2)$$
$$\therefore\ 3 \times (-2) = -6$$

1. State the following products.
   (*a*) $3 \times (-2)$ (*c*) $16 \times (-3)$ (*e*) $6 \times (-9)$
   (*b*) $4 \times (-7)$ (*d*) $13 \times (-5)$ (*f*) $8 \times (-8)$

Does order matter when multiplying integers?

2. (*a*) What is the value of $3 \times (-5)$?
   (*b*) What is the value of $(-5) \times 3$?

3. Evaluate the following products.
   (*a*) $6 \times (-8)$ (*d*) $(-5) \times 7$ (*g*) $(-18) \times 4$
   (*b*) $(-11) \times 10$ (*e*) $(-7) \times 9$ (*h*) $(-9) \times 0$
   (*c*) $14 \times (-3)$ (*f*) $(-4) \times 12$ (*i*) $11 \times (-12)$

4. Complete the statement.

> The product of one negative integer and one positive integer is a ~~~~ integer.

C *Two Negative Integers*

1. Can you give a meaning to $(-3) \times (-2)$?

   We know that $(-3) \times 2 = -6$. You might guess that $(-3) \times (-2)$ is not -6.

   Before you answer this question, consider a couple of situations that are outside the realm of mathematics.

   (*a*) If you say, "I don't never watch TV!", you really are saying, "I always watch TV!"
   "...don't never..." is like $(-)(-)$.
   "...always..." is like $(+)$.

   Think about this!

   (*b*) The effect on a club of "good guys" or "bad guys" joining or leaving can be shown in a table.

	Good Guys +	*Bad Guys* −
Join +	+	−
Leave −	−	+

   If a good guy joins, that's a +.
   If a good guy leaves, that's a −.
   If a bad guy joins, that's a −.
   If a bad guy leaves, that's a +.

   If a bad guy (−) leaves (−), that's a good (+) result! You might guess that $(-3) \times (-2) = +6$.

   !

2. Here's another example that is more mathematical. The local hockey club is losing money at the rate of $100/game. The following time line illustrates its finances in the past, now, and in the future.

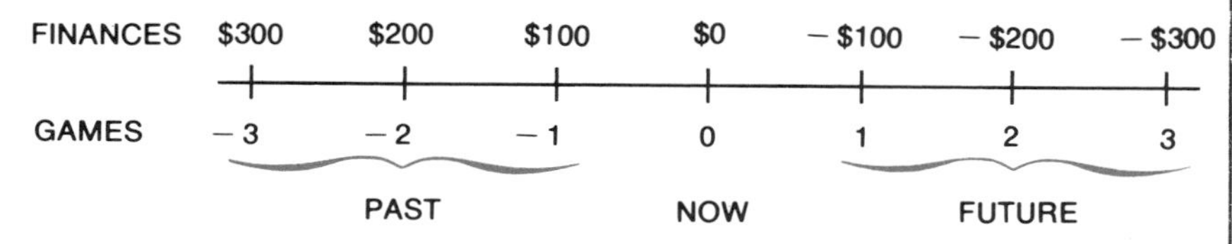

Notice that the team has *no* money now.

After 3 more games, the loss will be $300 more, and the team will be in debt $300; 3(−$100) or −$300.

Makes sense!

Two games ago, the loss was $200 less than now, and the team had $200; (−2)(−$100) or $200.

Do you see the pattern?

That's a little hard to believe, isn't it! *Multiplying two negative numbers gives a positive number!* The following pattern shows that this result really is quite reasonable.

$$(-3) \times 3 = -9$$
$$(-3) \times 2 = -6$$
$$(-3) \times 1 = -3$$
$$(-3) \times 0 = 0$$
$$(-3) \times (-1) = \square$$
$$(-3) \times (-2) = \square$$

What is happening?

3. Complete the statement.

> The product of two negative integers is a ~~~~ integer.

4. State the following products.

(a) $(-7)(-4)$
(b) $(-6)(-5)$
(c) $(-32)(-2)$
(d) $(-4)(-13)$
(e) $(-8)(-7)$
(f) $(-21)(-3)$

D You should now be able to solve problems involving substitution of integers, as illustrated below.

Example

Evaluate the following expressions when $a = 3$, $b = -4$, $c = -2$.

(a) abc (b) $a + 2b - 3c$ (c) $3a - 2(b + c)$

Solution

(a)
$$\begin{aligned} abc &= (a)(b)(c) \\ &= (3)(-4)(-2) \\ &= (-12)(-2) \\ &= 24 \end{aligned}$$

$a = 3$
$b = -4$
$c = -2$

(b)
$$\begin{aligned} a + 2b - 3c &= (a) + 2(b) - 3(c) \\ &= 3 + 2(-4) + (-3)(-2) \\ &= (3) + 2(-4) + (-3)(-2) \\ &= 3 + (-8) + (6) \\ &= -5 + 6 \\ &= 1 \end{aligned}$$

(*c*) $3a - 2(b + c) = 3(a) - 2[(b) + (c)]$
$= 3(3) - 2[(-4) + (-2)]$
$= 9 - 2(-6)$
$= 9 - (-12)$
$= 9 + 12$
$= 21$

Exercise 5.1

Discussion

1. Multiply 0×4, $0 \times (-3)$, 5×0, $(-1) \times 0$. What do you notice?

2. Multiply 1×2, 1×8, 1×14. What do you notice?

3. Multiply $(-1) \times 2$, $(-1) \times 8$, $(-1) \times 14$. What do you notice?

4. "Some number multiplied by 0 gives 1." Comment on this statement.

5. When two integers are multiplied, what kind of number is the product?

6. State the product.
   (*a*) $(-7) \times [2 \times (-3)]$
   (*b*) $[(-7) \times 2] \times (-3)$
   (*c*) $(-5)(-12)$
   (*d*) $(-12)(-5)$

   Compare your answers in (*a*) and (*b*). Is regrouping permitted in multiplication? Try an example of your own. Compare your answers in (*c*) and (*d*). Can you interchange integers when multiplying? Try an example of your own.

7. In your own words state how you would multiply *any* two integers.

8. State the product.
   (*a*) $(-1)(5)$
   (*b*) $(-6)(-2)$
   (*c*) $3(-5)$
   (*d*) $(-5)(-7)$
   (*e*) $(14)(3)$
   (*f*) $0(6)(-432)$
   (*g*) $(-3)(-2)(4)$
   (*h*) $6(-2)(5)$
   (*i*) $(-2)(-3)(4)(-1)$
   (*j*) $(-1)(-1)(-1)(-1)$

Times are changing!
12 cm

9(b) −6 (h) 320
(d) −126 (j) 105
(f) 4 (l) −80

10(a) −6 (c) −6

11(a) 5(−5) = −25
∴ The water level dropped 25 cm.
(c) 3(50) + 4(−75) = −150
∴ There is a net loss of $1.50.

12(c) 11 (g) −51
(e) −36 (h) −52

13(a) −23 (c) 6

Written Solutions

9. Find the product.

(*a*) $5(3)(2)$	(*e*) $(-1)(-2)(-3)$	(*i*) $(-4)(6)(-8)$
(*b*) $(-2)(3)$	(*f*) $(-2)^2$	(*j*) $(-3)(-7)(5)$
(*c*) $(-9)(-5)$	(*g*) $4(-3)^2$	(*k*) $(-1)^3(-1)^4$
(*d*) $18(-7)$	(*h*) $16(-4)(-5)$	(*l*) $(-5)(-2)^4$

10. Find the value of each of the following.
(*a*) $3ab$ where $a = 2, b = -1$
(*b*) $-5ry$ where $r = 3, y = -2$
(*c*) $3a + 2b$ where $a = -4, b = 3$
(*d*) $5r - 3s$ where $r = -2, s = 6$

11. Represent the following events using products of integers and state the result.
(*a*) The water level of the river dropped 5 cm/h for a period of 5 h.
(*b*) The temperature was −10°C at 08:00 and rose 5°C each hour until noon that day.
(*c*) The price of 1 share of Rusty Ironn stock rose 50¢/day for 3 days and then fell 75¢/day for 4 days.
(*d*) Desi Style, a fashion designer, raised the hem of dresses and skirts 3 cm each year for 4 years and then lowered the hems 2 cm each year for 3 years.

12. Simplify.
(*a*) $3(4 - 7)$
(*b*) $(-2)(6 - 5)$
(*c*) $2 - 3[1 + (-4)]$
(*d*) $2(-3)(4) + (-5) + 6(-1)$
(*e*) $(2 - 8)(8 - 2)$
(*f*) $3(-2) + (-1) - 5(-4)$
(*g*) $(-2)(-3 + 4) - 7[2 - (-5)]$
(*h*) $5(-6)(2) + 4[-3 - (-5)]$

13. Evaluate.
(*a*) $3a - 4b + c$ where $a = -2, b = 5, c = 3$
(*b*) $ab - 2bc$ where $a = 6, b = 1, c = -3$
(*c*) $4x - 2xy + 3yz$ where $x = -3, y = 3, z = 0$
(*d*) $2(a - b) - 3(a + b)$ where $a = -3, b = 5$

5.2 Powers of Integers

A

1. What is the short form for $a \times a \times a$?

2. What is *meant* by each of the following?

   (*a*) 2^3 (*b*) m^4 (*c*) b^{12} (*d*) 7^{29}

In the expression m^4, m is the *base*, 4 is the *exponent*, and m^4 is the *4th power of m*.

3. Complete the following statements.

   (*a*) In the expression 5^3, 5 is the ______, 3 is the ______, and 5^3 is the ______ power of ______.

   (*b*) In the expression x^7, ______ is the base, ______ is the exponent, and ______ is the 7th power of x.

   (*c*) In the expression ______, 4 is the base, 3 is the exponent, and ______ is the 3rd power of 4.

$2^5 = 2 \times 2 \times 2 \times 2 \times 2$. What do you notice about the exponent and the number of "twos" in the product?
$m^3 = m \times m \times m$. Here, m^3 is said to be in *exponential form*, and $m \times m \times m$ is said to be in *product form*.

1. State the exponential form of each of the following.

   (*a*) $6 \times 6 \times 6$
   (*b*) $3 \times 3 \times 3 \times 3 \times 3$
   (*c*) $t \times t$
   (*d*) $1 \times 1 \times 1 \times 1 \times 1$
   (*e*) $12 \times 12 \times 12$
   (*f*) $246 \times 246 \times 246 \times 246$

I'm glad I don't have to work out (f)!

2. State the product form of each of the following.

   (*a*) 7^3
   (*b*) 3^7
   (*c*) b^4
   (*d*) y^5
   (*e*) 2^{11}
   (*f*) k^6

1. In the expression $(-1)^3$, the base is ______, the exponent is ______, and $(-1)^3$ is the ______ power of ______.

2. Express $(-1)^3$ in product form.

3. Evaluate $(-1)^3$.

D 1. Evaluate $(-1)^2$, $(-1)^3$, $(-1)^4$, $(-1)^5$, $(-1)^6$, $(-1)^7$. What do you notice?

2. Evaluate $(-1)^{17}$, $(-1)^{49}$, $(-1)^{493}$, $(-1)^{624}$.

E 1. Evaluate $(-2)^2$, $(-2)^3$, $(-2)^4$, $(-2)^5$, $(-2)^6$.

2. Will $(-2)^{91}$ be a positive or a negative integer?

3. State whether the following represent positive or negative integers.

(*a*) $(-3)^4$ (*c*) $(-5)^{67}$ (*e*) $(-2)^{87}$
(*b*) $(-1)^{28}$ (*d*) $(-m)^{420}$ (*f*) $(15)^{21}$

Watch out here!

F 1. What is *meant* by $(-3)^2$? By $-(3)^2$?

Notice that in product form,
$(-3)^2 = (-3) \times (-3)$, while $-(3)^2 = -(3 \times 3)$

2. Evaluate $(-3)^2$ and $-(3)^2$.

3. Evaluate and compare.

(*a*) $(-2)^4$ and $-(2)^4$ (*c*) $(-1)^3$ and $-(1)^3$
(*b*) $(-5)^2$ and $-(5)^2$ (*d*) $(-4)^3$ and $-(4)^3$

Study the following examples.

Example 1 Evaluate (*a*) x^4 when $x = -3$
(*b*) $3x^2$ when $x = -5$
(*c*) $-2x^3$ when $x = -4$

Solution

(*a*) If $x = -3$, $\therefore x^4 = (x)^4 = (-3)^4 = (-3)(-3)(-3)(-3) = 81$

(*b*) If $x = -5$, $\therefore 3x^2 = 3(x)^2 = 3(-5)^2 = 3(25) = 75$

(*c*) If $x = -4$, $\therefore -2x^3 = (-2)(x)^3 = (-2)(-4)^3 = (-2)(-64) = 128$

Notice the difference.
$3a^2 = 3 \times a^2 = 3 \times a \times a$
$(3a)^2 = (3a) \times (3a) = 3 \times a \times 3 \times a$

Example 2

Find the value of (*a*) $2x^2 - 5x + 6$ when $x = -3$
(*b*) $-5y^3 + 6y^2 - 24$ when $y = -2$
(*c*) $a^2 - 2ab - 3b^2$ when $a = -1$, $b = -4$

Solution

(*a*) If $x = -3$, $\therefore 2x^2 - 5x + 6$
$= 2(x)^2 - 5(x) + 6$
$= 2(-3)^2 - 5(-3) + 6$
$= 2(9) + 15 + 6$
$= 39$

(*b*) If $y = -2$, $\therefore -5y^3 + 6y^2 - 24$
$= (-5)(y)^3 + 6(y)^2 - 24$
$= (-5)(-2)^3 + 6(-2)^2 - 24$
$= (-5)(-8) + 6(4) - 24$
$= 40$

(*c*) If $a = -1$, $b = -4$, $\therefore a^2 - 2ab - 3b^2$
$= (a)^2 - 2(a)(b) - 3(b)^2$
$= (-1)^2 - 2(-1)(-4) - 3(-4)^2$
$= 1 - 2(4) - 3(16)$
$= 1 + (-8) + (-48)$
$= -55$

Exercise 5.2

Discussion

1. Complete the following statements.
   (*a*) In the expression y^3, the base is ______, the exponent is ______, and ______ is the ______ power of ______.
   (*b*) In the expression ______, the base is 3, the exponent is ______, and ______ is the 3rd power of ______.

2. Express each of the following in exponential form.
   (*a*) $3 \times 3 \times 3$
   (*b*) 0.5×0.5
   (*c*) $k \times k \times k \times k$
   (*d*) $(-a) \times (-a) \times (-a) \times (-a)$

3. Express each of the following in product form.
   (*a*) $(-6)^5$
   (*b*) $(2)^3$
   (*c*) $(0)^2$
   (*d*) $(-r)^7$

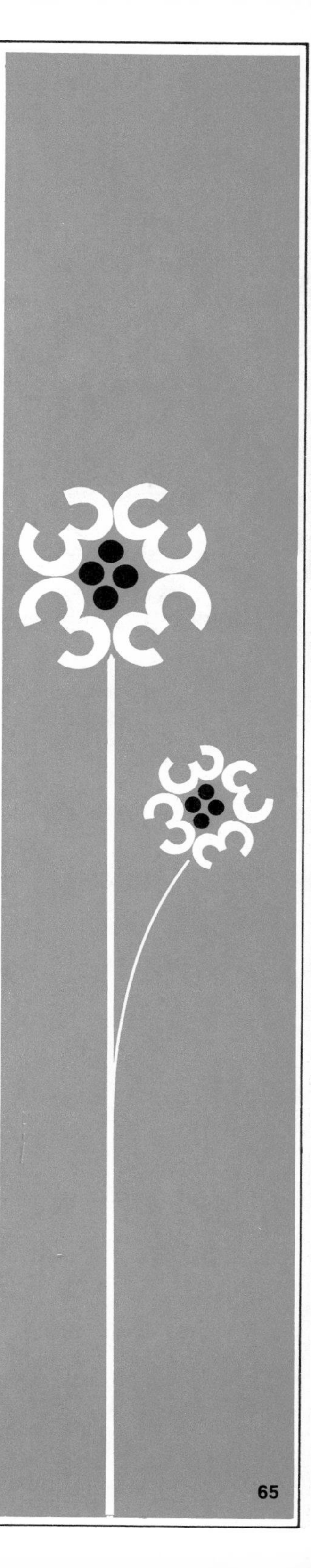

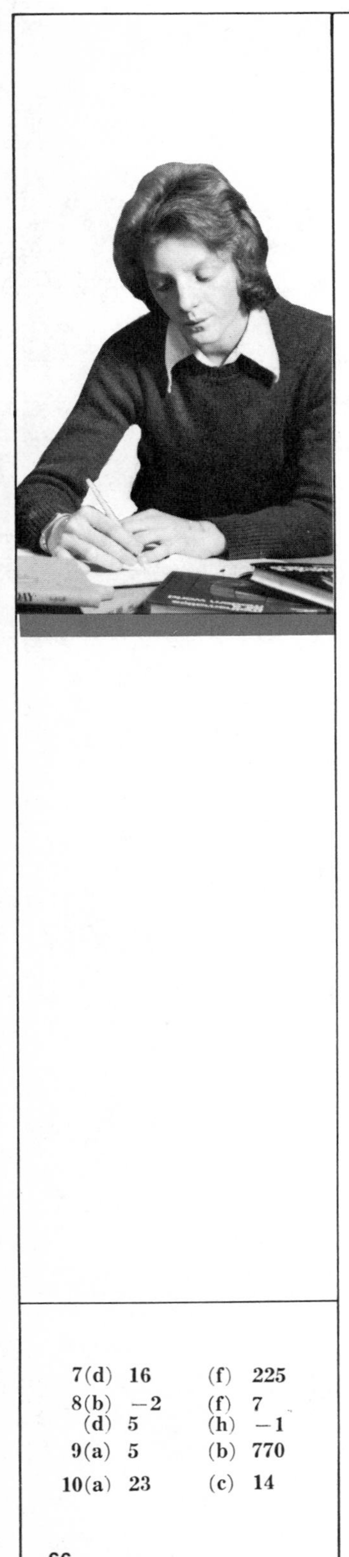

4. Are the following true? Why?
   (*a*) $(-2)^3 = 2^3$ (*b*) $2(-5)^2 = (-10)^2$

5. State the missing values.

Base	*Exponent*	*Power*
3	2	
m	3	
		$(-4)^2$
-5	4	
		t^7
-1	x	

6. Is the fourth power of a negative integer positive? Is the seventh power of a negative integer positive?

Written Solutions

7. Evaluate.
   (*a*) $(-3)^2$ (*d*) $(3 - 5)^4$ (*g*) $3(-2)^2$
   (*b*) $(-5)^2$ (*e*) $(-1)^{17}$ (*h*) -3^3
   (*c*) $(-4)^3$ (*f*) $(21 - 36)^2$ (*i*) $3(-2)^3$

8. Find the value of each of the following expressions.
   (*a*) $3a^2$ when $a = 2$
   (*b*) $-2b^2$ when $b = 1$
   (*c*) $3a + b^2$ when $a = -2, b = 4$
   (*d*) $a^2 - b^2$ when $a = 3, b = 2$
   (*e*) $3x^2 - 5y^2$ when $x = 5, y = -2$
   (*f*) $x^3 - y^3$ when $x = -1, y = -2$
   (*g*) $r^2 + s^2 - 2t^2$ when $r = -3, s = -2, t = 1$
   (*h*) $g(h + k)^2$ when $g = -1, h = 2, k = -3$

9. (*a*) If $v = u + at$, find v when $u = 20$, $a = -5$, and $t = 3$.
   (*b*) If $d = ut + \frac{1}{2}at^2$, find d when $u = -3$, $t = 10$, and $a = 16$.

10. Evaluate.
    (*a*) $4x^2 - 2x + 3$ when $x = -2$
    (*b*) $(x + 4y)(x - 2y)$ when $x = 3, y = -2$
    (*c*) $-3m^3 + 2m^2 - 4m + 5$ when $m = -1$
    (*d*) $5 - 2a + 6a^3$ when $a = -2$

7(d) 16 (f) 225
8(b) -2 (f) 7
(d) 5 (h) -1
9(a) 5 (b) 770
10(a) 23 (c) 14

5.3 Dividing Integers

A A partnership of 3 people suffers a \$6000 loss that is to be shared equally by the 3 partners.

1. What integer could be used to represent a loss of \$6000?
2. What would each partner's share of the loss be?
3. What operation did you use to arrive at an answer to Question 2?

B When dividing integers it is always possible to think in terms of multiplication, because multiplication and division are inverse operations. That is,

$\frac{24}{-6} = k$ and $k \times (-6) = 24$ mean the same thing.

Put these equations into words.

If the product form is easier to work with, use it. Think "What number times -6 gives 24?" The answer, -4, should come quite readily. Hence, $\frac{24}{-6} = -4$.

1. Complete the following table of equivalent statements.

	Division	*Multiplication*
(*a*)	$\frac{20}{4} = k$	$k \times 4 = 20$ $k = \square$
(*b*)	$\frac{-20}{-4} = k$	$k \times (-4) = -20$ $k = \square$
(*c*)	$\frac{20}{-4} = k$	$k \times (-4) = 20$ $k = \square$
(*d*)	$\frac{-20}{4} = k$	$k \times 4 = -20$ $k = \square$

2. Your written solution need not show the product step, but do not hesitate to write it down if you feel it will help you. State the quotients.

(*a*) $(-36) \div (-4)$ (*d*) $52 \div (-13)$ (*g*) $\frac{-48}{3}$

(*b*) $18 \div (-3)$ (*e*) $(-56) \div (-14)$ (*h*) $\frac{-64}{-16}$

(*c*) $(-12) \div 6$ (*f*) $0 \div (-5)$ (*i*) $\frac{28}{-7}$

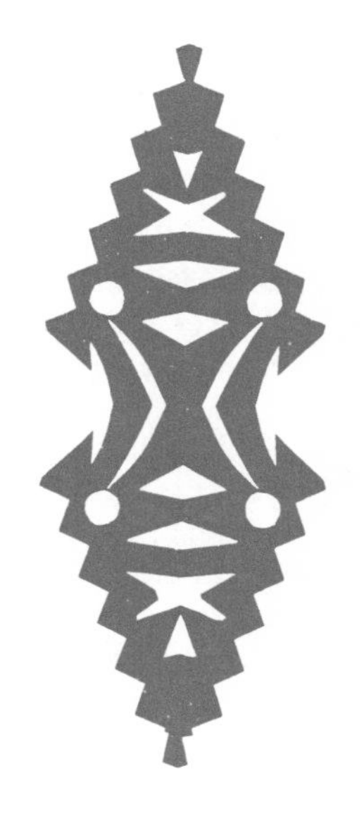

3. Recall how the sign of a *product* involving only 2 integers was found in Section 5.1. Can you find a similar method for determining the sign of the *quotient* of 2 integers?

4. Division of integers frequently occurs in evaluation by substitution. Study carefully the following examples.

Example 1

Evaluate $\frac{4p}{6q}$, when $p = -3$ and $q = 2$.

Solution

$$\frac{4p}{6q}$$

$$= \frac{4(p)}{6(q)}$$

$$= \frac{4(-3)}{6(2)}$$

$$= \frac{-12}{12}$$

$$= -1$$

$p = -3$
$q = 2$

Example 2

Evaluate $\frac{2(a^2 - b)}{ab + c^3}$, when $a = 2$, $b = -3$, and $c = -1$.

Solution

$$\frac{2(a^2 - b)}{ab + c^3}$$

$$= \frac{2[(a)^2 - (b)]}{(a)(b) + (c)^3}$$

$$= \frac{2[(2)^2 - (-3)]}{(2)(-3) + (-1)^3}$$

$$= \frac{2[4 + 3]}{-6 + (-1)}$$

$$= \frac{2(7)}{-7}$$

$$= -2$$

$a = 2$
$b = -3$
$c = -1$

Exercise 5.3

Discussion

1. To divide 10 by -2, what product step is involved? State the value of $10 \div (-2)$.

2. Consider $10 \div 0$. What is the product step? What conclusion can you draw?

3. Is $(-12) \div 4$ the same as $4 \div (-12)$? Does the order matter when dividing integers?

4. Does an integer result when an integer is divided by another integer?

5. How are the operations of division and multiplication related?

6. State the quotient.

(*a*) $14 \div 2$ (*b*) $(-15) \div 3$ (*c*) $\frac{-12}{-6}$ (*d*) $\frac{16}{-8}$ (*e*) $(-28) \div (-4)$ (*f*) $(-63) \div 7$

Written Solutions

7. Find the quotient.

(*a*) $(-144) \div 36$
(*b*) $72 \div (-24)$
(*c*) $(-84) \div (-12)$
(*d*) $256 \div (-16)$
(*e*) $(-54) \div (-18)$
(*f*) $(-441) \div 21$

8. Divide.

(*a*) $\frac{-91}{7}$ (*b*) $\frac{121}{-11}$ (*c*) $\frac{-196}{-14}$
(*d*) $\frac{225}{-15}$ (*e*) $\frac{-289}{17}$ (*f*) $\frac{-324}{-18}$
(*g*) $\frac{361}{-19}$ (*h*) $\frac{-400}{-20}$ (*i*) $\frac{143}{-11}$

9. Evaluate each of the following when $p = 6$, $q = -2$, $r = -1$.

(*a*) $\frac{3p}{rq}$ (*b*) $\frac{p+q}{r}$
(*c*) $(q - p) \div (qr)$ (*d*) $-3r^2 \div \left(\frac{p}{q}\right)$
(*e*) $5pqr \div (2qr^2)$ (*f*) $4q^2r \div (2q)$

10. Perform the operations indicated.

(*a*) $(-3) \times \frac{16}{-8}$
(*b*) $\frac{15}{-5} + \frac{-27}{3}$
(*c*) $\frac{3 - 15}{2(-3)}$
(*d*) $2(-3 + 7) \div (-1 - 3)$
(*e*) $\frac{-13 + (-8)}{4 - (-3)}$
(*f*) $\frac{-42}{14} + \frac{26}{-13}$

7(d) -16 (f) -21
8(e) -17 (g) -19
9(a) 9 (c) -4
10(a) 6 (c) 2 (e) -3

Maintaining Basic Skills

Exercise 1

1. Find the value in each of the following.

(*a*) $3 + 5 - 2$
(*b*) $6 - 8 + 3$
(*c*) $4 - 3 - 5$
(*d*) $2 - 6 + 3$
(*e*) $12 - 15 - 1$
(*f*) $6 - 9 - 4$
(*g*) $36 - 15 + 20$
(*h*) $-28 + 11 - 4$
(*i*) $3 + 4 - 6 - 1$
(*j*) $5 - 2 + 8 - 10$
(*k*) $-3 + 9 - 7 + 4$
(*l*) $-1 - 4 + 8 - 12$

2. Evaluate.

(*a*) 12×7
(*b*) $(-5) \times 8$
(*c*) $6 \times (-7)$
(*d*) $(-3) \times 8$
(*e*) $(-4) \times (-6)$
(*f*) $6 \times (-8)$
(*g*) $(-9) \times 4$
(*h*) $(-5) \times (-7)$
(*i*) $14 \times (-25)$
(*j*) $(-38) \times (-73)$
(*k*) $(-47) \times 85$
(*l*) $65 \times (-17)$

3. Find the quotient.

(*a*) $45 \div 9$
(*b*) $(-56) \div 7$
(*c*) $28 \div (-4)$
(*d*) $35 \div (-5)$
(*e*) $(-72) \div (-8)$
(*f*) $(-84) \div 12$
(*g*) $851 \div 23$
(*h*) $(-1148) \div 14$
(*i*) $(-2835) \div (-63)$
(*j*) $13\,041 \div (-27)$

4. Simplify.

(*a*) $5 + 8(6 - 2)$
(*b*) $10 - 9(3)$
(*c*) $-2 + 4(-3)$
(*d*) $6 - 5(9)$
(*e*) $(28 \div 4) \times (-3)$
(*f*) $(-6 + 2)(7)$
(*g*) $(-2)(3 + 8)$
(*h*) $5(7 - 15)$
(*i*) $(2 + 8)(6 - 3)$
(*j*) $(3 - 5)(8 - 2)$
(*k*) $5[6 - 2(3)] + 1$
(*l*) $3 + 2[1 - 5(3)]$

5. Evaluate.

(*a*) 3^4
(*b*) $(-2)^3$
(*c*) $(-7)^2$
(*d*) $(-5)^3$
(*e*) $2(5^2)$
(*f*) $(-3)(2)^3$
(*g*) $(-3 \times 2)^2$
(*h*) $5 + 4(-2)^3$
(*i*) $8 - (-3)^2$
(*j*) $5^3 + (-3)^4$
(*k*) $(-1)^5 - (-4)^2$
(*l*) $3(-2)^4 + (-2)5^2$

1(a) 6 **(b)** 1 **(c)** −4 **(j)** 1 **(k)** 3 **(l)** −9
2(a) 84 **(b)** −40 **(c)** −42 **(j)** 2774 **(k)** −3995 **(l)** −1105
3(a) 5 **(b)** −8 **(i)** 45 **(j)** −483
4(a) 37 **(b)** −17 **(c)** −14 **(j)** −12 **(k)** 1 **(l)** −25
5(a) 81 **(b)** −8 **(c)** 49 **(j)** 206 **(k)** −17 **(l)** −2

6. Evaluate the following expressions if $a = 3$, $b = -2$, $c = -1$, $d = 0$.

(a) $a + b + c + d$
(b) $ab - c$
(c) $ad + bc$
(d) $2a \div 3b$
(e) $a^2 + b^2$
(f) $3b - 2c$
(g) $-2a + 5b^2$
(h) $a^2 - 2b^3 + c$
(i) $5a^2 - 3b^2 - c$
(j) $-3a^3 + 2c + d$
(k) $d(a + b)$
(l) $6d \div 3a$

7. Solve the following equations. The domain is W.

(a) $x + 3 = 8$
(b) $y - 4 = 7$
(c) $5 - a = 12$
(d) $3 = b + 6$
(e) $2y + 6 = 14$
(f) $7 + 3y = 28$
(g) $4x - 2 = 10$
(h) $5 = 3h - 4$
(i) $10 = 3y + 4$
(j) $6 + 5w = 20$
(k) $31 = 2c - 15$
(l) $14 + 2s = 56$

8. Solve and graph the following inequations. The domain is W.

(a) $x + 3 > 5$
(b) $y - 3 < 1$
(c) $-2 + b > 1$
(d) $5 + x < 8$
(e) $b - 4 \geq -3$
(f) $3x < 6$
(g) $5y > 15$
(h) $3 + 4a \leq 11$
(i) $2 + 3h > 5$
(j) $4 + 3e \leq 20$
(k) $1 + 2x \geq 15$
(l) $5y - 24 < 6$

Number Curiosities

1. Write any 3-digit number and repeat the digits to make a 6-digit number. (For example, 742 742)
Have one person divide your number by 7.
Have another person divide the quotient by 13.
Have another person divide the last quotient by 11.
Does the final quotient surprise you?

2. Tricky 9.

Find the products.

999 999 × 2 = ☐
999 999 × 3 = ☐
999 999 × 4 = ☐
999 999 × 5 = ☐
999 999 × 6 = ☐
999 999 × 7 = ☐
999 999 × 8 = ☐
999 999 × 9 = ☐

3. Evaluate.

9 × 9 + 7 = ☐
98 × 9 + 6 = ☐
987 × 9 + 5 = ☐
9 876 × 9 + 4 = ☐
98 765 × 9 + 3 = ☐
987 654 × 9 + 2 = ☐
9 876 543 × 9 + 1 = ☐
98 765 432 × 9 + 0 = ☐

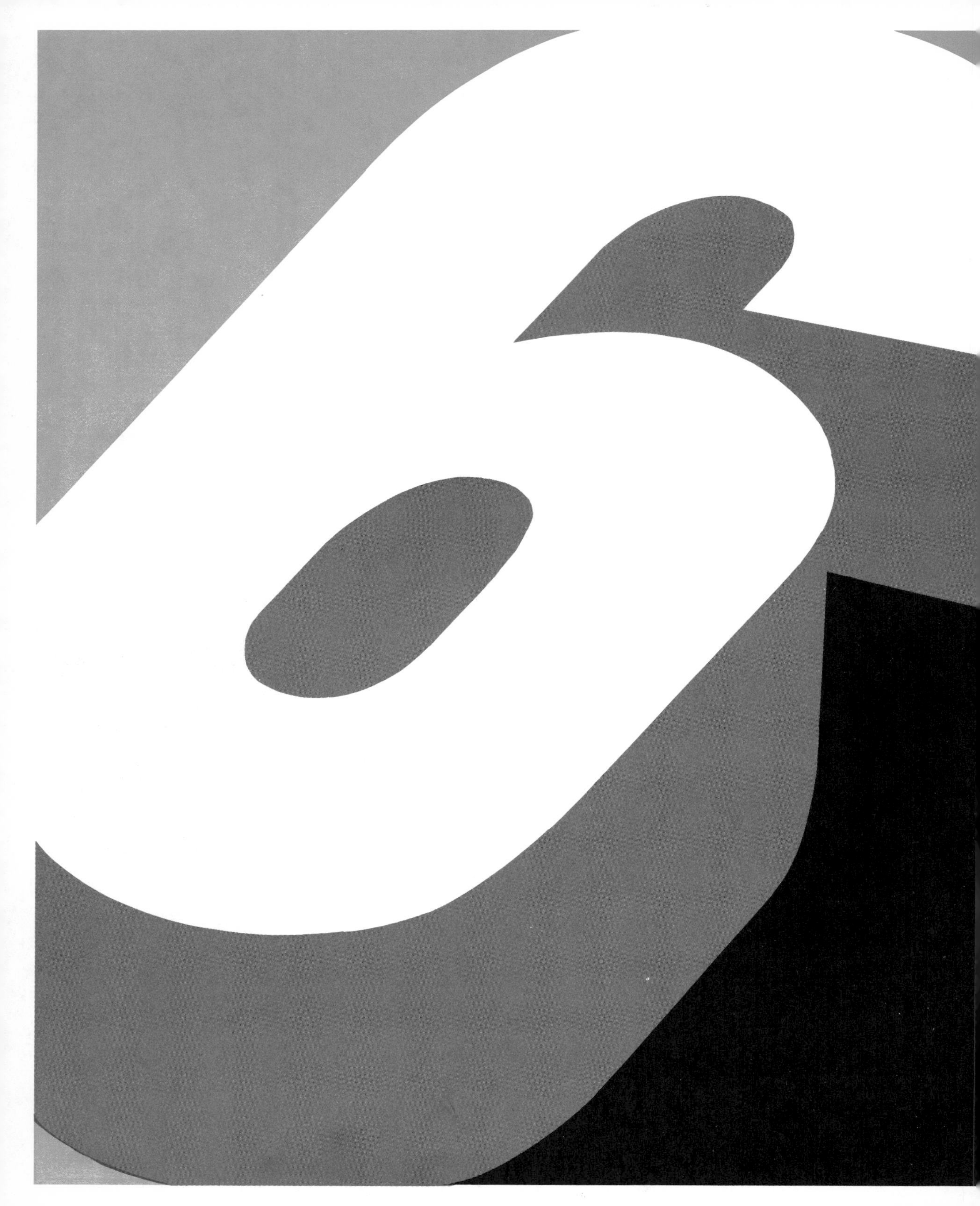

Unit 6
Solving Equations and Inequations Using Integers

Most problems begin as statements about one or more unknown quantities. These statements can be represented by equations containing variables, such as a, b, c, . . . x, y, z that stand for the unknown quantities. Some problems may be tackled by writing an equation to express the statement in mathematical terms and then solving the equation.

6.1 Solving Equations Using Integers

1. (*a*) State the sum of 3 and -7.
   (*b*) Read in words: "-7 added to 3 gives -4."
2. Find $-2 + 8$. Write a statement like 1(*b*).
3. (*a*) What number added to 3 gives -4?
   (*b*) What number added to -2 gives 6?
   (*c*) 4 added to ______ gives -1.
   (*d*) -3 added to ______ gives -7.
4. (*a*) Solve the equation $x + 5 = 12$, $x \in W$.
   (*b*) If $x \in I$, does the solution set change?
5. Solve.
   (*a*) $x + 6 = 4$. $x \in W$.
   (*b*) $x + 6 = 4$. $x \in I$.
   Watch the domain!
   Why are the solution sets different?

It appears that some equations have *no root* in W but may have a root if the domain of the variable is I.

6. Use the form of the example at the right to solve the following. $x \in I$.
   (*a*) $x + 5 = 4$
   (*b*) $4 + x = -2$
   (*c*) $-4 + x = 5$
   (*d*) $x + (-3) = -6$

You could answer Question 3 by using these equations.

(a) $3 + x = -4$
(b) $-2 + a = 6$
(c) $k + 4 = -1$
(d) $k + (-3) = -7$

A root of an equation is a number that makes the equation true!

Solve $x + 3 = -2$.

Solution

$\because \quad x + 3 = -2$

then $x + 3 - 3 = -2 - 3$

$\therefore \quad x = -5$

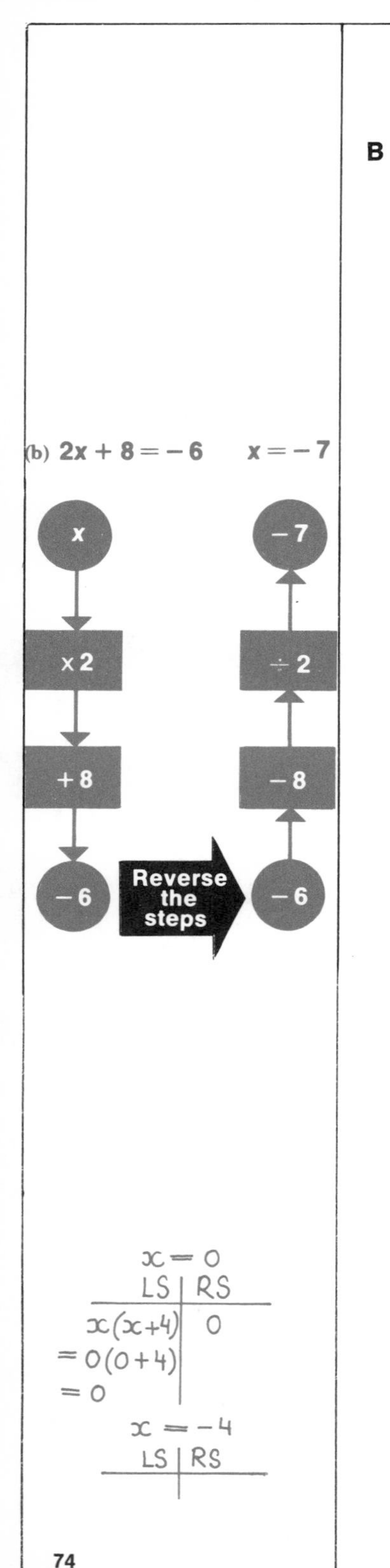

B The equations in Section A arose from addition problems that required you to use the integers to obtain an answer. Here are some questions that involve subtraction and multiplication.

Question	*Answer by Using this Equation*
What number subtracted from 3 gives -2?	$3 - x = -2$
What number subtracted from 4 gives 6?	$4 - x = 6$
What number multiplied by 5 gives -30?	$5x = -30$

The solution of equations involving integers follows the rules you already know.

Example 1

Solve (*a*) $3 - x = -2$ (*b*) $2x + 8 = -6, x \in I$.

Solution

(*a*)
$$\begin{aligned} \therefore \quad 3 - x &= -2 \\ \text{then} \quad 3 - 3 - x &= -2 - 3 \\ \therefore \quad -x &= -5 \\ \text{or} \quad (-1)(-x) &= (-1)(-5) \\ \therefore \quad x &= 5 \end{aligned}$$

(*b*)
$$\begin{aligned} \because \quad 2x + 8 &= -6 \\ \text{then} \quad 2x + 8 - 8 &= -6 - 8 \\ \therefore \quad 2x &= -14 \\ \text{or} \quad \frac{2x}{2} &= \frac{-14}{2} \\ \therefore \quad x &= -7 \end{aligned}$$

Check

LS	RS
$3 - x$	-2
$= 3 - 5$	
$= -2$	

$\therefore$ 5 is the root.

Check

LS	RS
$2x + 8$	-6
$= 2(-7) + 8$	
$= -14 + 8$	
$= -6$	

$\therefore$ -7 is the root.

Example 2

Solve (*a*) $x^2 = 16$ (*b*) $x(x + 4) = 0, x \in I$.

Solution

(*a*)
$$\begin{aligned} &\therefore x^2 = 16 \\ &\text{and } 4^2 = 16 \text{ or } (-4)^2 = 16 \\ &\therefore x = 4 \text{ or } -4 \end{aligned}$$

$\therefore \text{SS} = \{4, -4\}$

(*b*)
$$\begin{aligned} \therefore \quad x(x + 4) &= 0 \\ \therefore x = 0 \text{ or } x + 4 &= 0 \\ \text{then} \quad x + 4 - 4 &= 0 - 4 \\ \therefore \quad x &= -4 \end{aligned}$$

$\therefore \text{SS} = \{0, -4\}$

Exercise 6.1

Discussion

Note: Each variable has I as its domain.

1. Solve.
   (*a*) $5 - a = 2$ (*b*) $5 - b = 5$ (*c*) $5 - c = 8$

2. (*a*) To solve $x - (-2) = 5$ how should you simplify the equation?
   (*b*) Simplify and solve. $x - (-4) = 1$
   $3x - (-2) = 8$

3. Solve.
   (*a*) $x + 6 = 4$ (*d*) $2c = 0$
   (*b*) $2 - y = -1$ (*e*) $-3x = 0$
   (*c*) $r^2 = 4$ (*f*) $a(a + 1) = 0$

Psst! To subtract, add the opposite!

Written Solutions

4. Solve.
   (*a*) $x + 2 = 4$ (*c*) $a + 1 = -3$ (*e*) $c - 5 = -3$
   (*b*) $x + 5 = 2$ (*d*) $y - 2 = 1$ (*f*) $y - 2 = -7$

5. Solve.
   (*a*) $3x = -12$ (*c*) $-4r = 20$ (*e*) $-7n = 14$
   (*b*) $-2y = -10$ (*d*) $5t = -15$ (*f*) $3x = 0$

6. Solve and check.
   (*a*) $2x + 4 = 10$ (*d*) $-2 + 5z = 8$
   (*b*) $5 - 3b = -4$ (*e*) $3x + (-4) = -10$
   (*c*) $4 - 2a = 0$ (*f*) $2r - (-3) = 5$

7. Solve.
   (*a*) $x^2 = 25$ (*d*) $x(x + 2) = 0$
   (*b*) $c^2 = 81$ (*e*) $p(p - 7) = 0$
   (*c*) $a^2 - 16 = 0$ (*f*) $h(h + 3) = 0$

7(d)
HINT:
$\because x(x+2) = 0$
$\therefore x = 0$ or $x + 2 = 0$

8. Solve.
   (*a*) $-5 = 7 - 3m$ (*d*) $3 + 11s = 12$
   (*b*) $25 = 4a - 3$ (*e*) $4 + 6y = 20 \div 2$
   (*c*) $13 = 5 - 4n$ (*f*) $14 \div (-2) = 3 - 2x$

6(a)	**3**	**(d)**	**2**
7(a)	**5, −5**	**(d)**	**0, −2**
8(c)	**−2**	**(f)**	**5**

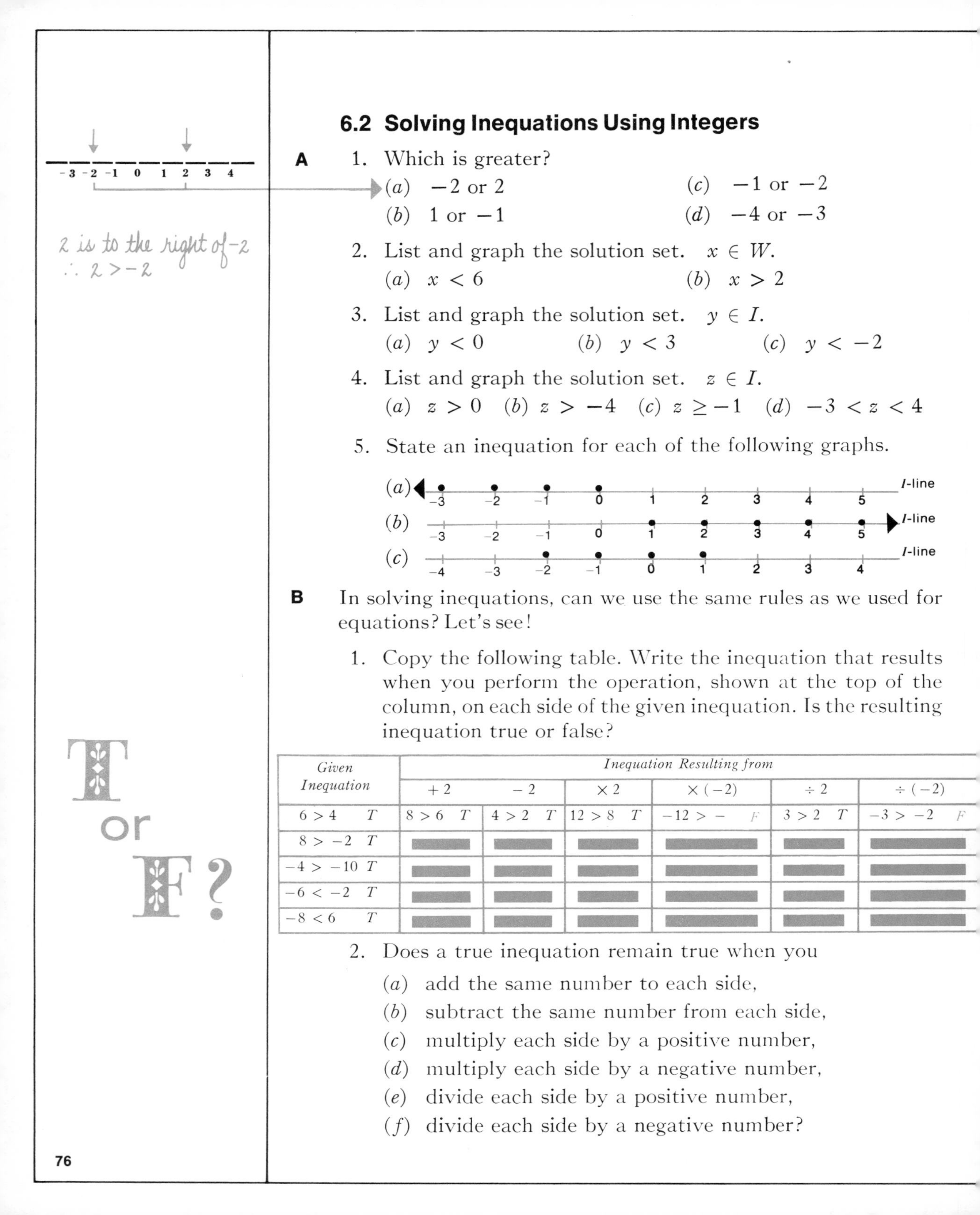

6.2 Solving Inequations Using Integers

A

1. Which is greater?
   (*a*) -2 or 2 (*c*) -1 or -2
   (*b*) 1 or -1 (*d*) -4 or -3

2. List and graph the solution set. $x \in W$.
   (*a*) $x < 6$ (*b*) $x > 2$

3. List and graph the solution set. $y \in I$.
   (*a*) $y < 0$ (*b*) $y < 3$ (*c*) $y < -2$

4. List and graph the solution set. $z \in I$.
   (*a*) $z > 0$ (*b*) $z > -4$ (*c*) $z \geq -1$ (*d*) $-3 < z < 4$

5. State an inequation for each of the following graphs.

B In solving inequations, can we use the same rules as we used for equations? Let's see!

1. Copy the following table. Write the inequation that results when you perform the operation, shown at the top of the column, on each side of the given inequation. Is the resulting inequation true or false?

Given Inequation	*Inequation Resulting from*					
	$+2$	-2	$\times 2$	$\times(-2)$	$\div 2$	$\div(-2)$
$6 > 4$ *T*	$8 > 6$ *T*	$4 > 2$ *T*	$12 > 8$ *T*	$-12 > -$ *F*	$3 > 2$ *T*	$-3 > -2$ *F*
$8 > -2$ *T*						
$-4 > -10$ *T*						
$-6 < -2$ *T*						
$-8 < 6$ *T*						

2. Does a true inequation remain true when you
   (*a*) add the same number to each side,
   (*b*) subtract the same number from each side,
   (*c*) multiply each side by a positive number,
   (*d*) multiply each side by a negative number,
   (*e*) divide each side by a positive number,
   (*f*) divide each side by a negative number?

Do you see that the *true* inequation $8 > -2$ became $-16 > 4$ (a *false* inequation!) when you *multiplied* each side by -2? Study the table again. A true inequation also became false whenever you *divided* each side by -2.

> When you multiply or divide each side of an inequation by a negative number, you must *reverse* the sign of inequality to keep the resulting inequation true.

For example, when multiplying by -2,
  $8 > -2$ should become $-16 < 4$, to remain true;
when dividing by -2,
  $8 > -2$ should become $-4 < 1$, to remain true.

3. By reversing the sign of inequality when multiplying or dividing by a negative number, state a true inequation.

Given Inequation	*Operation*	*Resulting True Inequation*
$6 > -2$ *T*	$\div(-1)$	
$-2 > -6$ *T*	$\times(-5)$	
$-4 < -2$ *T*	$\div(-2)$	
$-4 < 4$ *T*	$\times(-3)$	

The following examples illustrate the use of rules for solving inequations.

Example 1 Solve and graph. $x + 3 > -5,\ x \in I$

Solution

$\because\ x + 3 > -5$

then $x + 3 - 3 > -5 - 3$

or $x > -8$

−9 −8 −7 −6 −5 −4 −3 −2 −1 0 1 2 3 4 *I*

Spot check!
Test 1 or 2 numbers in the SS and 1 or 2 numbers outside the SS.

For $x > -8$, we want integers to the right of -8 on the *I*-line.
$\therefore$ SS $= \{-7, -6, -5, \ldots\}$

Is each number in the SS greater than −8?

Check your result by trying 1 or 2 members of the solution set in the original inequation.
Therefore, subtracting a number from each side of an inequation works, as it did for equations.

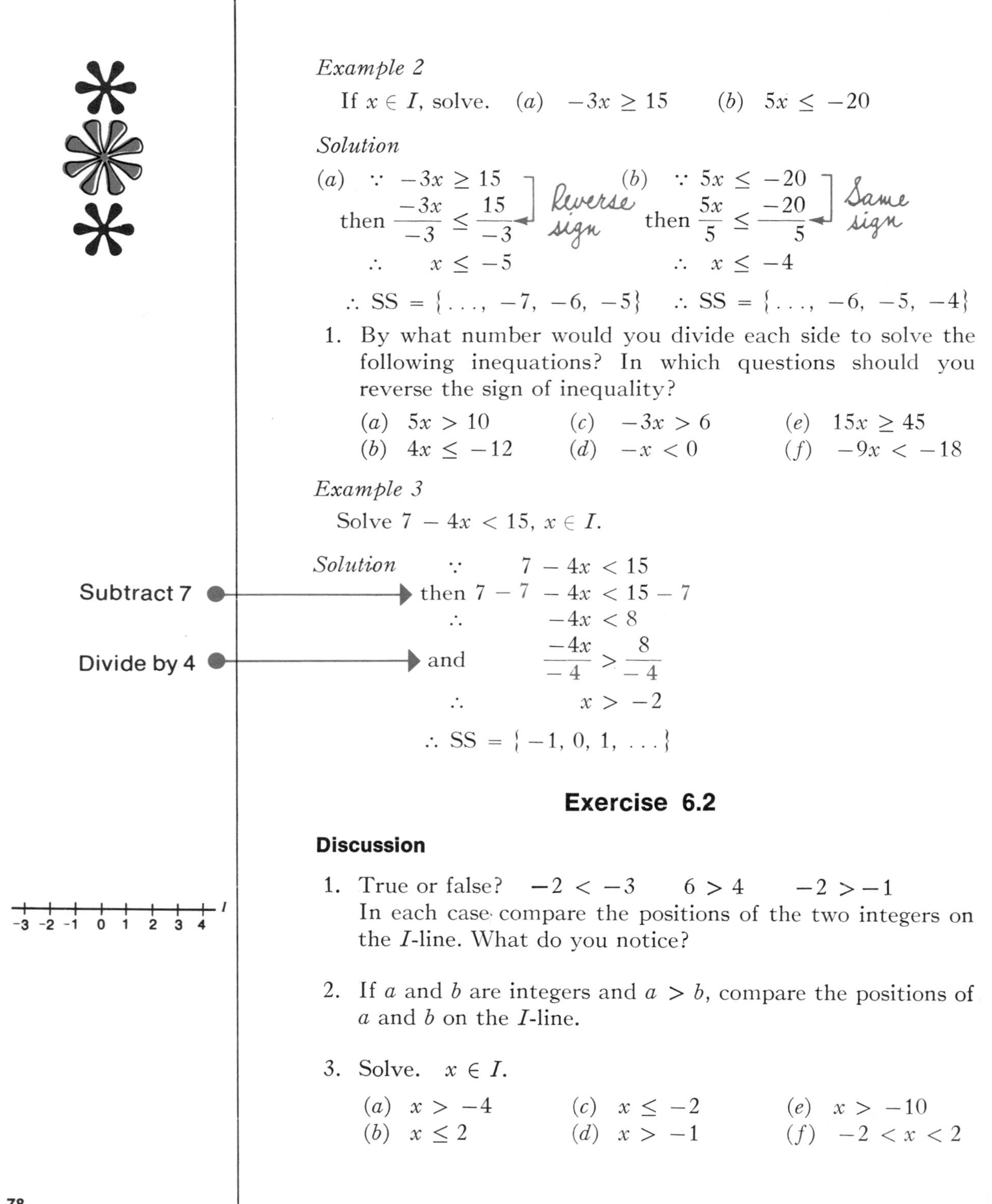

Example 2

If $x \in I$, solve. (*a*) $-3x \geq 15$ (*b*) $5x \leq -20$

Solution

(*a*) $\because \quad -3x \geq 15$

then $\dfrac{-3x}{-3} \leq \dfrac{15}{-3}$ ← Reverse sign

$\therefore \quad x \leq -5$

$\therefore$ SS $= \{\ldots, -7, -6, -5\}$

(*b*) $\because \quad 5x \leq -20$

then $\dfrac{5x}{5} \leq \dfrac{-20}{5}$ ← Same sign

$\therefore \quad x \leq -4$

$\therefore$ SS $= \{\ldots, -6, -5, -4\}$

1. By what number would you divide each side to solve the following inequations? In which questions should you reverse the sign of inequality?

(*a*) $5x > 10$	(*c*) $-3x > 6$	(*e*) $15x \geq 45$
(*b*) $4x \leq -12$	(*d*) $-x < 0$	(*f*) $-9x < -18$

Example 3

Solve $7 - 4x < 15$, $x \in I$.

Solution

$\because \quad 7 - 4x < 15$

Subtract 7 → then $7 - 7 - 4x < 15 - 7$

$\therefore \quad -4x < 8$

Divide by 4 → and $\dfrac{-4x}{-4} > \dfrac{8}{-4}$

$\therefore \quad x > -2$

$\therefore$ SS $= \{-1, 0, 1, \ldots\}$

Exercise 6.2

Discussion

1. True or false? $-2 < -3$ $\quad 6 > 4$ $\quad -2 > -1$
   In each case compare the positions of the two integers on the *I*-line. What do you notice?

2. If a and b are integers and $a > b$, compare the positions of a and b on the *I*-line.

3. Solve. $x \in I$.

(*a*) $x > -4$	(*c*) $x \leq -2$	(*e*) $x > -10$
(*b*) $x \leq 2$	(*d*) $x > -1$	(*f*) $-2 < x < 2$

4. State which graphs are correctly drawn. Correct those that are wrong.

Sentence — *Graph*

(*a*) $x < 4$

(*b*) $t \geq -3$

(*c*) $-1 \leq m < 2$

(*d*) $a^2 < 9$

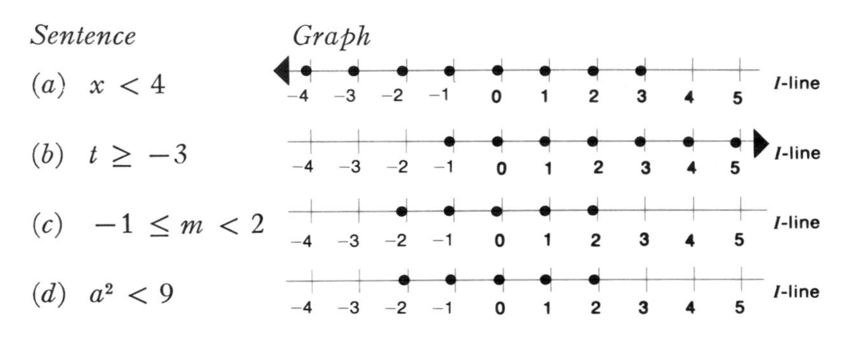

5. State the first step in solving each of the following inequations.

(*a*) $2x > -10$ (*c*) $-5x \leq 10$ (*e*) $7x > -14$

(*b*) $3x < 9$ (*d*) $-4x > -12$ (*f*) $3x + 2 < 5$

Written Solutions

Note: The domain of all variables is I.

6. List the solution set.

(*a*) $x < 2$ (*c*) $0 < k < 4$ (*e*) $b > -4$

(*b*) $a > 4$ (*d*) $s < -2$ (*f*) $-5 \leq w < -1$

7. Test whether the number given is in the solution set of the inequation.

(*a*) $p < -2;\quad -1$ (*c*) $2h < -6;\quad -3$

(*b*) $n > -5;\quad 2$ (*d*) $4 - 2x \geq 0;\quad 2$

8. List and graph the solution set.

(*a*) $x + 5 > 0$ (*d*) $k - 5 > -2$

(*b*) $q - 3 < 1$ (*e*) $r + 4 \leq 3$

(*c*) $c + 2 > -3$ (*f*) $5 - d < 4$

9. Solve and graph.

(*a*) $2x < 10$ (*c*) $-2a < 6$

(*b*) $4n > -12$ (*d*) $3y \geq -9$

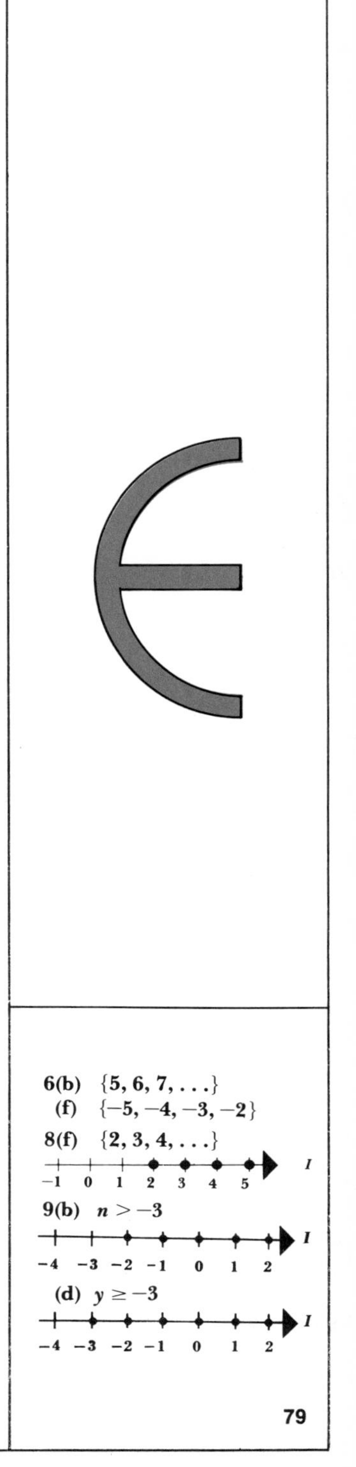

10. List the solution set.

(a) $2x + 1 > 5$
(b) $5x - 3 \leq 12$
(c) $-3x + 4 > 10$
(d) $9 - 10x < -11$
(e) $3 - x \geq 4$
(f) $4x - 15 < -3$

11. Rewrite with the variable on the left side, then solve.

(a) $10 < 2x$
(b) $15 \geq 3x$
(c) $5 > 3x - 4$
(d) $-4 \leq 1 - x$

12. Solve and graph.

(a) $-6 \leq 2x < 8$
(b) $-9 < 3t \leq 12$
(c) $x^2 \leq 4$
(d) $a^2 < 25$

6.3 Solving Problems Using Integers

A

1. If $2 + 3$ represents the integer that is 3 greater than 2, represent the integer that is

(a) 3 greater than x,
(b) 2 less than a.

2. If 2×3 represents the integer that is 2 times as large as 3, represent the integer that is

(a) 2 times as large as an integer x,
(b) 3 times as large as an integer b,
(c) 1 more than twice an integer i,
(d) 3 less than 5 times an integer t.

B

1. By calling x "some integer," translate the following equations into words.

(a) $5 - x = 6$
(b) $2x - 7 = -5$
(c) $3x + 5 = 2$

2. Form equations or inequations that represent the following statements.

(a) 4 added to an integer equals 2.
(b) If 3 is subtracted from an integer, the result is 1.
(c) 5 is 3 more than twice an integer.
(d) 3 times an integer is less than 6.

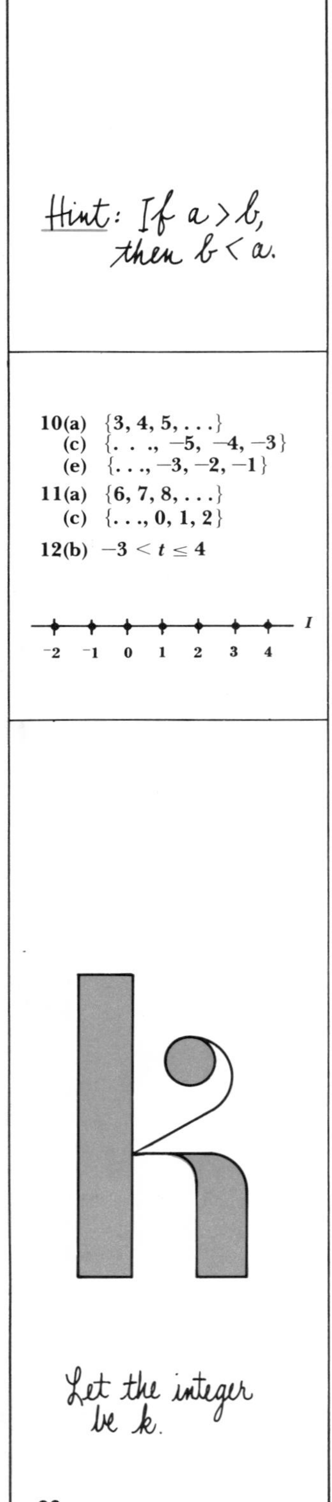

Use a "let" statement to introduce the variable, and then form an equation that could be used to solve the given problem.

1. Find an integer which when added to 4 gives -1.
2. If -3 is subtracted from an integer, the result is 7. Find the integer.

Check whether the answer given is the correct one for the problem.

1. An integer is doubled and then subtracted from 7, giving 13. Find the integer. (Answer -3)
2. The sum of -2 and three times an integer is 4. Find the integer. (Answer -4)

On a winter day in Calgary, the temperature at 04:00 is -20°C, and by 08:00 it has risen to 10°C as the result of a chinook. Find the average hourly increase in temperature.

1. What are you asked to find?
2. Use a "let" statement to represent this unknown quantity by a variable.
3. What facts are given concerning the temperature change?
4. Use this information to write an equation.
5. Solve the equation.
6. Check the answer against the given information.
7. Make a concluding statement.

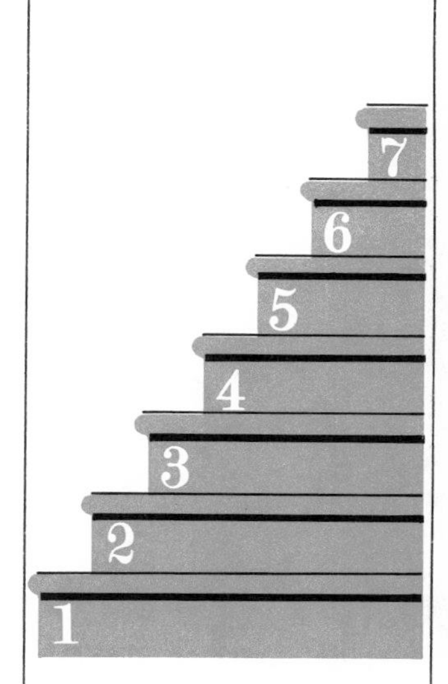

Exercise 6.3

Discussion

1. Represent by an algebraic expression.
   (*a*) the integer 3 greater than twice an integer a
   (*b*) the sum of two consecutive integers
   (*c*) 3 times an integer c, increased by 4
   (*d*) an integer d subtracted from 1
   (*e*) two integers that differ by 3
   (*f*) two integers that add to give 10

3. −10	8. {5, 6, 7, 8, . . .}
4. −3	9. −18°C, −42°C
5. 5	10. 3, −3
6. −15	11. {−2, −1, 0, 1, . . .}
7. −3, 3	12. 4 s

2. Represent by an algebraic sentence using i as the unknown integer.
   (*a*) Three times an integer lies between -2 and 9.
   (*b*) The sum of two consecutive integers is -13.
   (*c*) An integer is subtracted from 4 and the result is -7.
   (*d*) One less than 4 times an integer is less than 7.
   (*e*) Two more than 3 times an integer is -1.

Written Solutions

3. An integer is added to 8 giving a sum of -2. Find the integer.

4. If you double an integer and then add 5, the result is -1. Find the integer.

5. Three times an integer is subtracted from 2 and the result is -13. Find the integer.

6. An integer is increased by 3. The result is divided by 2 and gives -6. Find the integer.

7. Two integers differ by 6 and add to give 0. Find the integers.

8. The sum of -8 and twice an integer must be greater than 1. Find all such integers.

9. The temperatures in Peace River and Churchill differ by 24°C, and the sum of the temperatures is -60°C. Find the temperatures.

10. The square of an integer is doubled and then increased by 3. If the result is 21, find the integer.

11. An integer is subtracted from 2, and the result is less than 5. Find the integers that satisfy this condition.

12. In the 1967 Canadian Grand Prix car racing event at Mosport Park, Dennis Hulme was leading Jimmy Clark by 34 s after 22 laps of the track. Thirteen laps later, however, Hulme was trailing Clark by 18 s. Determine the average number of seconds lost by Hulme during each of the 13 laps.

Topology

Topology is a branch of mathematics often referred to as "the rubber sheet geometry." One of the most interesting examples of topology is a Moëbius strip.

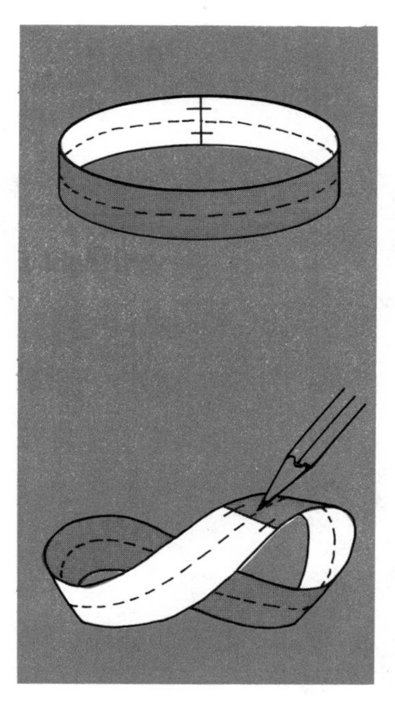

First, let us examine an ordinary strip of paper, its ends stapled to form a *loop* as shown. Notice that this loop has two *sides* (an "inside" and an "outside", if you wish!) and two *edges*. In order to travel from one side of the loop to the other, it is necessary to cross over an edge.

Now, let's take a second strip of paper, but before stapling its ends, give one end a half-twist, so that the result looks like the diagram. The interesting thing about this Moëbius strip is that it has only *one* side and *one* edge. To prove this to yourself hold the strip in one hand as shown, mark an "x" on the paper, and then trace along the centre of the strip. The result is rather startling!

No less amazing than the "one-sidedness" of the strip are the results of cutting the strips as shown—try it!

Cut halfway in from the edge.

Fold a third strip and cut one-third of the way in from the edge.

Note: Keep cutting until you return to your starting point.

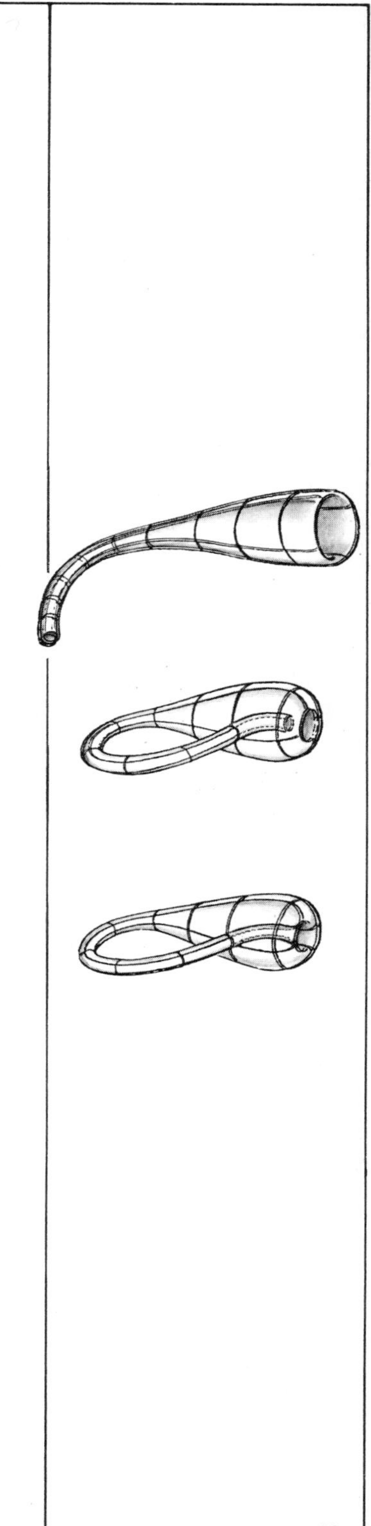

Unit 7

Rational Numbers

Throughout history the number system has been expanded as people encountered situations in life that required "new" numbers.

When the need arose for representing part of a whole object, for instance, the fractions were invented. Then, in order to have a set of numbers in which subtraction can always be performed, the integers came into being.

Then came the set of rational numbers, Q, containing all the positive and negative fractions and zero, so that division can always be performed (except by zero). Each element of Q can be expressed as a quotient.

Here are some examples of rational numbers.

$$\frac{2}{3}, \frac{-5}{7}, \frac{19}{8}, \frac{25}{5}, \frac{14}{-7}, \frac{0}{9}, \frac{2}{2}$$

Operation	*Whole Numbers*	*Integers*	*Rationals*
Subtraction	$4 - 10$ Impossible	$4 - 10 = -6$	$4 - 10 = -6$
Division	$7 \div 5$ Impossible	$7 \div 5$ Impossible	$7 \div 5 = 1.4$

$W = \{0, 1, 2, 3, \ldots\}$

$F = \{0, \frac{1}{1}, \frac{1}{2}, \frac{1}{3}, \ldots, \frac{2}{1}, \frac{2}{2}, \frac{2}{3}, \ldots,\}$

$I = \{\ldots, -3, -2, -1, 0, 1, 2, 3, \ldots\}$

$Q = \{$0 and all positive and negative fractions$\}$

Get-Set Exercise with Rational Numbers

Q?
rational numbers?
fractions?

Note: Reduce all answers to lowest terms.

1. Reduce to lowest terms.

(*a*) $\frac{4}{8}$ (*c*) $\frac{21}{35}$ (*e*) $\frac{16}{24}$ (*g*) $\frac{42}{36}$

(*b*) $\frac{6}{15}$ (*d*) $\frac{40}{60}$ (*f*) $\frac{48}{60}$ (*h*) $\frac{72}{54}$

2. Add.

(*a*) $\frac{2}{3}+\frac{4}{3}$ (*c*) $\frac{3}{10}+\frac{5}{10}+\frac{1}{10}$ (*e*) $\frac{4}{25}+\frac{7}{25}+\frac{9}{25}$

(*b*) $\frac{4}{5}+\frac{1}{5}$ (*d*) $\frac{1}{8}+\frac{5}{8}+\frac{7}{8}$ (*f*) $\frac{14}{100}+\frac{73}{100}+\frac{52}{100}$

3. Find the missing numerators.

(*a*) $\frac{2}{3}=\frac{\blacksquare}{12}$ (*c*) $\frac{5}{6}=\frac{\blacksquare}{24}$ (*e*) $\frac{4}{9}=\frac{\blacksquare}{36}$

(*b*) $\frac{3}{5}=\frac{\blacksquare}{10}$ (*d*) $\frac{2}{7}=\frac{\blacksquare}{35}$ (*f*) $\frac{7}{8}=\frac{\blacksquare}{48}$

12 is the Lowest Common Multiple (LCM) of 3, 4. →

4. Find the smallest number into which each set of numbers will divide.

(*a*) 3, 4 (*c*) 5, 7 (*e*) 3, 5, 9

(*b*) 4, 6, 8 (*d*) 5, 10, 12 (*f*) 8, 12, 20

Before adding, what must you do to the fractions? →

5. Add.

(*a*) $\frac{3}{5}+\frac{7}{10}$ (*e*) $1\frac{3}{7}+2\frac{1}{5}$

(*b*) $\frac{1}{3}+\frac{5}{6}$ (*f*) $\frac{5}{6}+\frac{3}{8}+1\frac{7}{12}$

(*c*) $\frac{3}{4}+\frac{1}{3}$ (*g*) $2\frac{4}{5}+1\frac{2}{3}+3\frac{1}{2}$

(*d*) $\frac{2}{5}+\frac{4}{9}$ (*h*) $\frac{7}{20}+\frac{5}{8}+\frac{1}{10}$

6. Subtract.

(*a*) $\frac{5}{8}-\frac{3}{8}$ (*c*) $\frac{2}{3}-\frac{1}{6}$ (*e*) $3\frac{3}{4}-2\frac{1}{2}$ (*g*) $3\frac{9}{10}-1\frac{3}{4}$

(*b*) $\frac{9}{5}-\frac{4}{5}$ (*d*) $\frac{7}{10}-\frac{2}{5}$ (*f*) $1\frac{3}{8}-\frac{5}{6}$ (*h*) $\frac{5}{9}-\frac{2}{7}$

1(a) $\frac{1}{2}$ **(e)** $\frac{2}{3}$
(c) $\frac{3}{5}$ **(g)** $\frac{7}{6}$
2(a) 2 **(c)** $\frac{9}{10}$ **(e)** $\frac{4}{5}$
3(a) 8 **(c) 20** **(e) 16**
4(a) 12 **(c) 35** **(e) 45**
5(a) $\frac{13}{10}$ **(e)** $3\frac{22}{35}$
(c) $\frac{13}{12}$ **(g)** $7\frac{29}{30}$
6(a) $\frac{1}{4}$ **(e)** $1\frac{1}{4}$
(c) $\frac{1}{2}$ **(g)** $2\frac{29}{60}$

7. Evaluate.

(a) $\frac{4}{3} + \frac{1}{2} - \frac{3}{4}$

(b) $3\frac{1}{8} - 1\frac{2}{3} + \frac{5}{6}$

(c) $2\frac{1}{2} - \frac{4}{5} + \frac{5}{4}$

(d) $2\frac{1}{4} + 3\frac{3}{8} - 1\frac{5}{6}$

(e) $3\frac{1}{2} - 5 + 2\frac{3}{4}$

(f) $4\frac{1}{3} - 5\frac{2}{5} + 1\frac{1}{2}$

8. Multiply.

(a) $8 \times \frac{1}{2}$

(b) $\frac{2}{3} \times 9$

(c) $\frac{5}{6} \times 9$

(d) $7 \times \frac{2}{5}$

(e) $7 \times 1\frac{2}{7}$

(f) $10 \times 3\frac{2}{5}$

9. Find the product.

(a) $\frac{1}{2} \times \frac{2}{3}$

(b) $\frac{3}{4} \times \frac{4}{7}$

(c) $\frac{5}{8} \times \frac{3}{5}$

(d) $\frac{9}{10} \times \frac{4}{9}$

(e) $\frac{2}{3} \times \frac{3}{4} \times \frac{4}{5}$

(f) $\frac{5}{8} \times \frac{1}{4} \times \frac{8}{9}$

(g) $\frac{3}{8} \times 1\frac{1}{4}$

(h) $5\frac{1}{2} \times 6$

10. Divide.

(a) $6 \div \frac{1}{2}$

(b) $5 \div \frac{3}{4}$

(c) $\frac{15}{8} \div 3$

(d) $\frac{2}{3} \div 4$

(e) $\frac{5}{2} \div \frac{1}{2}$

(f) $\frac{5}{8} \div \frac{5}{4}$

(g) $\frac{2}{5} \div \frac{7}{8}$

(h) $\frac{7}{10} \div \frac{3}{5}$

11. Find the quotient.

(a) $1\frac{1}{2} \div 3$

(b) $3\frac{1}{8} \div 5$

(c) $1 \div 2\frac{1}{5}$

(d) $5 \div 4\frac{1}{2}$

(e) $1\frac{5}{7} \div 2\frac{2}{5}$

(f) $3\frac{2}{3} \div 1\frac{4}{7}$

(g) $2\frac{7}{10} \div 3\frac{5}{10}$

(h) $1\frac{4}{5} \div 1\frac{2}{3}$

12. Evaluate.

(a) $\frac{3}{4} \times \frac{5}{6} \div \frac{1}{2}$

(b) $1\frac{1}{2} \div \frac{3}{5} \times \frac{1}{4}$

(c) $1\frac{2}{3} \times \left(3\frac{1}{2} \div 5\right)$

(d) $\frac{9}{10} \times 20 \div \frac{1}{3}$

7(a) $\frac{13}{12}$ **(b)** $2\frac{7}{24}$ **(c)** $2\frac{19}{20}$ **(d)** $3\frac{19}{24}$ **(e)** $1\frac{1}{4}$ **(f)** $\frac{13}{30}$
8(a) 4 **(c)** $\frac{15}{2}$ **(e)** 9
9(a) $\frac{1}{3}$ **(c)** $\frac{3}{8}$ **(e)** $\frac{2}{5}$ **(g)** $\frac{15}{32}$
10(a) 12 **(b)** $\frac{20}{3}$ **(c)** $\frac{5}{8}$ **(d)** $\frac{1}{6}$ **(e)** 5 **(f)** $\frac{1}{2}$ **(g)** $\frac{16}{35}$ **(h)** $\frac{7}{6}$
11(a) $\frac{1}{2}$ **(c)** $\frac{5}{11}$ **(e)** $\frac{5}{7}$ **(g)** $\frac{27}{35}$
12(a) $\frac{5}{4}$ **(b)** $\frac{5}{8}$ **(c)** $\frac{7}{6}$ **(d)** 54

$1\frac{2}{7} = \frac{7}{7} + \frac{2}{7} = \frac{9}{7}$

Is a common denominator needed here?

BODMAS!

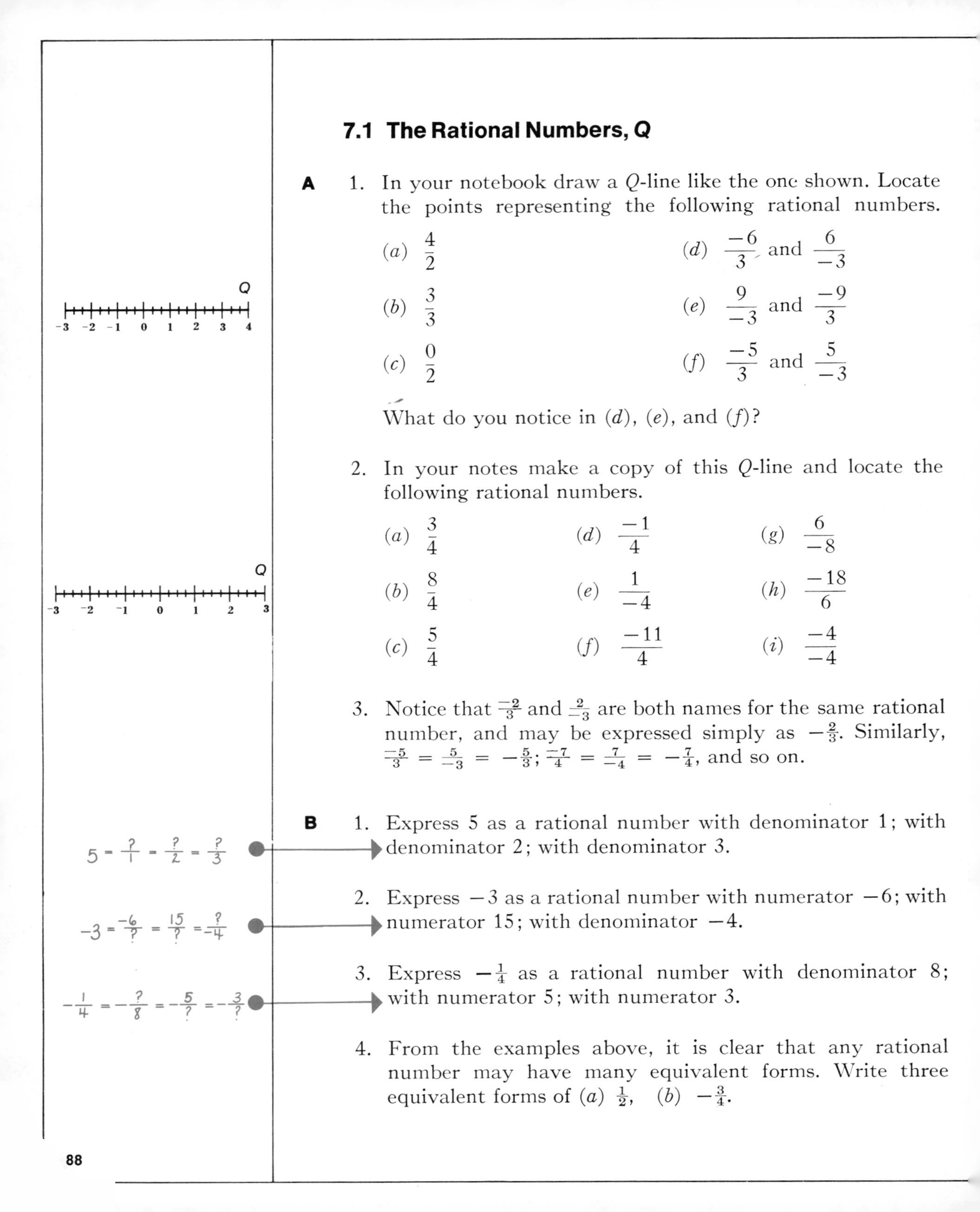

7.1 The Rational Numbers, Q

A 1. In your notebook draw a Q-line like the one shown. Locate the points representing the following rational numbers.

(*a*) $\frac{4}{2}$ (*d*) $\frac{-6}{3}$ and $\frac{6}{-3}$

(*b*) $\frac{3}{3}$ (*e*) $\frac{9}{-3}$ and $\frac{-9}{3}$

(*c*) $\frac{0}{2}$ (*f*) $\frac{-5}{3}$ and $\frac{5}{-3}$

What do you notice in (*d*), (*e*), and (*f*)?

2. In your notes make a copy of this Q-line and locate the following rational numbers.

(*a*) $\frac{3}{4}$ (*d*) $\frac{-1}{4}$ (*g*) $\frac{6}{-8}$

(*b*) $\frac{8}{4}$ (*e*) $\frac{1}{-4}$ (*h*) $\frac{-18}{6}$

(*c*) $\frac{5}{4}$ (*f*) $\frac{-11}{4}$ (*i*) $\frac{-4}{-4}$

3. Notice that $\frac{-2}{3}$ and $\frac{2}{-3}$ are both names for the same rational number, and may be expressed simply as $-\frac{2}{3}$. Similarly, $\frac{-5}{3} = \frac{5}{-3} = -\frac{5}{3}$; $\frac{-7}{4} = \frac{7}{-4} = -\frac{7}{4}$, and so on.

B 1. Express 5 as a rational number with denominator 1; with denominator 2; with denominator 3.

2. Express -3 as a rational number with numerator -6; with numerator 15; with denominator -4.

3. Express $-\frac{1}{4}$ as a rational number with denominator 8; with numerator 5; with numerator 3.

4. From the examples above, it is clear that any rational number may have many equivalent forms. Write three equivalent forms of (*a*) $\frac{1}{2}$, (*b*) $-\frac{3}{4}$.

Make a copy of the diagram, which shows a portion of a scale on a wheel-alignment machine. Note that the scale is divided into quarters.

1. Locate the following readings on your scale.
2. What reading is associated with point A? Point B? Point C? Point D? Point E?
3. How are readings of 2 and -2 related?
4. What is the relationship between readings of $\frac{1}{2}$ and $-\frac{1}{2}$? Of $\frac{7}{4}$ and $-\frac{7}{4}$?
5. State the opposites of the following rational numbers.

$$\frac{4}{4}, \frac{2}{7}, -\frac{3}{8}, -5, \frac{17}{10}, -\frac{21}{3}, 82, 0$$

Rational numbers are also used in equation-solving.

1. State the solution to each equation.

   (*a*) $x + 4 = 2, \quad x \in W$ (*d*) $2x = 1, \quad x \in W$
   (*b*) $x + 4 = 2, \quad x \in I$ (*e*) $2x = 1, \quad x \in I$
   (*c*) $x + 4 = 2, \quad x \in Q$ (*f*) $2x = 1, \quad x \in Q$

2. Solve.

   (*a*) $3x + 1 = 0, \quad x \in W$
   (*b*) $3x + 1 = 0, \quad x \in I$
   (*c*) $3x + 1 = 0, \quad x \in Q$

By extending the domain of the variable to the set Q, many equations that had no solution in I or W do have solutions in Q.

Example

Solve $4 - 3x = -6, \quad x \in Q$

Solution

$$\begin{aligned} \because \quad & 4 - 3x = -6 \\ \text{then } & 4 - 4 - 3x = -6 - 4 \\ \therefore \quad & -3x = -10 \\ \text{and } \quad & \frac{-3x}{-3} = \frac{-10}{-3} \\ \therefore \quad & x = \tfrac{10}{3} \end{aligned}$$

Check

LS	RS
$= 4 - 3x$	-6
$= 4 - 3\left(\frac{10}{3}\right)$	
$= 4 - 10$	
$= -6$	

$\therefore x = \frac{10}{3}$ is correct.

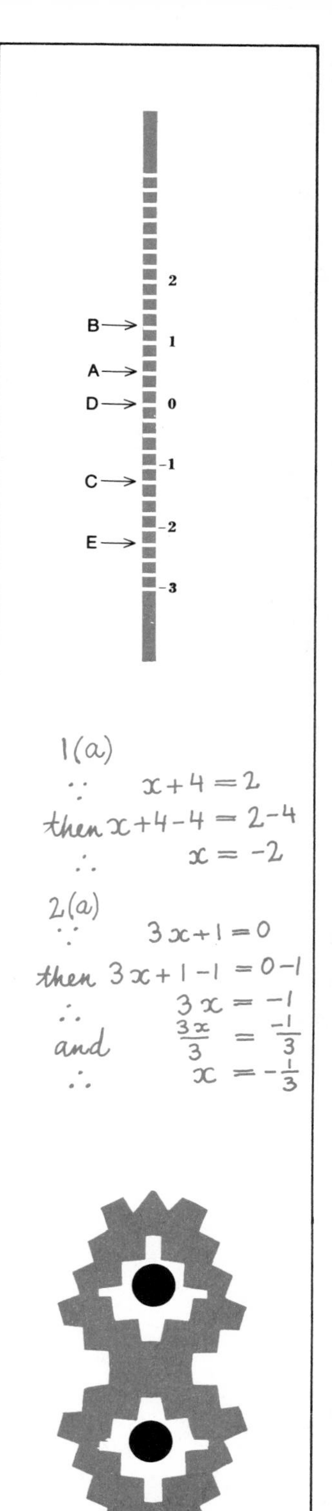

Exercise 7.1

Discussion

1. Does the set Q contain all the elements of N? Of W? Of I?

2. Is 0 an element of Q? Explain.

3. State the opposites of the following numbers.

$$\frac{2}{3},\quad -\frac{5}{1},\quad -\frac{7}{16},\quad \frac{5}{2},\quad 0,\quad 3\frac{1}{4},\quad -\frac{0}{11},\quad \frac{31}{59}$$

4. State two other ways of writing $\frac{-7}{2}$.

5. Using the integers -3, 2, and -5, make up four different rational numbers.

6. The rational number $\frac{4}{2}$ is also a member of I and W. To what sets do each of the following numbers belong?

$$3,\quad 4,\quad 2\frac{1}{2},\quad -\frac{14}{7},\quad \frac{3}{9},\quad \frac{-21}{3},\quad \frac{-6}{-6}.$$

7. The Q-line shown below is marked off in tenths. Name the rational numbers represented by the points A, B, C, D, E, F, and G.

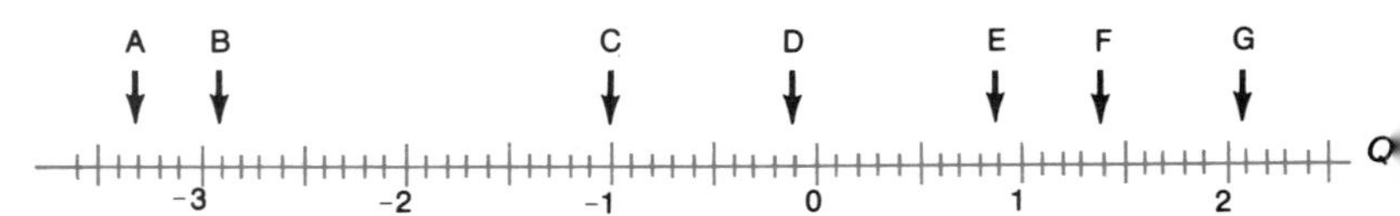

8. The Q-line below is marked off in eighths. Name the rational numbers represented by points M, N, P, Q, R, S, and T.

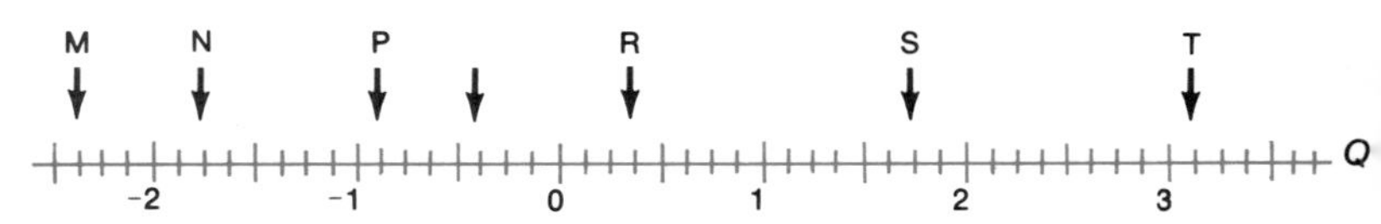

9. Name a rational number between 1 and 2. Now name a rational number between your answer and 2. Next name still another rational number between this new answer and 2. Can this procedure be carried out indefinitely? Explain.

Written Solutions

10. Draw a Q-line marked off in tenths. Locate the following rational numbers.

$$\frac{5}{10},\ -\frac{3}{5},\ \frac{15}{10},\ \frac{14}{5},\ -\frac{7}{10},\ -1\frac{4}{10},\ 2\frac{3}{5},\ -1\frac{1}{2}$$

11. Draw a Q-line marked off in one-hundredths. Locate the following rational numbers.

$$\frac{3}{100},\ -\frac{3}{4},\ \frac{1}{2},\ -\frac{7}{10},\ \frac{59}{100},\ -\frac{11}{10},\ \frac{1}{4},\ -\frac{9}{10},\ \frac{0}{100}$$

12. Arrange the following rational numbers in descending order. (greatest → least)

(*a*) $\frac{3}{4}, \frac{1}{4}, \frac{9}{20}, \frac{2}{5}, \frac{13}{40}$ (*b*) $\frac{3}{10}, \frac{7}{20}, \frac{23}{50}, \frac{2}{5}, \frac{49}{100}$

13. Solve and graph on a number line.

(*a*) $7x = 14,\ x \in I$ (*d*) $3x = -2,\ x \in Q$

(*b*) $4x = 1,\ x \in Q$ (*e*) $4x - 2 = 0,\ x \in I$

(*c*) $2x = \frac{1}{2},\ x \in W$ (*f*) $7x + 4 = 0,\ x \in Q$

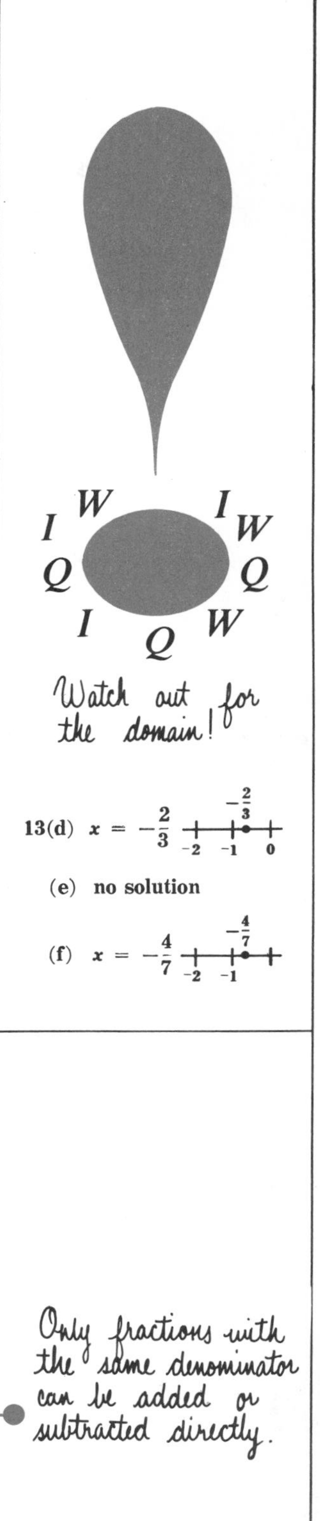

W I W
I Q Q
I Q W
Watch out for the domain!
13(d) x = −2/3
−2/3
−2 −1 0
(e) no solution
(f) x = −4/7
−4/7
−2 −1
Only fractions with the same denominator can be added or subtracted directly.

7.2 Addition and Subtraction in Q

Since the sets W and I are contained in the set Q, we would expect that the methods used for addition and subtraction in these sets also apply to Q.

1. Add.

7	−5	4	−2	$1\frac{1}{4}$	$2\frac{1}{8}$
2	3	−6	−8	$3\frac{1}{4}$	$3\frac{5}{8}$

2. What is the first step in adding $\frac{1}{2}$ and $\frac{3}{4}$? $\frac{4}{5}$ and $\frac{3}{10}$? $1\frac{5}{8}$ and $\frac{7}{16}$?

The only addition performed is with integers! It's easy!

3. State the numbers required to complete these examples.

(a) $\frac{1}{2} + \frac{3}{4}$
$= \frac{2}{4} + \frac{3}{4}$
$= \frac{2+3}{4}$
$= \frac{\square}{4}$

(b) $\frac{3}{2} + \left(-\frac{1}{4}\right)$
$= \frac{3}{2} + \frac{-1}{4}$
$= \frac{\square + (-1)}{\square}$
$= \square$

(c) $\frac{5}{2} + \left(-\frac{7}{3}\right)$
$= \frac{5}{2} + \frac{-7}{3}$
$= \frac{\square + \square}{\square}$
$= \square$

B

1. Subtract 8 from -3.
   $-3 - 8 = -11$

2. Subtract -16 from 22.
   $22 - (-16) = 22 + 16 = 38$

3. State the numbers required to complete the following.

(a) $-\frac{5}{6} - \frac{3}{4}$
$= \frac{-5}{6} + \frac{-3}{4}$
$= \frac{\square + \square}{12}$
$= \square$

(b) $-1\frac{5}{6} - 3\frac{3}{4}$
$= -\frac{11}{6} - \frac{\square}{4}$
$= \frac{-22 + (-\square)}{12}$
$= \frac{\square}{12}$

(c) $\frac{3}{4} + \left(-\frac{5}{6} - 1\frac{2}{5}\right)$
$= \frac{3}{4} + \left(\frac{\square}{6} + \frac{\square}{5}\right)$
$= \frac{3}{4} + \left(\frac{\square + \square}{30}\right)$
$= \frac{3}{4} + \frac{-67}{30}$
$= \frac{\square + \square}{\square}$
$= \square$

We simply add integers.

C

1. Evaluate $x - y + z$, where $x = 1\frac{2}{3}$, $y = -\frac{4}{5}$, and $z = -2$.

$x - y + z = \left(1\frac{2}{3}\right) - \left(-\frac{4}{5}\right) + (-2)$
$= \frac{5}{3} + \frac{4}{5} + (-2)$
$= \frac{25 + 12 + -30}{15}$
$= \frac{7}{15}$

Forgotten substitution? See Section 1.3.

2. Evaluate $a + b - c$, where $a = 0$, $b = -2\frac{5}{8}$, $c = \frac{3}{4}$.

$$
\begin{aligned}
& a + b - c \\
&= 0 + \left(-2\frac{5}{8}\right) - \left(\frac{3}{4}\right) \\
&= \frac{\square}{8} + \frac{\square}{4} \\
&= \frac{\square + \square}{8} \\
&= \frac{\square}{8}
\end{aligned}
$$

Exercise 7.2

Discussion

1. When adding $\frac{3}{5}$ and $-\frac{7}{4}$, what common denominator is used? How is it determined?

2. In subtracting two rational numbers, tell what steps you follow.

3. Do you think it is possible to add or subtract two rational numbers and get an answer that is *not* a rational number?

4. Add.

$2\frac{1}{2}$	$1\frac{5}{8}$	$5\frac{1}{6}$	$1\frac{1}{5}$	$1\frac{3}{4}$	$9\frac{1}{16}$
$3\frac{1}{4}$	$\frac{7}{8}$	$2\frac{2}{3}$	$3\frac{4}{10}$	$\frac{3}{8}$	$3\frac{1}{4}$

Written Solutions

5. Add the following sets of numbers.

   (*a*) $\frac{2}{5}, -\frac{7}{2}$

   (*b*) $-1\frac{3}{4}, -\frac{5}{3}$

   (*c*) $\frac{1}{6}, -\frac{3}{4}, \frac{2}{5}$

   (*d*) $4\frac{1}{2}, -3\frac{3}{4}, 1\frac{7}{8}$

6. Find the difference.

   (*a*) $\frac{3}{8} - \frac{3}{4}$

   (*b*) $-\frac{5}{6} - \left(-\frac{2}{3}\right)$

   (*c*) $-\frac{3}{5} - \frac{1}{4}$

   (*d*) $1\frac{2}{3} - \left(-2\frac{1}{2}\right)$

5(a) $-\frac{31}{10}$ **(c)** $-\frac{11}{60}$

6(a) $-\frac{3}{8}$ **(c)** $-\frac{17}{20}$

7(a) $\frac{13}{24}$ (b) $\frac{13}{24}$
8(a) $\frac{101}{24}$ (b) $-\frac{101}{24}$
9(a) $\frac{49}{60}$ (b) $\frac{40}{60}$
10(a) $-\frac{1}{24}$ (b) $-\frac{37}{24}$
11(a) $\frac{9}{15}$ (b) $\frac{49}{24}$

12. By addition, Sam butchered 31 full carcasses. However, the types of sections suggest that he must have butchered 34 carcasses.

7. Find the sum.

   (a) $2\frac{3}{8} + \left(-1\frac{5}{6}\right)$ (b) $-1\frac{5}{6} + 2\frac{3}{8}$

8. Find the difference.

   (a) $2\frac{3}{8} - \left(-1\frac{5}{6}\right)$ (b) $-1\frac{5}{6} - 2\frac{3}{8}$

9. Simplify.

   (a) $-\frac{3}{5} + \left(\frac{2}{3} + \frac{3}{4}\right)$ (b) $\left(-\frac{3}{5} + \frac{2}{3}\right) + \frac{3}{4}$

10. Simplify.

    (a) $-\frac{1}{6} - \left(\frac{5}{8} - \frac{3}{4}\right)$ (b) $\left(-\frac{1}{6} - \frac{5}{8}\right) - \frac{3}{4}$

11. Find the value.

    (a) $p + q - r$, where $p = \frac{2}{3}$, $q = -1$, $r = -1\frac{3}{5}$

    (b) $-a + b - c$, where $a = -\frac{5}{4}$, $b = \frac{1}{8}$, $c = -\frac{2}{3}$

    (c) $x - y - z$, where $x = 0$, $y = \frac{3}{10}$, $z = -1\frac{2}{5}$

12.

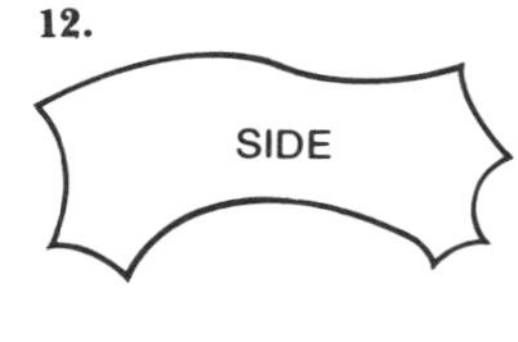

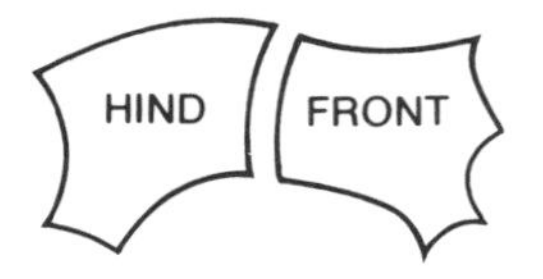

12. Shivering Sam, the butcher, counts 23 sides of beef (halves), 35 hindquarters, and 43 front quarters in his meat freezer. How many full carcasses did Sam butcher?

13. Joe and Judy are selling advertising space in the school yearbook. Joe has sold 3 full pages, 5 half-pages, 13 quarter-pages, and 42 eighth-pages of advertising space. Judy has sold 1 fewer full pages, 3 more half-pages, 2 fewer quarter-pages, and 4 more eighth-pages.

    (a) Find the total advertising space sold by each student.

    (b) If 35 pages of advertising are needed, how much space is yet to be sold?

7.3 Multiplication and Division in *Q*

A

1. Multiply.

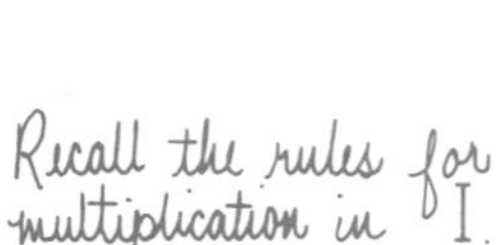

3	7	−4	−8
5	−2	5	−3

2. Multiply.

   (a) $\frac{3}{4} \times \frac{5}{2}$ (b) $\frac{1}{3} \times \frac{4}{7}$ (c) $\frac{3}{8} \times \frac{5}{4}$ (d) $\frac{5}{6} \times \frac{7}{8}$

3. State the numbers required to complete the following examples.

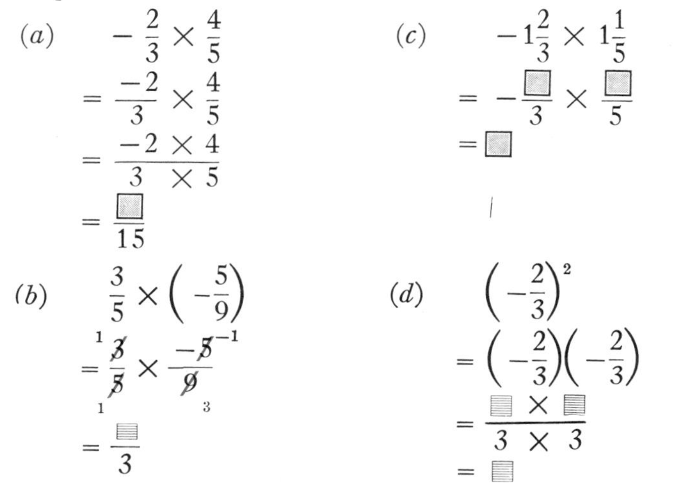

(a) $-\frac{2}{3} \times \frac{4}{5}$

$= \frac{-2}{3} \times \frac{4}{5}$

$= \frac{-2 \times 4}{3 \times 5}$

$= \frac{\square}{15}$

(b) $\frac{3}{5} \times \left(-\frac{5}{9}\right)$

$= \frac{\cancel{3}^{1}}{\cancel{5}_{1}} \times \frac{-\cancel{5}^{-1}}{\cancel{9}_{3}}$

$= \frac{\square}{3}$

(c) $-1\frac{2}{3} \times 1\frac{1}{5}$

$= -\frac{\square}{3} \times \frac{\square}{5}$

$= \square$

(d) $\left(-\frac{2}{3}\right)^2$

$= \left(-\frac{2}{3}\right)\left(-\frac{2}{3}\right)$

$= \frac{\square \times \square}{3 \times 3}$

$= \square$

Notice that multiplying rationals simply involves multiplying integers.

B From Section A we see that no new methods are required for multiplication of rational numbers. Evaluation by substitution is also treated as in *I*.

Example 1 Evaluate $3a + 4b$, where $a = \frac{5}{6}$ and $b = -\frac{1}{2}$.

Solution $3a + 4b = \cancel{3}^{1}\left(\frac{5}{\cancel{6}_{2}}\right) + \cancel{4}^{2}\left(-\frac{1}{\cancel{2}_{1}}\right)$

$= \frac{5}{2} + (-2)$

$= \frac{5}{2} + \frac{-4}{2}$

$= \frac{1}{2}$

$a = \frac{5}{6}$

$b = -\frac{1}{2}$

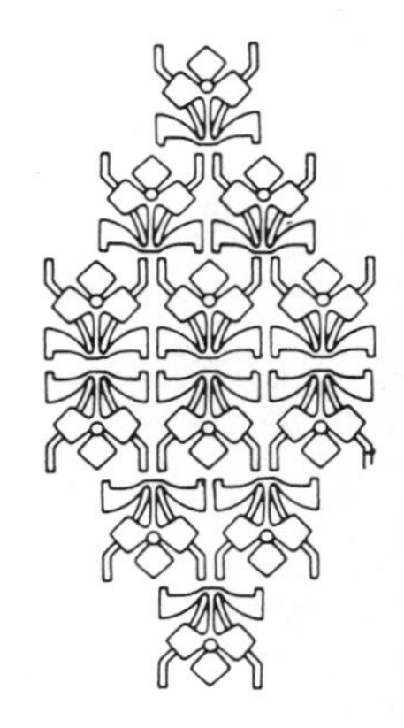

Example 2

Evaluate $2p - 3q + r$, where $p = -\frac{2}{3}$, $q = \frac{4}{5}$ and $r = -\frac{1}{3}$.

Solution $2p - 3q + r = 2\left(-\frac{2}{3}\right) - 3\left(\frac{4}{5}\right) + \left(-\frac{1}{3}\right)$

$= \frac{-4}{3} + \frac{-12}{5} + \frac{-1}{3}$

$= \frac{-20 + (-36) + (-5)}{15}$

$= -\frac{61}{15}$

$p = -\frac{2}{3}$

$q = \frac{4}{5}$

$r = -\frac{1}{3}$

C 1. Divide.

$14 \div 7 \qquad -25 \div 5 \qquad 24 \div -6 \qquad -12 \div -3$

You have probably learned a rule for dividing by fractions. Some students say "invert and multiply"; others use "multiply by the reciprocal." Whatever you *say*, here is what you *do*:

$$\frac{2}{5} \div \frac{3}{4} = \frac{2}{5} \times \frac{4}{3}$$

Replace division by multiplication. Here is why it works.

$\times \frac{4}{3}$

$\div \frac{3}{4}$

$$\frac{2}{5} \div \frac{3}{4} = \frac{\frac{2}{5}}{\frac{3}{4}} = \frac{\frac{2}{5} \times \frac{4}{3}}{\frac{3}{4} \times \frac{4}{3}} = \frac{\frac{2}{5} \times \frac{4}{3}}{1} = \frac{2}{5} \times \frac{4}{3}$$

Multiplying both the numerator and the denominator by $\frac{4}{3}$ does not change the value of the fraction.

Use the same method when you are working with rational numbers.

2. Restate each quotient as a product.

(*a*) $\frac{-2}{3} \div \frac{4}{5}$ (*b*) $1\frac{5}{6} \div \left(-\frac{2}{3}\right)$ (*c*) $\left(-1\frac{3}{8}\right) \div \left(-\frac{3}{4}\right)$

Example Evaluate $-1\frac{3}{8} \div 2\frac{4}{5}$.

Solution

$$-1\frac{3}{8} \div 2\frac{3}{4} = -\frac{\cancel{11}}{\cancel{8}} \div \frac{\cancel{11}}{\cancel{4}}$$
$$= -\frac{\cancel{11}}{\cancel{8}_2} \times \frac{\cancel{4}}{\cancel{11}}$$
$$= -\frac{1}{2}$$

Mixed numbers are changed to improper fractions before dividing.

3. Evaluate each of the following quotients.

(*a*) $\frac{3}{7} \div \frac{15}{21}$ (*b*) $\frac{5}{6} \div \left(-\frac{2}{3}\right)$ (*c*) $-1\frac{1}{16} \div \left(-\frac{5}{32}\right)$

Exercise 7.3

Discussion

1. State the product.

   (*a*) $\left(\frac{2}{3}\right)\left(\frac{3}{2}\right)$ (*b*) $\left(-\frac{7}{5}\right)\left(-\frac{5}{7}\right)$ (*c*) $\left(1\frac{3}{4}\right)\left(\frac{4}{7}\right)$

   What do you notice?

2. State the reciprocal of each.

   $\frac{4}{5}, -\frac{1}{2}, \frac{5}{7}, -\frac{3}{5}, 0, 1, -1$

3. State the product.

   (*a*) $\frac{2}{3} \times 6$ (*c*) $4\left(-\frac{5}{2}\right)$ (*e*) $0 \times \left(-\frac{3}{8}\right)\left(\frac{5}{9}\right)$

   (*b*) $\left(-\frac{3}{5}\right)^2$ (*d*) $\frac{2}{5}\left(-\frac{45}{100}\right)$ (*f*) $\left(\frac{-5}{3}\right)\left(-\frac{9}{15}\right)$

4. Express as a product.

   (*a*) $-\frac{5}{3} \div \frac{1}{2}$ (*c*) $2 \div \left(-1\frac{1}{2}\right)$

   (*b*) $3\frac{1}{2} \div \left(-\frac{4}{3}\right)$ (*d*) $-3 \div 2\frac{1}{4}$

5. Note that

   (*a*) $\frac{2}{3} - \left(-\frac{5}{3}\right) = \frac{2}{3} + \frac{5}{3}$ and (*b*) $\frac{2}{3} \div \left(-\frac{5}{3}\right) = \frac{2}{3} \times \left(-\frac{3}{5}\right)$

6. What rational number cannot be used as a divisor?

Written Solutions

7. Find the product.

   (*a*) $5\frac{1}{4} \times 3\frac{1}{2}$ (*b*) $-3\frac{1}{4} \times \left(-\frac{9}{2}\right)$ (*c*) $-5\frac{2}{5} \times 1\frac{5}{9}$

8. Multiply.

   (*a*) $3 \times \frac{7}{4} \times \frac{12}{9}$ (*c*) $-1\frac{7}{8} \times 3\frac{2}{3} \times 2\frac{2}{5}$

   (*b*) $3\frac{1}{3} \times \frac{3}{10} \times 4\frac{3}{5}$ (*d*) $3\frac{3}{4}\left(-4\frac{4}{5}\right)\left(-\frac{7}{10}\right)$

$\frac{2}{3} \times \frac{3}{2}$

Reciprocals are 2 numbers like $\frac{3}{4}$ and $\frac{4}{3}$ whose product is 1.

How is the subtraction done in (a)? How is the division done in (b)?

7(a) $\frac{34}{9}$ (b) $\frac{147}{8}$ (c) $\frac{117}{8}$ (d) $-\frac{42}{5}$

8(a) 7 (c) $-\frac{33}{2}$

9. Evaluate.

(*a*) $-\frac{3}{4} \div \frac{1}{4}$ (*c*) $\frac{3}{5} \div \frac{4}{5}$ (*e*) $\frac{3}{4} \div \frac{5}{8}$

(*b*) $\frac{2}{3} \div \left(-\frac{7}{3}\right)$ (*d*) $\frac{5}{6} \div \left(-\frac{4}{3}\right)$ (*f*) $\left(-\frac{3}{10}\right) \div \left(-\frac{7}{15}\right)$

10. Divide.

(*a*) $-\frac{3}{4}$ by $\frac{6}{5}$ (*c*) $\frac{4}{9}$ by $-\frac{5}{3}$ (*e*) $-1\frac{3}{5}$ by -2

(*b*) $\frac{3}{8}$ by $-2\frac{2}{3}$ (*d*) $-2\frac{3}{5}$ by $4\frac{1}{4}$ (*f*) $-4\frac{1}{8}$ by $1\frac{3}{8}$

What do you do with mixed numbers before dividing?

11. Divide.

(*a*) $2\frac{5}{8} \div 4\frac{1}{5}$ (*d*) $-2\frac{4}{5} \div \left(-1\frac{1}{8}\right)$

(*b*) $-3\frac{1}{2} \div \frac{7}{10}$ (*e*) $-\frac{7}{8} \div \frac{14}{20}$

(*c*) $\frac{7}{10} \div 5\frac{1}{4}$ (*f*) $-\frac{4}{10} \div \left(-3\frac{20}{100}\right)$

12. Simplify the following expressions in the easiest way possible.

(*a*) $-20\left(\frac{5}{4} + \frac{7}{5}\right)$ (*d*) $\frac{3}{4}\left(-2\right) + \frac{5}{16} \times 0$

(*b*) $\frac{5}{8}\left(-\frac{3}{4}\right)\left(\frac{4}{3}\right)$ (*e*) $\frac{2}{3}\left(\frac{5}{8}\right) + \frac{2}{3}\left(-\frac{1}{8}\right)$

(*c*) $7\left(\frac{4}{3} - \frac{5}{6}\right)$ (*f*) $\left(-\frac{18}{4}\right)\left(\frac{5}{9}\right)\left(-\frac{8}{10}\right)$

Use short cuts where you can!

13. Simplify.

(*a*) $\left(-\frac{5}{3}\right) \times \frac{5}{7} \times 0$ (*d*) $-\frac{5}{9} \times \left(\frac{3}{2}\right)^2 \times \frac{6}{-10}$

(*b*) $\left(-\frac{3}{4} + \frac{5}{7}\right) \times 28$ (*e*) $\frac{3}{8} \times \left(-\frac{7}{10}\right) \times \left(\frac{8}{3}\right)$

(*c*) $-\frac{1}{2}\left(-\frac{5}{3}\right) - \frac{1}{2}\left(\frac{7}{3}\right)$ (*f*) $-5\left(-\frac{3}{4} + \frac{5}{8}\right)$

14. Evaluate. $x = \frac{2}{3}$, $y = -\frac{1}{2}$, $z = \frac{5}{6}$

(*a*) xyz (*b*) $x + y + z$ (*c*) $x - y - 2z$

9(d)	$-\frac{5}{8}$	**(f)**	$\frac{9}{14}$
10(a)	$-\frac{5}{8}$	**(c)**	$-\frac{4}{15}$
11(a)	$\frac{5}{8}$	**(c)**	$\frac{2}{15}$
12(a)	-53	**(c)**	$\frac{7}{2}$
13(b)	-1	**(d)**	$\frac{3}{4}$
14(a)	$-\frac{5}{18}$	**(c)**	$-\frac{1}{2}$

15. Evaluate.

(*a*) $3p - 2q + 5r$, where $p = \frac{1}{2}$, $q = -\frac{1}{2}$, and $r = 0$

(*b*) $\frac{1}{2}a + \frac{2}{3}b - c$, where $a = -\frac{2}{3}$, $b = \frac{3}{2}$, and $c = -1$

(*c*) $2(l + w)$, where $l = 20\frac{3}{5}$ and $w = 13\frac{7}{10}$

(*d*) $\frac{1}{2}bh$, where $b = 2\frac{1}{2}$ and $h = \frac{58}{100}$

16. Evaluate.

(*a*) $\frac{2}{3} \div \left(-\frac{8}{3}\right) \times 6$

(*b*) $-\frac{4}{5} \div \frac{1}{2} + \left(-\frac{3}{5}\right) \div \frac{2}{3}$

(*c*) $3\frac{1}{2} - 6 \times \frac{2}{5} \div \left(-\frac{4}{5}\right)$

(*d*) $\dfrac{\frac{1}{2} + \frac{1}{3}}{\frac{1}{2} - \frac{1}{3}}$

(*e*) $\dfrac{-\frac{3}{8} + 2}{4 - \frac{3}{4}}$

(*f*) $\dfrac{-\frac{2}{3} + \frac{5}{6}}{\frac{1}{4} + \frac{5}{3}}$

(*g*) $\left(2\frac{5}{8} \div 4\frac{1}{5}\right) + \left(-\frac{7}{8} \div \frac{7}{10}\right)$

15(a) $\frac{5}{2}$ (b) $\frac{5}{3}$ (c) $68\frac{3}{5}$ (d) $\frac{29}{40}$
16(a) $-\frac{3}{2}$ (c) $\frac{13}{2}$ (e) $\frac{1}{2}$ (g) $-\frac{5}{8}$

7.4 Solving Equations and Inequations Using Rational Numbers

Rational numbers may appear in an equation such as

$$\tfrac{1}{2}x + \tfrac{3}{4} = 0,$$

and we need new methods to solve such equations.

To solve the equation $3x = 15$, you divide each side by 3. Suppose that the equation were

$$\tfrac{1}{3}x = 15.$$

Then what would you do? If you suggested *multiplying* each side by 3, you have the idea, since

$$3 \times \tfrac{1}{3}x = x.$$

1. What would you do to each side of the following equations in order to solve them?

(*a*) $\frac{1}{2}x = 5$ (*b*) $\frac{1}{5}x = 2$ (*c*) $-\frac{1}{4}x = 8$

2. Solve the equations in Question 1.

Like this!
$\because \quad \frac{1}{3}x = 15$
then $3 \times \frac{1}{3}x = 3 \times 15$
$\therefore \quad x = 45$

Solution (b)

$\frac{2}{3}x = 8$ $x = 12$

x → ×2 → ÷3 → 8 | Reverse the steps | 8 → ×3 → ÷2 → 12

B You have probably discovered that in solving an equation the aim is to get the variable by itself on one side — not $5x$, $y - 7$, or $\frac{1}{5}z$, but just plain x, y, or z!

1. By what number would you multiply $\frac{2}{3}$ to get an answer of 1? Repeat for $\frac{5}{7}$, $\frac{3}{5}$, $-\frac{3}{8}$.
2. By what number would you multiply $\frac{1}{2}x$ to give an answer of x? Repeat for $\frac{2}{3}x$, $\frac{3}{5}x$, $-\frac{4}{7}x$.

Example 1 Solve $\frac{2}{3}x = 8$, $x \in Q$.

Solution

(a)
$$\because \quad \frac{2}{3}x = 8$$
$$\text{then } \frac{3}{2} \times \frac{2}{3}x = \frac{3}{2} \times 8$$
$$\therefore \quad x = 12$$

(b)
$$\because \quad \frac{2}{3}x = 8$$
$$\text{then } 3\left(\frac{2}{3}x\right) = 3(8)$$
$$\text{and } \quad 2x = 24$$
$$\therefore \quad x = 12$$

Solution (*a*) is faster, but with Solution (*b*) you will probably be more accurate.

3. Solve by using one method from Example 1, and check by using the other.

   (*a*) $\frac{3}{5}x = 12$ (*b*) $-\frac{5}{6}y = 10$

Sometimes there is more than one fraction present in an equation. Then it is best to *clear the fractions* before doing anything else.

Clear the fractions!

Example 2 Solve $\frac{7}{8}x + 5 = \frac{3}{4}$, $x \in Q$.

Solution

$$\because \quad \frac{7}{8}x + 5 = \frac{3}{4}$$
$$\text{then } \quad 8\left(\frac{7}{8}x + 5\right) = 8\left(\frac{3}{4}\right) \quad (1)$$
$$\therefore \quad 7x + 40 = 6$$
$$\text{and } 7x + 40 - 40 = 6 - 40$$
$$\therefore \quad 7x = -34$$
$$\text{and } \quad \frac{1}{7}(7x) = \frac{1}{7}(-34)$$
$$\therefore \quad x = -\frac{34}{7}$$

$8(\frac{7}{8}x + 5)$
$= 8 \times \frac{7}{8}x + 8 \times 5$

This is called expanding.

By what was each side of (1) multiplied? Why?

C Using rational numbers has a startling effect on the graphs of solution sets of inequations.

1. How many natural numbers are there between 1 and 2?
2. How many integers are there between 1 and 2?
3. How many rational numbers are there between 1 and 2? *
4. Study the following examples carefully.

* Quite a few I guess!
Notice the domain in Examples 1, 2, 3.
A solid dot means "is included". An open dot means "is not included".
Why is the graph a solid line?

Example 1

Graph $1 \leq x < 2$. $x \in N$.

Solution

Example 2

Graph $1 \leq x < 2$. $x \in I$.

Solution

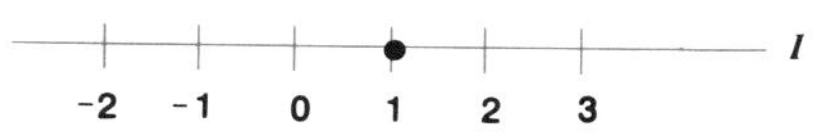

Example 3

Graph $1 \leq x < 2$. $x \in Q$.

Solution

Example 4

Graph $3y < 9$. $y \in Q$.

Solution

If $3y < 9$
$\therefore\ y < 3$

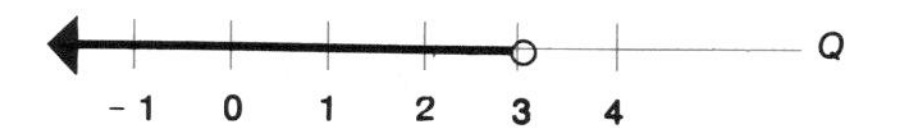

D

1. In solving $-3x < 9$, by what number do you divide each side?

2. What happens to an inequality sign when you divide by a negative number?

3. Try multiplying the following inequations by -2. What must you do to get true inequations?

$$6 < 8,\ 4 > 1,\ -3 < -1,\ 5 > -2$$

4. Solve.

   (*a*) $-\frac{1}{2}x > 3$ (*b*) $-\frac{2}{3}x < -8$

Exercise 7.4

Discussion

Note: Unless stated otherwise, the variable is a rational number.

1. State the first step in solving each of the following equations.

   (*a*) $\frac{1}{2}x = 4$ (*d*) $-\frac{1}{4}x = 1$ (*g*) $\frac{2}{3}x = 4$
   (*b*) $\frac{1}{3}x = 10$ (*e*) $5x = 1$ (*h*) $-\frac{7}{8}x = 14$
   (*c*) $-\frac{1}{5}x = 4$ (*f*) $-3x = 6$ (*i*) $\frac{5}{2}x = \frac{1}{2}$

Recall: Lowest Common Multiple (LCM) of some numbers is the smallest number into which each will divide.

2. State the lowest common multiple of

   (*a*) 4 and 8 (*b*) 5 and 7 (*c*) 2, 3, and 4

3. By what number would you multiply each side to clear the fractions?

   (*a*) $\frac{1}{2}x = \frac{3}{4}$ (*c*) $-\frac{2}{5}x = \frac{1}{4}$ (*e*) $\frac{5}{8}x = \frac{1}{6}$
   (*b*) $\frac{1}{3}x - \frac{5}{6} = 0$ (*d*) $\frac{2}{3} = \frac{1}{4}x$ (*f*) $\frac{9}{10}x = \frac{7}{100}$

4. Multiply.

   (*a*) $2(5 + 8)$ (*d*) $4(\frac{1}{4}x + 3)$
   (*b*) $3(6 - 4)$ (*e*) $-5(-\frac{2}{5}x + 1)$
   (*c*) $5(a + b)$ (*f*) $10(\frac{3}{10}x - \frac{1}{5})$

5. Correct the errors (if any) in each of the following graphs.

   (*a*) $x < 3,\ x \in I$
   (*b*) $x > -1,\ x \in Q$
   (*c*) $-1 < x \leq 1,\ x \in Q$
   (*d*) $x > 0,\ x \in I$

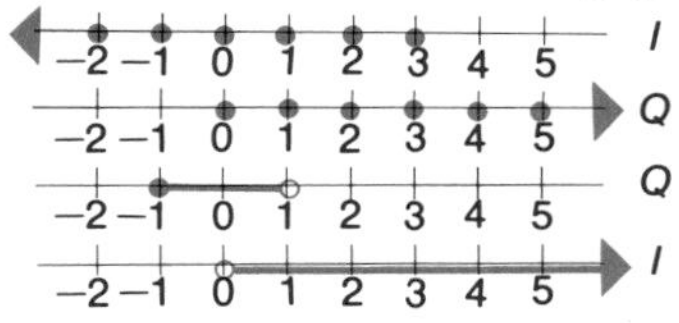

Written Solutions

6. Solve.

   (a) $\frac{1}{3}x = -2$
   (b) $\frac{1}{4}x = 4$
   (c) $\frac{1}{10}x = 1000$
   (d) $-\frac{1}{2}x = 8$
   (e) $\frac{1}{5}x + 3 = 0$
   (f) $6 - \frac{1}{3}x = 0$
   (g) $18 = -\frac{1}{4}x$
   (h) $-\frac{1}{7}x = 0$
   (i) $0 = \frac{1}{9}x - 3$

7. Solve.

   (a) $\frac{2}{3}x = 6$
   (b) $-\frac{3}{4}x = 9$
   (c) $1 - \frac{7}{10}x = 0$
   (d) $3 + \frac{4}{5}x = 11$
   (e) $28 = \frac{7}{2}x - 14$
   (f) $-\frac{5}{8}x = 16$
   (g) $-6 = 4 - \frac{3}{10}x$
   (h) $16 = 5 + \frac{2}{3}x - 7$

8. Find the lowest common multiple of each group of numbers.

   (a) 3, 4
   (b) 5, 10
   (c) 8, 12, 10
   (d) 6, 3, 20
   (e) 10, 100
   (f) 4, 5, 6

9. Solve.

   (a) $\frac{1}{4}x = \frac{5}{8}$
   (b) $\frac{1}{3}x + \frac{1}{6} = 0$
   (c) $-\frac{1}{5}x = \frac{7}{10}$
   (d) $3 - \frac{1}{4}x = \frac{1}{2}$
   (e) $\frac{4}{5}x = \frac{3}{4}$
   (f) $-\frac{9}{10}x = \frac{4}{100}$
   (g) $\frac{3}{8} = \frac{3}{10}x$
   (h) $0 = \frac{1}{5} - \frac{7}{10}x$

10. Solve.

    (a) $\frac{3}{5}x + \frac{1}{4} = 2$
    (b) $-\frac{2}{3}x + \frac{1}{6} = 9$
    (c) $\frac{7}{3}x - \frac{1}{5} = 1$
    (d) $1 - \frac{5}{9}x = 0$
    (e) $\frac{3}{4}x + \frac{5}{6} = \frac{1}{8}$
    (f) $-\frac{3}{10}x + \frac{1}{5} = \frac{3}{2}$
    (g) $\frac{5}{3}x - \frac{1}{4} = \frac{2}{5}$
    (h) $\frac{4}{9} = \frac{3}{5}x + 1$

11. Graph each of the following inequations.

    (a) $x < 3$
    (b) $-x \geq -2$
    (c) $x + 3 \leq 1$
    (d) $0 < x < 5$
    (e) $2x < -6$
    (f) $10 > 5x$
    (g) $-8 \leq \frac{1}{2}x$
    (h) $-\frac{1}{3}x > 9$

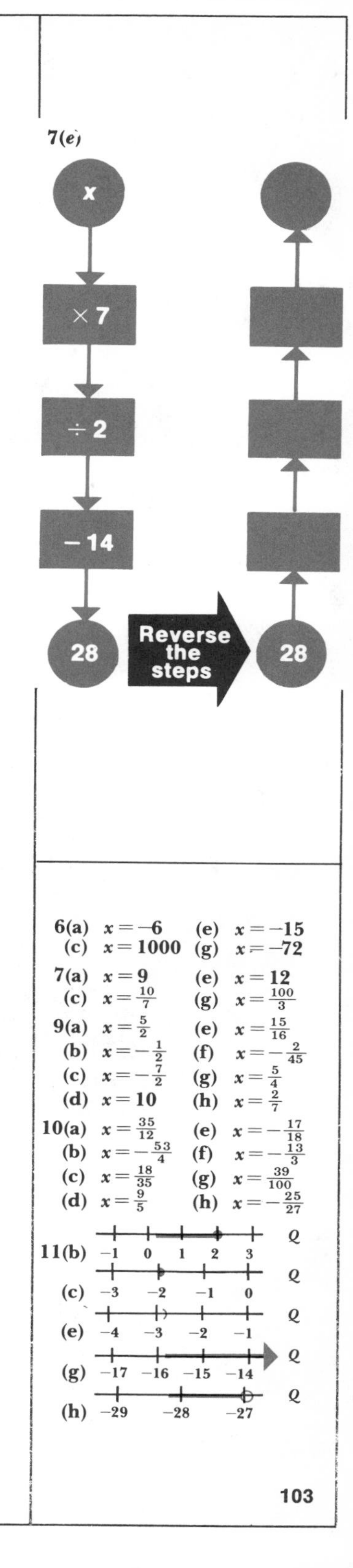

6(a) $x = -6$ (e) $x = -15$
(c) $x = 1000$ (g) $x = -72$

7(a) $x = 9$ (e) $x = 12$
(c) $x = \frac{10}{7}$ (g) $x = \frac{100}{3}$

9(a) $x = \frac{5}{2}$ (e) $x = \frac{15}{16}$
(b) $x = -\frac{1}{2}$ (f) $x = -\frac{2}{45}$
(c) $x = -\frac{7}{2}$ (g) $x = \frac{5}{4}$
(d) $x = 10$ (h) $x = \frac{2}{7}$

10(a) $x = \frac{35}{12}$ (e) $x = -\frac{17}{18}$
(b) $x = -\frac{53}{4}$ (f) $x = -\frac{13}{3}$
(c) $x = \frac{18}{35}$ (g) $x = \frac{39}{100}$
(d) $x = \frac{9}{5}$ (h) $x = -\frac{25}{27}$

11(b) −1 0 1 2 3
(c) −3 −2 −1 0
(e) −4 −3 −2 −1
(g) −17 −16 −15 −14
(h) −29 −28 −27

Unit 8
Decimal Numbers

Early in history, people used parts of their bodies to measure length. To refer to portions of these units, halves and quarters were used. Until the adoption of the metric system, rulers were graduated in inches, and the inch was divided into sixteenths, eighths, and quarters. This use of one-half and one-half of one-half (that is, one-quarter) is still evident in our measurement of time and money. Thus, town clocks strike the quarter and half-hour, and the quarter- and half-dollar are common coins.

However, our money system is basically decimal: the cent is 0.01 or $\frac{1}{100}$ of a dollar and the dime is 0.1 or $\frac{1}{10}$ of a dollar. Today, there is even a trend toward decimal parts of an hour. Parking garages use 6 min or 0.1 h to divide time, and auto mechanics often charge time for labor in the same way. Business also depends on the language of percent (a decimal relation), hence halves and quarters will be used less and less in the future.

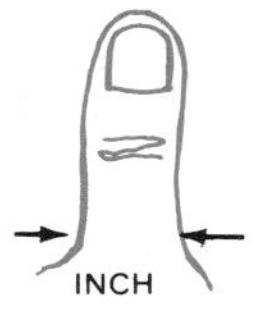

INCH

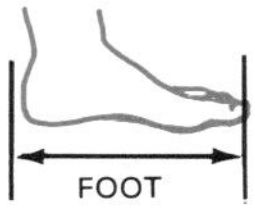

FOOT

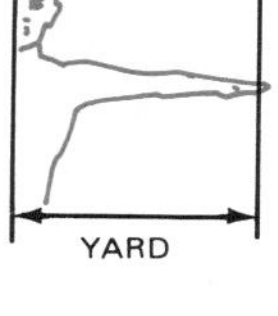

YARD

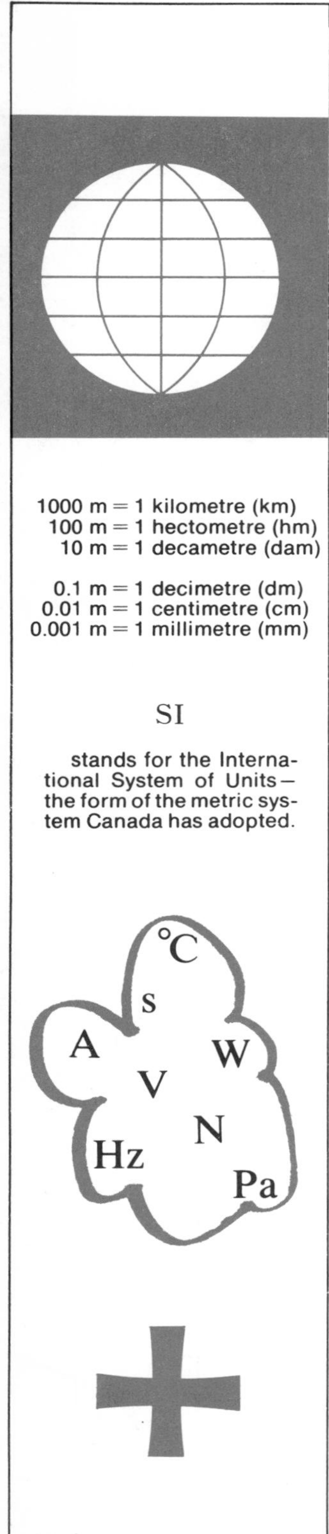

1000 m = 1 kilometre (km)
100 m = 1 hectometre (hm)
10 m = 1 decametre (dam)
0.1 m = 1 decimetre (dm)
0.01 m = 1 centimetre (cm)
0.001 m = 1 millimetre (mm)
SI
stands for the International System of Units—the form of the metric system Canada has adopted.
°C
s
A
W
V
N
Hz
Pa

The metric system is an entirely *decimal* system of measurement. It is a product of the French Revolution, which took place when nearly every village in France (in Europe, in fact) had its own system of measurement. Trade between villages was very difficult, since people didn't understand each other's measurements. The Revolutionists introduced a new, scientific system of measurement based on a natural constant.

The base unit of length, the *metre* (m), was originally defined by making the meridian through Paris from the North Pole to the equator 10 000 000 m long. The metre was multiplied and divided by powers of 10 to produce longer and shorter units of length. Additional units were introduced for capacity and mass. The capacity of a cube 10 cm long, 10 cm wide, and 10 cm high was defined as the *litre* (ℓ). The mass of 1 ℓ of water was defined as the *kilogram* (kg).

Since its birth, the metric system has grown and developed in many ways. Today, it includes a variety of units, such as seconds (time), degrees Celsius (temperature), amperes (electric current), volts (electric potential), watts (power), hertz (frequency), newtons (force), and pascals (pressure).

Now that we are using the metric system of measurement, most of our conversions will involve numbers such as 10, 100, 1000, 0.1, 0.01, and 0.001, and numbers in decimal form.

In this unit, you will review conversion from fractions to decimals, and vice versa. You will also have the opportunity to sharpen your skill in calculating with rational numbers in decimal form.

Get-Set Exercise with Decimal Numbers

1. Add.

(*a*) 3.8 + 5.9 + 4.6

(*b*) 1.94 + 3.27 + 13.05 + 14.92

(*c*) 0.58 + 0.97 + 0.05

(*d*) 38.2 + 14.81 + 1.9 + 17.34

(*e*) 14.623 + 15.917 + 2.063 + 29.596 + 72.004 + 8.637 + 9.438

2. Add.

(*a*) 4.63, 18.2, 0.87, 10.01
(*b*) $4.95, $15.72, $0.63, $1.98
(*c*) 0.57, 1.629, 42.6, 1.304
(*d*) $150.22, $497.89, $14.63, $1200.00
(*e*) 0.505, 0.509, 0.497, 0.493

3. Subtract, and check by addition.

(*a*)	(*b*)	(*c*)	(*d*)	(*e*)
4.62	32.04	1.607	62.573	803.01
1.31	18.23	0.234	39.692	688.92

4. Subtract and check.

(*a*) 4.62 from 8.97
(*b*) 38.64 from 51.32
(*c*) 1.049 from 2.18
(*d*) 0.063 from 0.090
(*e*) $436.80 from $518.76
(*f*) 1.011 from 10.101

5. Evaluate.

(*a*) $3.84 + 7.92 - 6.18$
(*b*) $52.9 - 26.01 + 42.3$
(*c*) $128.4 - 123.9 + 82.61$
(*d*) $46.2 - 58.4 + 36.1$
(*e*) $732.65 + $59.04 − $28.97 − $329.89
(*f*) $0.03 + 0.005 - 0.006 - 0.01$

6. Multiply.

(*a*) 5×2.683
(*b*) 10×42.8
(*c*) 100×0.035
(*d*) 65×3.207
(*e*) 143×6.03
(*f*) 1000×0.0058

7. Multiply.

(*a*) 3.8×5.7
(*b*) 9.2×7.3
(*c*) 84.6×9.1
(*d*) 3.682×1.8
(*e*) 5.63×0.051
(*f*) 1.006×3.80

8. Divide.

(*a*) 82.6 by 8
(*b*) 1.634 by 5
(*c*) 13.87 by 10
(*d*) 0.057 by 100
(*e*) 14.325 by 7
(*f*) 860.4 by 30

9. Divide.

(*a*) 453.1 by 6.8
(*b*) 29.03 by 5.3
(*c*) 0.069 by 2.3
(*d*) 529.3 by 60
(*e*) 16.8 by 14.7
(*f*) 2.69 by 15.87

2(a) 33.71 **(c)** 46.103 **(e)** 2.004
5(a) 5.58 **(c)** 87.11 **(e)** $432.83
6(d) 208.455 **(e)** 862.29
7(a) 21.66 **(c)** 769.86 **(e)** 0.287 13
8(a) 10.325 **(e)** 2.046 **(f)** 28.68
9(a) 66.632 **(b)** 5.477 **(c)** 0.03 **(d)** 8.822 **(e)** 1.143 **(f)** 0.170

3.682 → 3 decimals
1.8 → 1 decimal
29456
3682
6.6276 → 4 decimals

6.8) 453.1 → 68) 4531

10(a) 11.3 (c) 3.429 (d) 0.8 (f) 2.075

11(a) 5112 (c) 0.9 (d) 3.5 (f) 69

12(d) 10.08 (e) 126.25 (f) 91.98

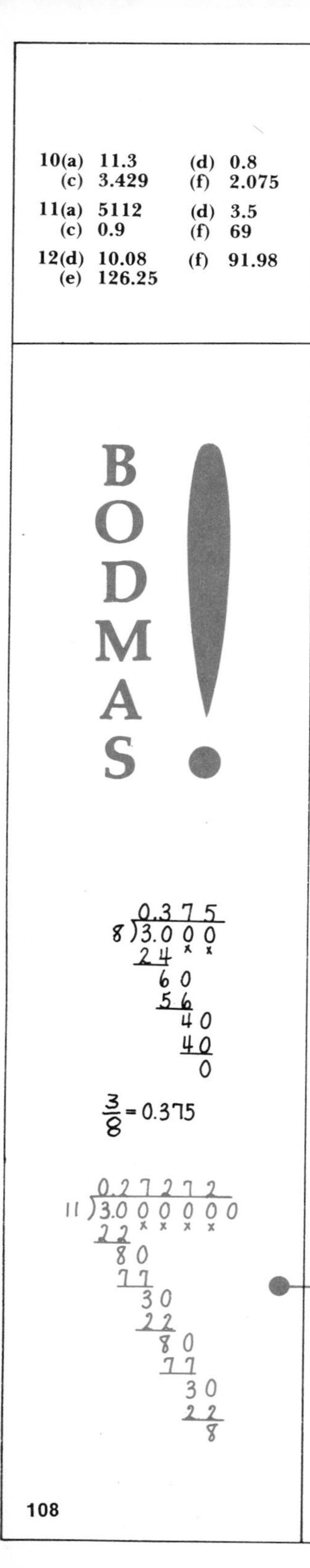

10. Evaluate.

(a) $\frac{5 \times 6.8}{3}$ (d) $1000 \times \frac{4.6}{250 \times 23}$

(b) $\frac{4.8 \times 3.5}{5 \times 6}$ (e) $\frac{6.3}{7} \times \frac{8.1}{0.9}$

(c) $\frac{42 \times 8}{7 \times 14}$ (f) $\frac{4.82 \times 3.1}{7.2}$

11. Evaluate.

(a) $1000(4.75) + 100(3.62)$ (e) $\frac{0.01}{0.002} + \frac{0.1}{0.01}$

(b) $\frac{6.47}{100} + \frac{3.95}{1000}$ (f) $\frac{0.81}{0.09} + \frac{1.8}{0.03}$

(c) $100(0.01) - 1000(0.0001)$ (g) $\frac{100}{0.01} - \frac{1000}{0.5}$

(d) $0.06 \times 100 - 0.05(50)$ (h) $\frac{0.1}{1.0} + \frac{1.0}{0.1}$

12. Evaluate.

(a) $(0.1)^2 + (0.2)^2$ (d) $(4.8)^2 - (3.6)^2$

(b) $(0.4)^2 - (0.3)^2$ (e) $\frac{1000(0.505)}{4}$

(c) $\frac{2 \times 0.01}{100}$ (f) $\frac{6}{100} \times 365 \times 4.20$

8.1 Decimal Equivalents of Rational Numbers

A Any rational number can be expressed in decimal form by dividing the numerator by the denominator.

1. Express each of the following as a decimal.

(a) $\frac{1}{2}$ (b) $\frac{3}{4}$ (c) $\frac{5}{8}$

2. Consider the decimal equivalent of $\frac{3}{11}$

$$\frac{3}{11} = 0.27\ 27\ 27\ \ldots$$

Will this division ever end? That is, will the remainder ever be zero? Why?

3. Find the decimal equivalent of $\frac{4}{9}$.

Decimals such as 0.4444... and 0.27 27 27... are called *repeating* or *periodic* decimals. For such a decimal number, the *period* is the set of digits that is repeated, and the *length* of the period is the number of digits in the period. The period of 0.4444... is 4 and the length is 1. The period of 0.27 27 27... is 27 and the length is 2.

0.27 27 27...

2 digits, so the length of the period is 2.

1. For each of the periodic decimals given below, state the period and its length.

   (*a*) 0.31 31 ...
   (*b*) 2.089 089 ...
   (*c*) −16.3333 ...
   (*d*) 0.1432 1432 ...
   (*e*) 7.165 37 37 ...
   (*f*) 17.925 000 0 ...

It is customary to abbreviate the writing of periodic decimals by placing a dot above the first and last digits of the period.

$$0.45\ 45\ 45 \ldots = 0.\dot{4}\dot{5}$$
$$-16.183\ 183 \ldots = -16.\dot{1}8\dot{3}$$
$$0.06421\ 6421 \ldots = 0.0\dot{6}42\dot{1}$$
$$15.7777 \ldots = 15.\dot{7}$$

Notice that only one dot is needed here.

2. Abbreviate the following periodic decimals.

   (*a*) 1.39 39 39 ...
   (*b*) 0.81222 ...
   (*c*) −60.3152 3152 3152 ...

3. Express the following as periodic decimals, and state the period and the length.

   (*a*) $\frac{5}{11}$ (*b*) $\frac{7}{8}$ (*c*) $\frac{5}{16}$

$$11\overline{)5.000} \quad 0.4,\ 44$$

Decimals with period 0 are often called *terminating* decimals. For instance, $\frac{1}{2} = 0.50000\ldots = 0.5\dot{0} = 0.5$

If no period is indicated, as in 0.5, we will assume it is 0.

1. Which of the following decimals are terminating decimals?

   (*a*) 0.666 ...
   (*b*) $0.4\dot{9}$
   (*c*) $13.625\dot{0}$
   (*d*) −1.375
   (*e*) 92.413 413 413 ...
   (*f*) $2.30\dot{8}4\dot{1}$

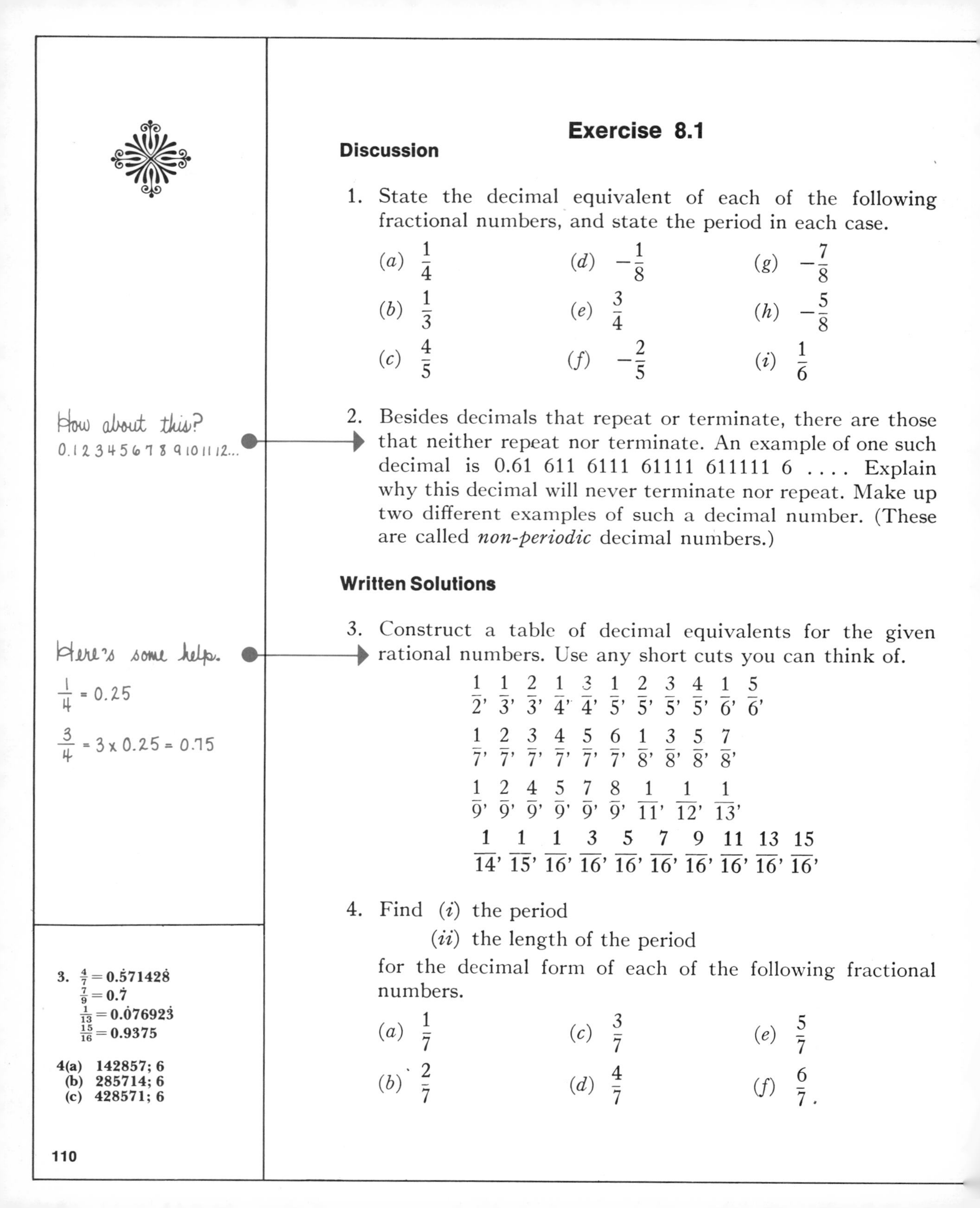

Exercise 8.1

Discussion

1. State the decimal equivalent of each of the following fractional numbers, and state the period in each case.

   (*a*) $\frac{1}{4}$ (*d*) $-\frac{1}{8}$ (*g*) $-\frac{7}{8}$

   (*b*) $\frac{1}{3}$ (*e*) $\frac{3}{4}$ (*h*) $-\frac{5}{8}$

   (*c*) $\frac{4}{5}$ (*f*) $-\frac{2}{5}$ (*i*) $\frac{1}{6}$

How about this?
0.123456789101112...

2. Besides decimals that repeat or terminate, there are those that neither repeat nor terminate. An example of one such decimal is 0.61 611 6111 61111 611111 6 . . . . Explain why this decimal will never terminate nor repeat. Make up two different examples of such a decimal number. (These are called *non-periodic* decimal numbers.)

Written Solutions

Here's some help.
$\frac{1}{4} = 0.25$
$\frac{3}{4} = 3 \times 0.25 = 0.75$

3. Construct a table of decimal equivalents for the given rational numbers. Use any short cuts you can think of.

   $\frac{1}{2}, \frac{1}{3}, \frac{2}{3}, \frac{1}{4}, \frac{3}{4}, \frac{1}{5}, \frac{2}{5}, \frac{3}{5}, \frac{4}{5}, \frac{1}{6}, \frac{5}{6},$

   $\frac{1}{7}, \frac{2}{7}, \frac{3}{7}, \frac{4}{7}, \frac{5}{7}, \frac{6}{7}, \frac{1}{8}, \frac{3}{8}, \frac{5}{8}, \frac{7}{8},$

   $\frac{1}{9}, \frac{2}{9}, \frac{4}{9}, \frac{5}{9}, \frac{7}{9}, \frac{8}{9}, \frac{1}{11}, \frac{1}{12}, \frac{1}{13},$

   $\frac{1}{14}, \frac{1}{15}, \frac{1}{16}, \frac{3}{16}, \frac{5}{16}, \frac{7}{16}, \frac{9}{16}, \frac{11}{16}, \frac{13}{16}, \frac{15}{16},$

4. Find (*i*) the period
   (*ii*) the length of the period

   for the decimal form of each of the following fractional numbers.

   (*a*) $\frac{1}{7}$ (*c*) $\frac{3}{7}$ (*e*) $\frac{5}{7}$

   (*b*) $\frac{2}{7}$ (*d*) $\frac{4}{7}$ (*f*) $\frac{6}{7}$.

3. $\frac{4}{7} = 0.\dot{5}7142\dot{8}$
$\frac{7}{9} = 0.\dot{7}$
$\frac{1}{13} = 0.\dot{0}7692\dot{3}$
$\frac{15}{16} = 0.9375$

4(a) 142857; 6
(b) 285714; 6
(c) 428571; 6

5. (*a*) Determine how digits in the period of the decimal form of $\frac{1}{7}$ and $\frac{2}{7}$ are related.

   (*b*) Compare the digits in the period of $\frac{1}{7}$ and $\frac{3}{7}$.

6. List the remainders that occur in finding the decimal equivalent of $\frac{5}{7}$.

   Are there other numbers that could be remainders? State the next six digits in the answer.

   What happens to the answer when a remainder repeats?

```
    0.714285
 7)5.000000
   4 9
     10
      7
      30
      28
       20
       14
        60
        56
         40
         35
          5
```

7. State the possible remainders when dividing by 5; by 8; by 11; by 15; by any natural number. What eventually must happen to the remainders? What effect does this have on the answer?

8. Why must the decimal equivalent of a rational number either terminate or be a repeating decimal? (Use the results of Questions 5, 6, and 7 to help you answer.)

8.2 The Fractional Equivalent of a Decimal Number

You know that 0.5 and $\frac{1}{2}$ are different ways of expressing the same number. Since we use each form frequently, it is important to know how to change from one to the other. In the previous section, the problem was to find the decimal form when the fractional form was given. In this section we will find the fractional equivalent of a given decimal number.

Finding the fractional equivalent just means putting it into the form $\frac{a}{b}$.

Notice the number of decimal places in 0.75 and the number of zeros in the multiplier.

A 1. Study the following examples carefully.

(a) $0.75 = 0.75 \times \frac{100}{100} = \frac{75}{100} = \frac{3}{4}$

(b) $-1.875 = -1.875 \times \frac{1000}{1000} = -\frac{1875}{1000} = -\frac{15}{8}$

(c) $4.0625 = 4.0625 \times \frac{10\,000}{10\,000} = \frac{40\,625}{10\,000} = \frac{65}{16}$

2. Find the fractional equivalent.

(a) 0.8 (b) 0.125 (c) −0.039 (d) 2.375

B With a repeating decimal, the process is quite different than that shown in Part A. Suppose you want to find the fractional equivalent of $0.\dot{2}$.

1

The length of the period is 1, so we multiply by 10.

$$\begin{aligned} \text{Let} \quad x &= 0.\dot{2} = 0.2222\ldots \\ \therefore\ 10x &= 2.2222\ldots \\ \text{But} \quad 1x &= 0.2222\ldots \\ \text{Subtract} \quad 9x &= 2 \\ \therefore\ x &= \frac{2}{9} \\ \therefore\ 0.\dot{2} &= \frac{2}{9} \end{aligned}$$

Notice that the decimal portions cancel out when you subtract.

C 1. Complete the following example for finding the fractional equivalent of $0.\dot{3}2\dot{1}$.

3

The length of the period is 3, so we multiply by 1000.

$$\begin{aligned} \text{Let} \quad x &= 0.\dot{3}2\dot{1} = 0.321\ 321\ldots \\ \therefore\ 1000x &= 321.321\ 321\ 321\ldots \\ \text{But} \quad 1x &= \square \\ \text{Subtract} \quad 999x &= \square \\ \therefore\ x &= \frac{321}{999} = \frac{107}{333} \\ \therefore\ 0.\dot{3}2\dot{1} &= \square \end{aligned}$$

2. Complete the following example for finding the fractional equivalent of $0.\dot{1}\dot{7}$.

Let	$x = \square$
$\therefore$	$100x = \square$
But	$1x = \square$
Subtract	$\square = \square$
$\therefore$	$x = \square$
$\therefore$	$0.\dot{1}\dot{7} = \square$

3. Find the fractional equivalent for each of the following.

   (*a*) $0.\dot{3}$ (*b*) $0.\dot{4}\dot{5}$ (*c*) $0.\dot{6}\dot{9}$

Note: From the work in this section and in Section 8.1, we see that it is possible to find a periodic decimal for every fractional number, and a fractional number for every periodic decimal.

Exercise 8.2

Discussion

1. To what form may every fractional number be changed? Is the reverse change always possible?

2. Are there decimal numbers that do not repeat or terminate? If there are, do they have fractional equivalents?

3. Express the following terminating decimals as fractions and reduce to lowest terms.

   (*a*) 0.4 (*d*) 0.005 (*g*) 0.75
   (*b*) 0.02 (*e*) 0.125 (*h*) 0.625
   (*c*) 0.08 (*f*) 0.44 (*i*) 1.875

4. State the number you would use to multiply each of the following in finding its fractional equivalent.

   (*a*) $0.\dot{6}\dot{8}$ (*c*) 0.5555 . . . (*e*) $0.\dot{2}5\dot{3}$
   (*b*) $0.\dot{3}0\dot{2}$ (*d*) $0.\dot{4}16\dot{2}$ (*f*) 0.27 27 27 . . .

2
The length of the period is 2. We multiply by 100.

5(a) $\frac{1}{4}$ (c) $\frac{1}{20}$

6(a) $\frac{3}{10}$ (c) $\frac{18}{25}$

7(a) $\frac{3}{11}$ (d) $\frac{1}{2}$

Written Solutions

5. Convert to fractional form.

   (*a*) 0.25 (*c*) 0.05 (*e*) 0.525

   (*b*) 0.85 (*d*) 0.0001 (*f*) 1.450

6. Express in fractional form.

   (*a*) 0.3 (*c*) 0.72 (*e*) 0.121

   (*b*) $0.\dot{3}$ (*d*) $0.\dot{7}\dot{2}$ (*f*) $0.\dot{1}2\dot{1}$

7. Find the fractional equivalents.

   (*a*) $0.\dot{2}\dot{7}$ (*c*) $0.\dot{4}\dot{7}$

   (*b*) $0.\dot{2}3\dot{4}$ (*d*) $0.4\dot{9}$

8.3 Applications of Rational Numbers

A Complete the following examples.

Example 1

Find the value of $3x - 4y + 5z$ if $x = 2.8$, $y = -0.8$, $z = -2.2$.

Solution

$$\begin{aligned} & 3x - 4y + 5z \\ &= 3(2.8) - 4(-0.8) + 5(-2.2) \\ &= \square + \square + \square \\ &= 0.6 \end{aligned}$$

$x = 2.8$
$y = -0.8$
$z = -2.2$

Example 2

If $I = \frac{E}{R}$, find I when $E = 220$ and $R = 5.5$.

Solution

$$\begin{aligned} I &= \frac{E}{R} \\ &= \frac{\square}{\square} \\ &= \square \end{aligned}$$

$E = 220$
$R = 5.5$

Example 3

Find x.

(*a*) $0.2x = 14$ (*b*) $0.75x = 0.\dot{3}$

Solution

(*a*) $\because \quad 0.2x = 14$
then $10(0.2x) = 10(14)$
or $2x = 140$
$\therefore \quad x = 70$

(*b*) $\because \quad 0.75x = 0.\dot{3}$
then $100(0.75x) = 100(\frac{1}{3})$
or $75x = \frac{100}{3}$
and $x = \frac{100}{3 \times 75}$
$\therefore \quad x = \frac{4}{9}$

$\frac{100}{3} \div 75$
$= \frac{100}{3} \times \frac{1}{75}$
$= \frac{100}{3 \times 75}$

Exercise 8.3

Discussion

1. State the value of each of the following.

(*a*) $0.01 + 0.001$ (*c*) $\frac{4}{9} \div \frac{2}{9}$ (*e*) 0.4×0.5

(*b*) $(0.02)^2$ (*d*) 1.2×0.06 (*f*) $\frac{0.002}{0.01}$

2. Solve. (All variables have domain Q.)

(*a*) $0.2x = 0.3$ (*c*) $0.6y = 9$ (*e*) $\frac{3}{8} = 0.5q$

(*b*) $\frac{2}{3}m = 4$ (*d*) $\frac{1}{8}y = 0.4$ (*f*) $0.75s = 12$

Written Solutions

3. Evaluate when $a = -0.2$, $b = 0.3$, and $c = 0.4$.

(*a*) $3a + b$ (*c*) abc (*e*) $2b^2$

(*b*) $ab - c^2$ (*d*) $(b - c)^2$ (*f*) $4a - 2bc$

4. Solve. (All variables have domain Q.)

(*a*) $0.375x = 18$ (*c*) $0.8k = 15 \times 2$

(*b*) $0.75x = 2\frac{3}{4} + 4\frac{3}{4}$. (*d*) $1.25m = 120 - 30$

3(a) -0.3 **(c)** -0.024
4(a) $x = 48$ **(c)** $k = 37.5$
(b) $x = 10$ **(d)** $m = 72$

5. A line 6 m long is divided into 8 equal parts. What is the length of each segment?

6. Toni Tourist drives 600 km in 7 h 20 min. What is her average speed, as a periodic decimal?

7. Patti Kake sells the following goods in Patti's Variety:

Item	*Price*
beans	3 tins/$1.00
bread	5 loaves/$1.69
baking powder	9 packages/$2.00
carrots	24 tins/$3.00
flour	5 kg/$1.95

Find the cost per unit (¢/kg, ¢/tin) and express your answer as a decimal.

8. Find the total cost of each of the following.
   (*a*) 24 kg at $0.375/kg
   (*b*) 360 bags at $0.44/bag
   (*c*) 450 g at $1.60/kg
   (*d*) 99 ℓ at $0.66/ℓ
   (*e*) 48 tins at 6.25¢/tin
   (*f*) 6600 bags at $0.09/bag

9. Determine the cost per 100 g or 100 ml (to the nearest 0.1¢) of each of the following items.
   (*a*) 300 g can of soup at 2 cans/45¢
   (*b*) 500 g can of peas at 2 cans/49¢
   (*c*) 50 ml tube of toothpaste at 3 tubes/$1.39

10. Soup that regularly sells for 2 cans/31¢ is on special at 7 cans/95¢.
    (*a*) Find the cost per can at the regular rate and at the special rate, to the nearest 0.1¢.
    (*b*) How much money would be saved on a purchase of 7 cans?

11. A supermarket sells Detergent "X" at $1.25 for a 1.5 kg box and $2.00 for a 2.5 kg box. Which is the better buy?

6. $81.\dot{8}\dot{1}$ km/h

8(a) $9 (c) $27 (e) $3

9(a) 7.5¢ (c) 92.7¢

10(b) 13.5¢

11. The 2.5 kg box is the better buy, by $3\frac{1}{3}$¢/kg.

12. Jim and Debbie are comparing the gas economy of their cars. Debbie has driven 575 km on 105 ℓ of gas, while Jim has covered 750 km on 90 ℓ of gas. Whose car is consuming more gas per 100 km, and by how much?

13. Ruth Luss purchased shares in several companies through the Toronto Stock Exchange. Following is a list of the stocks and the prices at which she purchased them. Calculate Ruth's costs before any commission or tax is included.

Stock	*Cost Per Share*	*Number of Shares Purchased*
Bramalea	$ 5.20	300
Mattagami	14.80	125
Home Oil A	39.40	75
Rio Algom	24.70	50
Stelco	27.30	100

14. Russ and Ann Tique, interior decorators, calculate that to decorate a living room and dining room they need 40 m^2 of carpet at $11.50/$m^2$ for carpet and $4.00/$m^2$ for installation and underlay. If, in addition, they need 35 m^2 of drapery at $6.95/$m^2$, including making the drapes, what should Russ and Ann charge in total for carpet and drapery?

15. Penny Pincher and Sam Spender are comparing their wages for a 2-week period. Penny receives $2.43/h and works 37.5 h/week. Sam earns $2.30/h but works 42.5 h/week. Who receives the larger gross pay and by how much?

12. Debbie, by 6.3 ℓ/100 km.
13. $10 330
14. $863.25
15. Sam, by $13.25/week.

Unit 9

Decimal Numbers in Standard Form

150 000 000 km

You have been working with rational numbers in fractional and decimal form. There is a third way of writing rational numbers that simplifies writing and calculation when working with very large and very small numbers.

The sun is approximately 150 000 000 km from earth.

Operations in a computer take place in 0.000 001 s.

Take a big breath and hold it. You have just inhaled about 50 000 000 000 000 000 000 000 molecules of air! (Don't forget to exhale!)

Can you think of other examples where either very large or very small numbers are needed?

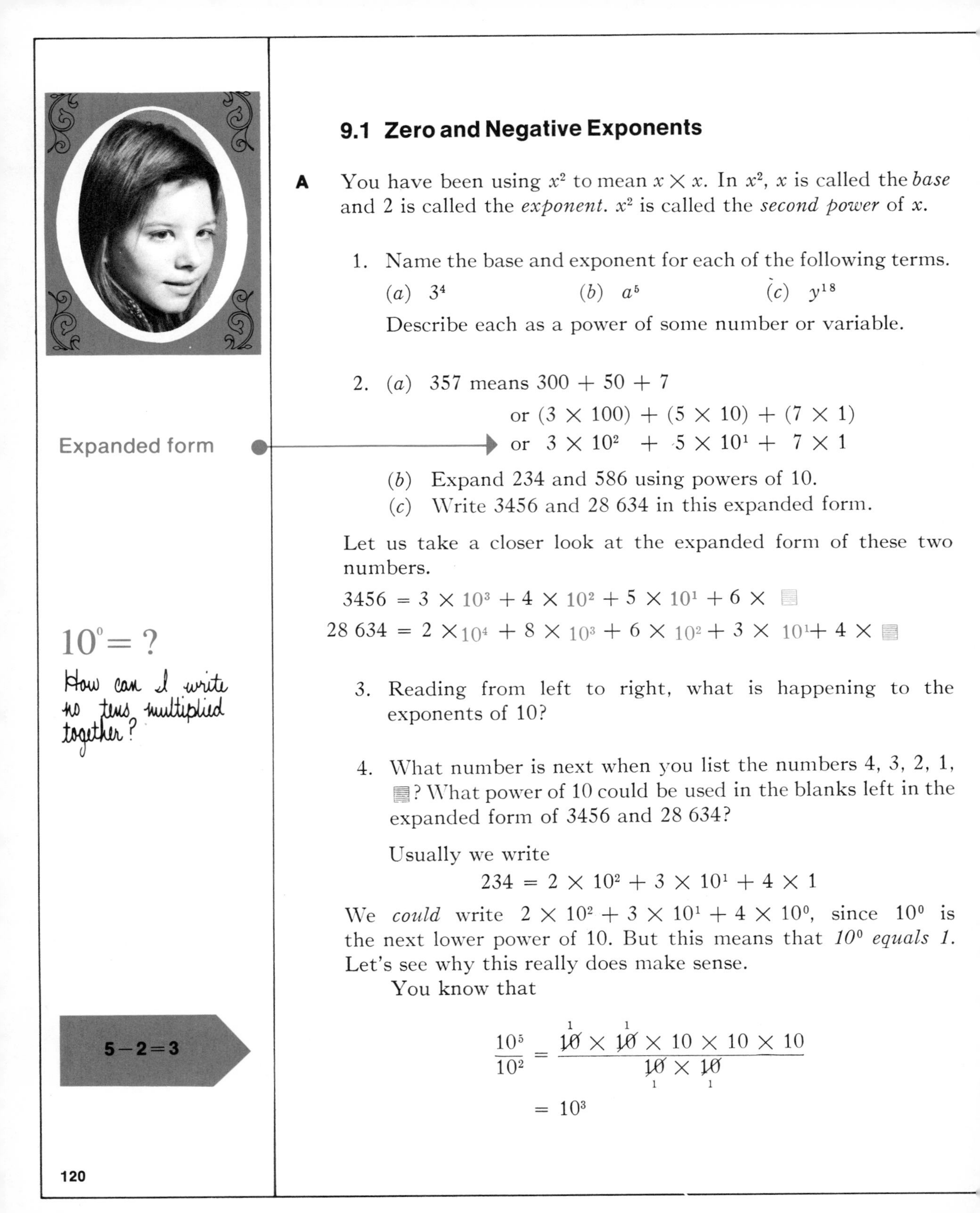

9.1 Zero and Negative Exponents

A You have been using x^2 to mean $x \times x$. In x^2, x is called the *base* and 2 is called the *exponent*. x^2 is called the *second power* of x.

1. Name the base and exponent for each of the following terms.

   (*a*) 3^4 (*b*) a^5 (*c*) y^{18}

   Describe each as a power of some number or variable.

2. (*a*) 357 means $300 + 50 + 7$

   or $(3 \times 100) + (5 \times 10) + (7 \times 1)$

   Expanded form → or $3 \times 10^2 + 5 \times 10^1 + 7 \times 1$

   (*b*) Expand 234 and 586 using powers of 10.

   (*c*) Write 3456 and 28 634 in this expanded form.

Let us take a closer look at the expanded form of these two numbers.

$$3456 = 3 \times 10^3 + 4 \times 10^2 + 5 \times 10^1 + 6 \times \square$$

$$28\,634 = 2 \times 10^4 + 8 \times 10^3 + 6 \times 10^2 + 3 \times 10^1 + 4 \times \square$$

$10^0 = ?$

How can I write no tens multiplied together?

3. Reading from left to right, what is happening to the exponents of 10?

4. What number is next when you list the numbers 4, 3, 2, 1, $\square$? What power of 10 could be used in the blanks left in the expanded form of 3456 and 28 634?

   Usually we write

$$234 = 2 \times 10^2 + 3 \times 10^1 + 4 \times 1$$

We *could* write $2 \times 10^2 + 3 \times 10^1 + 4 \times 10^0$, since 10^0 is the next lower power of 10. But this means that *10^0 equals 1.* Let's see why this really does make sense.

You know that

$5 - 2 = 3$

$$\frac{10^5}{10^2} = \frac{\overset{1}{\cancel{10}} \times \overset{1}{\cancel{10}} \times 10 \times 10 \times 10}{\underset{1}{\cancel{10}} \times \underset{1}{\cancel{10}}}$$

$$= 10^3$$

5. Using this method, find the value of the following.

(*a*) $\frac{10^7}{10^3}$ (*b*) $\frac{10^5}{10^4}$ (*c*) $\frac{10^6}{10^4}$ (*d*) $\frac{10^8}{10^3}$

Do you see a short cut for finding the answer in each?

6. Evaluate.

(*a*) $\frac{10^5}{10^2}$ (*b*) $\frac{10^4}{10^2}$ (*c*) $\frac{10^3}{10^2}$ (*d*) $\frac{10^2}{10^2}$

Your answer to 6(*d*) should be 10^0.

But you know that $\frac{10^2}{10^2} = \frac{100}{100} = 1$

$\therefore 10^0 = 1$ makes sense!

> Thus, if we use 10^0 we must insist that $10^0 = 1$.

$10^0 = 1$

Remember that

$$43.82 = 4 \times 10^1 + 3 \times 10^0 + 8 \times \frac{1}{10} + 2 \times \frac{1}{100}$$

$$= 4 \times 10^1 + 3 \times 10^0 + 8 \times \frac{1}{10} + 2 \times \frac{1}{10^2}$$

1. Expand in the same way.

(*a*) 68.57 (*b*) 5.834 (*c*) 432.65

Your answer to 1(*c*) should be

$$4 \times 10^2 + 3 \times 10^1 + 2 \times 10^0 + 6 \times \frac{1}{10} + 5 \times \frac{1}{10^2}$$

To replace $\frac{1}{10}$ and $\frac{1}{10^2}$ by powers of 10 we need to study the pattern 10^2, 10^1, 10^0, ▤, ▤.

$10^4 = 10\,000$
$10^3 = 1000$
$10^2 = 100$
$10^1 = 10$
$10^0 = 1$
$10^? = \frac{1}{10^1} = 0.1$
$10^? = \frac{1}{10^2} = 0.01$
$10^? = \frac{1}{10^3} = 0.001$

2. What powers of 10 could be used to fill in the blanks?

It appears that

$$432.65 = 4 \times 10^2 + 3 \times 10^1 + 2 \times 10^0 + 6 \times \frac{1}{10} + 5 \times \frac{1}{10^2}$$

$$= 4 \times 10^2 + 3 \times 10^1 + 2 \times 10^0 + 6 \times 10^{-1} + 5 \times 10^{-2}$$

$\therefore 10^{-1} = \frac{1}{10}$, $10^{-2} = \frac{1}{10^2}$

Remember?

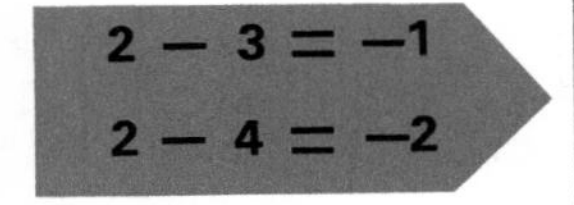

3. To see that these make sense, use the short cut to evaluate.

   (*a*) $\frac{10^3}{10^2}$ (*b*) $\frac{10^2}{10^2}$ (*c*) $\frac{10^2}{10^3}$ (*d*) $\frac{10^2}{10^4}$

In 3(*c*) we could say

$$\text{that } \frac{10^2}{10^3} = \frac{\cancel{10} \times \cancel{10}}{\cancel{10} \times \cancel{10} \times 10} = \frac{1}{10}$$

$$\text{but } \frac{10^2}{10^3} = 10^{2-3} = 10^{-1}$$

If we want 10^{-1} to have meaning, then $\boxed{10^{-1} = \frac{1}{10}}$.

In 3(*d*) using the short cut,

$$\frac{10^2}{10^4} = 10^{2-4}$$
$$= 10^{-2}$$

$$\text{But } \frac{10^2}{10^4} = \frac{\cancel{10} \times \cancel{10}}{\cancel{10} \times \cancel{10} \times 10 \times 10}$$
$$= \frac{1}{10^2}$$

$$\therefore \; 10^{-2} = \frac{1}{10^2} \text{ makes sense.}$$

4. Write as powers of 10.

   (*a*) $\frac{1}{10^3}$ (*b*) $\frac{1}{10^5}$ (*c*) $\frac{1}{10^7}$ (*d*) $\frac{1}{10^{12}}$

5. Express as a fraction and as a decimal.

   (*a*) 10^{-3} (*b*) 10^{-6} (*c*) 10^{-11}

6. Expand 39.456 using powers of 10.

Exercise 9.1

Discussion

1. State the value.

   (*a*) $10^2 \times 10^3$ (*b*) $10^5 \times 10^3$ (*c*) $10^4 \times 10$

2. State the value.

(*a*) $\frac{10^5}{10^2}$ (*b*) $\frac{10^3}{10^7}$ (*c*) $\frac{10^5}{10^5}$ (*d*) $10^2 \div 10^{-1}$

3. Evaluate.

(*a*) $10^2 \times 10^{-2}$ (*b*) $10^5 \times 10^{-5}$ (*c*) $10^7 \times 10^{-7}$

4. What name do you give to numbers, such as the pairs in Question 3, whose product is 1?

Written Solutions

5. Expand using powers of 10.

(*a*) 536 (*c*) 28.69 (*e*) 5.864
(*b*) 4320 (*d*) 356.12 (*f*) 50.32

6. State each number represented.

(*a*) $3 \times 10^2 + 5 \times 10 + 6 \times 10^0 + 3 \times 10^{-1}$
(*b*) $4 \times 10^3 + 2 \times 10 + 3 \times 10^0 + 5 \times 10^{-1}$
(*c*) $6 \times 10 + 4 \times 10^{-1} + 2 \times 10^{-3}$

7. Add the following integers.

(*a*) $3 + (-1)$ (*b*) $-2 + 6$ (*c*) $\begin{array}{r} -3 \\ \underline{-4} \end{array}$ (*d*) $\begin{array}{r} 3 \\ \underline{-5} \end{array}$

8. Express each product as a power of 10.

(*a*) $10^7 \times 10^3$ (*c*) $10^{-1} \times 10^{-3}$
(*b*) $10^5 \times 10^{-1}$ (*d*) $10^2 \times 10^{-3}$

9. Subtract the following integers.

(*a*) $3 - (-2)$ (*b*) $-2 - (4)$ (*c*) $\begin{array}{r} -2 \\ \underline{-5} \end{array}$ (*d*) $\begin{array}{r} -2 \\ \underline{6} \end{array}$

10. Express each quotient as a power of 10.

(*a*) $10^6 \div 10^2$ (*c*) $10^{-3} \div 10^{-3}$
(*b*) $10^2 \div 10^{-1}$ (*d*) $10^{-2} \div 10^2$

11. Express each as a fraction and as a decimal.

(*a*) 10^{-2} (*b*) 10^{-4} (*c*) 10^{-1}

12. Find the product.

(*a*) 6.26×10 (*c*) 1.25×10^{-1}
(*b*) 3.84×10^2 (*d*) 3.5×10^{-3}

5(a) $5\times10^2+3\times10^1+6\times10^0$
(c) $2\times10^1+8\times10^0+6\times10^{-1}+9\times10^{-2}$
(e) $5\times10^0+8\times10^{-1}+6\times10^{-2}+4\times10^{-3}$
6(a) 356.3 **(b)** 4023.5
8(a) 10^{10} **(c)** 10^{-4}
10(a) 10^4 **(c)** 10^0
11(a) $\frac{1}{100}$, 0.01
12(a) 62.6 **(c)** 0.125

9.2 Standard Notation

Wow!

Your heart beats more than 30 000 000 times each year! The nearest star is estimated to be 4 light-years away from our earth. This means that the star's light, travelling 300 000 km every second, reaches earth 4 years after leaving the star! This star is 37 800 000 000 000 km away from us.

In this section you will learn to use powers of 10 in expressing very large and very small numbers.

A Study these examples.

(*a*) 2.3×10
$= 23$

(*b*) 2.3×10^2
$= 2.3 \times 100$
$= 230$

(*c*) 2.3×10^3
$= 2.3 \times 1000$
$= 2300$

1. Express as a whole number.

(*a*) 3.8×10^5 (*b*) 2.69×10^3 (*c*) 4.35×10^2

Did you notice that in each case multiplication by a power of 10 can be done by moving the decimal point? How do you know how far to move the decimal point?

How many places was the decimal point moved?

What is the exponent?

2. State the decimal form.

(*a*) 5.12×10
(*b*) 4.86×10^2
(*c*) 3.85×10^4
(*d*) 5.03×10^0

Numbers like 3.85×10^4 are said to be in *standard form*. When a number is in standard form, there must be exactly one digit (not a zero) to the left of the decimal point.

3. Rewrite the following numbers in standard form.

(*a*) 528 (*b*) 64 (*c*) 1230 (*d*) 32.6

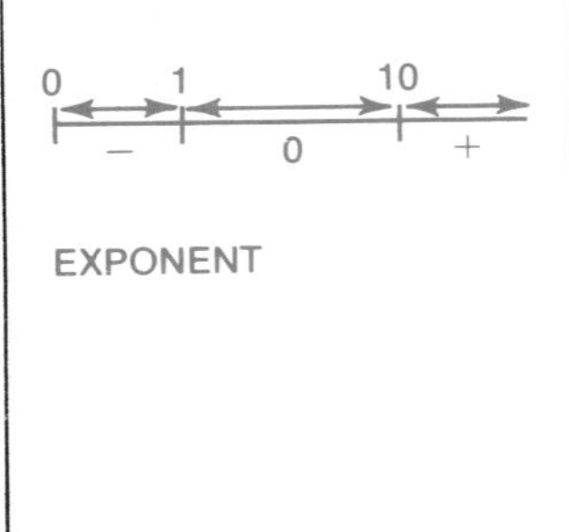

B Study the following examples.

(*a*) 2.3×10^{-1}
$= 2.3 \times \frac{1}{10}$
$= 0.23$

(*b*) 2.3×10^{-2}
$= 2.3 \times \frac{1}{10^2}$
$= 2.3 \times \frac{1}{100}$
$= 0.023$

(*c*) 2.3×10^{-3}
$= 2.3 \times \frac{1}{10^3}$
$= 2.3 \times \frac{1}{1000}$
$= 0.0023$

1. Find the product.

   (*a*) 6.5×10^{-2} (*b*) 3.52×10^{-4} (*c*) 1.6×10^{-6}

2. What is the effect on the decimal point of a number when the number is multiplied by a *negative* power of 10?

3. Multiply.

   (*a*) 2.4×10^{-1} (*b*) 3.14×10^{-2} (*c*) 1.6×10^{-3}

4. Express in standard form.

   (*a*) 0.0415 (*b*) 0.000 063 (*c*) 0.502

Exercise 9.2

Discussion

1. Multiply.

   (*a*) 5.62×10^{2} (*d*) 4.8×10^{-1} (*g*) 1.5×10^{4}

   (*b*) 4.8×10^{3} (*e*) 6.31×10^{-2} (*h*) 3.82×10^{-5}

   (*c*) 3.9×10 (*f*) 4.37×10^{2} (*i*) 4.87×10^{0}

2. Express in standard form.

   (*a*) 527 (*d*) 1250 (*g*) 2 000 000

   (*b*) 63 (*e*) 0.0075 (*h*) 52.6

   (*c*) 0.581 (*f*) 0.000 000 92 (*i*) 320 000 000 000

Written Solutions

3. Rewrite the following using standard form for each number.

   (*a*) 600×900 (*e*) $\dfrac{72 \times 395}{561}$

   (*b*) $\dfrac{400\,000}{200}$ (*f*) $\dfrac{0.297}{0.058}$

   (*c*) 387×542 (*g*) $58 \times 87 \times 42$

   (*d*) 0.0685×0.0019 (*h*) $\dfrac{0.68}{5.29 \times 37.1}$

3(a) $6 \times 10^{2} \times 9 \times 10^{2}$
(c) $3.87 \times 10^{2} \times 5.42 \times 10^{2}$
(e) $\dfrac{7.2 \times 10^{1} \times 3.95 \times 10^{2}}{5.61 \times 10^{2}}$
(h) $\dfrac{6.8 \times 10^{-1}}{5.29 \times 10^{0} \times 3.71 \times 10^{1}}$

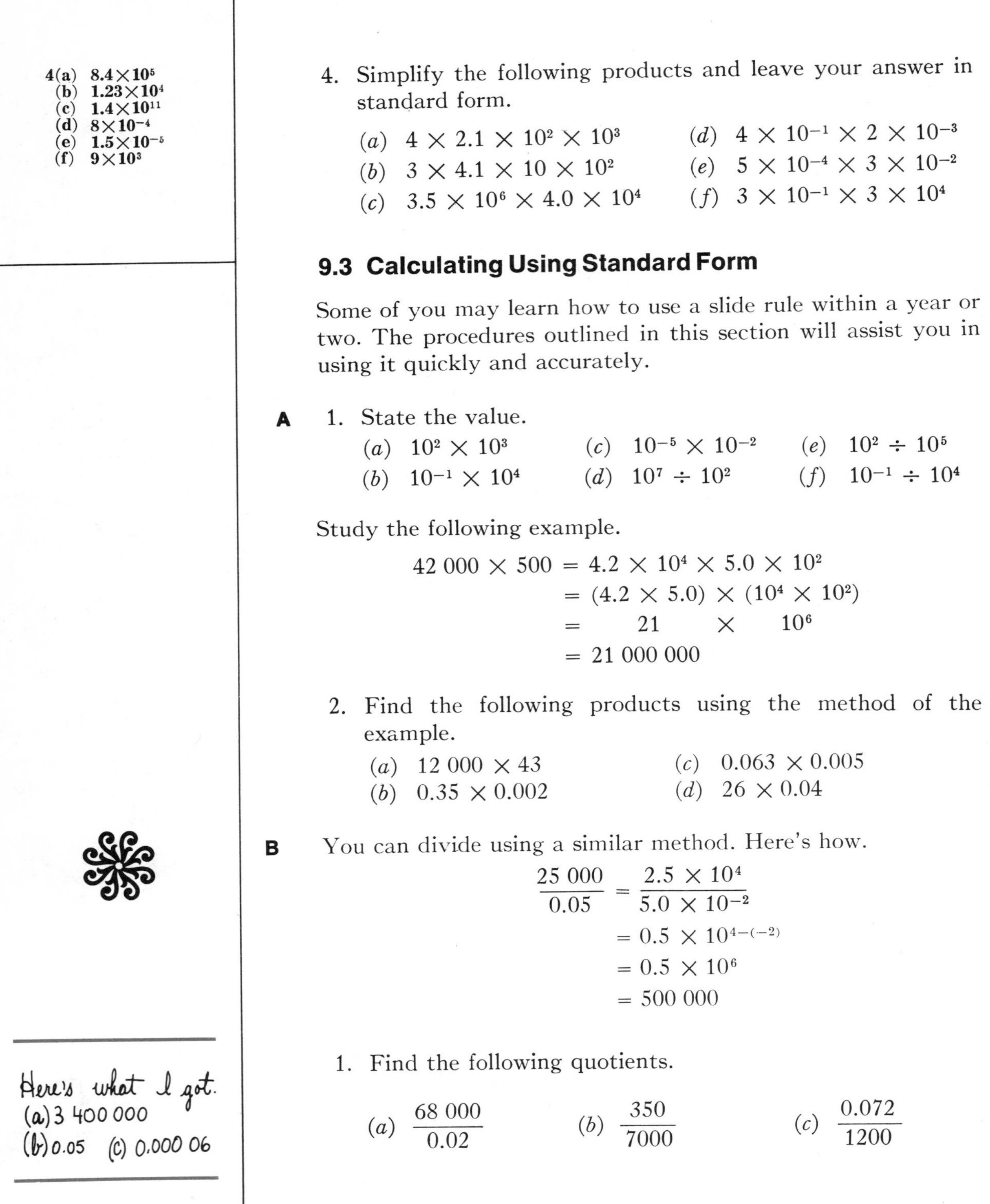

4(a) 8.4×10^5
(b) 1.23×10^4
(c) 1.4×10^{11}
(d) 8×10^{-4}
(e) 1.5×10^{-5}
(f) 9×10^3

4. Simplify the following products and leave your answer in standard form.

(*a*) $4 \times 2.1 \times 10^2 \times 10^3$
(*b*) $3 \times 4.1 \times 10 \times 10^2$
(*c*) $3.5 \times 10^6 \times 4.0 \times 10^4$
(*d*) $4 \times 10^{-1} \times 2 \times 10^{-3}$
(*e*) $5 \times 10^{-4} \times 3 \times 10^{-2}$
(*f*) $3 \times 10^{-1} \times 3 \times 10^4$

9.3 Calculating Using Standard Form

Some of you may learn how to use a slide rule within a year or two. The procedures outlined in this section will assist you in using it quickly and accurately.

A

1. State the value.

(*a*) $10^2 \times 10^3$
(*b*) $10^{-1} \times 10^4$
(*c*) $10^{-5} \times 10^{-2}$
(*d*) $10^7 \div 10^2$
(*e*) $10^2 \div 10^5$
(*f*) $10^{-1} \div 10^4$

Study the following example.

$$\begin{aligned} 42\,000 \times 500 &= 4.2 \times 10^4 \times 5.0 \times 10^2 \\ &= (4.2 \times 5.0) \times (10^4 \times 10^2) \\ &= 21 \times 10^6 \\ &= 21\,000\,000 \end{aligned}$$

2. Find the following products using the method of the example.

(*a*) $12\,000 \times 43$
(*b*) 0.35×0.002
(*c*) 0.063×0.005
(*d*) 26×0.04

B You can divide using a similar method. Here's how.

$$\begin{aligned} \frac{25\,000}{0.05} &= \frac{2.5 \times 10^4}{5.0 \times 10^{-2}} \\ &= 0.5 \times 10^{4-(-2)} \\ &= 0.5 \times 10^6 \\ &= 500\,000 \end{aligned}$$

Here's what I got.
(a) 3 400 000
(b) 0.05 (c) 0.000 06

1. Find the following quotients.

(*a*) $\dfrac{68\,000}{0.02}$ (*b*) $\dfrac{350}{7000}$ (*c*) $\dfrac{0.072}{1200}$

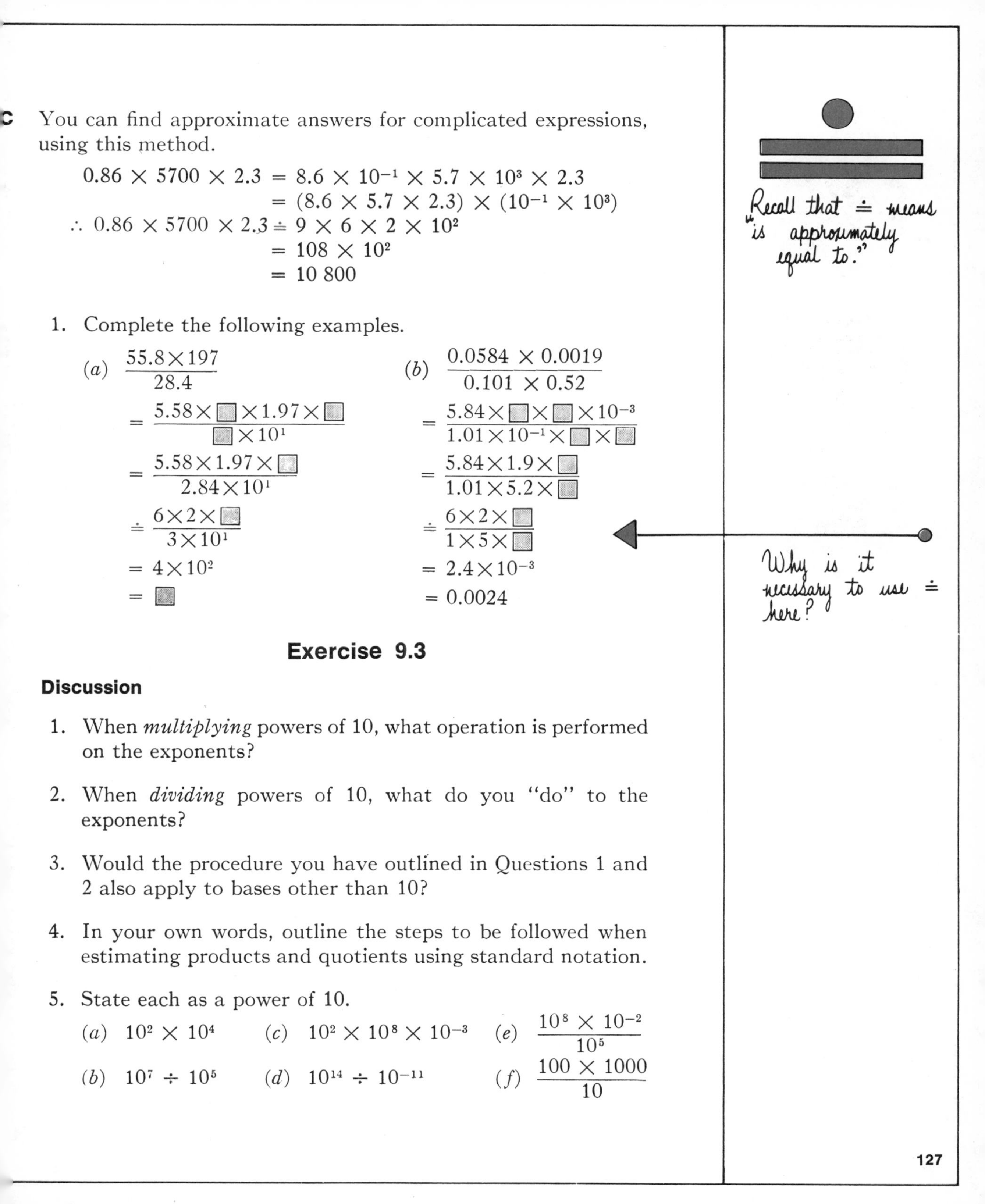

C You can find approximate answers for complicated expressions, using this method.

$$0.86 \times 5700 \times 2.3 = 8.6 \times 10^{-1} \times 5.7 \times 10^{3} \times 2.3$$
$$= (8.6 \times 5.7 \times 2.3) \times (10^{-1} \times 10^{3})$$
$$\therefore\ 0.86 \times 5700 \times 2.3 \doteq 9 \times 6 \times 2 \times 10^{2}$$
$$= 108 \times 10^{2}$$
$$= 10\,800$$

Recall that $\doteq$ means "is approximately equal to."

1. Complete the following examples.

(*a*) $\dfrac{55.8 \times 197}{28.4}$

$= \dfrac{5.58 \times \square \times 1.97 \times \square}{\square \times 10^{1}}$

$= \dfrac{5.58 \times 1.97 \times \square}{2.84 \times 10^{1}}$

$\doteq \dfrac{6 \times 2 \times \square}{3 \times 10^{1}}$

$= 4 \times 10^{2}$

$= \square$

(*b*) $\dfrac{0.0584 \times 0.0019}{0.101 \times 0.52}$

$= \dfrac{5.84 \times \square \times \square \times 10^{-3}}{1.01 \times 10^{-1} \times \square \times \square}$

$= \dfrac{5.84 \times 1.9 \times \square}{1.01 \times 5.2 \times \square}$

$\doteq \dfrac{6 \times 2 \times \square}{1 \times 5 \times \square}$

$= 2.4 \times 10^{-3}$

$= 0.0024$

Why is it necessary to use $\doteq$ here?

Exercise 9.3

Discussion

1. When *multiplying* powers of 10, what operation is performed on the exponents?

2. When *dividing* powers of 10, what do you "do" to the exponents?

3. Would the procedure you have outlined in Questions 1 and 2 also apply to bases other than 10?

4. In your own words, outline the steps to be followed when estimating products and quotients using standard notation.

5. State each as a power of 10.

(*a*) $10^{2} \times 10^{4}$ (*c*) $10^{2} \times 10^{8} \times 10^{-3}$ (*e*) $\dfrac{10^{8} \times 10^{-2}}{10^{5}}$

(*b*) $10^{7} \div 10^{5}$ (*d*) $10^{14} \div 10^{-11}$ (*f*) $\dfrac{100 \times 1000}{10}$

Written Solutions

(If your answer is very large or very small, express it in standard form.)

6. Approximate the following products and quotients.
   (*a*) 742×0.043
   (*b*) $3160 \div 29.5$
   (*c*) $14 \times 72 \times 812$
   (*d*) $\dfrac{6740 \times 15\,210}{94}$
   (*e*) $39\,600 \div 247$
   (*f*) $\dfrac{69\,500\,000 \times 0.003}{219}$
   (*g*) $\dfrac{64 \times 89.5}{0.13 \times 5.8}$
   (*h*) $\dfrac{16.9 \times 7.3 \times 410.8}{64 \times 3.19}$

7. On the average, a sleeping person breathes 15 times each minute. Find the number of breaths you would take during an 8 h sleep.

8. A concrete retaining wall is 1 m high, 30 cm thick, and 30 m long. If the density of concrete is 2400 kg/m^3, find the mass of the wall.

9. Astra Notte pilots her spacecraft around the earth at a speed of 27 350 km/h.
   (*a*) How far does she travel in 2 days?
   (*b*) If her orbit is 80 900 km long, how many orbits does she make in 2 days?

10. The total value of goods and services produced in Canada in 1972 was $103 407 000 000, and the average number of persons employed was 8 329 000. Find the average value of goods and services produced by each member of Canada's labor force that year.

11. The number of loops required to complete one row of a hooked rug is 111, and the rug is 152 rows long. If each loop requires 6.4 cm of yarn, how many metres of yarn does it take to hook the rug?

12. The construction of the partitions of a house requires 325 studs. If each stud requires 6 nails and a waste factor of 20% must be added, find
    (*a*) the number of kilograms of nails required if 110 nails have a mass of 1 kg,
    (*b*) the total cost of the nails at 82.5¢/kg.

7. 7200
8. 2.16×10^4 kg
9(a) 1.3128×10^6 km
(b) 16.23
10. $12 415.30
11. 1079.808 m
12(a) 21.3 kg **(b)** $17.57

13. A needle-point picture has 174 rows, each 43.2 cm long. If it takes approximately 3.6 min to stitch 10 cm, how many hours does it take to sew the picture?

14. The Market Research Department of Ding-A-Ling Cosmetics estimates that a tube of lipstick lasts 3.5 months on the average. Find the yearly consumption of lipstick in a population of 4 372 000 women.

15. A car burns 0.4 ml of oil per kilometre. On a trip of 5075 km, find

 (*a*) how much oil is consumed,
 (*b*) the total cost of the oil burned at \$1.15/ℓ.

16. A googol = 10^{100}
 How many billions are there in 1 googol?

13. 45 h
14. 1.5×10^7 tubes
15(a) 2030 ml (b) \$2.33
16. 10^{91}

Number Activities

1. Evaluate $(111\ 111\ 111)^2$.

2. You may use the operations of +, −, × and ÷ to form the following numbers.
 (*a*) Express 24 using three identical digits.
 (*b*) Express 30 using three identical digits.
 (*c*) Express 10 using five 9's.
 (*d*) Express 100 using five identical digits.
 (*e*) Express 100 using four 9's.

3. Use four 4's to express all the whole numbers from 1 to 30.

4. Find the number of litres of milk consumed by your class in a year.

5. Find the cost of 1 tonne of honey, based on supermarket prices.

6. Estimate the area of the classroom floor by using floor tiles.

Maintaining Basic Skills

Exercise 2

1. Find the value.

(*a*) $\frac{3}{4} + \frac{5}{8} - \frac{3}{8}$ (*d*) $\frac{5}{8} - \frac{3}{5} + \frac{1}{4}$ (*g*) $10\frac{3}{10} - 4\frac{3}{5}$

(*b*) $\frac{2}{5} - \frac{7}{10} + \frac{1}{5}$ (*e*) $1\frac{2}{3} - \frac{5}{6} - \frac{1}{3}$ (*h*) $-1\frac{1}{4} + \frac{7}{8} - \frac{5}{6}$

(*c*) $\frac{2}{3} + \frac{5}{4} - \frac{1}{3}$ (*f*) $5\frac{3}{4} - 2\frac{1}{8}$ (*i*) $1\frac{2}{3} - \left(1\frac{1}{6} + \frac{3}{8}\right)$

2. Find the sum in each part.

(*a*) 3.5, 14.9, 1.58, 2.37, 12.7, 8.75
(*b*) 0.038, 0.0065, 1.094, 2.103, 5.003
(*c*) \$1.56, \$28.07, \$0.56, \$129.63, \$49.75

3. Find the product or quotient.

(*a*) 0.4×0.375 (*d*) 1.68×0.75 (*g*) $2\frac{7}{8} \div \left(-\frac{3}{16}\right)$

(*b*) $-\frac{3}{4} \times \frac{5}{6}$ (*e*) $5\frac{1}{6} \times 3\frac{3}{4}$ (*h*) $14.873 \div 2.14$

(*c*) $1\frac{2}{3} \div \frac{5}{9}$ (*f*) $3.62 \div .02$ (*i*) $\frac{2}{7} \times \frac{14}{5} \div 1.1$

4. Express in fractional form.

(*a*) 3^{-1} (*c*) 5^{-2} (*e*) $(-1)^0$
(*b*) 4^0 (*d*) 10^{-4} (*f*) -4^{-2}

5. Simplify.

(*a*) $8 + 20 \div 5 - 3(-2)$ (*e*) $\frac{2}{3} \times \frac{3}{5} + \frac{7}{10} \div 7$

(*b*) $3(-2)^3 + (5 - 8)^2$ (*f*) $24\left(\frac{3}{8} - \frac{5}{6}\right)$

(*c*) $2 + (-8) - (-3)$ (*g*) $1\frac{2}{3} + \frac{1}{6} \times \frac{3}{4}$

(*d*) $\frac{(-3) \times (-5)}{4 \times (-2)}$ (*h*) $3[12 \div (2 + 1)] - 3(8 - 2)$

1(a) 1 **(h)** $-\frac{29}{24}$
(b) $-\frac{1}{10}$ **(i)** $\frac{1}{8}$
(c) $\frac{19}{12}$
2(a) 43.8 **(c)** \$209.57
(b) 8.2445
3(a) 0.15 **(h)** 6.95
(b) $-\frac{5}{8}$ **(i)** $\frac{8}{11}$
4(d) $\frac{1}{10\ 000}$ **(f)** $-\frac{1}{16}$
5(a) 18 **(g)** $\frac{43}{24}$
(b) −15 **(h)** −6

6. Convert to decimal form.

(*a*) $\frac{3}{8}$ (*b*) $1\frac{4}{5}$ (*c*) $\frac{3}{50}$ (*d*) $-10\frac{6}{100}$ (*e*) $\frac{27}{16}$

7. Convert to fraction form.

(*a*) 0.35 (*b*) 0.0875 (*c*) 3.216 (*d*) $0.\dot{7}$ (*e*) $1.\dot{3}\dot{6}$

8. Evaluate the following expressions.

(*a*) $5(2a + 3b)$; $a = 2, b = 3$
(*b*) $2mn - 3n^2$; $m = -3, n = -2$
(*c*) $x^5 - x^4$; $x = -1$
(*d*) $\frac{2}{3}x - \frac{3}{4}y$; $x = 3, y = 2\frac{2}{3}$
(*e*) $p^2 - 2pq + q^2$; $p = \frac{1}{3}, q = -\frac{3}{2}$
(*f*) $\frac{1}{3}(p + 2m + 3n)$; $p = 12, m = 3, n = 1$

9. Solve and graph the following. The domain is Q.

(*a*) $2x + 3 = -1$
(*b*) $3x - 4 < 2$
(*c*) $0.6y = 0.4$
(*d*) $\frac{1}{3}x + 5 = \frac{3}{4}$
(*e*) $0.2a = 1.86$
(*f*) $-3x + 2 \geq 11$
(*g*) $-1.6x = 4.8$
(*h*) $\frac{3}{8}a - 1 = \frac{5}{6} + 2$

10. Express in standard form.

(*a*) 2356 (*b*) 0.003 94 (*c*) 56 000 000 (*d*) 0.5920

11. Change to regular form.

(*a*) 4.631×10^3
(*b*) 3.05×10^0
(*c*) 9.8×10^{-3}
(*d*) 1.694×10^2
(*e*) 3.2×10^6
(*f*) 2.50×10^{-5}

12. Find the following products or quotients, expressing your answers in standard form.

(*a*) $4.60 \times 10^2 \times 5.90 \times 10^3$
(*b*) $3.26 \times 10^{-1} \times 1.68 \times 10^2$
(*c*) $(8.96 \times 10^5) \div (3.14 \times 10^2)$
(*d*) $(1.57 \times 10^4) \div (3.60 \times 10^{-1})$
(*e*) $3.50 \times 10^{-2} \times 5.80 \times 10^{-3}$
(*f*) $(5.20 \times 10^{-1}) \div (7.80 \times 10^2)$

6(a) 0.375 **(b)** 1.8 **(c)** 0.06 **(d)** -10.06 **(e)** 1.6875
7(a) $\frac{7}{20}$ **(b)** $\frac{7}{80}$ **(c)** $3\frac{27}{125}$ **(d)** $\frac{7}{9}$ **(e)** $1\frac{4}{11}$
8(a) 65 **(b)** 0 **(e)** $\frac{121}{36}$ **(f)** 7
9(a) $x = -2$ **(c)** $y = \frac{2}{3}$ **(e)** $a = 9.3$ **(h)** $a = \frac{92}{9}$
10(a) 2.356×10^3
11(a) 4631 **(f)** 0.000 025
12(a) 2.71×10^6 **(e)** 2.03×10^{-4}

Summary of Units 1 to 9

	Do you understand...?	*Can you...?*
Unit 1 **The Whole Numbers**		
1.1 Approximations in W	approximation $\doteq$	add, subtract, multiply, and divi whole numbers *accurately* find a good approximation to a calculation determine whether an answer is reasonable
1.2 Simplifying Number Phrases	order of operations BODMAS	simplify expressions using BODMAS
1.3 Evaluation by Substitution	variable algebraic expression domain substitution	evaluate algebraic expressions by substitution
Unit 2 **Mathematical Equations**		
2.1 Solving Equations by Inspection	equation solution set solving an equation identity ϕ	solve an equation by inspection check the solution set of an equation graph the solution set of an equation
2.2 Solving Equations by Adding and Subtracting	equivalent equations when to use addition or subtraction to solve an equation	solve an equation by adding the same number to each side solve an equation by subtracting the same number from each sid
2.3 Solving Equations by Dividing	when to use division to solve an equation the 3 steps necessary to solve an equation $\{\ \}$	solve an equation by dividing eac side by the same number follow the 3 steps to solve an equation

	Do you understand...?	*Can you...?*
Unit 3 **Inequations and Word Problems**		
3.1 Inequations	inequality signs inequations containing *or* or *and*	find the solution set of an inequation by inspection graph the solution set of an inequation
3.2 Methods for Solving Inequations	when to use addition, subtraction, or division to solve an inequation	solve an inequation using addition, subtraction, or division apply the 3 steps for solving an equation to an inequation check the solution set of an inequation
3.3 Word Problems	sum, difference product, quotient	translate an English sentence into a mathematical equation solve a word problem algebraically
Unit 4 **Addition and Subtraction of Integers**		
4.1 Adding Integers	integers negative, positive addition of integers opposites	locate integers on an I-line add integers
4.2 Subtracting Integers	subtraction by addition	subtract integers substitute using integers
4.3 Summary of Addition and Subtraction of Integers	the rules for adding integers the rule for subtracting integers	group positive integers and negative integers before adding them
Unit 5 **Multiplication and Division of Integers**		
5.1 Multiplying Integers	multiplication as a short cut for addition why the product of 2 negative integers is a positive integer	determine the sign of the product of 2 integers multiply integers

	Do you understand...?	*Can you...?*
5.2 Powers of Integers	base exponent power exponential form product form	change exponential form to product form change product form to exponenti form evaluate powers by substitution
5.3 Dividing Integers	inverse operations	determine the sign of the quotien of 2 integers divide integers

Unit 6
Solving Equations and Inequations Using Integers

6.1 Solving Equations Using Integers	root of an equation the rules for solving equations	by inspection, solve an equation involving integers solve an equation using addition, subtraction, or division check the solution set of an equation involving integers
6.2 Solving Inequations Using Integers	when to reverse the sign of inequality the rules for solving inequations	graph the solution set of an inequation on an I-line form a true inequation by performing the same operation on each side solve an inequation involving integers using addition, subtraction, or division
6.3 Solving Problems Using Integers	"let" statements	translate an English sentence intc a mathematical equation involving integers solve a word problem algebraicall

Unit 7
Rational Numbers

7.1 The Rational Numbers, Q	rational numbers Q-line lowest common multiple (LCM) common denominator	add, subtract, multiply, and divic fractions *accurately* solve an equation involving ratioı numbers using addition, subtraction, or division check a rational root
7.2 Addition and Subtraction in Q	why rational numbers are added and subtracted like integers	add and subtract rational number

	Do you understand...?	*Can you...?*
7.3 Multiplication and Division in Q	why rational numbers are multiplied like integers reciprocal division by multiplication	multiply and divide rational numbers evaluate by substitution, using rational numbers
7.4 Solving Equations and Inequations Using Rational Numbers	when to use multiplication to solve an equation clearing fractions expanding	solve an equation by multiplication graph the solution set of an inequation

Unit 8
Decimal Numbers

8.1 Decimal Equivalents of Rational Numbers	repeating (periodic) decimal period length of a period terminating decimal non-periodic decimal	add, subtract, multiply, and divide decimal numbers *accurately* find the decimal equivalent of a rational number abbreviate a periodic decimal
8.2 The Fractional Equivalent of a Decimal Number	fractional equivalent	find the fractional equivalent of a terminating or periodic decimal
8.3 Applications of Rational Numbers		substitute, using decimal numbers solve equations involving decimal numbers

Unit 9
Decimal Numbers in Standard Form

9.1 Zero and Negative Exponents	expanded form of a number the meaning of 10^0	write a decimal number in expanded form determine the quotient of 2 powers of 10
9.2 Standard Notation	standard form of a number	write a decimal number in standard form
9.3 Calculating Using Standard Form	$\doteq$ the rules for multiplying and dividing powers of 10	evaluate or approximate a product or quotient, using standard notation

Review Exercise, Units 1 to 9

Unless otherwise stated, assume that all variables represent rational numbers.

1. Evaluate.

   (*a*) $12 - 3 \times 4$
   (*b*) $14 + 2 \times 8 \div 4$
   (*c*) $8 \times 6 - 9 \div 3$
   (*d*) $47 - \frac{2}{3}$ of 24
   (*e*) $7 \times 9 + 10 \div 5 - 3$
   (*f*) $95 \div (12 + 14 \div 2)$
   (*g*) $48 \div 2 \times 3 \div (8 \times 9)$
   (*h*) $2[4 - 16 \div (12 - 2 \times 2)]$
   (*i*) $(9 \times 8 + 5) \div (6 - 3 \times 2)$

2. Evaluate.

   (*a*) $6x + y$ when $x = 2, y = 3$
   (*b*) $2(3m - n)$ when $m = 1, n = 2$
   (*c*) $3st - 2t$ when $s = 4, t = 1$
   (*d*) $p - 2q + r$ when $p = 10, q = 3, r = 0$
   (*e*) $(a + b) \div cd$ when $a = 5, b = 3, c = 2, d = 0$
   (*f*) $2x^2 - y^3$ when $x = 3, y = 2$

3. Choose the best approximation to each of the following expressions.

   (*a*) 16×29; 46, 464, 4640
   (*b*) 170×42; 714, 7140, 71 400
   (*c*) $3 \times 68 \times 7$; 1428, 14 280, 142 800
   (*d*) $15 \times 62 \times 31$; 288, 2883, 28 830
   (*e*) $343 \div 49$; 7, 70, 700
   (*f*) $1102 \div 58$; 2, 19, 190
   (*g*) $1004 \div 12$; 81, 810, 8100
   (*h*) $42 \times 73 \div 18$; 17, 170, 1700

4. Solve.

   (*a*) $x - 7 = 13$
   (*b*) $x + 4 = 4$
   (*c*) $2x - 5 = 1$
   (*d*) $14 - 3x = 5$
   (*e*) $2(x + 3) = 8$
   (*f*) $x^2 + 6 = 15$

5. Solve ($x \in I$).

   (*a*) $3x > 6$
   (*b*) $\frac{1}{3}x < 4$
   (*c*) $x + 6 > -1$
   (*d*) $5 > x - 3$
   (*e*) $2x < 8$
   (*f*) $\frac{2}{3}x \geq 10$

6. Which of the following are true, and which are false?

   (*a*) $15 > 3 + 7$
   (*b*) $2 \leq 14 \div 7$
   (*c*) $4 \ngtr 6$
   (*d*) $5 + 3 \nless 12$
   (*e*) $16 - 12 \div 4 > 2 \times 4$
   (*f*) $4 + 3 \nless 8$
   (*g*) $2(5 - 3) \geq 5 + 2$
   (*h*) $17 \ngtr 12 + 5$

1(a) 0 **(h)** 4
(b) 18 **(i)** Impossible
2(a) 15 **(f)** 10
(e) Impossible
3(c) 1428 **(g)** 81
(d) 28 830 **(h)** 170
4(a) $x = 20$
(f) $x = 3, x = -3$
5(b) {. . ., 9, 10, 11}
(d) {. . ., 5, 6, 7}
(f) {15, 16, 17, . . .}
6(a) T **(c)** T **(e)** T **(g)** F
(b) T **(d)** F **(f)** F **(h)** T

7. Solve and graph.

(*a*) $6x + 5 = 11$
(*b*) $3 + 2y = 19$
(*c*) $24 - 5t = 9$
(*d*) $x^2 + 4 = 20$
(*e*) $4m < 0$
(*f*) $p + 3 < 5$
(*g*) $16 \leq 4r$
(*h*) $2w + 1 \geq 1$

8. Evaluate.

(*a*) $14 - 30 \div 2$
(*b*) $65 \div 13 + (-24) \div 3$
(*c*) $(-2)(-4) + (5)(-6)$
(*d*) $\dfrac{25 \div 5 \times 9 - 3}{2 \times 4 - 28 \div 2}$

9. Find the value of each of the following when $a = 1, b = -2, c = -3, d = 0$.

(*a*) $6ab - 3d$
(*b*) $5a(2b + c)$
(*c*) $abcd + 1$
(*d*) $3b^2 - 2ac$
(*e*) $c^3 - a^2b$
(*f*) $\dfrac{b^2 + 3c}{b + c}$

10. Solve.

(*a*) $a + 3 = 5 - 2$
(*b*) $3y + 2 = -4$
(*c*) $5s + 12 = 12$
(*d*) $2x > -3, x \in I$
(*e*) $\frac{2}{3}q = -4$
(*f*) $\dfrac{5m}{2} = -10$

11. Solve and graph.

(*a*) $s + 5 = -7$
(*b*) $5 + t > -4$
(*c*) $6 + 3c = 0$
(*d*) $-2 < r \leq 1$
(*e*) $-2 \leq 2p < 8$
(*f*) $k^2 \leq 4$
(*g*) $m \geq 3$ and $m \leq 0$
(*h*) $y \leq 2$ and $y \geq -1$

12. Evaluate.

(*a*) $\dfrac{2}{3} + \dfrac{5}{6} - \dfrac{1}{2}$
(*b*) $1\frac{5}{8} - 3\frac{1}{4}$
(*c*) $\dfrac{6}{7} + \left(\dfrac{-3}{14}\right) - \dfrac{9}{28}$
(*d*) $-2\frac{5}{6} + 7\frac{1}{4} - 2\frac{5}{8}$
(*e*) $\left(\dfrac{-1}{3}\right)\left(\dfrac{3}{4}\right)\left(\dfrac{4}{-5}\right)$
(*f*) $2\frac{5}{8} \times \left(-3\frac{3}{7}\right)$

13. Evaluate.

(*a*) 3.26×5.4
(*b*) $49.6 \div 7.2$
(*c*) $(3.6 + 5.8) \div 6.1$
(*d*) $42.7 \times 1.4 \div 2$
(*e*) $0.001 \div 0.1$
(*f*) 0.03×0.54

7(a) 0 1 2 Q
(b) 6 7 8 9 Q
(g) 3 4 5 6 7 Q
(h) 0 1 2 3 4 Q
8(a) -1 **(d)** -7
9(a) -12 **(c)** 1
10(a) $a = 0$
(d) $\{-1, 0, 1, 2, \ldots\}$
11(a) -13 -12 -11 -10 Q
(b) -9 -8 -7 -6 -5 -4 Q
12(a) 1 **(b)** $-\frac{13}{8}$
13(c) 1.54 (2 decimal places)
(d) 29.89

14. Find the value of each of the following.

(a) $6pq + r$ when $p = -\frac{1}{4}$, $q = \frac{2}{3}$, $r = -\frac{5}{6}$

(b) $\frac{a+b}{c}$ when $a = -\frac{3}{8}$, $b = 2$, $c = 3\frac{1}{4}$

(c) m^2n when $m = -0.8$, $n = -1.25$

(d) $x^2 + 2y^3$ when $x = -0.75$, $y = -0.5$

15. List the solution set.

(a) $0.1x = 5$ (b) $0.5x = 2.5$ (c) $3x = 0.18$

16. Graph the solution set.

(a) $\frac{1}{3}m = 0.5$ (c) $4x = 0.4$ (e) $\frac{1}{4}k = 12$

(b) $2r = 2.6$ (d) $2a = 1$ (f) $2c = 0.375 - 0.2$

17. State the period and length of the period of each of the following.

(a) $0.6\dot{8}$ (d) $-3.\dot{6}5\dot{0}$

(b) 12.13 13 13 . . . (e) 12.41111 . . .

(c) $0.0\dot{1}5\dot{2}$ (f) $0.1\dot{9}36\dot{7}$

18. Write in abbreviated form.

(a) 1.3205 205 205 . . . (d) 6.1273 73 73 . . .

(b) 0.019 19 19 19 . . . (e) 128.61111 . . .

(c) −6.65555 . . . (f) −4.82153 82153 82153 . . .

19. Change the following fractions to decimal numbers, and state the period and its length.

(a) $-\frac{1}{2}$ (b) $\frac{4}{5}$ (c) $\frac{2}{11}$ (d) $-\frac{5}{7}$

20. Determine the fractional equivalent of each of the following.

(a) 0.375 (c) −4.18 (e) $2.\dot{3}$

(b) 6.65 (d) $1.\dot{6}$ (f) $0.\dot{2}\dot{4}$

21. Evaluate the following.

(a) $(-2)^4$ (d) $2^3 \times 2^2$ (g) $10^6 \times 10^{-2}$

(b) $6^0 + 3^2$ (e) $3^5 \div 3^3$ (h) $5^5 \times 5^{-3} \times 5^{-2}$

(c) $(-1)^{25}$ (f) 4^{-2} (i) $\left(\frac{1}{3}\right)^{-2}$

14(a) $-1\frac{5}{6}$ **(c)** −0.8
(b) $\frac{1}{2}$ **(d)** 0.3125

15(a) {50} **(c)** {0.06}
(b) {5}

16(a) 1.5; 0 1 2 3 Q

(c) 0.1; 0 1 2 Q

19(a) 0, 1 **(c)** 18, 2
(b) 0, 1 **(d)** 714285, 6

20(a) $\frac{3}{8}$ **(d)** $1\frac{2}{3}$
(b) $6\frac{13}{20}$ **(e)** $2\frac{1}{3}$

21(a) 16 **(g)** 10^4
(b) 10 **(h)** 1
(c) −1 **(i)** 9

22. Express 27 as a power of 3.

23. Write 29.3 in expanded form, using powers of 10.

24. Express in standard form.

(*a*) 129	(*c*) 17.58	(*e*) 0.0058
(*b*) 42 000	(*d*) 0.17	(*f*) 6.3

Solve the following word problems algebraically.

25. The sum of a whole number and 6 is less than or equal to 11. Find all such numbers.

26. The product of 5 and a number, decreased by 12, is 23. Find the number.

27. A stack of 8 bricks, each the same thickness, is 20 cm short of 0.60 m high. Find the thickness of 1 brick.

28. Isobel Ringing's bank account contains $92. After depositing $3/week for several weeks, she finds her account contains $149. How many weekly deposits has Isobel made?

29. The product of an integer and 4 is subtracted from 15, and the result is 3. Find the integer.

30. Find the integer whose square, decreased by 39, gives -14.

31. A lathe is set to decrease the diameter of a piece of work by 0.1 mm/rev. Determine the number of revolutions to reduce the diameter from 2.86 cm to 2.61 cm.

In the following problems use a diagram if it helps in answering the question. An algebraic solution is not required.

32. A large bowl of punch is made by combining the following ingredients.

500 ml grape juice	150 ml lemon juice
1.25 ℓ pineapple juice	2 ℓ ginger ale

Determine the total quantity of punch produced.

25. 0, 1, 2, 3, 4, 5
26. 7
27. 5 cm
28. 19
29. 3
30. 5, –5
31. 25
32. 3.9 ℓ

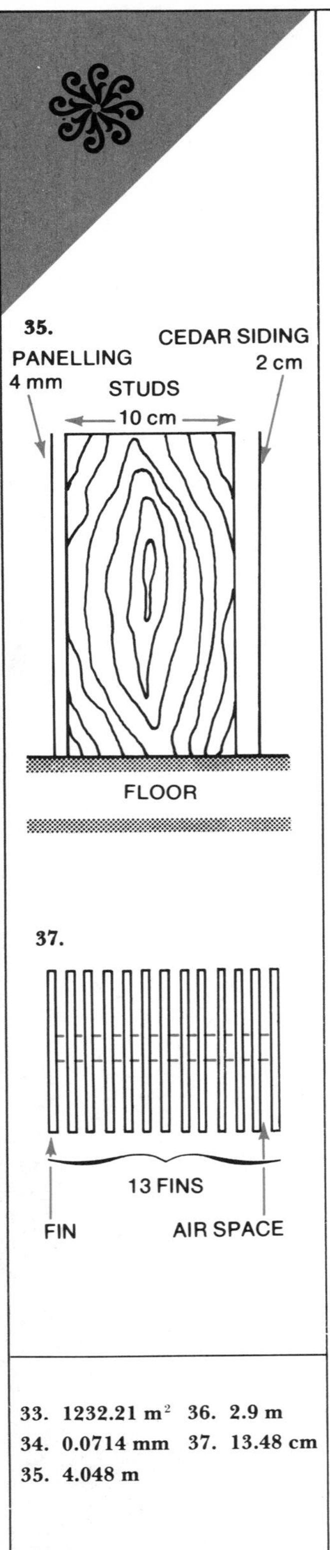

33. How many square metres of lawn must be mowed if the rectangular lawn measures 20.3 m by 60.7 m?

34. Calculate the thickness of 1 sheet of paper if 350 sheets measure 2.5 cm thick.

35. The inside measurement of a garage is 3.8 m. If the outside walls consist of 4 mm panelling, 5 cm by 10 cm studs, and 2 cm cedar siding, determine the total outside dimension of the garage.

36. Lengths of 2.5 m, 3.2 m, and 1.6 m are cut from a bolt of cloth 10.2 m long. How many metres of material are left over?

37. The heating unit on an electric baseboard heater consists of a "finned" element, as shown. If each fin is 1.6 mm thick and the air space between fins is 9.5 mm, calculate the overall length of the unit.

38. In football, quarterbacks are rated by their Passes Completed Record. Midway through the 1974 CFL schedule, the following passing records were published.

Western Conference	*Attempted*	*Completed*
Liske, Calgary Stampeders	199	121
Lancaster, Saskatchewan Roughriders	221	122
Moorehead, B.C. Lions	160	82
Wilkinson, Edmonton Eskimos	126	89
Ealey, Winnipeg Blue Bombers	132	72

Eastern Conference	*Attempted*	*Completed*
Jones, Montreal Alouettes	171	86
Jonas, Hamilton Tiger Cats	171	90
Rae, Toronto Argonauts	173	77
Keeling, Ottawa Roughriders	125	60
Cassata, Ottawa Roughriders	107	44

Calculate, to 3 decimal places, the completion rate

$$\frac{\text{No. of passes completed}}{\text{No. of passes attempted}} \text{ for each quarterback.}$$

33. 1232.21 m² 36. 2.9 m
34. 0.0714 mm 37. 13.48 cm
35. 4.048 m

More About the Moëbius Strip

This dramatic variation of the Moëbius strip requires a paper strip that is at least six times longer than it is wide.

1. First fold the strip to locate the centre line at one end of the strip.

2. Fold the strip so that B falls on the centre line and the resulting crease AC passes through A. What kind of triangle is ABC?

3. Fold the strip back so that the crease CD falls along CB. What kind of triangle is CDA? Next fold forward along DA, forming another triangle. Continue folding back and forth until ten equilateral triangles have been formed. Cut off the excess of the strip as well as the first right-angled triangle ABC.

4. Lay the strip in the position shown and number the triangles accordingly.

5. Turn the strip over and continue numbering as shown. Be sure that triangle 11 is behind triangle 1. Coloring each triangle or drawing designs on them will add to the attractiveness of the *hexaflexagons*.

6. To fold the *hexaflexagon*, hold the strip with triangle 1 at your left. Fold triangle 1 over triangle 2. Then fold triangle 15 on triangle 14 and triangle 8 on triangle 7. If your folding now gives you the arrangements shown, glue triangle 1 to 10. If you do not have this arrangement, recheck the directions given.

Your hexagon will now open and give you three surfaces or six designs. The designs open easily by folding in the three single edges, forming a three-cornered star and opening out the centre.

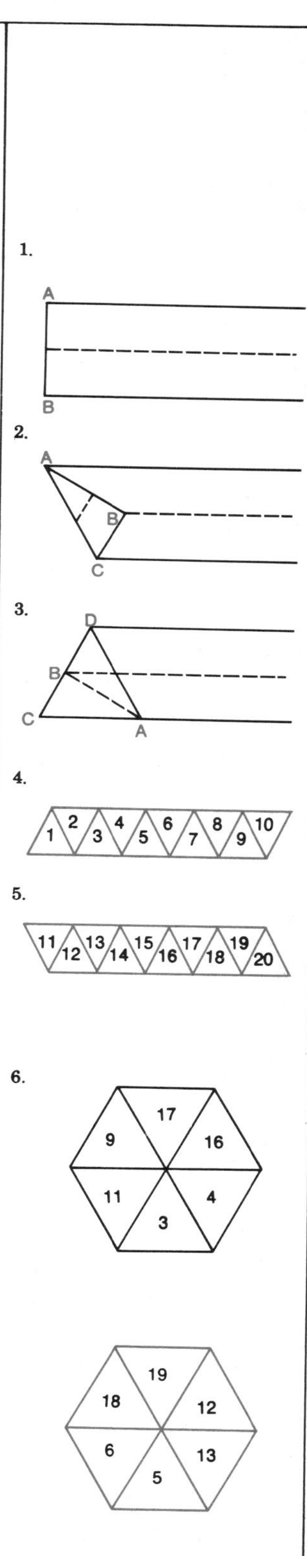

Unit 10

Square Root • Part 1

If you are told that a card table is 75 cm long and 75 cm wide, you can easily determine the area of the table top by *squaring* 75 cm. The inverse operation to squaring—finding the *square root*—is somewhat more difficult. For example, given that the area of a square table top is 3812 cm^2, you may have some trouble in determining the length of the sides of the table. In the next 2 units, we shall study methods for calculating square roots.

$a = (75\text{ cm})^2$
$= 75\text{ cm} \times 75\text{ cm}$
$= 5625\text{ cm}^2$
Nothing to it!

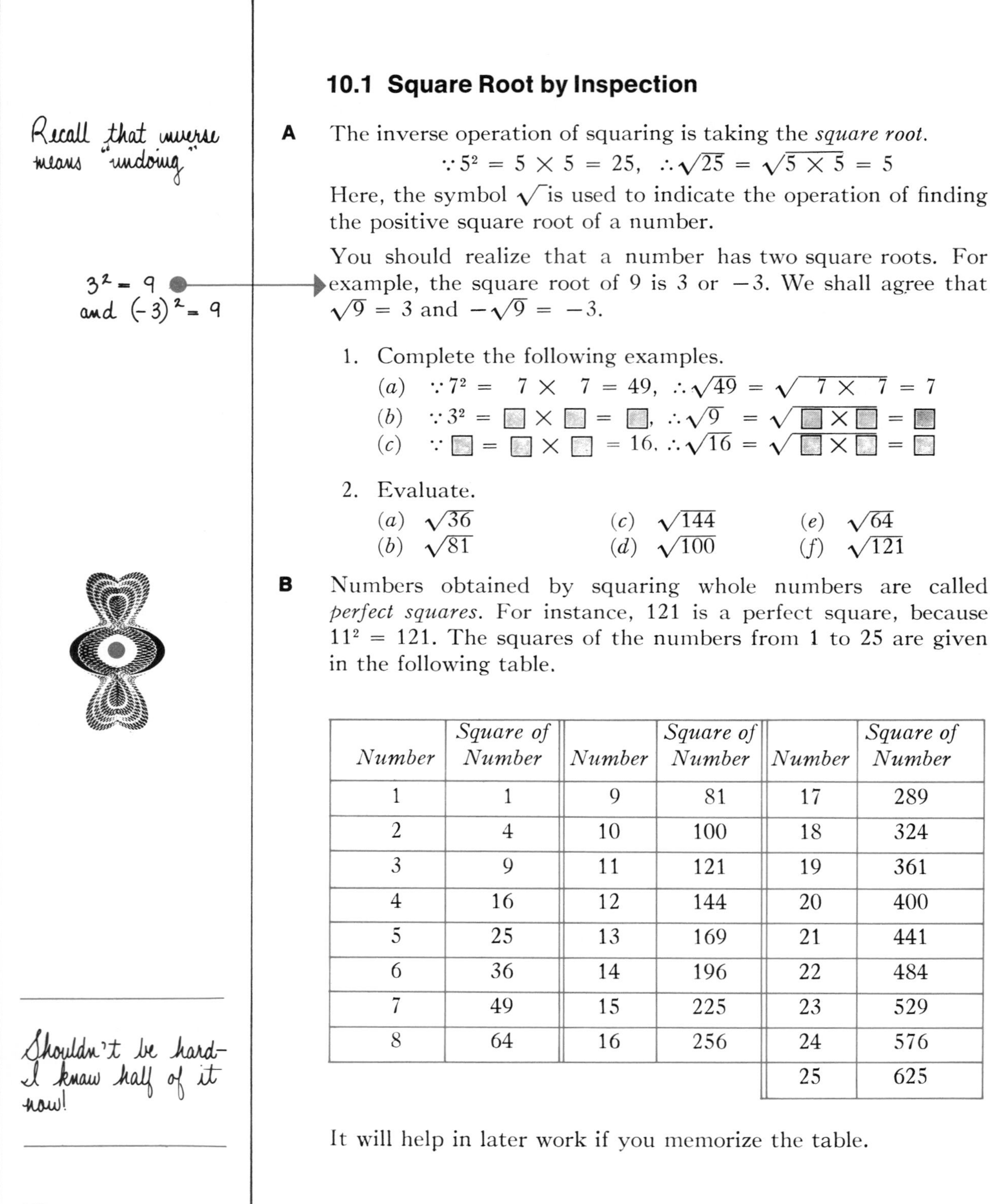

10.1 Square Root by Inspection

Recall that inverse means "undoing"

A The inverse operation of squaring is taking the *square root*.

$$\because 5^2 = 5 \times 5 = 25, \quad \therefore \sqrt{25} = \sqrt{5 \times 5} = 5$$

Here, the symbol $\sqrt{\ }$ is used to indicate the operation of finding the positive square root of a number.

You should realize that a number has two square roots. For example, the square root of 9 is 3 or -3. We shall agree that $\sqrt{9} = 3$ and $-\sqrt{9} = -3$.

$3^2 = 9$ and $(-3)^2 = 9$

1. Complete the following examples.
   (*a*) $\because 7^2 = 7 \times 7 = 49, \therefore \sqrt{49} = \sqrt{7 \times 7} = 7$
   (*b*) $\because 3^2 = \square \times \square = \square, \therefore \sqrt{9} = \sqrt{\square \times \square} = \square$
   (*c*) $\because \square = \square \times \square = 16, \therefore \sqrt{16} = \sqrt{\square \times \square} = \square$

2. Evaluate.
   (*a*) $\sqrt{36}$ (*c*) $\sqrt{144}$ (*e*) $\sqrt{64}$
   (*b*) $\sqrt{81}$ (*d*) $\sqrt{100}$ (*f*) $\sqrt{121}$

B Numbers obtained by squaring whole numbers are called *perfect squares*. For instance, 121 is a perfect square, because $11^2 = 121$. The squares of the numbers from 1 to 25 are given in the following table.

Number	*Square of Number*	*Number*	*Square of Number*	*Number*	*Square of Number*
1	1	9	81	17	289
2	4	10	100	18	324
3	9	11	121	19	361
4	16	12	144	20	400
5	25	13	169	21	441
6	36	14	196	22	484
7	49	15	225	23	529
8	64	16	256	24	576
				25	625

Shouldn't be hard— I know half of it now!

It will help in later work if you memorize the table.

1. Evaluate. (Refer to the table only if necessary.)

(*a*) $\sqrt{121}$ (*d*) $\sqrt{484}$

(*b*) $\sqrt{361}$ (*e*) $\sqrt{\frac{25}{49}}$

(*c*) $\sqrt{529}$ (*f*) $\sqrt{\frac{16}{9}}$

To find the square root of a perfect square greater than 625, it is necessary to first *factor* the number into a product of prime factors. For example,

$$\because \quad 1089 = 3 \times 3 \times 11 \times 11$$
$$\therefore \quad \sqrt{1089} = \sqrt{3 \times 3 \times 11 \times 11}$$
$$= 3 \times 11$$
$$= 33$$

1. Evaluate by first expressing as a product of prime factors.

(*a*) $\sqrt{1764}$ (*b*) $\sqrt{1936}$ (*c*) $\sqrt{5929}$

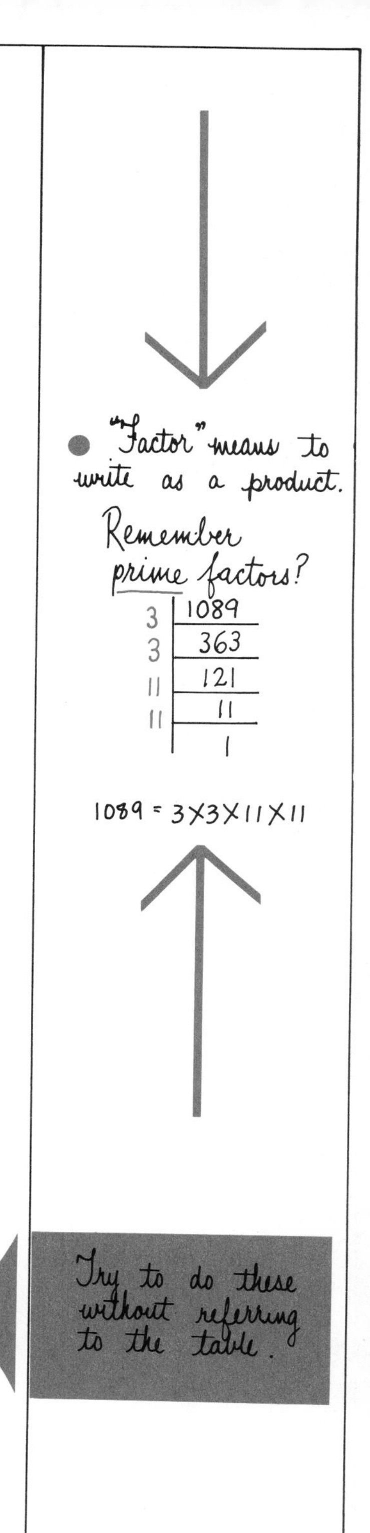

"Factor" means to write as a product.
Remember prime factors?
3 | 1089
3 | 363
11 | 121
11 | 11
1
1089 = 3×3×11×11
Try to do these without referring to the table.

Exercise 10.1

Discussion

1. Continue the list as far as you can.

$$1^2 = 1, \quad 2^2 = 4, \quad 3^2 = 9, \ldots$$

2. Can you express $\sqrt{2 \times 2 \times 5 \times 5}$ and $\sqrt{3 \times 7 \times 11 \times 11}$ as whole numbers? Explain.

3. In your own words, state the condition concerning the prime factors of a perfect square.

4. Evaluate.

(*a*) $\sqrt{36}$ (*d*) $\sqrt{225}$ (*g*) $\sqrt{529}$

(*b*) $\sqrt{81}$ (*e*) $\sqrt{169}$ (*h*) $\sqrt{256}$

(*c*) $\sqrt{400}$ (*f*) $\sqrt{196}$ (*i*) $\sqrt{576}$

5. Will the method of prime factors work for finding the square root of *any* number? Explain.

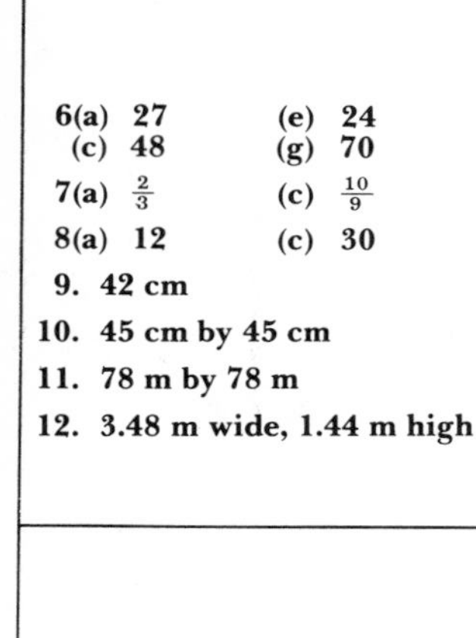
6(a) 27 (e) 24
(c) 48 (g) 70
7(a) $\frac{2}{3}$ (c) $\frac{10}{9}$
8(a) 12 (c) 30
9. 42 cm
10. 45 cm by 45 cm
11. 78 m by 78 m
12. 3.48 m wide, 1.44 m high

Written Solutions

6. Evaluate by factoring first.

(*a*) $\sqrt{729}$	(*d*) $\sqrt{1024}$	(*g*) $\sqrt{4900}$
(*b*) $\sqrt{1225}$	(*e*) $\sqrt{576}$	(*h*) $\sqrt{4356}$
(*c*) $\sqrt{2304}$	(*f*) $\sqrt{2401}$	(*i*) $\sqrt{2601}$

7. Evaluate.

(*a*) $\sqrt{\frac{36}{81}}$ (*b*) $\sqrt{\frac{64}{121}}$ (*c*) $\sqrt{\frac{100}{81}}$

8. Solve for the positive value of x.

(*a*) $x^2 = 144$ (*c*) $2x^2 = 1800$

(*b*) $x^2 + 100 = 356$ (*d*) $\frac{x^2}{3} = 432$

9. The area of the top of a square table is 1764 cm². How wide is the table top?

10. In the ventilation system of a coal mine, a round pipe whose cross-sectional area is 2025 cm² joins onto a square pipe with the same area of cross section. What are the dimensions of the square pipe?

11.

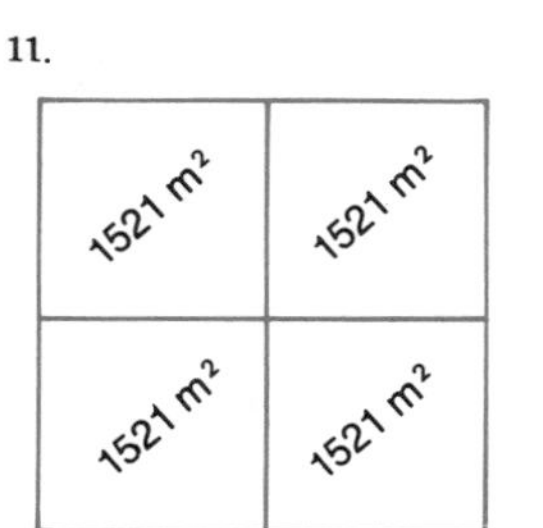

11. A square field is fenced off into 4 smaller fields, as shown. If the area of each small field is 1521 m², find the dimensions of the field.

12. A square window has an area of 12 996 cm². Find the dimensions of drapery material for the window if 30 cm are allowed on either side and 15 cm at top and bottom. Double the width of the material to permit pleating.

10.2 Square Root from Tables

A Quite often it is necessary to find the square root of a number that is not a perfect square. A very convenient way to find the square roots of numbers such as 13, 27, 89, and so on, is to look them up in a table of square roots constructed for this very purpose. Part of such a table follows.

Square Root Table

n	$\sqrt{n}$	n	$\sqrt{n}$	n	$\sqrt{n}$	n	$\sqrt{n}$	n	$\sqrt{n}$
1	1.00	21	4.58	41	6.40	61	7.81	81	9.00
2	1.41	22	4.69	42	6.48	62	7.87	82	9.06
3	1.73	23	4.80	43	6.56	63	7.94	83	9.11
4	2.00	24	4.90	44	6.63	64	8.00	84	9.17
5	2.24	25	5.00	45	6.71	65	8.06	85	9.22
6	2.45	26	5.10	46	6.78	66	8.12	86	9.27
7	2.65	27	5.20	47	6.86	67	8.19	87	9.33
8	2.83	28	5.29	48	6.93	68	8.25	88	9.38
9	3.00	29	5.39	49	7.00	69	8.31	89	9.43
10	3.16	30	5.48	50	7.07	70	8.37	90	9.49
11	3.32	31	5.57	51	7.14	71	8.43	91	9.54
12	3.46	32	5.66	52	7.21	72	8.49	92	9.59
13	3.61	33	5.74	53	7.28	73	8.54	93	9.64
14	3.74	34	5.83	54	7.35	74	8.60	94	9.70
15	3.87	35	5.92	55	7.42	75	8.66	95	9.75
16	4.00	36	6.00	56	7.48	76	8.72	96	9.80
17	4.12	37	6.08	57	7.55	77	8.77	97	9.85
18	4.24	38	6.16	58	7.62	78	8.83	98	9.90
19	4.36	39	6.24	59	7.68	79	8.89	99	9.95
20	4.47	40	6.32	60	7.75	80	8.94	100	10.00

See page 371 for a more complete Square Root Table.

Note that numbers in this table are correct to 2 decimal places only.

8.31 × 8.31
= 69.0561
$\sqrt{69}$ is nearly 8.31

In later work, you will find out how values in this table were determined.

1. Evaluate by using the square root table.

(*a*) $\sqrt{29}$ (*c*) $\sqrt{10}$ (*e*) $\sqrt{8}$

(*b*) $\sqrt{46}$ (*d*) $\sqrt{92}$ (*f*) $\sqrt{54}$

Since finding square root is the inverse operation of squaring, the table may also be used to find the value of the square of certain numbers. For instance,

$$\because \sqrt{59} \doteq 7.68, \quad \therefore 7.68^2 \doteq 59$$

Remember what $\doteq$ means?

1. Evaluate.

(*a*) 6.16^2 (*c*) 8.06^2 (*e*) 1.73^2

(*b*) 4.90^2 (*d*) 6.93^2 (*f*) 3.46^2

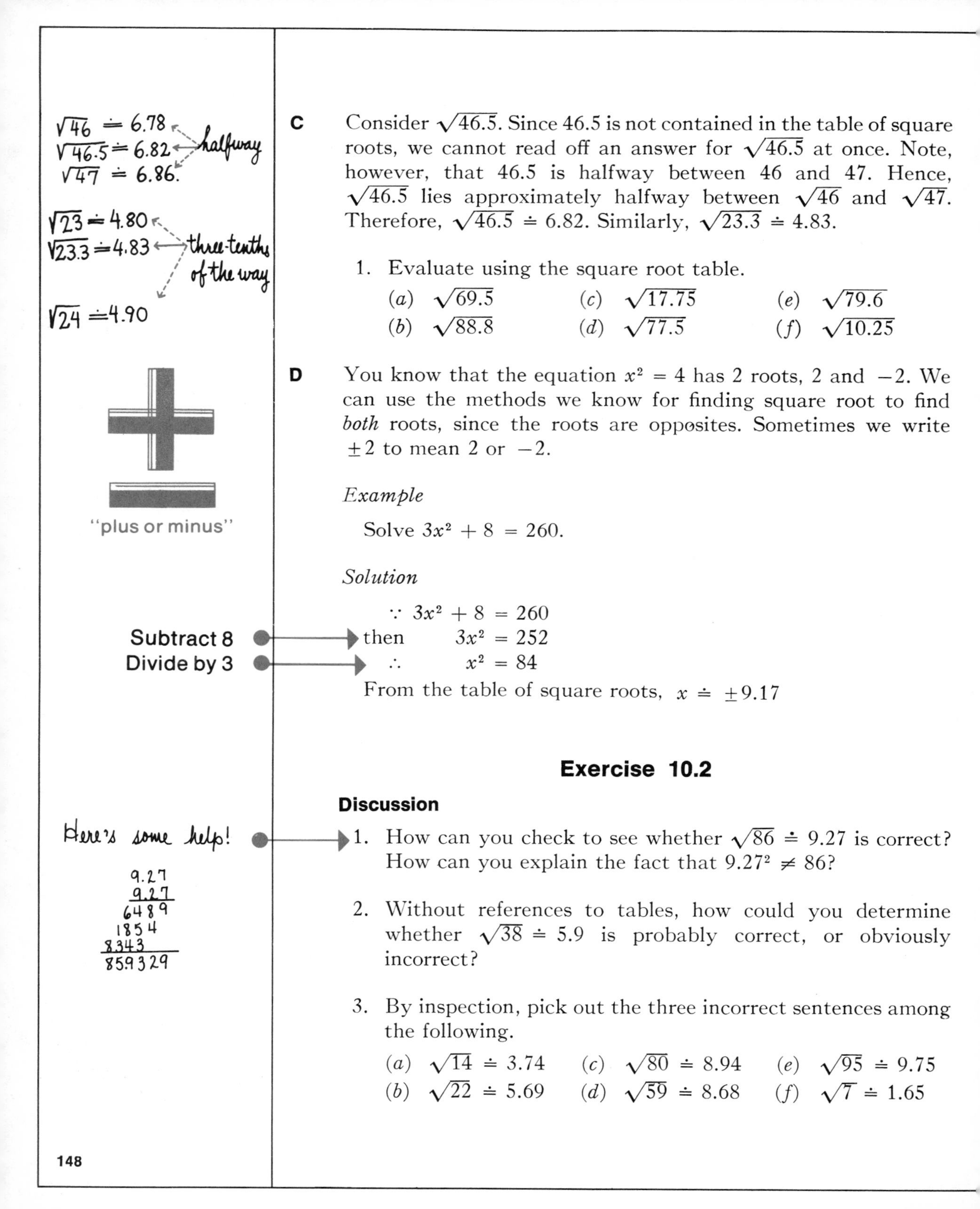

C Consider $\sqrt{46.5}$. Since 46.5 is not contained in the table of square roots, we cannot read off an answer for $\sqrt{46.5}$ at once. Note, however, that 46.5 is halfway between 46 and 47. Hence, $\sqrt{46.5}$ lies approximately halfway between $\sqrt{46}$ and $\sqrt{47}$. Therefore, $\sqrt{46.5} \doteq 6.82$. Similarly, $\sqrt{23.3} \doteq 4.83$.

1. Evaluate using the square root table.

(*a*) $\sqrt{69.5}$	(*c*) $\sqrt{17.75}$	(*e*) $\sqrt{79.6}$
(*b*) $\sqrt{88.8}$	(*d*) $\sqrt{77.5}$	(*f*) $\sqrt{10.25}$

D You know that the equation $x^2 = 4$ has 2 roots, 2 and -2. We can use the methods we know for finding square root to find *both* roots, since the roots are opposites. Sometimes we write ± 2 to mean 2 or -2.

Example

Solve $3x^2 + 8 = 260$.

Solution

$$\because\ 3x^2 + 8 = 260$$

Subtract 8 → then $3x^2 = 252$

Divide by 3 → $\therefore\ x^2 = 84$

From the table of square roots, $x \doteq \pm 9.17$

Exercise 10.2

Discussion

1. How can you check to see whether $\sqrt{86} \doteq 9.27$ is correct? How can you explain the fact that $9.27^2 \neq 86$?

2. Without references to tables, how could you determine whether $\sqrt{38} \doteq 5.9$ is probably correct, or obviously incorrect?

3. By inspection, pick out the three incorrect sentences among the following.

(*a*) $\sqrt{14} \doteq 3.74$	(*c*) $\sqrt{80} \doteq 8.94$	(*e*) $\sqrt{95} \doteq 9.75$
(*b*) $\sqrt{22} \doteq 5.69$	(*d*) $\sqrt{59} \doteq 8.68$	(*f*) $\sqrt{7} \doteq 1.65$

4. Evaluate using square root tables.

(*a*) $\sqrt{19}$ (*d*) $\sqrt{13}$ (*g*) $\sqrt{85}$
(*b*) $\sqrt{24}$ (*e*) $\sqrt{41}$ (*h*) $\sqrt{30}$
(*c*) $\sqrt{97}$ (*f*) $\sqrt{50}$ (*i*) $\sqrt{69}$

5. Evaluate.

(*a*) $\sqrt{64}$ (*d*) $\sqrt{169}$ (*g*) $\sqrt{4}$
(*b*) $\sqrt{17^2}$ (*e*) $\sqrt{75^2}$ (*h*) $\sqrt{576}$
(*c*) $\sqrt{28}$ (*f*) $\sqrt{81}$ (*i*) $\sqrt{x^2}$

6. Solve.

(*a*) $x^2 = 1$ (*b*) $x^2 = 4$ (*c*) $2x^2 = 32$

Written Solutions

7. Using the square root tables, evaluate.

(*a*) $\sqrt{35.5}$ (*d*) $\sqrt{84.4}$ (*g*) $\sqrt{94.2}$
(*b*) $\sqrt{73.5}$ (*e*) $\sqrt{79.2}$ (*h*) $\sqrt{26.8}$
(*c*) $\sqrt{7.5}$ (*f*) $\sqrt{16.25}$ (*i*) $\sqrt{12.6}$

8. Solve.

(*a*) $p^2 = 25$ (*d*) $a^2 = 72.5$
(*b*) $r^2 = 64$ (*e*) $x^2 + 19 = 28$
(*c*) $m^2 = 37$ (*f*) $42 - y^2 = 21$

9. A checkered tablecloth is made up of squares each having an area of 90 cm². If there are 26 squares along the length of the tablecloth, how long is it?

10. How many pieces of square floor tile, each having an area of 400 cm², can be placed along a wall measuring 6.8 m?

11. Grandpa Sew-em-up has a piece of material 2 m by 1 m which he plans to use to make squares for a quilt. His pattern indicates that he can use squares that are 324 cm² or 225 cm². Since all squares must be the same size, how many of each size can he make? Which size makes more efficient use of the material?

7(a) 5.96 **(c)** 2.74 **(e)** 8.90 **(g)** 9.71 **(i)** 3.55
8(a) ±5 **(c)** ±6.08
9. 247 cm
10. 34

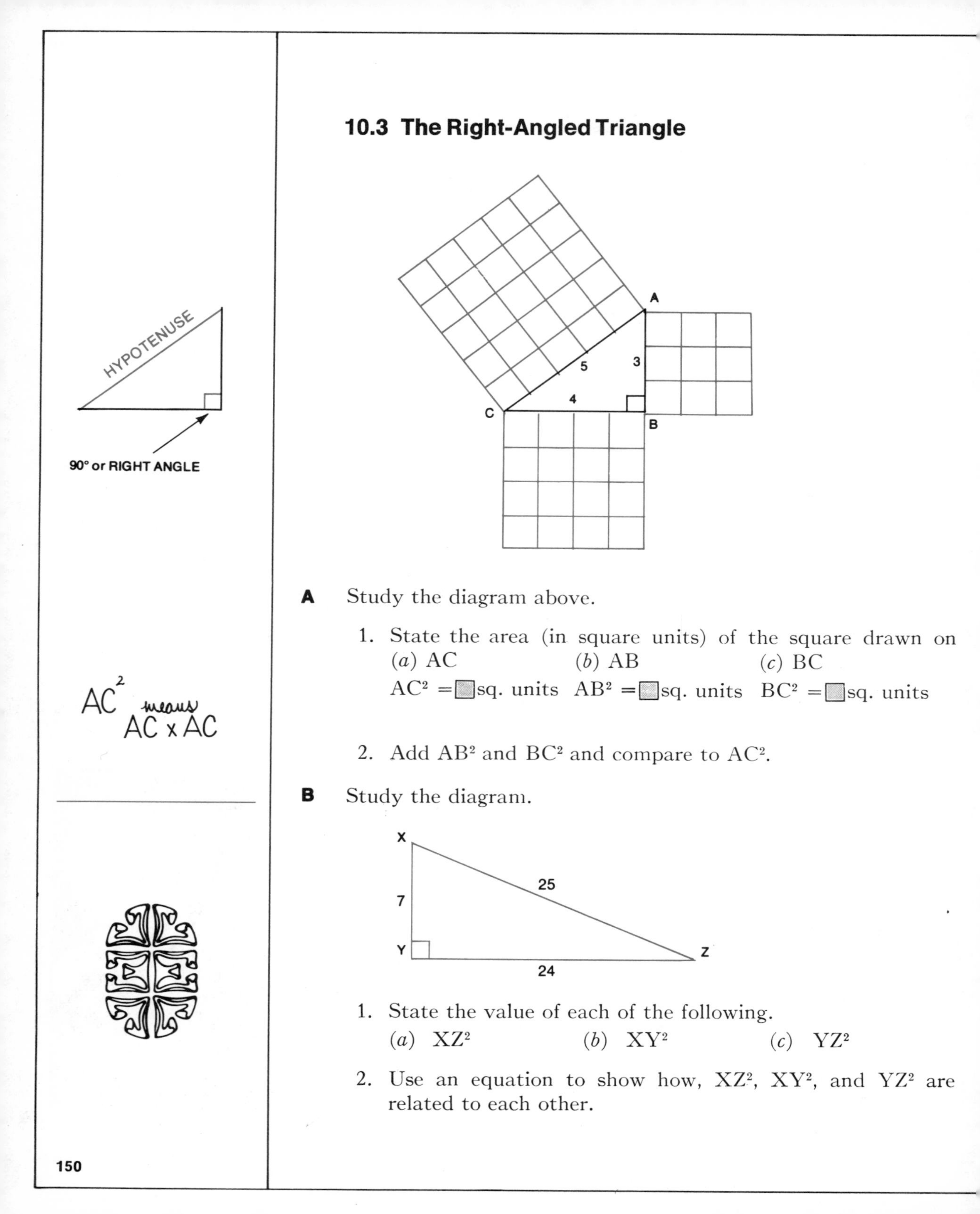

10.3 The Right-Angled Triangle

A Study the diagram above.

1. State the area (in square units) of the square drawn on
   (*a*) AC (*b*) AB (*c*) BC
   AC^2 = ▢ sq. units AB^2 = ▢ sq. units BC^2 = ▢ sq. units

2. Add AB^2 and BC^2 and compare to AC^2.

B Study the diagram.

1. State the value of each of the following.
   (*a*) XZ^2 (*b*) XY^2 (*c*) YZ^2

2. Use an equation to show how, XZ^2, XY^2, and YZ^2 are related to each other.

C Study the diagram.

$h^2 = ▨ + ▨$

a h b

In words:

> The area of the square on the hypotenuse equals the sum of the areas of the squares on the other 2 sides.

1. Write the equation relating the sides in each of the triangles.

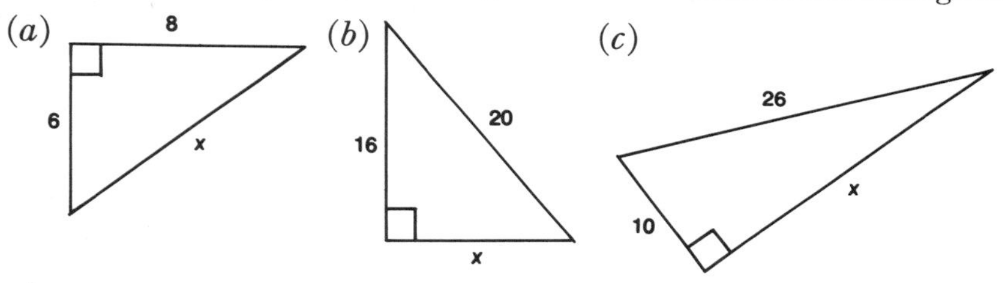

2. This is how you can find x in 1(b).

$$\because\ x^2 + 16^2 = 20^2$$
$$\text{then } x^2 + 256 = 400$$
$$\text{and } x^2 = 144$$
$$\therefore\ x = 12\ *$$

Find x in 1(a) and 1(c).

Example

How long is a ladder that reaches 12 m up a vertical wall when its foot is 5 m from the wall?

Solution

Let the length of the ladder be k metres.

$$\therefore\ k^2 = 12^2 + 5^2$$
$$= 144 + 25$$
$$= 169$$
$$\therefore\ k = 13$$

$\therefore$ The ladder is 13 m long.

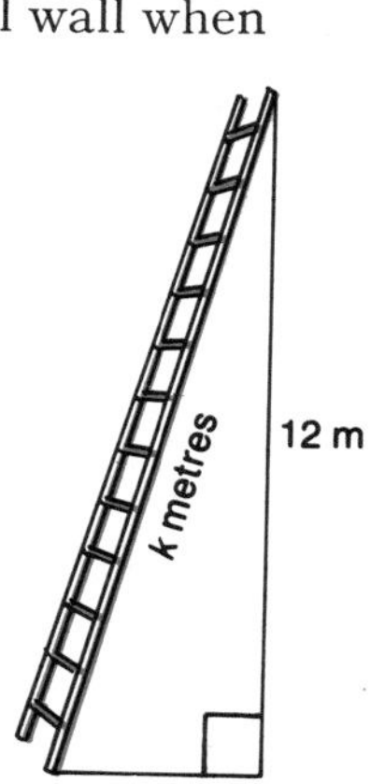

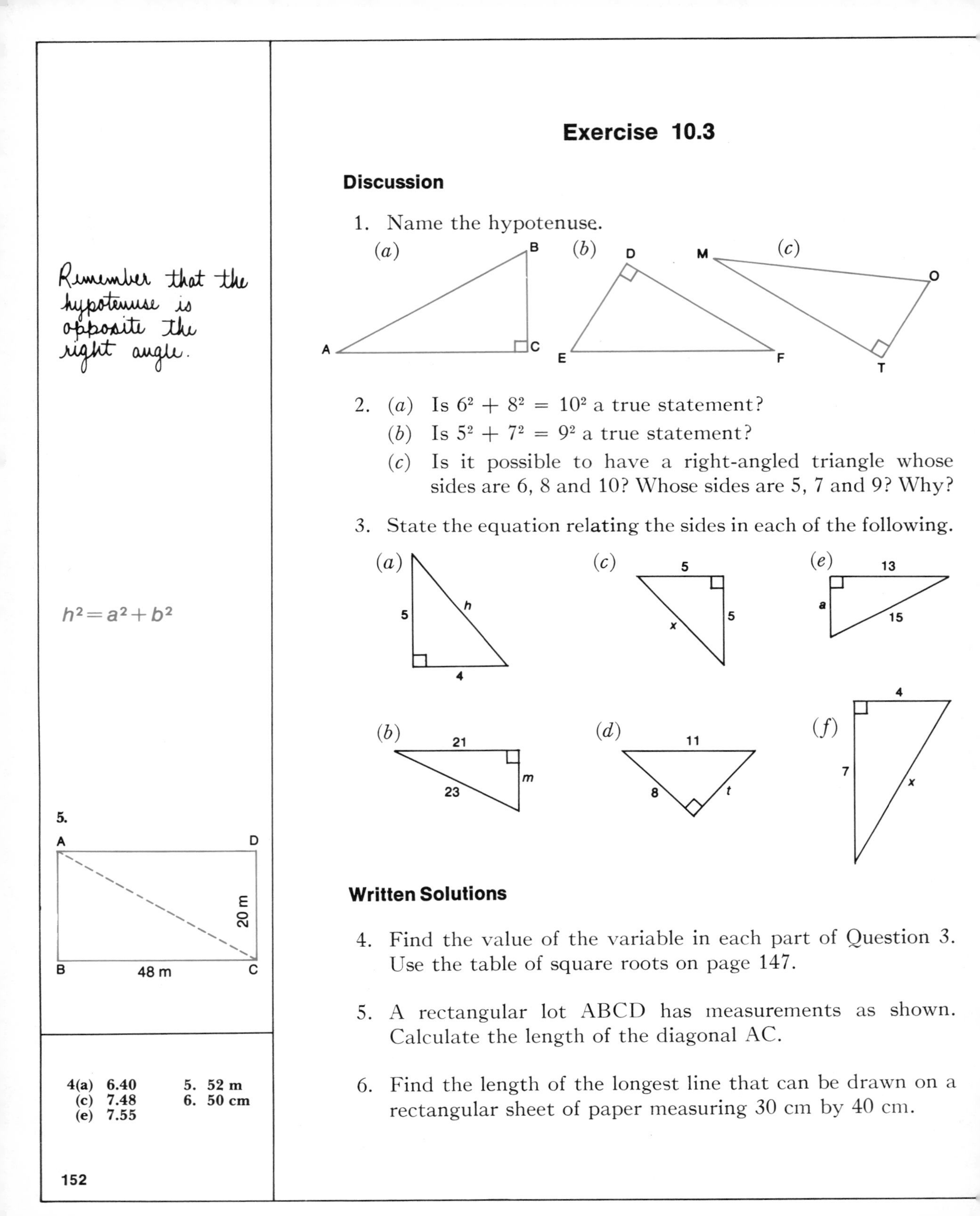

Remember that the hypotenuse is opposite the right angle.

$h^2 = a^2 + b^2$

Exercise 10.3

Discussion

1. Name the hypotenuse.

2. (a) Is $6^2 + 8^2 = 10^2$ a true statement?
   (b) Is $5^2 + 7^2 = 9^2$ a true statement?
   (c) Is it possible to have a right-angled triangle whose sides are 6, 8 and 10? Whose sides are 5, 7 and 9? Why?

3. State the equation relating the sides in each of the following.

Written Solutions

4. Find the value of the variable in each part of Question 3. Use the table of square roots on page 147.

5. A rectangular lot ABCD has measurements as shown. Calculate the length of the diagonal AC.

5.

6. Find the length of the longest line that can be drawn on a rectangular sheet of paper measuring 30 cm by 40 cm.

4(a) 6.40
(c) 7.48
(e) 7.55

5. 52 m
6. 50 cm

7. A radio broadcasting tower is secured by guy wires 61 m long. Find the distance k.

8. A 10 m ladder is placed against a vertical wall with its foot 2 m from the wall. How far up the wall does it reach?

9. Sky King has built an experimental model flying saucer in his basement workshop. The door leading outside measures 75 cm by 2 m. If the model has a diameter of 3 m, show that it must be dismantled before it can be removed from the workshop.

10. A square kerchief is folded along a diagonal measuring 90 cm. Find the dimensions of the kerchief.

11. The rafters in a house must span 8 m. If they meet at a right angle, how long must each rafter be? How far is the peak above the top of the wall?

12. Penelope Punchpress, a machinist at the Drill & Borem Tooling Company, carries the drill bits for her machine in a metal box with inside dimensions 8 cm by 10 cm by 5 cm. If she is issued a new drill bit 15 cm long, will Penelope be able to fit it into the metal box?

13. A ladder 13 m long is placed against a vertical wall, as shown. If the top of the ladder slides 4 m down the wall, how far will the foot of the ladder slide? Give your answer to the nearest centimetre.

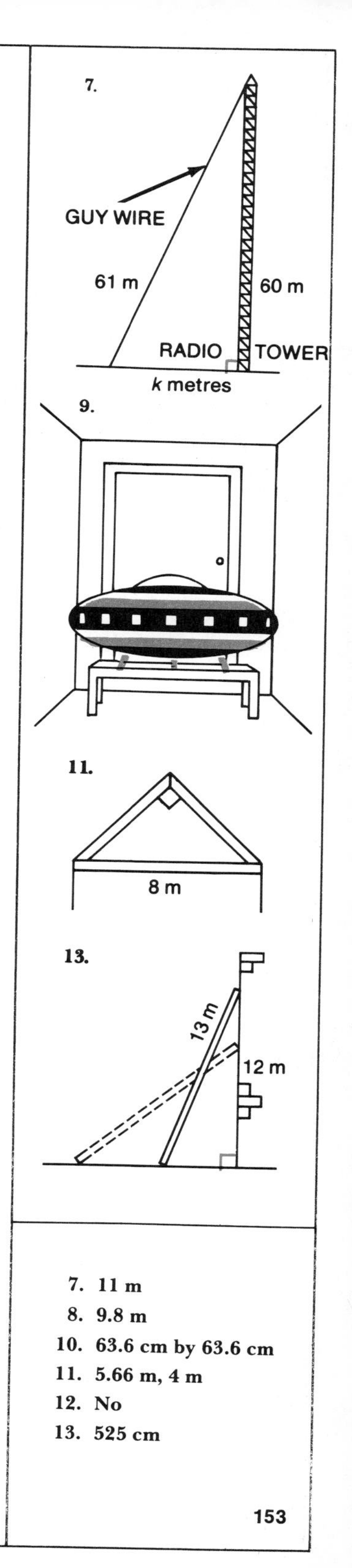

7. **11 m**
8. **9.8 m**
10. **63.6 cm by 63.6 cm**
11. **5.66 m, 4 m**
12. **No**
13. **525 cm**

Unit 11

Square Root • Part 2

The methods we have examined so far for finding the square root of a number have involved special numbers only. The numbers either were perfect squares or could be found readily in a table. In this unit, you will learn a method for finding the square root of *any* whole or decimal number.

11.1 Calculating Square Root — Newton's Method

You know that $\sqrt{100} = 10$ and that $\sqrt{121} = 11$, but all you can say about the value of $\sqrt{108}$ is that it lies somewhere between 10 and 11.

1. The following square roots lie between 2 consecutive numbers. Name the numbers.

   (*a*) $\sqrt{28}$ (*b*) $\sqrt{58}$ (*c*) $\sqrt{91}$ (*d*) $\sqrt{135}$ (*e*) $\sqrt{150}$

Like this!
$2 < \sqrt{7} < 3$

Your answer to Question 1 (*a*) should have been that $\sqrt{28}$ lies between 5 and 6; that is, $5 < \sqrt{28} < 6$.

$\because$ 28 is closer to 25 than it is to 36,

$\therefore$ $\sqrt{28}$ is closer to 5 than it is to 6.

First, try $\sqrt{28} = 5.2$ *Check:* $5.2^2 = 27.04$

Next, try $\sqrt{28} = 5.3$ $5.3^2 = 28.09$

$\because \quad 27.04 < 28 < 28.09$

$\therefore \quad 5.2 < \sqrt{28} < 5.3$

$\because$ 28 is much closer to 28.09 than it is to 27.04,

$\therefore$ $\sqrt{28} = 5.3$, correct to 1 decimal place.

```
  5.2
  5.2
  ---
  104
 260
 ----
27.04
```

The method we used to find $\sqrt{28}$ depends on good *estimation*. Some of this guesswork can be eliminated.

Suppose you don't know that $\sqrt{25} = 5$ and you estimate that $\sqrt{25} = 4$. To check, divide 25 by 4. The answer, 6.25, shows that 4 is wrong but, more important, it means that $4 < \sqrt{25} < 6.25$. ← *Why?*

$\frac{4+6.25}{2} = \frac{10.25}{2}$
$= 5.125$

The average of 4 and 6.25, which is 5.125, should be a good second approximation. And it is!

Try using 3 as a first estimate. You will see that the average, 5.6, is *still* fairly close to 5!

Example 1 Find $\sqrt{18}$ to 1 decimal place.

Solution

Try 4 as a first approximation.

Divide: $\frac{18}{4} = 4.5$

Average: $\frac{4 + 4.5}{2} = 4.25$

$\therefore \quad \sqrt{18} \doteq 4.25$ is a second approximation.

Repeat the steps with 4.25.

Divide: $\frac{18}{4.25} = 4.23$

Average: $\frac{4.25 + 4.23}{2} = 4.24$

By rounding off, $\sqrt{18} = 4.2$ (1 decimal place)

This method is called Newton's Method* for finding square root. The work involved can be summarized in a table.

Sir Isaac Newton, that is, not Mr. Newton, the author!

Example 2 Find $\sqrt{5}$ to 2 decimal places.

Solution

Follow the arrows, starting from a first approximation of 2.

Approximation	2	2.25	2.235
Division	$\frac{5}{2} = 2.5$	$\frac{5}{2.25} = 2.22$	$\frac{5}{2.235} = 2.237$
Average	$\frac{2 + 2.5}{2} = 2.25$	$\frac{2.25 + 2.22}{2} = 2.239$	
Next approximation	2.25	2.235	

Do you think this process will end in an exact answer?

From the last column, $2.235 < \sqrt{5} < 2.237$

$\therefore \sqrt{5} = 2.24$ (2 decimal places)

Exercise 11.1

Discussion

1. "Trap" each of the following square roots between 2 consecutive numbers.
   (*a*) $\sqrt{20}$ (*b*) $\sqrt{75}$ (*c*) $\sqrt{110}$ (*d*) $\sqrt{160}$ (*e*) $\sqrt{405}$

2. State a good first approximation to each square root.
   (*a*) $\sqrt{40}$ (*b*) $\sqrt{70}$ (*c*) $\sqrt{150}$ (*d*) $\sqrt{600}$ (*e*) $\sqrt{1000}$

3. Discuss the differences between numbers like $\sqrt{16}$, $\sqrt{49}$, and $\sqrt{100}$ and numbers like $\sqrt{5}$ and $\sqrt{18}$.

Written Solutions

4. Use estimation and multiplication to evaluate each of the following square roots, to 1 decimal place.
   (*a*) $\sqrt{22}$ (*c*) $\sqrt{8}$ (*e*) $\sqrt{78}$ (*g*) $\sqrt{350}$
   (*b*) $\sqrt{2}$ (*d*) $\sqrt{40}$ (*f*) $\sqrt{500}$ (*h*) $\sqrt{800}$

5. Evaluate to 2 decimal places, using Newton's Method. Make a table in each case.
   (*a*) $\sqrt{7}$ (*c*) $\sqrt{29}$ (*e*) $\sqrt{20}$ (*g*) $\sqrt{160}$
   (*b*) $\sqrt{13}$ (*d*) $\sqrt{33}$ (*f*) $\sqrt{68}$ (*h*) $\sqrt{300}$

6. Find the square root of each number, by Newton's Method.
   (*a*) 484 (*b*) 676 (*c*) 1024 (*d*) 2209

4(a) 4.7 (c) 2.8 (e) 8.8 (g) 18.7
5(a) 2.65 (c) 5.39 (e) 4.47 (g) 12.65
6(a) 22 (c) 32

11.2 Calculating Square Root — The Formal Method

The long division required in Newton's Method is time consuming, unless you have a calculator. Another method avoids this operation and may be done with pencil and paper only.

1. Copy and complete the following table. You may have to square some numbers to do this.

Range of n	1–9	10–99	100–999	1000–9999	10 000 –99 999	100 000 –999 999
Number of digits in n	1	2	3	4	5	6
Number of digits in $\sqrt{n}$	1	1				

2. State the number of digits in the square root of each of the following numbers.

   (*a*) 64 (*c*) 256 (*e*) 2304 (*g*) 22 500
   (*b*) 144 (*d*) 576 (*f*) 6400 (*h*) 202 500

B If the area of a square is 9, then the length of its side is 3.

1. State the length of the side of the squares having each of the following areas.

   (*a*) 49 (*b*) 144 (*c*) 400 (*d*) 900 (*e*) 1600

Example 1

Find the length of the side of a square whose area is 1024.

Solution

Let the required length be x.

Step 1

$\because 30^2 = 900$
and $40^2 = 1600$
$\therefore 30 < x < 40$

Thus we know that the answer is between 30 and 40. To find x, we need to find the width, w, of the L-shaped figure.

Step 2

Now the area of the L-shaped figure $= 1024 - 900$
$= 124$

Swing part of the figure down, as shown, to form a rectangle.

Step 3

$\therefore$ Width of rectangle $= \dfrac{\text{Area}}{\text{Length}}$
$\doteq \dfrac{124}{60}$
$\doteq 2$

$\therefore$ Length of rectangle $= 30 + 2 + 30$
$= 62$

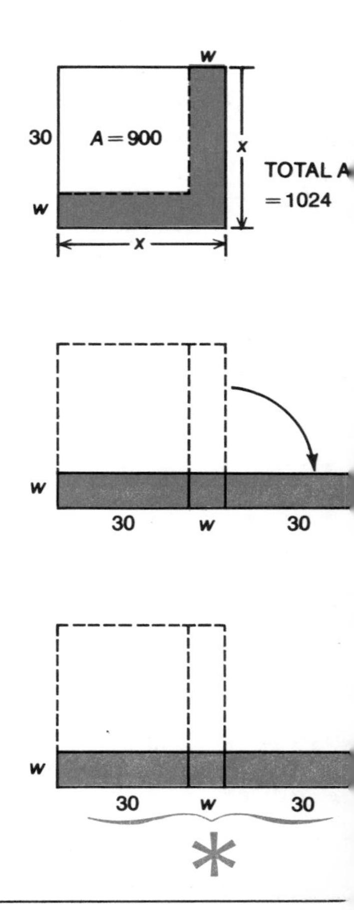

*

If $a = lw$, $\therefore w = \frac{a}{l}$, where 60 is an approximation of the length.

Check on area

Area of rectangle $= 62 \times 2$
$= 124$

Step 4 $\therefore x = 30 + 2$
$= 32$

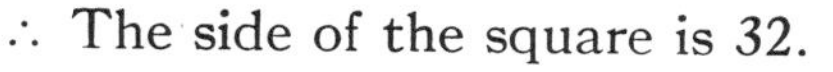

$\therefore$ The side of the square is 32.

2. Use the diagram method to find the sides of squares whose areas are (*a*) 441 and (*b*) 2809.

The diagrams take time to do so we'll shorten the work and write our solution as follows.

Example 2

Find $\sqrt{1024}$. (The same problem as Example 1.)

Solution

Step 1 "Pair off" the digits from the decimal point.

Step 2 Find the largest digit (3) which, when squared, is less than or equal to the first pair (10).

Step 3 Square this digit and put the result under the first pair. Then subtract, and bring down the next pair.

Step 4 To find a *trial divisor*, double the answer so far (3 ▤); and put this trial divisor (6 ▤) opposite the 124.

Step 5 Divide the trial divisor (6 ▤) into the 124. It goes 2 times. The *final* divisor is then 62 and the next digit in the answer is 2.

Step 6 Finally, multiply 2×62 and subtract the answer from 124.

Since the remainder is 0, we find that $\sqrt{1024} = 32$.

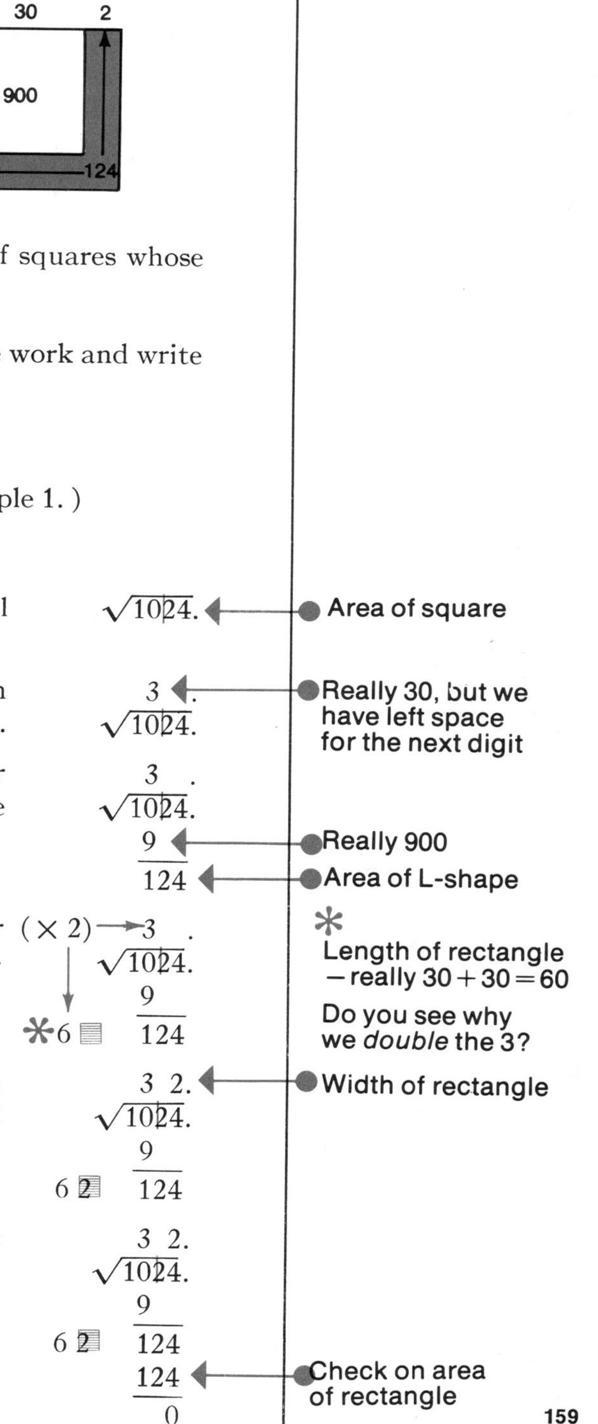

EXTRACTION OF THE SQUARE ROOT

The root of your first
period you
Must place in quote
if you work true:
Whose square from your
said period then
You must subtract;
and to th' remain
Another period being
brought,
You must divide as
here is taught,
By the double of your
quote, but see
Your unit's place you
do leave free;
Which place will be
supply'd by th' square
Of your next quoted
figure there:
Next multiply, subtract,
and then
Repeat your work unto
the end;
And if your number
be irrational
Add pairs of cyphers
for a decimal.

From Arithmetic
Both in the
Theory and Practice
by John Hill, Gent.
Edinburgh

(Courtesy of
Mr. P. Templin)

Example 3

Find $\sqrt{64\,009}$.

Solution

Step 1

```
    2     .
 √6|40|09|.
  | 4
  | 240
```

You may think this should be 6, but 46×6=276, which is greater than 240!

Step 2

```
(×2)←2  5     .
    ↓ √6|40|09|.
    4 5 | 4
        | 240
        | 225
        | 1509
```

Step 3

```
(×2)←2  5  3 .
     √6|40|09|.
  45  | 4
      | 240
      | 225
  503 | 1509
      | 1509
      |    0
```

$\therefore \sqrt{64\,009} = 253$

The solution in your notebook would look like this!

Exercise 11.2

Discussion

1. State the first digit of the answer.

   (*a*) $\sqrt{324}$ (*c*) $\sqrt{1849}$ (*e*) $\sqrt{15\,129}$

   (*b*) $\sqrt{841}$ (*d*) $\sqrt{7569}$ (*f*) $\sqrt{294\,849}$

"Pa... of...

2. What trial divisor would you use for the next step in each of the following questions?

(*a*)
```
   3   .
 √15|21|.
  | 9
  | 621
```

(*b*)
```
     2  3   .
   √5|47|56|.
     | 4
  43 | 147
     | 129
     | 1856
```

(*c*)
```
     3  6    .
   √13|03|21|.
     | 9
  66 | 403
     | 396
     | 721
```

Double, double, toil and trouble

3. What is the next digit in the answer in each case?

(*a*)
```
     7   .
   √54|76|.
     | 49
 14▒ | 576
```

(*b*)
```
     3   .
   √14|44|.
     | 9
  6▒ | 544
```

(*c*)
```
     2     .
   √6|60|49|.
     | 4
  4▒ | 260
```

4. Why do you "pair off" the digits when you find a square root?

Written Solutions

5. Find the square root of the following numbers.
   (*a*) 529 (*c*) 2704 (*e*) 961
   (*b*) 1156 (*d*) 5041 (*f*) 7225

6. Evaluate.
   (*a*) $\sqrt{6084}$ (*c*) $\sqrt{1444}$ (*e*) $\sqrt{841}$
   (*b*) $\sqrt{3481}$ (*d*) $\sqrt{2209}$ (*f*) $\sqrt{7744}$

7. Determine each square root.
   (*a*) $\sqrt{15\,129}$ (*c*) $\sqrt{209\,764}$ (*e*) $\sqrt{83\,521}$
   (*b*) $\sqrt{46\,656}$ (*d*) $\sqrt{277\,729}$ (*f*) $\sqrt{585\,225}$

8. An outdoor swimming pool measures 60 m by 25 m (see diagram). Sally swims around the edge of the pool from A until she returns to A. Sam swims the route A to C to D to B. Who swims farther and by how much?

9. A rectangular table is 135 cm long and 72 cm wide. Find the length of a diagonal cross brace necessary to support the table top.

10. Write a computer program for finding the square root of a number using Newton's Method.

5(a) 23 (c) 52 (e) 31
6(a) 78 (c) 38 (e) 29
7(a) 123 (c) 458 (e) 289
8. Sally, by 15 m
9. 153 cm

Don't leave this space when finding the square root!

8.

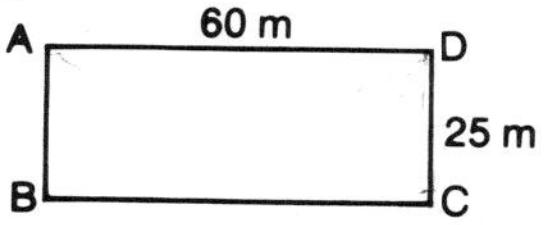

9.

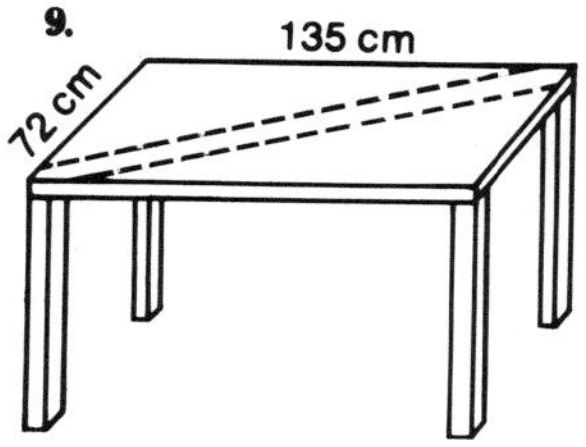

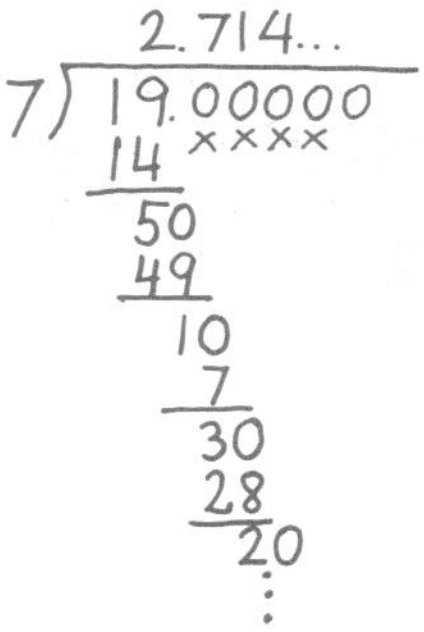

11.3 Calculating Approximate Square Roots — The Formal Method

Up to this point, you have been using the Formal Method to find the square roots of perfect squares. The zero remainder at the end of each question served to check that the answer was exact. In a practical situation, you are far more likely to meet the square root of a number that is *not* a perfect square. When this happens, you handle the question in a way very similar to *inexact division*; you keep going until you have the required number of digits to the right of the decimal point.

```
     2.714...
7 ) 19.00000
    14
     50
     49
      10
       7
      30
      28
       20
        ⋮
```

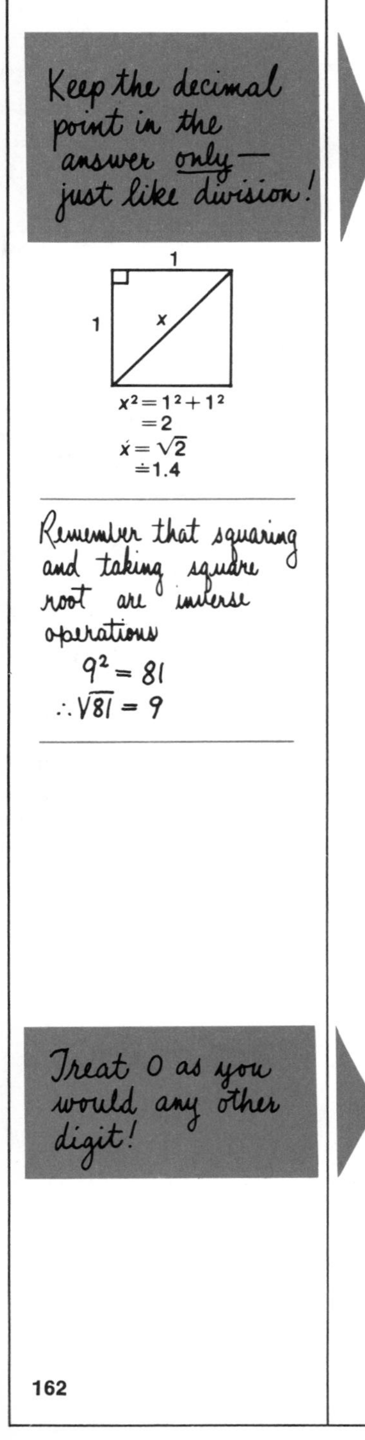

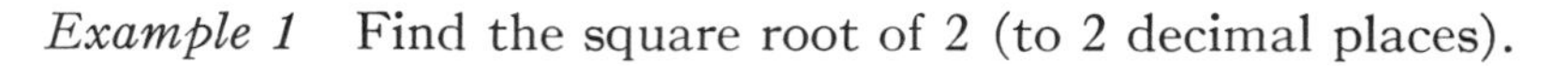

Example 1 Find the square root of 2 (to 2 decimal places).

Solution

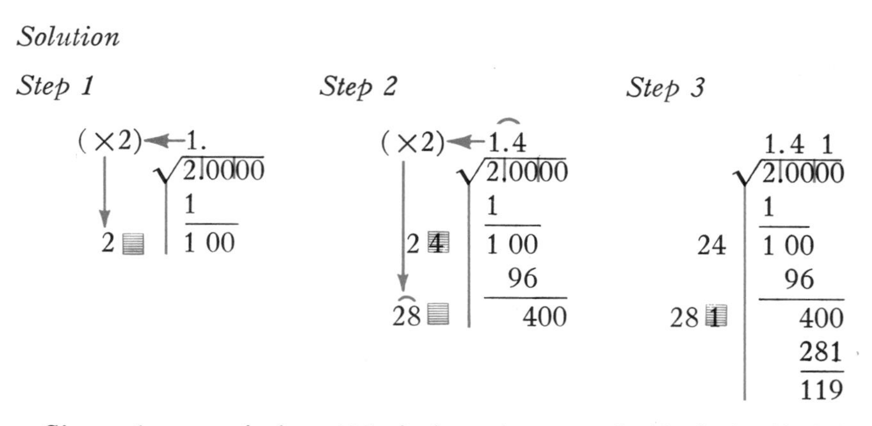

Since the remainder, 119, is less than one-half of the "trial divisor", 281, the next digit in the answer would be less than 5.

$\therefore \sqrt{2} = 1.41$ (to 2 decimal places)

You *could* calculate 1.41×1.41 to check your work. The answer, 1.9881, indicates that 1.41 is an approximate value of $\sqrt{2}$. Finding more digits to the right of the decimal point will increase your accuracy. To 3 decimal places, $\sqrt{2} = 1.414$ and $1.414^2 = 1.999\,396$.

1. Find $\sqrt{3}$ and $\sqrt{5}$ (to 2 decimal places).

Take care when a 0 appears in the answer of a square root question. A similar problem occurs in division.

1. Divide 11 368 by 56.

Example 2 Find $\sqrt{116.68}$, to 1 decimal place.

Solution

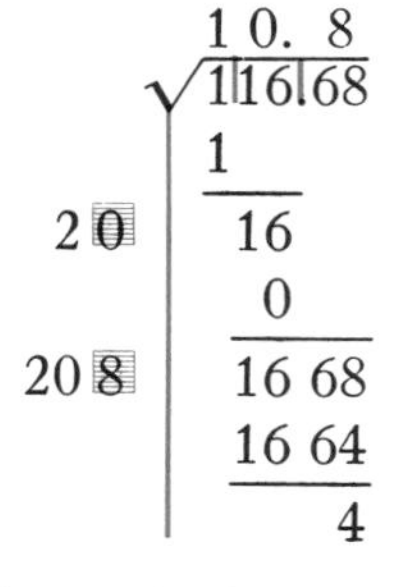

$\therefore \sqrt{116.68} = 10.8$ (to 1 decimal place)

Exercise 11.3

Discussion

1. Does the table of square roots on page 371 give exact or approximate values?

2. In a practical problem, how would you know how many decimal places to include in your answer?

3. $\sqrt{3} = 1.7$ (to 1 decimal place) and $1.7^2 = 2.89$
   $\sqrt{3} = 1.73$ (to 2 decimal places) and $1.73^2 = 2.9929$
   $\sqrt{3} = 1.732$ (to 3 decimal places) and $1.732^2 = 2.999\ 824$
   ⋮
   (*a*) Will this process ever end?
   (*b*) Is the approximation you use for $\sqrt{3}$ ever larger than $\sqrt{3}$? *Careful here!*
   (*c*) Here's a toughie! Is $\sqrt{3}$ a rational number? *

4. State the next digit in the answer in each of the following questions.

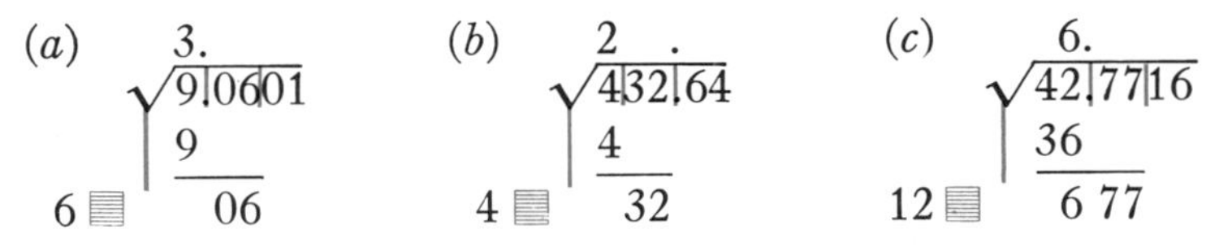

(a) 3.
9.06 01
9
6 ▒ 06
(b) 2 .
4 32.64
4
4 ▒ 32
(c) 6.
42.77 16
36
12 ▒ 6 77

Written Solutions

5. Calculate each of the following square roots to 1 decimal place.

(*a*) $\sqrt{5}$	(*c*) $\sqrt{28}$	(*e*) $\sqrt{342}$
(*b*) $\sqrt{8}$	(*d*) $\sqrt{75}$	(*f*) $\sqrt{854}$

6. Find the square root (to 2 decimal places) of each of the following numbers.

(*a*) 105	(*c*) 50	(*e*) 4.05
(*b*) 16.24	(*d*) 82.65	(*f*) 36.01

7. Calculate the square root of each number, correct to 1 decimal place.

(*a*) 42 682	(*c*) 1.68	(*e*) 239 416
(*b*) 3541.4	(*d*) 283.72	(*f*) 8397

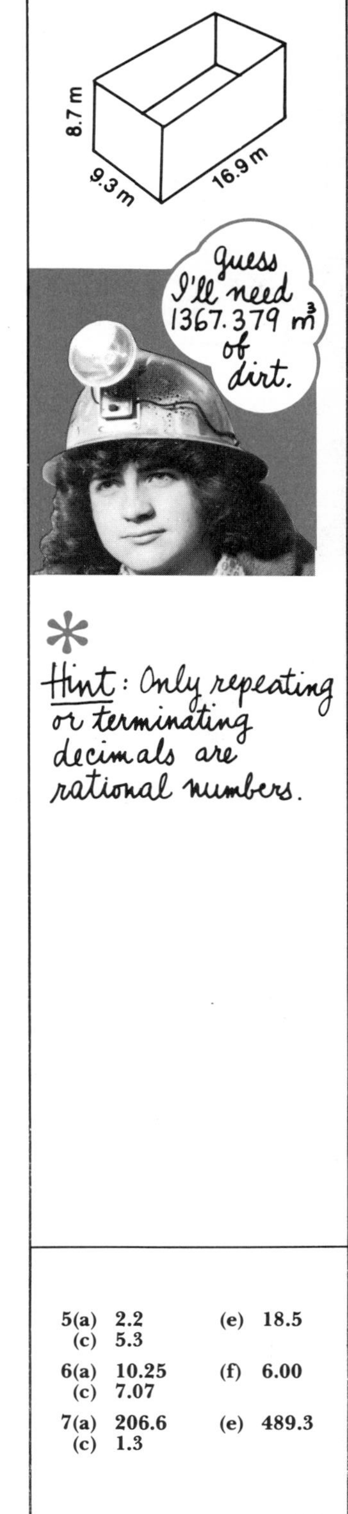

*
Hint: Only repeating or terminating decimals are rational numbers.

5(a) 2.2 (e) 18.5
(c) 5.3
6(a) 10.25 (f) 6.00
(c) 7.07
7(a) 206.6 (e) 489.3
(c) 1.3

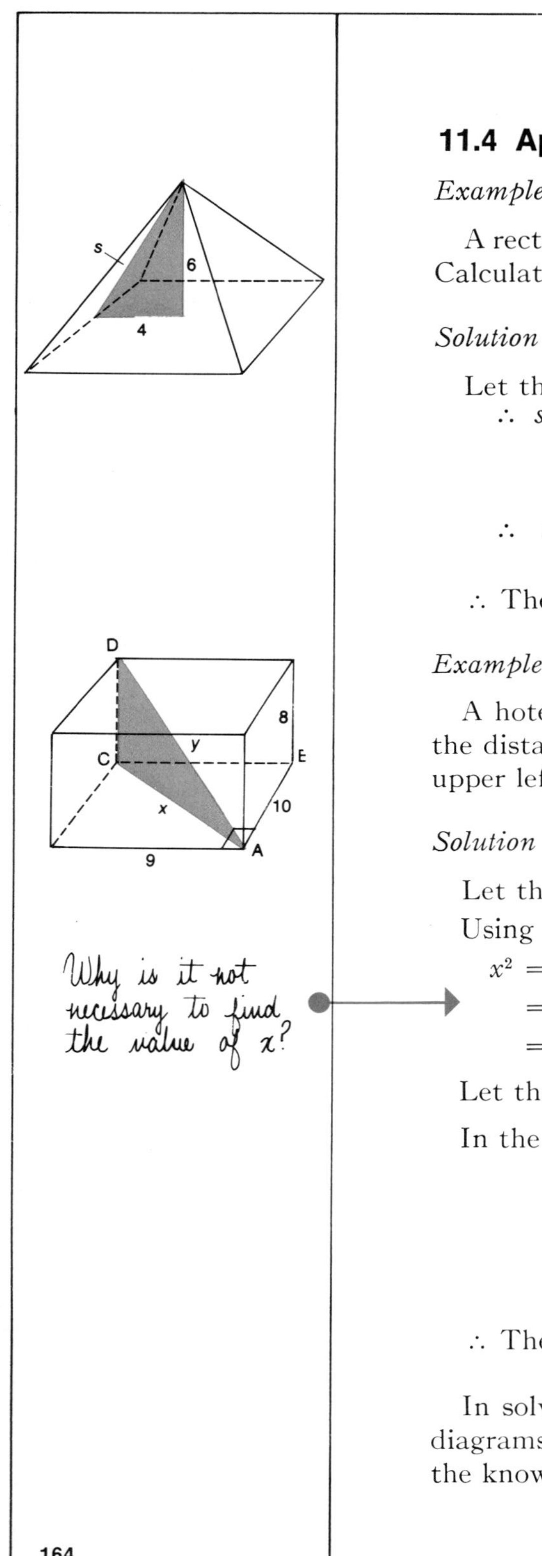

11.4 Applications of Square Root

Example 1

A rectangular pyramid 6 m high has a square base 8 m by 8 m. Calculate the slant height of the pyramid.

Solution

Let the slant height be s metres.

$$\begin{aligned} \therefore\ s^2 &= 6^2 + 4^2 \\ &= 36 + 16 \\ &= 52 \\ \therefore\ s &= \sqrt{52} \\ &\doteq 7.2 \end{aligned}$$

$\therefore$ The slant height is 7.2 m.

Example 2

A hotel foyer is 8 m high and measures 10 m by 9 m. Find the distance from a lower right-hand corner of the foyer to the upper left-hand corner at the other end of the foyer.

Solution

Let the diagonal AC (across the floor) be x metres.

Using $\triangle$ABC on the floor,

$$\begin{aligned} x^2 &= 9^2 + 10^2 \\ &= 81 + 100 \\ &= 181 \end{aligned}$$

Let the diagonal AD by y metres.

In the shaded triangle,
$$\begin{aligned} y^2 &= x^2 + 8^2 \\ &= 181 + 64 \\ &= 245 \\ \therefore\ y &= \sqrt{245} \\ &\doteq 15.6 \end{aligned}$$

$\therefore$ The required distance is 15.6 m.

In solving problems like these, it is important to draw neat diagrams that are fairly large and clear. Mark on the diagram the known dimensions and the unknown ones you want to find.

Exercise 11.4

Discussion

1. State the equation involving the sides of each of the following triangles.

   (*a*)

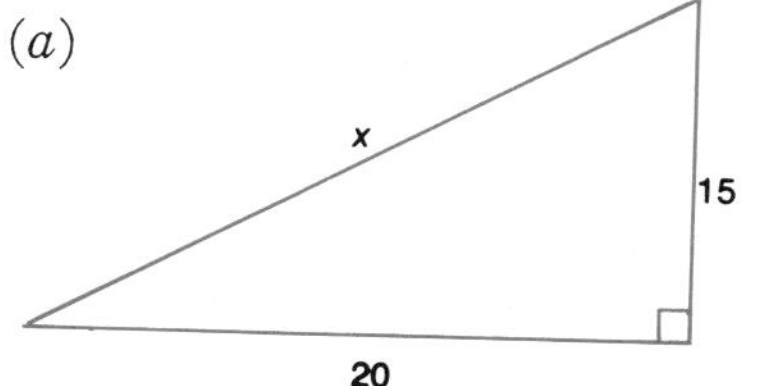

   (*b*)

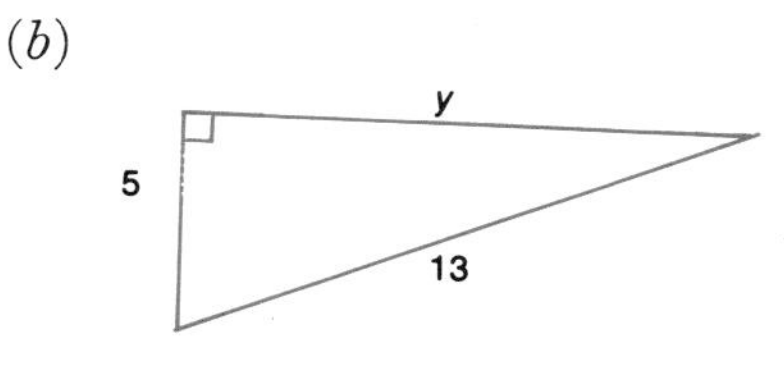

2. State the area.

   (*a*) (*b*)

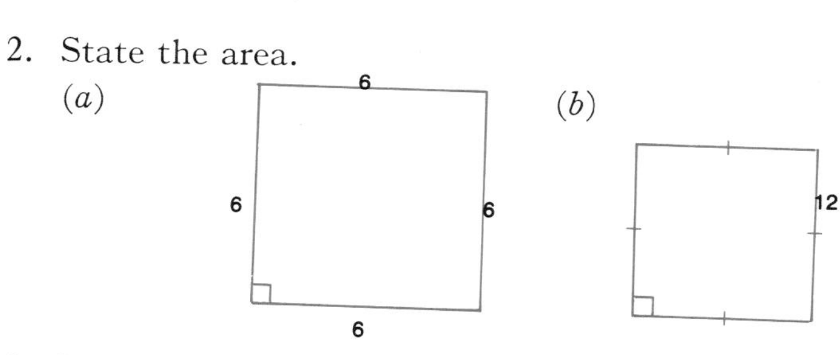

3. How long is the side of a square whose area is

   (*a*) 16 cm^2? (*b*) 100 mm^2? (*c*) 45 m^2?

   State the perimeter of the squares in (*a*) and (*b*).

Written Solutions

4. A farm gate 4 m wide is 2 m high. Find the length of a diagonal brace used to support the gate (nearest centimetre).

5. Mr. Dryweather has a rectangular back yard that measures 15 m by 25 m. Where should he put posts to support a clothes line to obtain the longest possible line? Find how long this line would be. (Answer to the nearest metre.)

6. A 14 m ladder is placed on level ground with its foot 3 m from a vertical wall. How far up the wall will it reach (to the nearest 0.1 m)?

7. The area of a square is 890 cm^2. Find the perimeter of the square, to the nearest centimetre.

8. Find the dimensions (nearest 0.1 cm) of the largest square box that will fit in a circular pipe of inside diameter 24 cm.

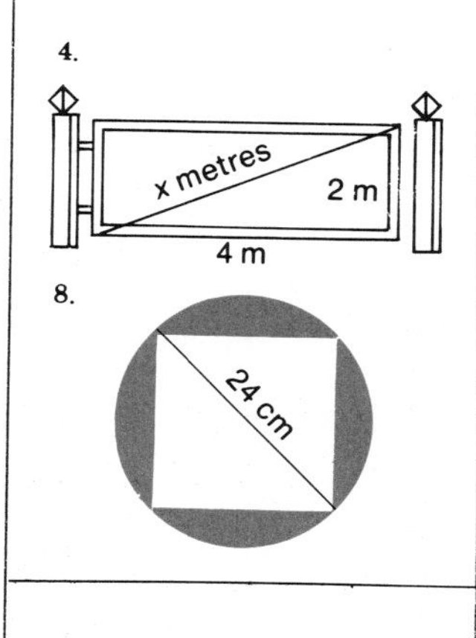

4. **447 cm**
5. **29 m**
6. **13.7 m**
7. **119 cm**
8. **17.0 cm by 17.0 cm**

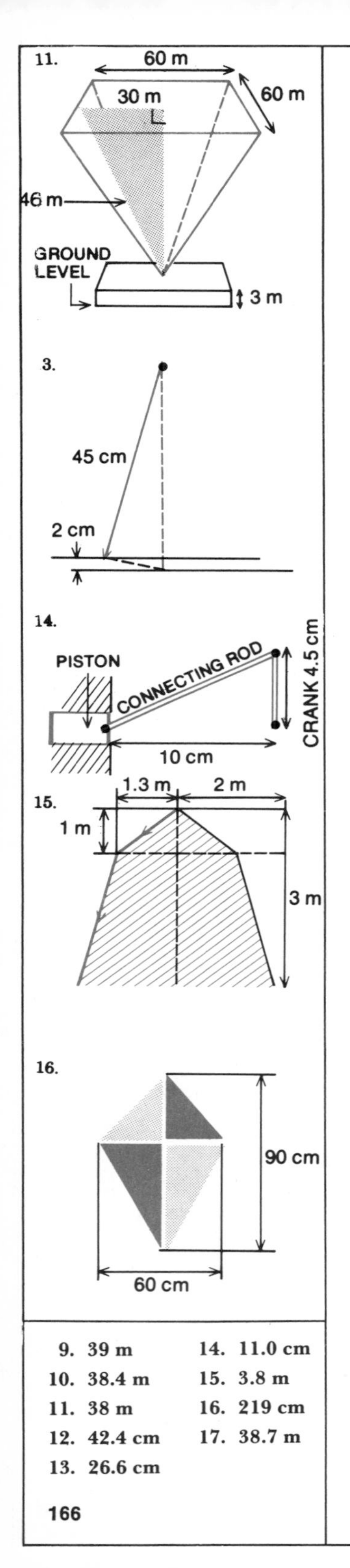

9. James Tiredman cuts diagonally across a lot 50 m by 110 m instead of walking down one side and across the end. How much shorter, to the nearest metre, is his short cut?

10. An ocean freighter is unloaded by an overhead crane that dumps the cargo of grain on a platform on the dock. The grain falls into a cone-shaped pile 16 m high, whose slant height is 25 m. How wide (to the nearest 0.1 m) must the platform be to hold the grain?

11. The "Katimavik" part of the Canadian Pavilion at Expo '67 in Montreal was an inverted rectangular pyramid. Using the dimensions shown, find the height of the observation level above the ground, to the nearest metre.

12. A Christmas cake is 30 cm square. What is the diameter of the smallest round cake tin that will hold the cake?

13. The pendulum of a grandfather clock is 45 cm long. It swings so that its end is 2 cm above the lowest level of the swing. What is the minimum inside width, to the nearest 0.1 cm, of the cabinet containing the pendulum if the pendulum is to avoid hitting the sides of the cabinet?

14. A crank and piston assembly is in the position shown in the diagram. Find, to one decimal place, the length of the connecting rod.

15. Kathryn Kamper is awakened from a sound sleep in a tent by a squirrel running from the peak of the tent to the ground. Using the sketch, find the shortest distance travelled by the squirrel in reaching the ground (to the nearest 0.1 m)..

16. The shorter strut of a kite is 60 cm long and is fastened at right angles to the 90 cm strut at a point one-third of the way along it. Find the perimeter of the kite (to the nearest centimetre).

17. A baseball diamond is a square measuring 27.4 m by 27.4 m. Find the distance the catcher throws from home plate in order to cut off a runner who is trying to steal second base.

9. 39 m
10. 38.4 m
11. 38 m
12. 42.4 cm
13. 26.6 cm
14. 11.0 cm
15. 3.8 m
16. 219 cm
17. 38.7 m

More Fun with Topology

The old city of Koenigsberg was built along a river and on two islands. The river was crossed by seven bridges. The story is told that a prize was offered to anyone who could cross each of the bridges but cross each bridge only once. Sketch the bridges and try to decide if anyone collected the prize.

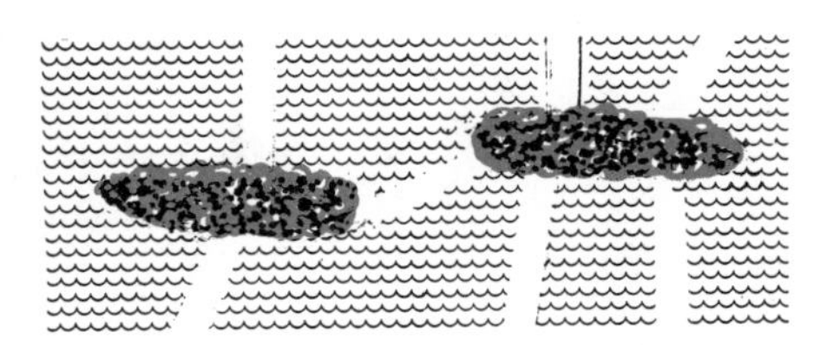

A mathematician named Leonard Euler worked out an answer to the problem. Instead of walking through the city, Euler did what mathematicians usually do—he made a diagram. The paths you would walk he called *arcs* and the points where the arcs cross, *vertices*. The whole diagram is a *network*.

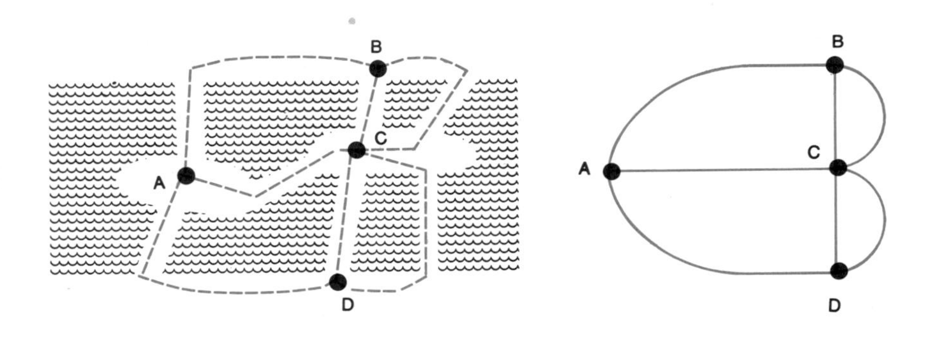

By studying this network and others, Euler noticed that the number of arcs to some vertices was *odd*, and the number of arcs to some vertices was *even*. Euler was able to make some statements about networks based on whether the vertices were even or odd.

Check the network for the Koenigsberg bridges. Are the vertices odd or even? Suppose one bridge was washed away in a flood. Draw a network. Could you win the prize for the Koenigsberg walk now?

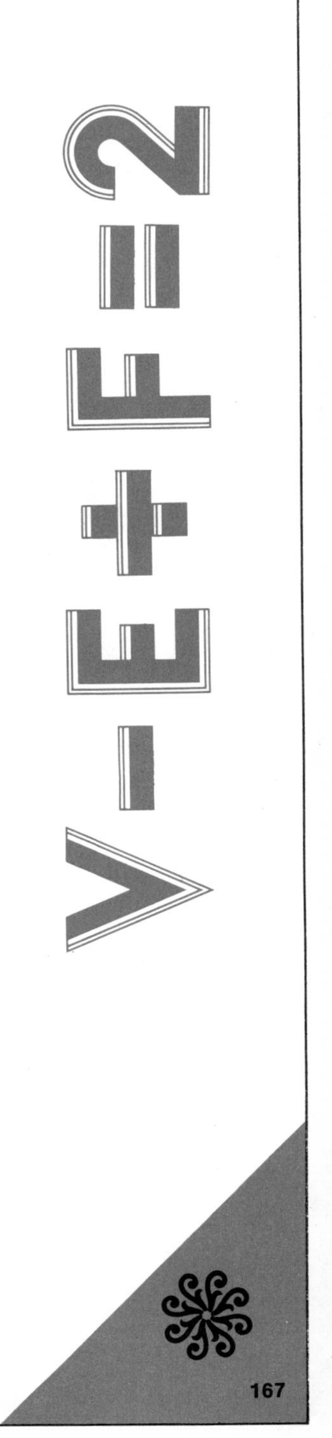

Unit 12

Operations With Polynomials

In arithmetic you study how to add, subtract, multiply, divide, and take square root. These are operations with *numbers.*

The next 5 units deal with how you add, subtract, multiply, and divide variable expressions like $x + y$, $3a - 4b + c$, and $7a^2$. These are operations with *polynomials.*

$$\begin{array}{r} 5 \\ \underline{2} \\ 7 \end{array} \qquad \begin{array}{r} 5a \\ \underline{2a} \\ ? \end{array}$$

12.1 Adding and Subtracting Terms

Recall that $4a$ means $4 \times a$ or the sum $a + a + a + a$. Similarly, $x + x + x$ can be written as the product $3x$.

1. Express as a sum.
   (*a*) $5x$ (*b*) $2x$

2. Express as a product.
   (*a*) $a + a + a + a + a$ (*b*) $a + a$

Thus $5x + 2x = (x + x + x + x + x) + (x + x)$
$= x + x + x + x + x + x + x$ ← Count the x's!
$= 7x$

or $5x + 2x = (5 + 2)x$
$= 7x$

3. Complete the following.

(*a*) $4a + 3a = (\square + \square)a = \square$

(*b*) $6b + 5b = (\square + \square)b = \square$

(*c*) $-2x + 3x = (\square + \square)x = \square$

4. Find the sum where possible.

(*a*) $4a + 6a$

(*b*) $7xy + (-5)xy$

(*c*) $-2b + 5b$

(*d*) $3a + 5b$

(*e*) $-2y^2 + 5y^2$

(*f*) $5y^2 + 3y$

Why can we not find the sum in (d) and (f)?

B Subtraction is performed in a similar way.

Addition! $5x + 8x = (5 + 8)x = 13x$

Subtraction! $5x - 8x = (5 - 8)x = -3x$

1. Subtract.

(*a*) $12a - 7a$

(*b*) $4x - 6x$

(*c*) $-5a^2 - 2a^2$

(*d*) $3xy - xy$

(*e*) $6s^3 - 4s^3$

(*f*) $5xy^2 - 7xy^2$

C $3x$, $5x^2$, $-7xyz$ are all called *terms*. $3x$ is a term in x and 3 is the *coefficient*. $-7xyz$ is a term in xyz and the coefficient is -7.

A "term" results from multiplying numbers and variables.

A "coefficient" is the number part of a term.

1. Describe $5x^2$ in the same way.

2. Describe $-4xy$, $5a^3$, $15ab^2$.

3. Terms that have identical variable parts are *like* terms. $3x$ and $5x$ are like terms. $4x^2$ and $7x$ are not like terms.

4. Select two pairs of like terms from $-2xy$, $5y^2$, $5xy$, $-y^2$.

Exercise 12.1

Discussion

Careful in (c)!

1. Add where possible.

(*a*) $\begin{array}{r} 5x \\ 7x \\ \hline \end{array}$ (*b*) $\begin{array}{r} -2x \\ 4x \\ \hline \end{array}$ (*c*) $\begin{array}{r} -3a \\ -5a^2 \\ \hline \end{array}$ (*d*) $\begin{array}{r} 6ab \\ -4ab \\ \hline \end{array}$

Remember to add the opposite!

2. Subtract where possible.

(*a*) $\begin{array}{r} 12b \\ 5b \\ \hline \end{array}$ (*b*) $\begin{array}{r} 3m \\ 7m \\ \hline \end{array}$ (*c*) $\begin{array}{r} -4xy \\ -6xy \\ \hline \end{array}$ (*d*) $\begin{array}{r} -3a \\ 5ab \\ \hline \end{array}$

3. Simplify where possible.

(*a*) $3a + (-5a)$

(*b*) $7x - 9x$

(*c*) $3a^2 + 4a$

(*d*) $-3ab - 5ab$

(*e*) $2x^2 - x^2$

(*f*) $-3ab^2 + 5ab^2$

4. State the coefficient of each term.

$a, \quad -2a^2, \quad 5b, \quad 6ab, \quad -y$

5. What kind of terms can be added or subtracted to form a single term?

Written Solutions

6. Simplify.

(*a*) $3a + 5a$

(*b*) $4x - 3x$

(*c*) $2a - 5a$

(*d*) $3x + 8x$

(*e*) $-3ab + 7ab$

(*f*) $4x + 5x - 2x$

7. Simplify.

(*a*) $2x^2 + 4x^2$

(*b*) $5xy - 6xy$

(*c*) $-3a^2 - 2a^2$

(*d*) $3a^3 + 4a^3$

(*e*) $x^5 + 3x^5$

(*f*) $2x^2y - 3x^2y$

8. Copy and add.

(*a*)	(*b*)	(*c*)	(*d*)
$3x$	$3a$	$-b$	$4x^2$
$2x$	$5a$	$8b$	$-3x^2$
$7x$	$7a$	$-6b$	$-7x^2$

9. The value of 2 quarters is (25×2)¢

(*a*) State the value of x quarters.

(*b*) State the value of x dimes.

(*c*) Find the total value of the x dimes and x quarters.

(*d*) Check your answer using 7 dimes and 7 quarters.

10. Find the perimeter of the figure in the diagram.

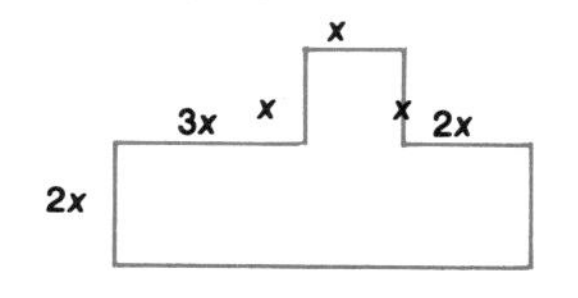

11. Find the total distance around the figure shown.

9(a) $25x$¢ (c) $35x$¢

10. $18x$

11. $9x + 4y$

12.2 Adding and Subtracting Polynomials

Can any of these terms be combined?

A Because x^2, $2x$, 1 are unlike terms, we represent their sum by $x^2 + 2x + 1$. $x^2 + 2x + 1$ is called a *polynomial* in x. Other examples of polynomials in x are $3x^2 - 4$ and $x^5 + 3x - 1$. There are *three* terms in $x^2 + 2x + 1$ and it is called a *trinomial*. $3x^2 - 4$ is a *binomial*, since it contains *two* terms.

In a polynomial the terms are separated by + and − signs only.

1. Make up
   (*a*) a trinomial in a,
   (*b*) a binomial in m.

$5a \times b$ is the single term $5ab$, but $5a+b$ contains 2 terms, $5a$ and b.

A polynomial, such as $4x^3$, that is just a single term is called a *monomial*.

2. Make separate lists of the (*a*) monomials, (*b*) binomials, and (*c*) trinomials from the following.

$x^2 - y^2$	$a + b - c$	5
$-3x^5$	$3x - 2yz$	$3x^4 - 2x^2 + 1$

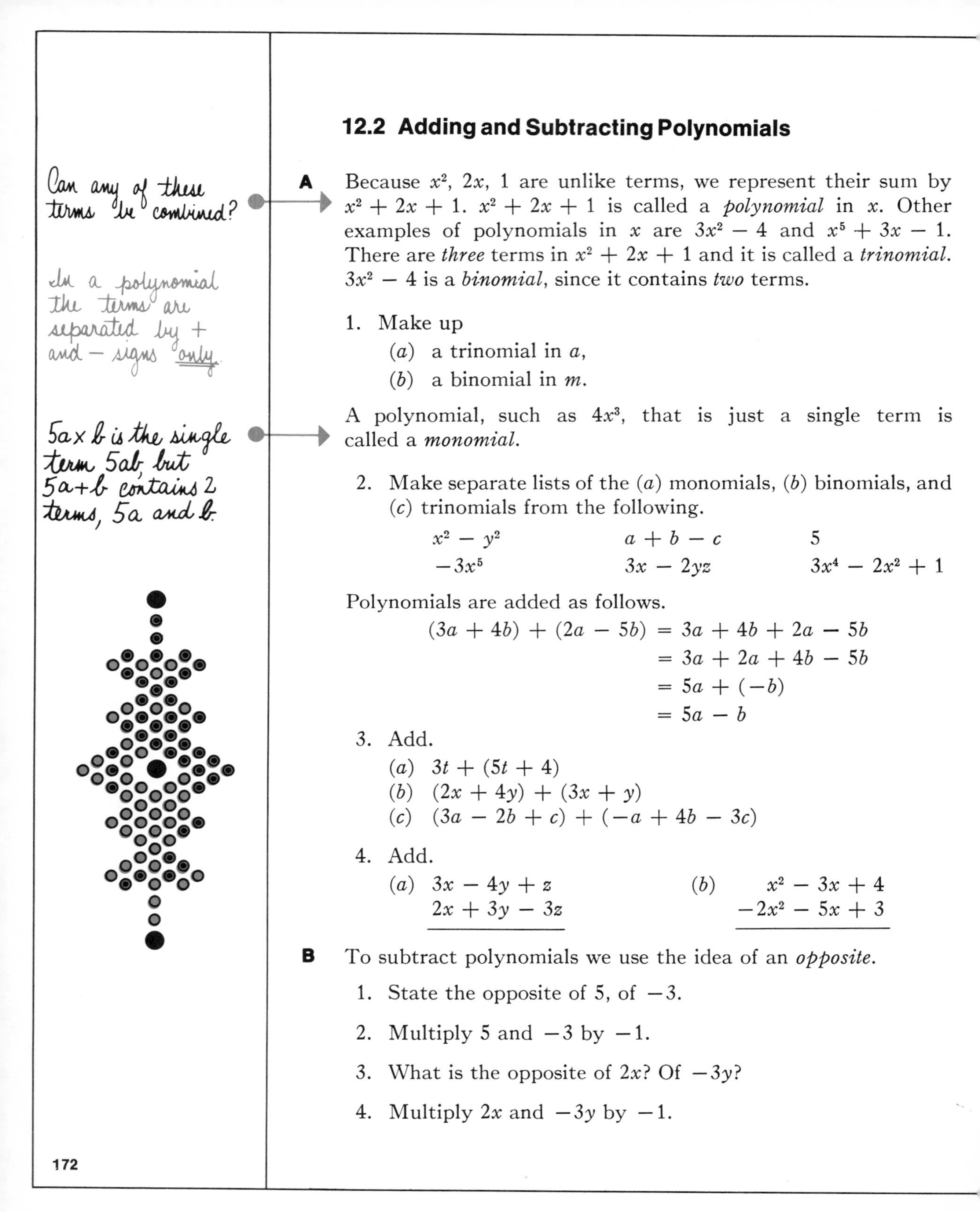

Polynomials are added as follows.

$$\begin{aligned}(3a + 4b) + (2a - 5b) &= 3a + 4b + 2a - 5b \\ &= 3a + 2a + 4b - 5b \\ &= 5a + (-b) \\ &= 5a - b\end{aligned}$$

3. Add.
   (*a*) $3t + (5t + 4)$
   (*b*) $(2x + 4y) + (3x + y)$
   (*c*) $(3a - 2b + c) + (-a + 4b - 3c)$

4. Add.
   (*a*) $\begin{array}{r} 3x - 4y + z \\ 2x + 3y - 3z \\ \hline \end{array}$
   (*b*) $\begin{array}{r} x^2 - 3x + 4 \\ -2x^2 - 5x + 3 \\ \hline \end{array}$

B To subtract polynomials we use the idea of an *opposite*.

1. State the opposite of 5, of -3.
2. Multiply 5 and -3 by -1.
3. What is the opposite of $2x$? Of $-3y$?
4. Multiply $2x$ and $-3y$ by -1.

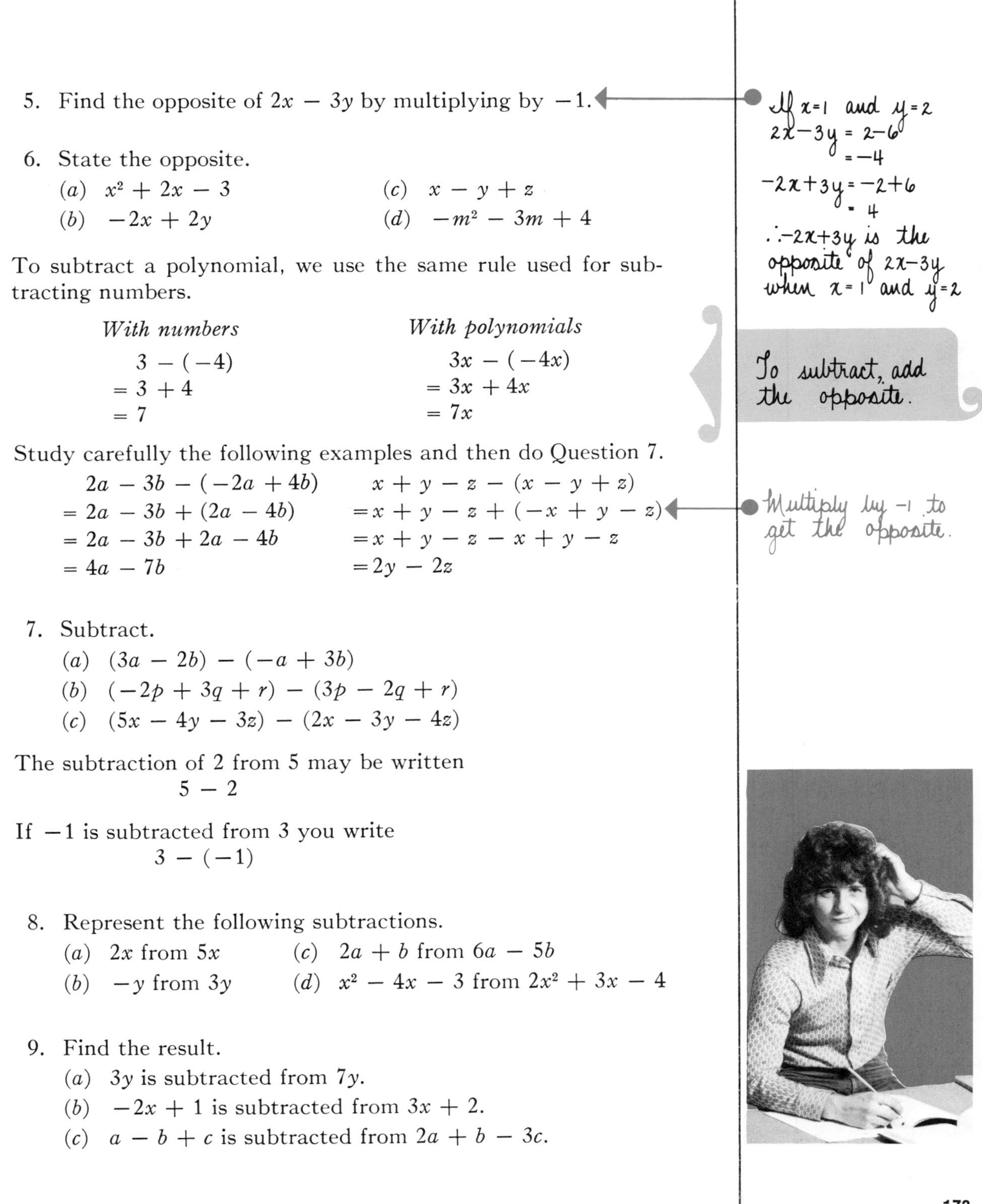

5. Find the opposite of $2x - 3y$ by multiplying by -1.

If $x = 1$ and $y = 2$
$2x - 3y = 2 - 6$
$= -4$
$-2x + 3y = -2 + 6$
$= 4$
$\therefore -2x + 3y$ is the opposite of $2x - 3y$ when $x = 1$ and $y = 2$

6. State the opposite.
   (a) $x^2 + 2x - 3$
   (b) $-2x + 2y$
   (c) $x - y + z$
   (d) $-m^2 - 3m + 4$

To subtract a polynomial, we use the same rule used for subtracting numbers.

With numbers

$$3 - (-4)$$
$$= 3 + 4$$
$$= 7$$

With polynomials

$$3x - (-4x)$$
$$= 3x + 4x$$
$$= 7x$$

To subtract, add the opposite.

Study carefully the following examples and then do Question 7.

$$2a - 3b - (-2a + 4b)$$
$$= 2a - 3b + (2a - 4b)$$
$$= 2a - 3b + 2a - 4b$$
$$= 4a - 7b$$

$$x + y - z - (x - y + z)$$
$$= x + y - z + (-x + y - z)$$
$$= x + y - z - x + y - z$$
$$= 2y - 2z$$

Multiply by -1 to get the opposite.

7. Subtract.
   (a) $(3a - 2b) - (-a + 3b)$
   (b) $(-2p + 3q + r) - (3p - 2q + r)$
   (c) $(5x - 4y - 3z) - (2x - 3y - 4z)$

The subtraction of 2 from 5 may be written

$$5 - 2$$

If -1 is subtracted from 3 you write

$$3 - (-1)$$

8. Represent the following subtractions.
   (a) $2x$ from $5x$
   (b) $-y$ from $3y$
   (c) $2a + b$ from $6a - 5b$
   (d) $x^2 - 4x - 3$ from $2x^2 + 3x - 4$

9. Find the result.
   (a) $3y$ is subtracted from $7y$.
   (b) $-2x + 1$ is subtracted from $3x + 2$.
   (c) $a - b + c$ is subtracted from $2a + b - 3c$.

They look pretty easy to me!

9(a) $3x+4y$
(c) $3x^2-x$

Exercise 12.2

Discussion

1. In the following list of polynomials name
   (*a*) the monomials, (*b*) the binomials, (*c*) the trinomials.
   $3x^2+2$, $5x^7$, $7a-6b-5c$, $x+y$, -1, p^2-q^2, $-4x^5$, $2x^2-5x+4$

2. Add.

$$\begin{array}{r} 3x+5y \\ -2x+6y \\ \hline \end{array} \qquad \begin{array}{r} 2x^2-5x-3 \\ 4x^2-x+4 \\ \hline \end{array} \qquad \begin{array}{r} -3a+2b \\ -a-3b \\ \hline \end{array}$$

3. Subtract.

$$\begin{array}{r} 4a+3b+2c \\ a+4b-3c \\ \hline \end{array} \qquad \begin{array}{r} 2a^2-b \\ -3a-2b \\ \hline \end{array} \qquad \begin{array}{l} 3m-4n \\ 4m+n \\ \hline \end{array}$$

4. Simplify where possible.
   (*a*) x^2+2x+1
   (*b*) $3x^4+x^2-x^4$
   (*c*) $2xy+3x^2y$
   (*d*) $3a^2-a^2$
   (*e*) $3x^2-x^3$
   (*f*) $4m^2-2m^2+3m$

5. Change the following subtractions to additions.
   (*a*) $3x-(-5x)$
   (*b*) $5q-(3q-2)$
   (*c*) $(4a+3b)-(-2a+3b)$
   (*d*) $(6s-3t)-(4s+5t)$

6. Simplify.
   (*a*) $-1(x-y+z)$
   (*b*) $-1(-x^2+2x-4)$

7. State the opposite.
   (*a*) $x-y+z$
   (*b*) $-x^2+2x-4$

8. Compare your answers to Questions 6 and 7. What do you notice? Can you use this result in subtracting polynomials?

Written Solutions

9. Simplify
   (*a*) $x+2x+y+3y$
   (*b*) $3a-a+5b-6b$
   (*c*) $x^2+3x^2-x^2+3x-4x$

10. Simplify.

(*a*) $x + (2x + 4)$ (*d*) $(3p + 5) + 2p$
(*b*) $3a + (-2a + 1)$ (*e*) $(-2y + z) + 5y$
(*c*) $(3x - 5) + 2$ (*f*) $-2a + (1 - 5a)$

11. Simplify.

(*a*) $(x + 2) + (x - 4)$ (*c*) $(x - y) + (-2x + 5y)$
(*b*) $(3a - b) + (b - 2a)$ (*d*) $(p + 2q) + (3p - 5q)$

12. Simplify.

(*a*) $(2x + 7) - 4$ (*d*) $(2k - 1) - 4k$
(*b*) $(3a - 2) - 2a$ (*e*) $(3 - 4t) + t - 5$
(*c*) $(3p - 4) - 5$ (*f*) $3 - (4p + 2)$

13. Simplify.

(*a*) $2t - (1 + 2t)$ (*d*) $-2m - (1 + 5m)$
(*b*) $5x - (2x - 4)$ (*e*) $4 - (5 - 2t) + t$
(*c*) $3y - (-2y + 5)$ (*f*) $(x + y) - (x - y)$

14. Simplify.

(*a*) $(2a + b) - (a + b)$
(*b*) $(2p - 3r) - (p - 2r)$
(*c*) $(x^2 - 2x) - (3x^2 + x)$
(*d*) $x^2 + 5x - 4 - (3x^2 - 10x + 3)$
(*e*) $(-3a + 6b - c) - (2a - 3b - 4c)$
(*f*) $(2m + 4n - k) - (-m - 2n + 3k) + (-5m - 2n - k)$

15. Simplify.

(*a*) $(2x + 4y) + (3x - 2y)$ (*d*) $3a + (2a - 5) - 4a$
(*b*) $1 - (2t - 3) - 3t$ (*e*) $(2x^2 - y^2) - (3x^2 + 5y^2)$
(*c*) $(-3x + 5) - (2 - 4x)$ (*f*) $4b - (3c - 5) + 2b$

16. Write the following groups of polynomials one under the other and add.

(*a*) $2a + 5b - 4c, \quad -3a + 2b - c, \quad 2a - c$
(*b*) $2x^2 + 5x, \quad -x + 4, \quad -3x^2 + 5$
(*c*) $p - q + r, \quad -5q + p - 2r, \quad -r + 3q + 2p$

17. Represent using brackets and simplify.

(*a*) The sum of $4a - 3b$, $7a + 5b$, $-2a + b$.
(*b*) The difference when $3x - 5y$ is subtracted from $-2x + y$.
(*c*) $2x - 3$ subtracted from the sum of $5x + 4$ and $-3x + 2$.

10(a) $3x + 4$ **(e)** $3y + y$
(c) $3x - 3$

11(a) $2x - 2$ **(c)** $-x + 4y$

12(a) $2x + 3$ **(e)** $-3t - 2$
(c) $3p - 9$

13(a) -1 **(e)** $3t - 1$
(c) $5y - 5$

14(a) a
(c) $-2x^2 - 3x$
(e) $-5a + 9b + 3c$

15(a) $5x + 2y$ **(e)** $-x^2 - 6y^2$
(c) $x + 3$

16(a) $a + 7b - 6c$
(b) $-x^2 + 4x + 9$
(c) $4p - 3q - 2r$

17(a) $9a + 3b$
(b) $-5x + 6y$
(c) 9

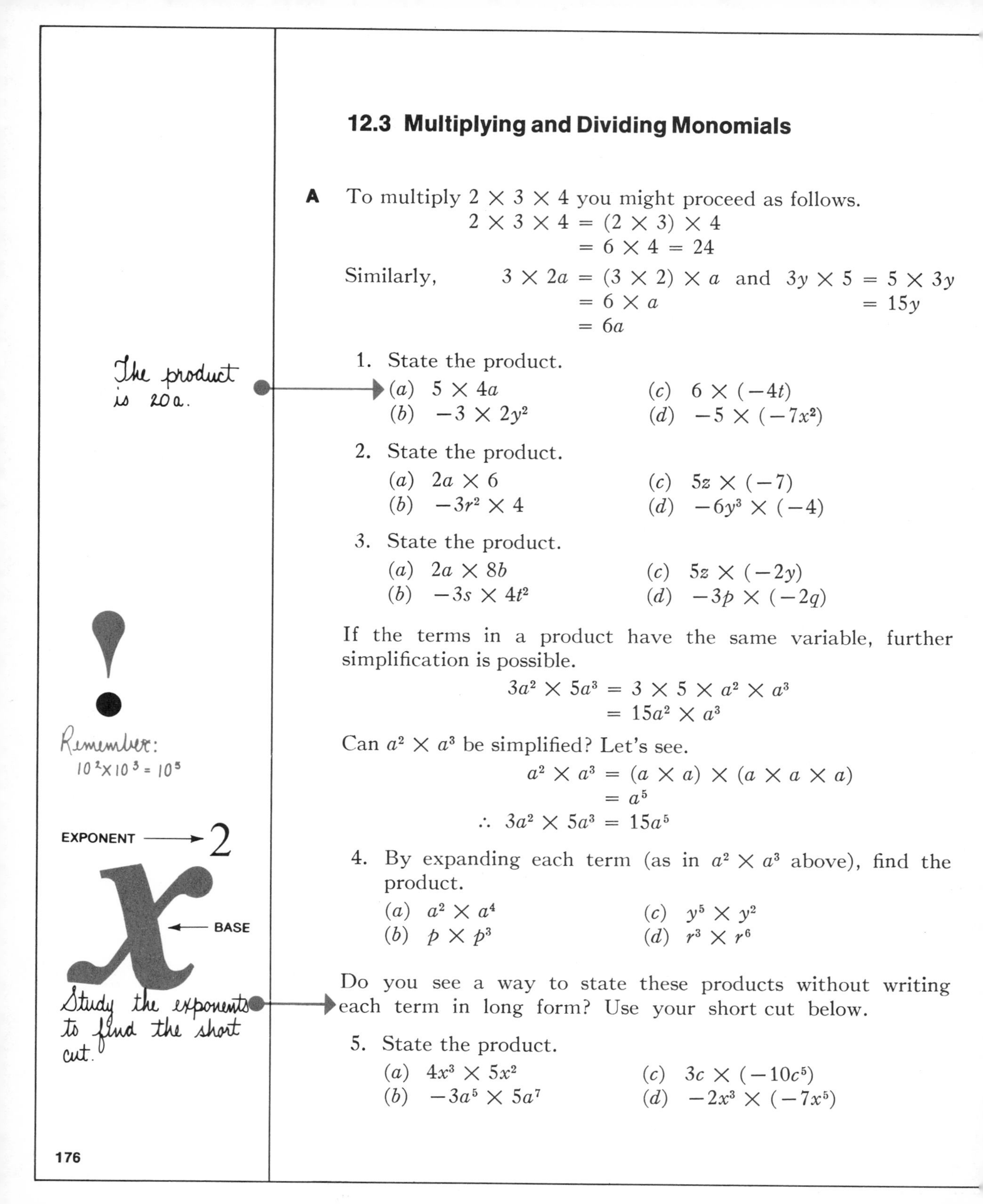
The product is 20a.
Remember:
$10^2 \times 10^3 = 10^5$
EXPONENT
BASE
Study the exponents to find the short cut.

12.3 Multiplying and Dividing Monomials

A To multiply $2 \times 3 \times 4$ you might proceed as follows.

$$\begin{aligned} 2 \times 3 \times 4 &= (2 \times 3) \times 4 \\ &= 6 \times 4 = 24 \end{aligned}$$

Similarly, $3 \times 2a = (3 \times 2) \times a = 6 \times a = 6a$ and $3y \times 5 = 5 \times 3y = 15y$

1. State the product.
   (a) $5 \times 4a$
   (b) $-3 \times 2y^2$
   (c) $6 \times (-4t)$
   (d) $-5 \times (-7x^2)$

2. State the product.
   (a) $2a \times 6$
   (b) $-3r^2 \times 4$
   (c) $5z \times (-7)$
   (d) $-6y^3 \times (-4)$

3. State the product.
   (a) $2a \times 8b$
   (b) $-3s \times 4t^2$
   (c) $5z \times (-2y)$
   (d) $-3p \times (-2q)$

If the terms in a product have the same variable, further simplification is possible.

$$\begin{aligned} 3a^2 \times 5a^3 &= 3 \times 5 \times a^2 \times a^3 \\ &= 15a^2 \times a^3 \end{aligned}$$

Can $a^2 \times a^3$ be simplified? Let's see.

$$\begin{aligned} a^2 \times a^3 &= (a \times a) \times (a \times a \times a) \\ &= a^5 \\ \therefore\ 3a^2 \times 5a^3 &= 15a^5 \end{aligned}$$

4. By expanding each term (as in $a^2 \times a^3$ above), find the product.
   (a) $a^2 \times a^4$
   (b) $p \times p^3$
   (c) $y^5 \times y^2$
   (d) $r^3 \times r^6$

Do you see a way to state these products without writing each term in long form? Use your short cut below.

5. State the product.
   (a) $4x^3 \times 5x^2$
   (b) $-3a^5 \times 5a^7$
   (c) $3c \times (-10c^5)$
   (d) $-2x^3 \times (-7x^5)$

$\frac{2}{3} \times \frac{5}{7} = \frac{2 \times 5}{3 \times 7}$ illustrates how we multiply fractions.
Therefore, $\frac{5 \times 7}{8 \times 3}$ can be written as the product $\frac{5}{8} \times \frac{7}{3}$.

1. Express as a product of 2 fractions and simplify.

   (a) $\dfrac{4 \times 9}{7 \times 11}$ (b) $\dfrac{5 \times 3}{8 \times 4}$ (c) $\dfrac{6 \times a}{3 \times y}$ (d) $\dfrac{4 \times a^5}{8 \times a^2}$

   Part (d) should be simplified as follows.

$$\frac{4 \times a^5}{8 \times a^2} = \frac{4}{8} \times \frac{a^5}{a^2} \; * $$
$$= \frac{1}{2}a^3$$

*
By expanding
$$\frac{a^5}{a^2} = \frac{a \times a \times a \times a \times a}{a \times a}$$

2. Simplify.

   (a) $\dfrac{a^7}{a^2}$ (c) $15y^6 \div 3y$

   (b) $\dfrac{x^5}{x^4}$ (d) $-12t^5 \div 4t^3$

Do you see a short cut that can be used to avoid the expanding of each term? Use it to do Question 3.

Study the exponents to find the short cut.

3. State the quotient.

   (a) $\dfrac{4a^5}{-2a^2}$ (c) $12y^3 \div 3y^2$

   (b) $\dfrac{-10x^3}{5x}$ (d) $-4r^6 \div (-8r^4)$

In some cases more than one variable is present in each term. Study the following examples and then do Question 4.

Example 1

Simplify $\dfrac{12a^5b^3}{4a^3b^2}$

Solution

$$\frac{12a^5b^3}{4a^3b^2} = \frac{12}{4} \times \frac{a^5}{a^3} \times \frac{b^3}{b^2}$$
$$= 3 \times a^2 \times b^1$$
$$= 3a^2b$$

Example 2

Simplify $\dfrac{25x^2y^5z}{-15xy^7}$

Solution

$$\begin{aligned}\frac{25x^2y^5z}{-15xy^7} &= \frac{25}{-15} \times \frac{x^2}{x} \times \frac{y^5}{y^7} \times z \\ &= -\frac{5}{3} \times x \times \frac{1}{y^2} \times z \\ &= -\frac{5xz}{3y^2}\end{aligned}$$

4. Divide.
   (*a*) $\dfrac{4a^2b^3}{2ab}$ (*b*) $\dfrac{-7x^2y^5}{14x^5y^2}$ (*c*) $\dfrac{6pq^2r}{-9pr}$ (*d*) $\dfrac{8r^5s^2t}{6rs^6}$

Exercise 12.3

Discussion

1. State the product.
   (*a*) $x^5 \times x^7$
   (*b*) $a^5 \times b^7$
   (*c*) $2x^7 \times 5y^2$
   (*d*) $-3a^2 \times 5a^3$

$3a \times 2b = 6\,ab$

2. When multiplying two terms, how do you find the coefficient of the answer?

$2a^3 \times 5a^2 = 10\,a^5$

3. When multiplying terms having the same variable, how do you find the exponent of the variable part of the answer?

4. State the quotient.
   (*a*) $a^5 \div a^2$
   (*b*) $x^7 \div x^4$
   (*c*) $3t^5 \div 6t$
   (*d*) $4y^8 \div y^5$
   (*e*) $-10x^5 \div 2y^2$
   (*f*) $-8x \div (-4x^3)$

$\dfrac{12a^7}{-4a^3} = ?$

5. When dividing two terms, how do you find the coefficient of the answer?

6. When dividing terms having the same variable, how do you find the exponent of the variable part of the answer?

Written Solutions

7. Find the product.

(*a*) $3a^2 \times 5a^5$ (*c*) $-8t^4 \times 3t^7$ (*e*) $0.5d^2 \times 8d^3$

(*b*) $7x^2 \times (-2x^3)$ (*d*) $-2a^2 \times (-5b^3)$ (*f*) $-\frac{3}{4}x^2 \times \frac{8}{15}y$

8. Find the product.

(*a*) $-4 \times 2x^5$ (*d*) $7 \times (-4c^3)$

(*b*) $5x^2 \times (-3)$ (*e*) $-3x^2 \times (-5)$

(*c*) $-x^2 \times y^3$ (*f*) $ab \times a^2b^3$

9. Find the product.

(*a*) $x^2 \times x^5 \times x^7$ (*d*) $-x^2 \times 3x \times (-4x)$

(*b*) $3a \times 5b \times c$ (*e*) $x^3y^5 \times x^2y^4$

(*c*) $2xy \times (-3x) \times 5y$ (*f*) $2a^2b^3 \times (-3ab^2)$

10. Find the quotient.

(*a*) $\frac{x^7}{x^3}$ (*c*) $\frac{4a^2}{a^5}$ (*e*) $\frac{-5t^7}{-10t^2}$

(*b*) $\frac{y^5}{y^2}$ (*d*) $\frac{12x^5}{-3x}$ (*f*) $\frac{-24r^5}{12r^7}$

11. Find the quotient.

(*a*) $\frac{15ab}{5a}$ (*d*) $16ab \div (-2ab)$

(*b*) $\frac{-24x^2y}{4xy}$ (*e*) $12x^2y^3 \div 6xy^2$

(*c*) $\frac{10st}{-2t}$ (*f*) $-20ab^6 \div 4b^4$

12. Find the areas of the following rectangles.

(*a*) 20 cm by 12 cm

(*b*) $5x$ metres by $3x$ metres

(*c*) $3a$ millimetres by a millimetres

(*d*) $5x$ centimetres by $4y$ centimetres

13. $12xy = 6x \times 2y$. Find four other ways of expressing $12xy$ as a product of two terms.

14. Express as a product of two terms in at least four ways.

(*a*) $16a^2$ (*b*) $6ab$ (*c*) $-8ab^2$ (*d*) $-3x^2y$

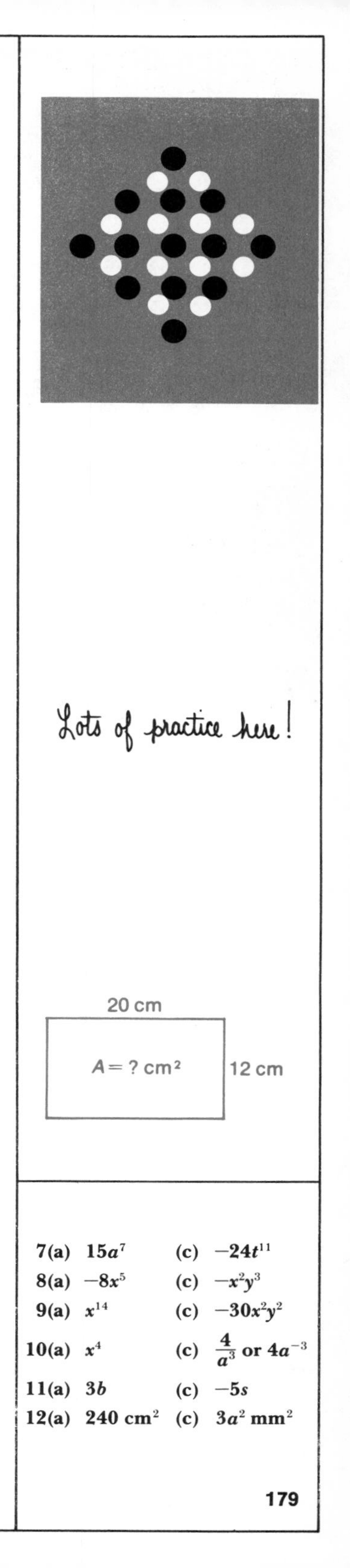

7(a) $15a^7$ **(c)** $-24t^{11}$
8(a) $-8x^5$ **(c)** $-x^2y^3$
9(a) x^{14} **(c)** $-30x^2y^2$
10(a) x^4 **(c)** $\frac{4}{a^3}$ or $4a^{-3}$
11(a) $3b$ **(c)** $-5s$
12(a) 240 cm² **(c)** $3a^2$ mm²

Unit 13
Equations and Inequations Revisited

You use your knowledge of mathematics to help you find solutions to problems in many other subjects. Frequently, relationships are expressed as *formulas*. Here are 2 examples.

$I = Prt$ is used in business subjects to calculate the interest earned on a principal P.

$d = vt$ is used in physics to give the distance travelled during time t at velocity v.

The rules for working with equations also apply to formulas, such as those above. In this unit you will learn how to work with formulas, equations, and inequations that are somewhat more complicated than those you studied earlier.

13.1 Equations and Inequations with Variables on Both Sides

You have already solved equations such as $3x + 5 = 20$. Remember that the aim was to get x by itself on the left side of the equation.

1. What would you do to each side of $3x + 5 = 20$ in order to solve it?

2. Solve $1 - 4x = 21$.

Consider the equation $5x = 3x + 10$. How can we get a single term in x on the left side of the equation? Here's a possible solution.

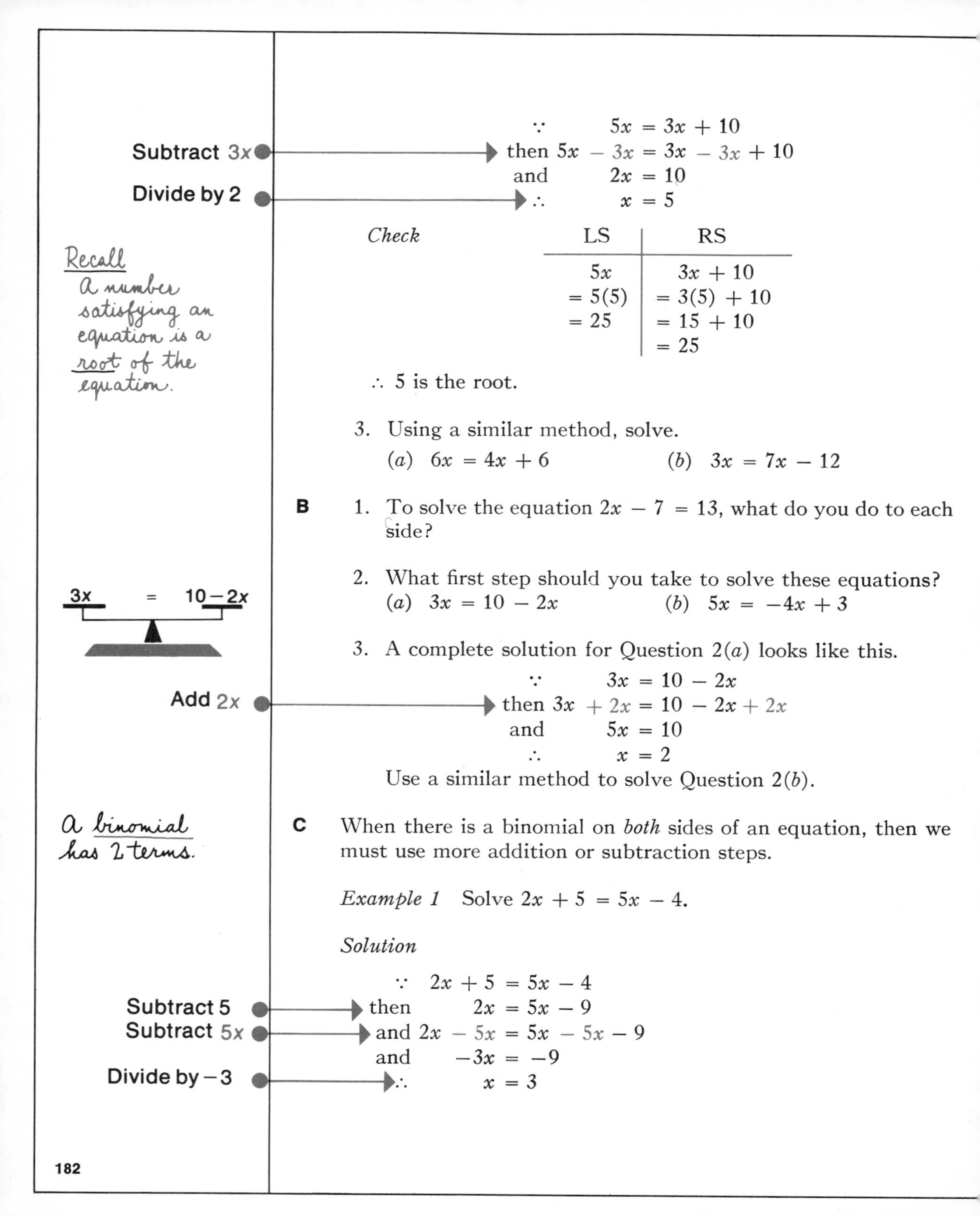

$$\begin{aligned} \because \quad 5x &= 3x + 10 \\ \text{then } 5x - 3x &= 3x - 3x + 10 \quad \text{(Subtract } 3x\text{)} \\ \text{and} \quad 2x &= 10 \\ \therefore \quad x &= 5 \quad \text{(Divide by 2)} \end{aligned}$$

Check

LS	RS
$5x$	$3x + 10$
$= 5(5)$	$= 3(5) + 10$
$= 25$	$= 15 + 10$
	$= 25$

$\therefore$ 5 is the root.

Recall
A number satisfying an equation is a root of the equation.

3. Using a similar method, solve.
   (*a*) $6x = 4x + 6$ (*b*) $3x = 7x - 12$

B 1. To solve the equation $2x - 7 = 13$, what do you do to each side?

2. What first step should you take to solve these equations?
   (*a*) $3x = 10 - 2x$ (*b*) $5x = -4x + 3$

3. A complete solution for Question 2(*a*) looks like this.

$$\begin{aligned} \because \quad 3x &= 10 - 2x \\ \text{then } 3x + 2x &= 10 - 2x + 2x \quad \text{(Add } 2x\text{)} \\ \text{and} \quad 5x &= 10 \\ \therefore \quad x &= 2 \end{aligned}$$

Use a similar method to solve Question 2(*b*).

C When there is a binomial on *both* sides of an equation, then we must use more addition or subtraction steps.

A binomial has 2 terms.

Example 1 Solve $2x + 5 = 5x - 4$.

Solution

$$\begin{aligned} \because \quad 2x + 5 &= 5x - 4 \\ \text{then} \quad 2x &= 5x - 9 \quad \text{(Subtract 5)} \\ \text{and } 2x - 5x &= 5x - 5x - 9 \quad \text{(Subtract } 5x\text{)} \\ \text{and} \quad -3x &= -9 \\ \therefore \quad x &= 3 \quad \text{(Divide by } -3\text{)} \end{aligned}$$

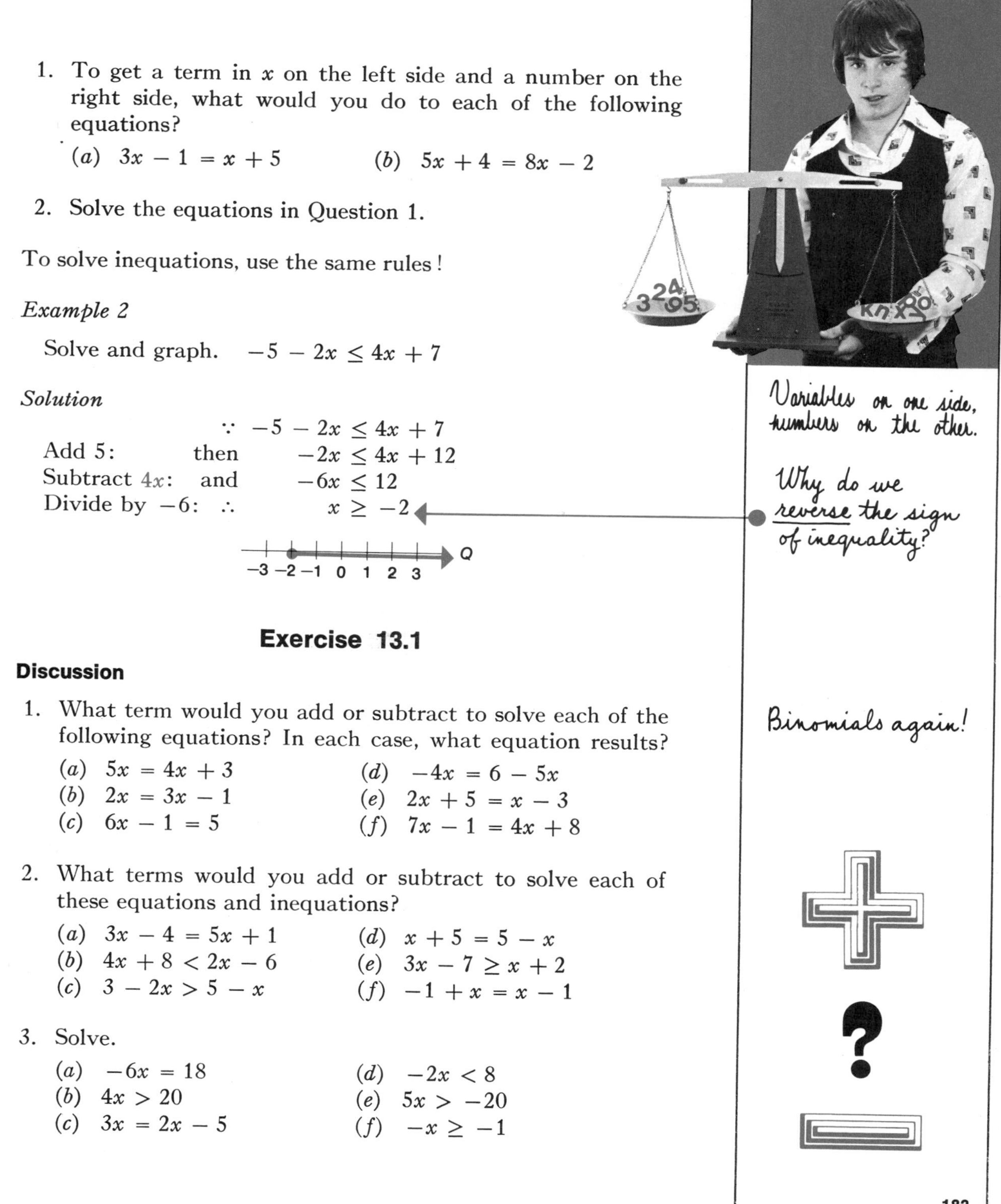

1. To get a term in x on the left side and a number on the right side, what would you do to each of the following equations?

   (*a*) $3x - 1 = x + 5$ (*b*) $5x + 4 = 8x - 2$

2. Solve the equations in Question 1.

To solve inequations, use the same rules!

Example 2

Solve and graph. $-5 - 2x \le 4x + 7$

Solution

	$\because$	$-5 - 2x \le 4x + 7$
Add 5:	then	$-2x \le 4x + 12$
Subtract $4x$:	and	$-6x \le 12$
Divide by -6:	$\therefore$	$x \ge -2$

Variables on one side, numbers on the other.

Why do we reverse the sign of inequality?

Exercise 13.1

Discussion

1. What term would you add or subtract to solve each of the following equations? In each case, what equation results?

   (*a*) $5x = 4x + 3$ (*d*) $-4x = 6 - 5x$
   (*b*) $2x = 3x - 1$ (*e*) $2x + 5 = x - 3$
   (*c*) $6x - 1 = 5$ (*f*) $7x - 1 = 4x + 8$

Binomials again!

2. What terms would you add or subtract to solve each of these equations and inequations?

   (*a*) $3x - 4 = 5x + 1$ (*d*) $x + 5 = 5 - x$
   (*b*) $4x + 8 < 2x - 6$ (*e*) $3x - 7 \ge x + 2$
   (*c*) $3 - 2x > 5 - x$ (*f*) $-1 + x = x - 1$

3. Solve.

   (*a*) $-6x = 18$ (*d*) $-2x < 8$
   (*b*) $4x > 20$ (*e*) $5x > -20$
   (*c*) $3x = 2x - 5$ (*f*) $-x \ge -1$

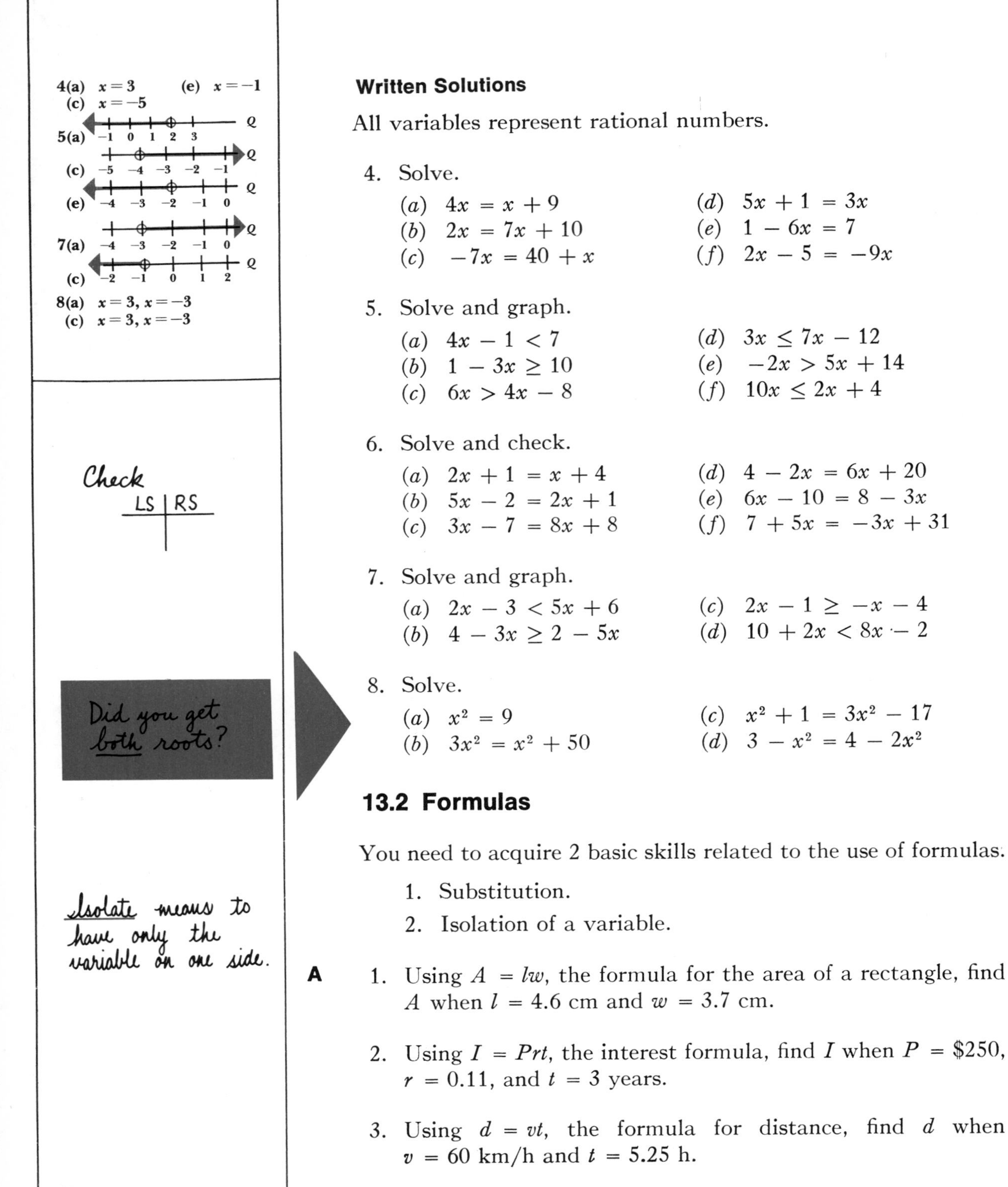

4(a) $x = 3$ (e) $x = -1$
(c) $x = -5$

5(a) –1 0 1 2 3 Q

(c) –5 –4 –3 –2 –1 Q

(e) –4 –3 –2 –1 0 Q

7(a) –4 –3 –2 –1 0 Q

(c) –2 –1 0 1 2 Q

8(a) $x = 3, x = -3$
(c) $x = 3, x = -3$

Written Solutions

All variables represent rational numbers.

4. Solve.
   (a) $4x = x + 9$
   (b) $2x = 7x + 10$
   (c) $-7x = 40 + x$
   (d) $5x + 1 = 3x$
   (e) $1 - 6x = 7$
   (f) $2x - 5 = -9x$

5. Solve and graph.
   (a) $4x - 1 < 7$
   (b) $1 - 3x \geq 10$
   (c) $6x > 4x - 8$
   (d) $3x \leq 7x - 12$
   (e) $-2x > 5x + 14$
   (f) $10x \leq 2x + 4$

Check

LS	RS

6. Solve and check.
   (a) $2x + 1 = x + 4$
   (b) $5x - 2 = 2x + 1$
   (c) $3x - 7 = 8x + 8$
   (d) $4 - 2x = 6x + 20$
   (e) $6x - 10 = 8 - 3x$
   (f) $7 + 5x = -3x + 31$

7. Solve and graph.
   (a) $2x - 3 < 5x + 6$
   (b) $4 - 3x \geq 2 - 5x$
   (c) $2x - 1 \geq -x - 4$
   (d) $10 + 2x < 8x - 2$

Did you get both roots?

8. Solve.
   (a) $x^2 = 9$
   (b) $3x^2 = x^2 + 50$
   (c) $x^2 + 1 = 3x^2 - 17$
   (d) $3 - x^2 = 4 - 2x^2$

13.2 Formulas

You need to acquire 2 basic skills related to the use of formulas.

1. Substitution.
2. Isolation of a variable.

Isolate means to have only the variable on one side.

A

1. Using $A = lw$, the formula for the area of a rectangle, find A when $l = 4.6$ cm and $w = 3.7$ cm.

2. Using $I = Prt$, the interest formula, find I when $P = \$250$, $r = 0.11$, and $t = 3$ years.

3. Using $d = vt$, the formula for distance, find d when $v = 60$ km/h and $t = 5.25$ h.

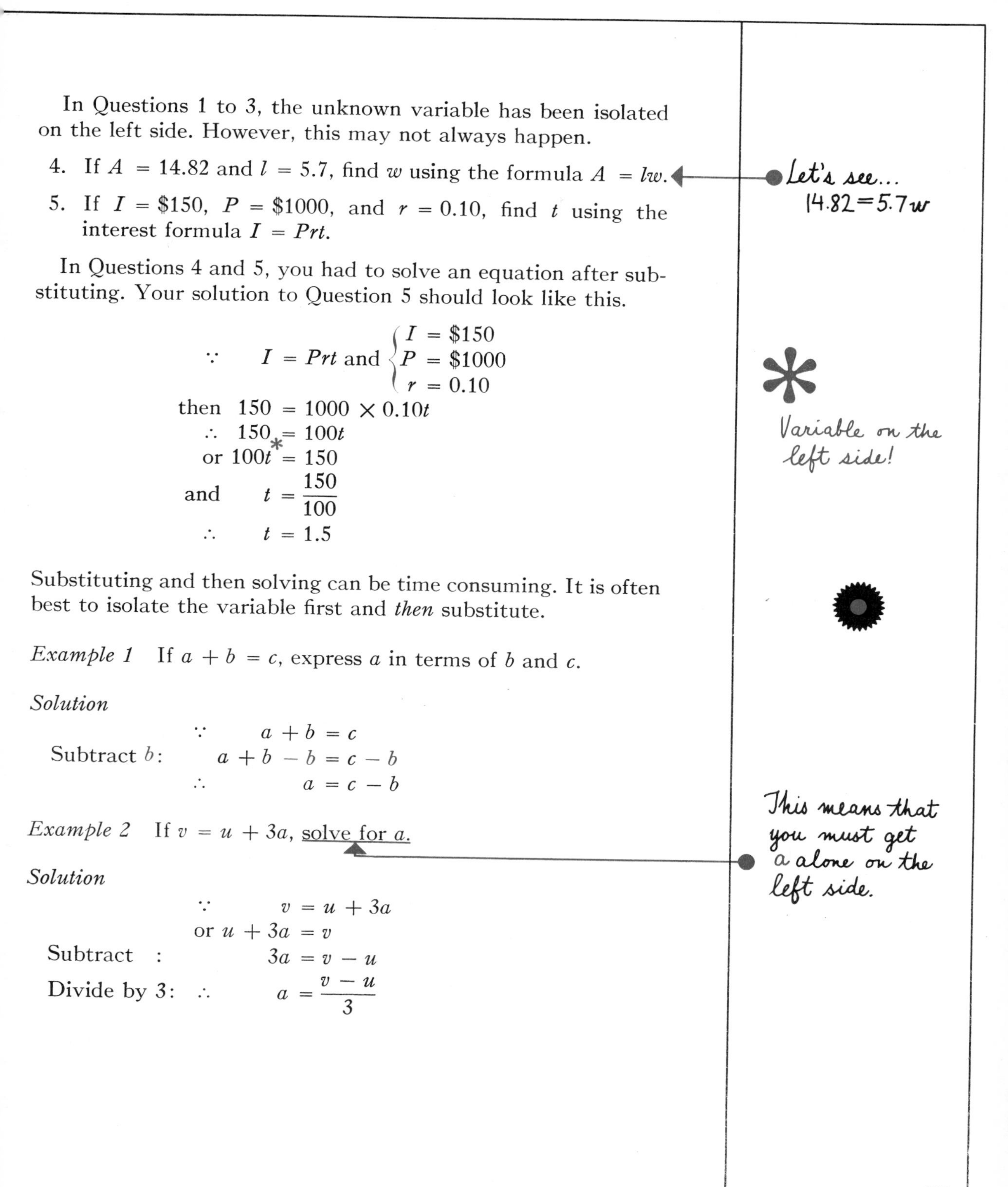

Let's see...
14.82=5.7w
Variable on the left side!
This means that you must get a alone on the left side.

In Questions 1 to 3, the unknown variable has been isolated on the left side. However, this may not always happen.

4. If $A = 14.82$ and $l = 5.7$, find w using the formula $A = lw$.
5. If $I = \$150$, $P = \$1000$, and $r = 0.10$, find t using the interest formula $I = Prt$.

In Questions 4 and 5, you had to solve an equation after substituting. Your solution to Question 5 should look like this.

$$\because \quad I = Prt \text{ and } \begin{cases} I = \$150 \\ P = \$1000 \\ r = 0.10 \end{cases}$$

$$\begin{aligned} \text{then} \quad 150 &= 1000 \times 0.10t \\ \therefore \quad 150 &= 100t \\ \text{or } 100t^{*} &= 150 \\ \text{and} \quad t &= \frac{150}{100} \\ \therefore \quad t &= 1.5 \end{aligned}$$

Substituting and then solving can be time consuming. It is often best to isolate the variable first and *then* substitute.

Example 1 If $a + b = c$, express a in terms of b and c.

Solution

$$\begin{aligned} \because \quad a + b &= c \\ \text{Subtract } b: \quad a + b - b &= c - b \\ \therefore \quad a &= c - b \end{aligned}$$

Example 2 If $v = u + 3a$, solve for a.

Solution

$$\begin{aligned} \because \quad v &= u + 3a \\ \text{or } u + 3a &= v \\ \text{Subtract } \quad : \quad 3a &= v - u \\ \text{Divide by 3:} \quad \therefore \quad a &= \frac{v - u}{3} \end{aligned}$$

2. Solve for y.
(*a*) $y + 2x = 5$ (*b*) $2x + 3y = 4$ (*c*) $x - y = 5$

Example 3 If $d = vt$, express t in terms of d and v.

Solution

$$\because d = vt$$
$$\text{or } vt = d$$
Divide by v: $$\text{then } \frac{vt}{v} = \frac{d}{v}$$
$$\therefore t = \frac{d}{v}$$

You know... at a speed (v) of 80 km/h, a distance (d) of 240 km is travelled in a time (t) of $\frac{240}{80}$ h!

3. If $E = IR$, solve for I.

Exercise 13.2

Discussion

1. Solve.
(*a*) $A = 100 \times 1.62$ (*c*) $s = \frac{150}{20}$ (*e*) $2x - 6 = 4$
(*b*) $I = 100 \times 0.08 \times 2$ (*d*) $\frac{E}{4} = 8$ (*f*) $v = 30 + 4(3)$

2. Solve for the variable indicated.
(*a*) $PN = I$; N (*d*) $I = Prt$; t (*g*) $a = \frac{b}{c}$; b
(*b*) $A = lw$; w (*e*) $\frac{d}{t} = v$; d (*h*) $R = \frac{E}{I}$; E
(*c*) $c = \pi d$; d (*f*) $\frac{V}{A} = l$; V (*i*) $r^2 = \frac{V}{\pi h}$; h

3. 7.85 cm
4. 6.5 m
5. 70 km/h

Written Solutions

3. The formula for the perimeter of a circle is $c = 3.14d$. Find c when $d = 2.5$ cm.

3.
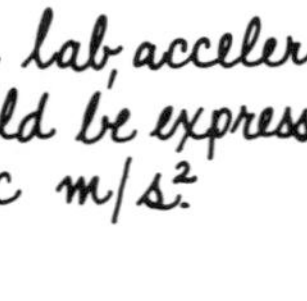

4. The area of a rectangle is 55.25 m². Find the width, if the length is 8.5 m.

5. Using the formula $v = u + at$, find the final velocity (v) of a car. From an initial velocity (u) of 20 km/h the car accelerates (a) at 0.8 km/h each second for a time (t) of 70 s.

In a lab acceleration would be expressed as x m/s².

6. Find the interest (I) on an investment (P) of \$650, invested for 5 years (t) at a rate (r) of 0.085. Use the formula $I = Prt$.

7. Find the value of the other variable.
   (a) $2x + y = 15$; $x = 2.8$
   (b) $3x - y = 10$; $y = 5.6$
   (c) $x + 5y - 3 = 0$; $y = 1.2$
   (d) $7x - 2y + 10 = 0$; $x = 4$
   (e) $y = 5x - 4$; $y = 6$
   (f) $y = \frac{3}{2}x + 8$; $x = \frac{5}{3}$

8. Solve for the variable indicated.
   (a) $2y = 4x + 5$; y
   (b) $3x + 2v = 6$; y
   (c) $5x - 2v + 1 = 0$; v
   (d) $a = b - c$; c
   (e) $v = \frac{d}{t}$; t
   (f) $P = \frac{c}{n}$; n

9. The distance, d metres, a falling object drops from rest in t seconds is given by $d = 9.8t^2$. Find
   (a) d if an object drops for 4 s (nearest metre).
   (b) t if $d = 100$ m (to the nearest 0.1 s).

10. An object dropped from rest is acted upon by gravity. It will have a velocity of v km/h after falling d metres (ignoring air resistance), according to the formula $v = 8.4\sqrt{d}$.
    (a) How fast will the object be going after falling 25 m? 100 m? 400 m? 825 m?
    (b) How far will the object have to fall before its velocity is 30 km/h? 80 km/h?

11. A simple pendulum is a rod free to pivot about a point O, as shown. The time for the *bob* of the pendulum to swing from A to B and return to A is called the *period* of the pendulum. The length of the pendulum, l, and the bob period, T, are related by the formula $T = 2\pi\sqrt{\frac{l}{980}}$, where T is the period in seconds, l is the length in centimetres, and $\pi \doteq 3.14$. Calculate the period of a pendulum 49 cm long, to 2 decimal places.

6. \$276.25
7(a) 9.4 **(c)** −3 **(e)** 2
8(a) $y = \frac{4x + 5}{2}$ **(c)** $y = \frac{5x + 1}{2}$ **(f)** $n = \frac{c}{P}$
9(a) 157 m **(b)** 3.2 s
10(b) 12.8 m, 90.7 m
11. 1.41 s

Neglecting air resistance!

Use $d = \frac{v^2}{70.56}$

11.

13.3 Strategy of Solving Equations

A

1. Expand.

   (*a*) $2(x + 5)$ (*c*) $-4(x + 7)$ (*e*) $5(3x - 4)$
   (*b*) $3(2x - 2)$ (*d*) $-2(-x + 4)$ (*f*) $-(2x - 1)$

Removal of brackets by expansion is sometimes the first step in solving an equation.

Example 1 Solve $3(x - 4) = -2(1 + x)$

Solution

$$\because 3(x - 4) = -2(1 + x)$$

Expand: $3x - 12 = -2 - 2x$

Add 12: $3x = 10 - 2x$

Add $2x$: $5x = 10$

$$\therefore x = 2$$

Check

LS	RS
$3(x - 4)$	$-2(1 + x)$
$= 3(2 - 4)$	$= -2(1 + 2)$
$= 3(-2)$	$= -2(3)$
$= -6$	$= -6$

$\therefore$ 2 is the root.

2. Solve.

   (*a*) $2(a + 5) = 16$ (*b*) $5(b - 3) = -2(b + 4)$

B You may remember from earlier work with equations that eliminating fractions simplifies the solution.

1. What number would you use as a multiplier to eliminate fractions in each of the following equations?

   (*a*) $\frac{2}{5}x + 1 = 3x$ (*b*) $x + \frac{3}{4} = \frac{1}{2}x$ (*c*) $\frac{1}{3}x = \frac{1}{4}$ (*d*) $\frac{5}{6}x = \frac{3}{4}$

2. Expand each of the following expressions.

   (*a*) $4(\frac{1}{2}x + 3)$ (*c*) $3(\frac{1}{3}x - \frac{2}{3})$ (*e*) $15(\frac{4}{5}x - \frac{1}{3})$
   (*b*) $5(2x + \frac{4}{5})$ (*d*) $12(\frac{1}{3}x + \frac{3}{4})$ (*f*) $24(-\frac{5}{6}x + \frac{7}{8})$

Example 2 Solve $\frac{4}{5}x - 3 = \frac{2}{3}x + 1$

Solution

	$\because$	$\frac{4}{5}x - 3 = \frac{2}{3}x + 1$
Multiply by 15:	$\therefore$	$15(\frac{4}{5}x - 3) = 15(\frac{2}{3}x + 1)$
Expand:	and	$12x - 45 = 10x + 15$
	then	$12x = 10x + 60$
	and	$2x = 60$
	$\therefore$	$x = 30$

Check

LS	RS
$\frac{4}{5}x - 2$	$\frac{2}{3}x + 1$
$= \frac{4}{5}(30) - 3$	$= \frac{2}{3}(30) + 1$
$= 24 - 3$	$= 20 + 1$
$= 21$	$= 21$

$\therefore$ 30 is the root.

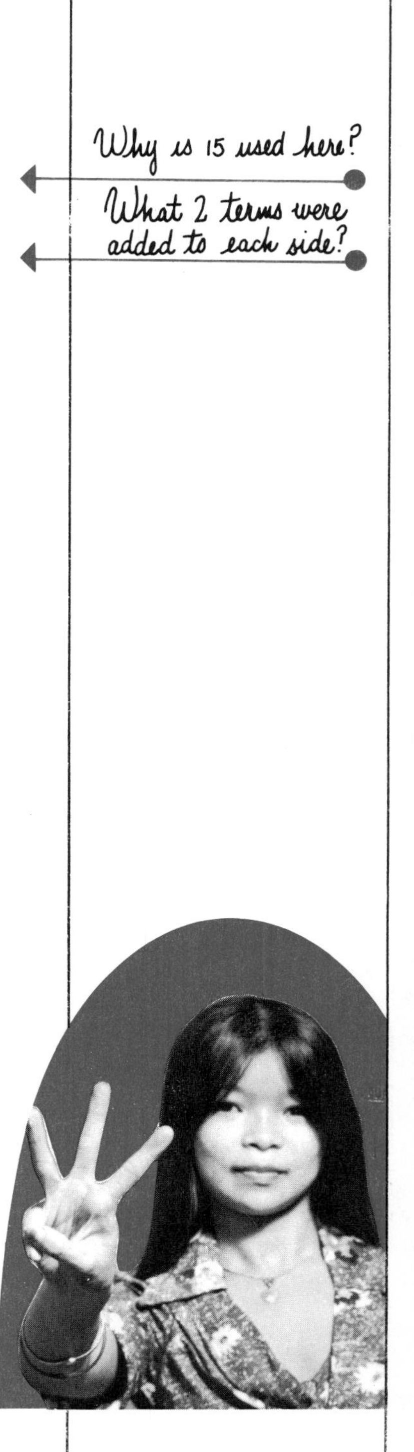

Why is 15 used here?
What 2 terms were added to each side?

3. What number would you use as a multiplier to eliminate fractions in the following equations? Solve each equation.

(*a*) $\dfrac{2}{5}x + \dfrac{1}{4} = 2$ (*c*) $\dfrac{1}{3}x = \dfrac{3}{4}$

(*b*) $\dfrac{5}{8}a = \dfrac{1}{4}a - 3$ (*d*) $\dfrac{5}{6}a = \dfrac{1}{4}$

Example 3 Solve $\dfrac{x - 1}{2} = \dfrac{x + 3}{4}$.

Solution

	$\because$	$\dfrac{x-1}{2} = \dfrac{x+3}{4}$
Multiply by 4:		$4\left(\dfrac{x-1}{2}\right) = 4\left(\dfrac{x+3}{4}\right)$
Expand:		$2(x - 1) = x + 3$
	then	$2x - 2 = x + 3$
	$\therefore$	$x = 5$

> *Steps in Solving Equations*
> 1. Remove fractions and brackets.
> 2. Isolate the variable term.
> 3. Solve for the variable.

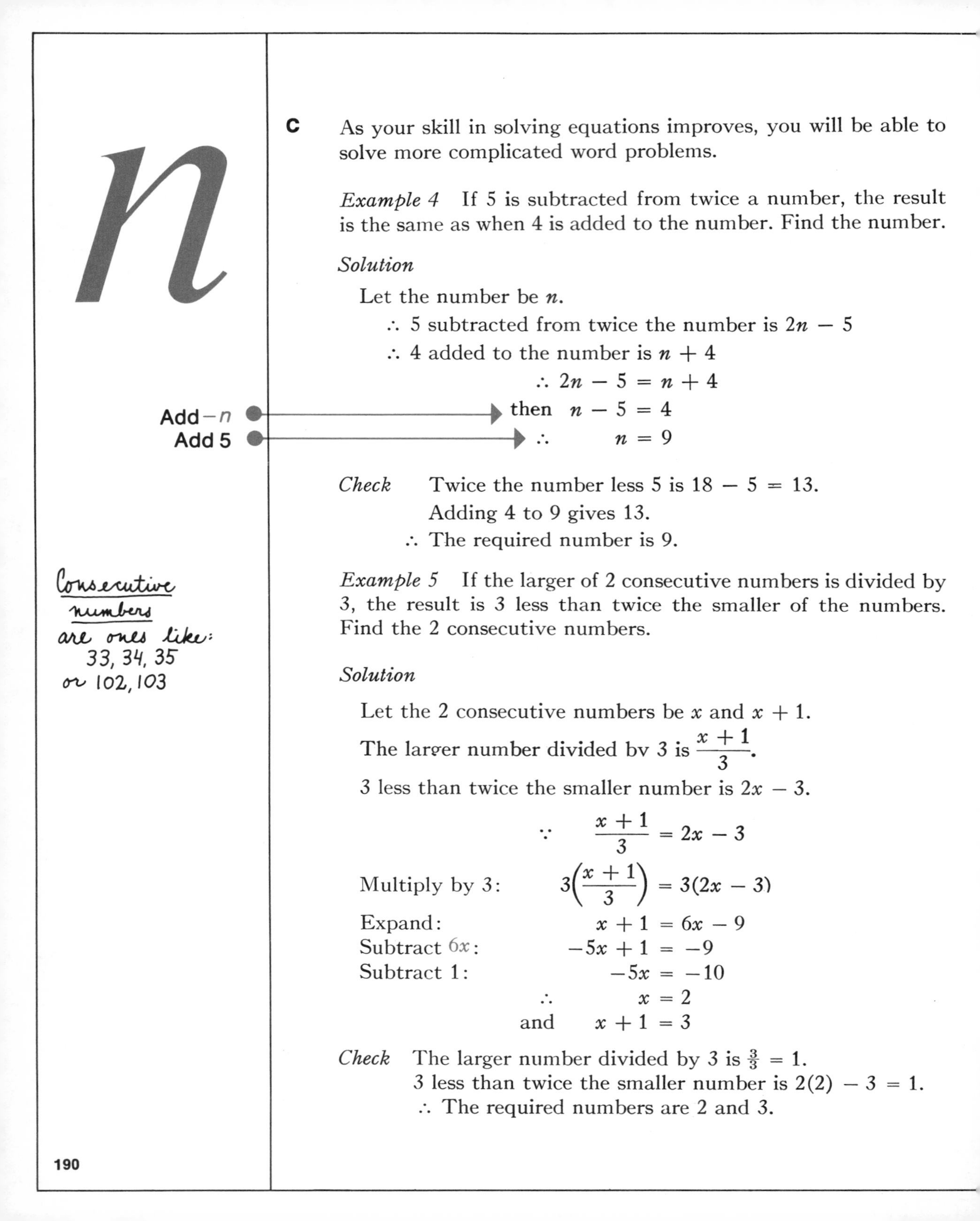

C As your skill in solving equations improves, you will be able to solve more complicated word problems.

Example 4 If 5 is subtracted from twice a number, the result is the same as when 4 is added to the number. Find the number.

Solution

Let the number be n.

$\therefore$ 5 subtracted from twice the number is $2n - 5$

$\therefore$ 4 added to the number is $n + 4$

$$\therefore 2n - 5 = n + 4$$

Add $-n$ → then $n - 5 = 4$

Add 5 → $\therefore n = 9$

Check Twice the number less 5 is $18 - 5 = 13$.
Adding 4 to 9 gives 13.
$\therefore$ The required number is 9.

Consecutive numbers are ones like: 33, 34, 35 or 102, 103

Example 5 If the larger of 2 consecutive numbers is divided by 3, the result is 3 less than twice the smaller of the numbers. Find the 2 consecutive numbers.

Solution

Let the 2 consecutive numbers be x and $x + 1$.

The larger number divided by 3 is $\frac{x+1}{3}$.

3 less than twice the smaller number is $2x - 3$.

$$\because \frac{x+1}{3} = 2x - 3$$

Multiply by 3: $3\left(\frac{x+1}{3}\right) = 3(2x - 3)$

Expand: $x + 1 = 6x - 9$

Subtract $6x$: $-5x + 1 = -9$

Subtract 1: $-5x = -10$

$\therefore x = 2$

and $x + 1 = 3$

Check The larger number divided by 3 is $\frac{3}{3} = 1$.
3 less than twice the smaller number is $2(2) - 3 = 1$.
$\therefore$ The required numbers are 2 and 3.

Exercise 13.3

Discussion

1. State the first step in solving the following equations.

   (*a*) $2x - 5 = 7$ (*d*) $2(x + 3) = -7$

   (*b*) $\frac{1}{2}x - 1 = \frac{3}{4}$ (*e*) $\frac{2}{3}x - \frac{2}{5} = x + 1$

   (*c*) $\dfrac{x - 1}{5} = \dfrac{x + 1}{6}$ (*f*) $3(x - 1) = 4(x + 3)$

2. State the lowest common multiple.

   (*a*) 2, 3 (*c*) 4, 6 (*e*) 8, 10

   (*b*) 2, 4 (*d*) 6, 8 (*f*) 4, 8, 12

3. State the multiplier needed to eliminate fractions in Questions 7 and 8, below.

4. Expand.

   (*a*) $3\left(\dfrac{x - 2}{3}\right)$ (*c*) $6\left(\dfrac{1}{3}x + \dfrac{1}{2}\right)$ (*e*) $-3(x - 2)$

   (*b*) $15\left(\dfrac{x + 1}{5}\right)$ (*d*) $-2(3a + 5)$ (*f*) $12\left(\dfrac{2x + 1}{3}\right)$

Written Solutions

All variables have domain Q.

5. Solve.

   (*a*) $2(x + 3) = 8$ (*d*) $4 = 3(2x - 5)$

   (*b*) $3(x - 4) = 6$ (*e*) $29 = 2(3x + 7)$

   (*c*) $-5(t + 1) = 10$ (*f*) $6 = -5(x - 1)$

6. Solve.

   (*a*) $2(a - 1) = 3(a + 2)$ (*d*) $3(y + 2) - 1 = 5$

   (*b*) $5(y + 3) = 4(y - 2)$ (*e*) $x + 5 = -4(x + 1) + 2$

   (*c*) $10(1 - 2x) = 3(2 - 6x)$ (*f*) $2(a - 5) - 3 = 4(a + 1)$

7. Solve.

   (*a*) $\dfrac{2}{5}a = \dfrac{1}{2}$ (*c*) $\dfrac{3}{4}x = \dfrac{1}{3}$ (*e*) $\dfrac{3}{5}z + 1 = \dfrac{1}{3}$

   (*b*) $\dfrac{4}{7}b = \dfrac{5}{3}$ (*d*) $\dfrac{2}{7}y - \dfrac{1}{2} = 2$ (*f*) $2 - \dfrac{5}{6}y = \dfrac{2}{3} + y$

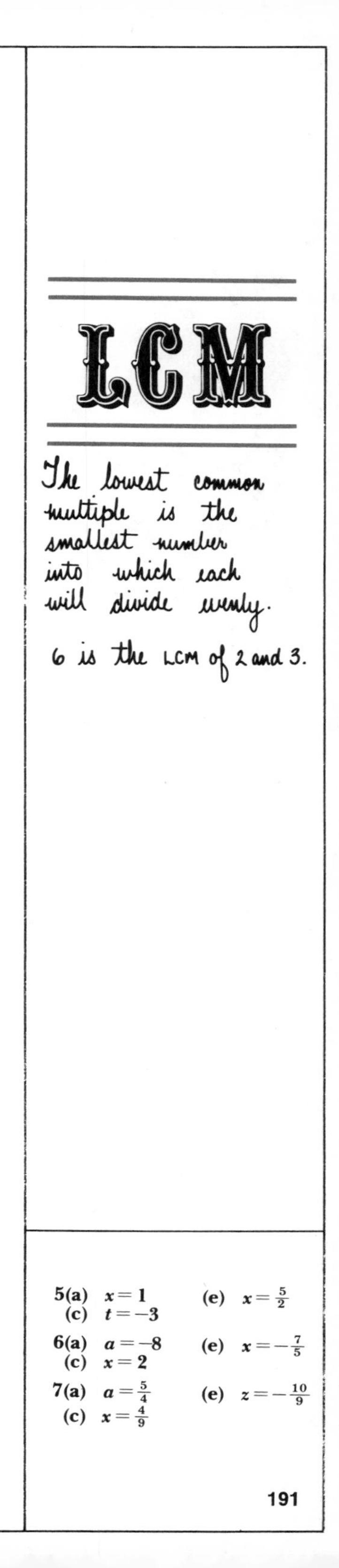

LCM
The lowest common multiple is the smallest number into which each will divide evenly.
6 is the LCM of 2 and 3.
5(a) x = 1 (e) x = 5/2
(c) t = −3
6(a) a = −8 (e) x = −7/5
(c) x = 2
7(a) a = 5/4 (e) z = −10/9
(c) x = 4/9

8. Solve and check.

(a) $\dfrac{x+1}{2} = \dfrac{x+3}{3}$ (d) $\dfrac{2a-3}{3} = \dfrac{24-a}{6}$

(b) $\dfrac{y-1}{5} = \dfrac{y+2}{8}$ (e) $\dfrac{5c-2}{6} = \dfrac{4c-8}{8}$

(c) $\dfrac{z+5}{2} = \dfrac{2z+10}{4}$ (f) $\dfrac{2-2t}{5} = \dfrac{-4-3t}{4}$

9. Solve.

(a) $3(x+1) + 2(x-3) = 1$ (d) $\frac{3}{5}x + \frac{2}{3} = x + \frac{1}{5}$

(b) $\dfrac{x+1}{3} + 2 = \dfrac{3}{2}$ (e) $\dfrac{3(x+1)}{4} = \dfrac{4(x-2)}{6}$

(c) $\dfrac{2x-7}{5} = \dfrac{3}{4}$ (f) $\frac{2}{3}(y-1) = \frac{5}{6}(y+2)$

10. Five times an integer is equal to a number 12 greater than the integer. Find the integer.

11. A number is doubled and then 13 is added, giving 25. Find the number.

12. 5 times a number is greater than 20 by the same amount as 2 times the same number is less than 15. Find the number.

Careful here!

13. Find the number such that, when it is multiplied by $\frac{2}{3}$, the result is 2 larger than the number.

14. The result is the same when a number is divided by 5, as when it is subtracted from 3. Find the number.

15. In multiplying a number by 3 you get the same answer as when you subtract 8 from the number. Find the number.

16. Adding 4 to 3 times a number gives the same answer as doubling the number and subtracting 1. Find the number.

17. The sum of 2 consecutive numbers is equal to 3 times the number that is 5 less than the smaller of the consecutive numbers. Find the 2 consecutive numbers.

18. The product of a number and the number increased by 3 is 6 less than the square of the number. Find the number.

9(a) $x = \frac{4}{5}$
(c) $x = \frac{43}{8}$
(e) $x = -25$
10. 3
11. 6
12. 5
13. −6
14. $\frac{5}{2}$
15. −4
16. −5
17. 16, 17
18. −2

Pattern and Design

These designs were drawn by a student using ruler and compasses only. Try making some of your own!

Maintaining Basic Skills

Exercise 3

1. Simplify.

   (*a*) $1\frac{3}{8} + 2\frac{3}{4} - 1\frac{5}{8}$

   (*b*) $12\frac{3}{5} - 2\frac{7}{10} + \frac{2}{5}$

   (*c*) $\frac{5}{6} - 1\frac{2}{3} + \frac{3}{4}$

   (*d*) $1\frac{7}{10} - 2\frac{3}{5} + 4\frac{1}{4}$

2. Simplify.

   (*a*) $-2 + (-6)$

   (*b*) $5 - (-2)$

   (*c*) $-6 - 4$

   (*d*) $-5 + 2$

   (*e*) $4 + (-3) - 5 - (-1)$

   (*f*) $-3 - 7 + 5 - 9$

   (*g*) $6 - (-4) + 3 - 5$

   (*h*) $3 + (-4) - 2 - (-5)$

3. Find the product or quotient.

   (*a*) $\frac{3}{4} \times \left(-\frac{8}{15}\right)$

   (*b*) $2\frac{1}{4} \times 5\frac{7}{8}$

   (*c*) $\frac{3}{5} \div \frac{9}{10}$

   (*d*) $6\frac{2}{3} \div 4\frac{5}{6}$

   (*e*) $(-2)(3)(-4)$

   (*f*) $5(-2)^2$

   (*g*) $\frac{3}{8} \div (-2)$

   (*h*) $\left(-1\frac{3}{5}\right)\left(-2\frac{1}{6}\right)$

4. Find the product or quotient.

   (*a*) 3.8×5.6

   (*b*) 0.02×53.5

   (*c*) $4.82 \div 3.2$

   (*d*) $12.4 \div 0.016$

   (*e*) $1.05 \times 25 \times 0.03$

   (*f*) $0.58 \div 12$

   (*g*) $6.7 \times 20\,000 \times 0.0045$

   (*h*) $0.0596 \div 0.32$

5. Find the exact value.

   (*a*) $\sqrt{81}$

   (*b*) $\sqrt{4900}$

   (*c*) $\sqrt{7225}$

   (*d*) $\sqrt{\frac{25}{4}}$

   (*e*) $\sqrt{\frac{64}{9}}$

   (*f*) $\sqrt{\frac{49}{4}}$

   (*g*) $\sqrt{46.24}$

   (*h*) $\sqrt{1369}$

   (*i*) $\sqrt{41\,616}$

6. Find the value to two decimal places.

(*a*) $\sqrt{15.36}$ (*b*) $\sqrt{381.54}$ (*c*) $\sqrt{0.9314}$ (*d*) $\sqrt{0.0638}$

7. Solve the following equations.

(*a*) $5x - 4 = 10$
(*b*) $-2y + 5 = 1$
(*c*) $5 + 7y = -3$
(*d*) $1 + 10a = 1$
(*e*) $1 - 3x = 22$
(*f*) $-6x + 2 = -7$

8. Solve the following equations.

(*a*) $0.5x + 3 = 0.75$
(*b*) $0.3x - 1 = 0.4$
(*c*) $\frac{1}{2}x - 3 = \frac{2}{3} + 11$
(*d*) $2.6y = 39$
(*e*) $0.2a - 3.1 = 4.2$
(*f*) $5.2 - 1.6x = 7.9$

9. Simplify.

(*a*) $(1.8 \times 10^2) \times (3.7 \times 10^3)$
(*b*) $(6.4 \times 10^3) \div (1.6 \times 10^2)$
(*c*) $(2.5 \times 10^{-1}) \times (9.1 \times 10^{-3})$
(*d*) $(7.2 \times 10) \div (2.4 \times 10^{-1})$

10. Simplify.

(*a*) $-15 \div 5 + (-2)(-1)$
(*b*) $\frac{20}{-10} + \frac{-12}{-4}$
(*c*) $(-4)^2 + 3^2$
(*d*) $2(-1)^3 - 3(-2)^2$
(*e*) $-5(2)^2 + 6(-1)^2$
(*f*) $\frac{-15}{5} - \frac{24}{-6}$

11. Evaluate the following expressions.

(*a*) $2a - 3b + c$ $a = 1.3$, $b = 2.1$, $c = 5.8$
(*b*) $a^2 - b^2$ $a = 5.1$, $b = 1.7$
(*c*) $p^2 - 2p + 3$ $p = 8.3$
(*d*) $3r - 2s + t$ $r = -2$, $s = 5$, $t = -6$
(*e*) $4a^2 + b^2 - 3c^2$ $a = 1$, $b = -2$, $c = 3$
(*f*) $3yz - 4z^2$ $y = 5$, $z = -1$

6(a) 3.92 **(c)** 0.97
7(a) $x = \frac{14}{5}$ **(e)** $x = -7$
8(a) $x = -4.5$ **(e)** $a = 36.5$
9(a) 6.66×10^5 or 666 000
(c) 2.275×10^{-3} or 0.002 275
10(a) -1 **(e)** -14
11(a) 2.1 **(c)** 55.29

14

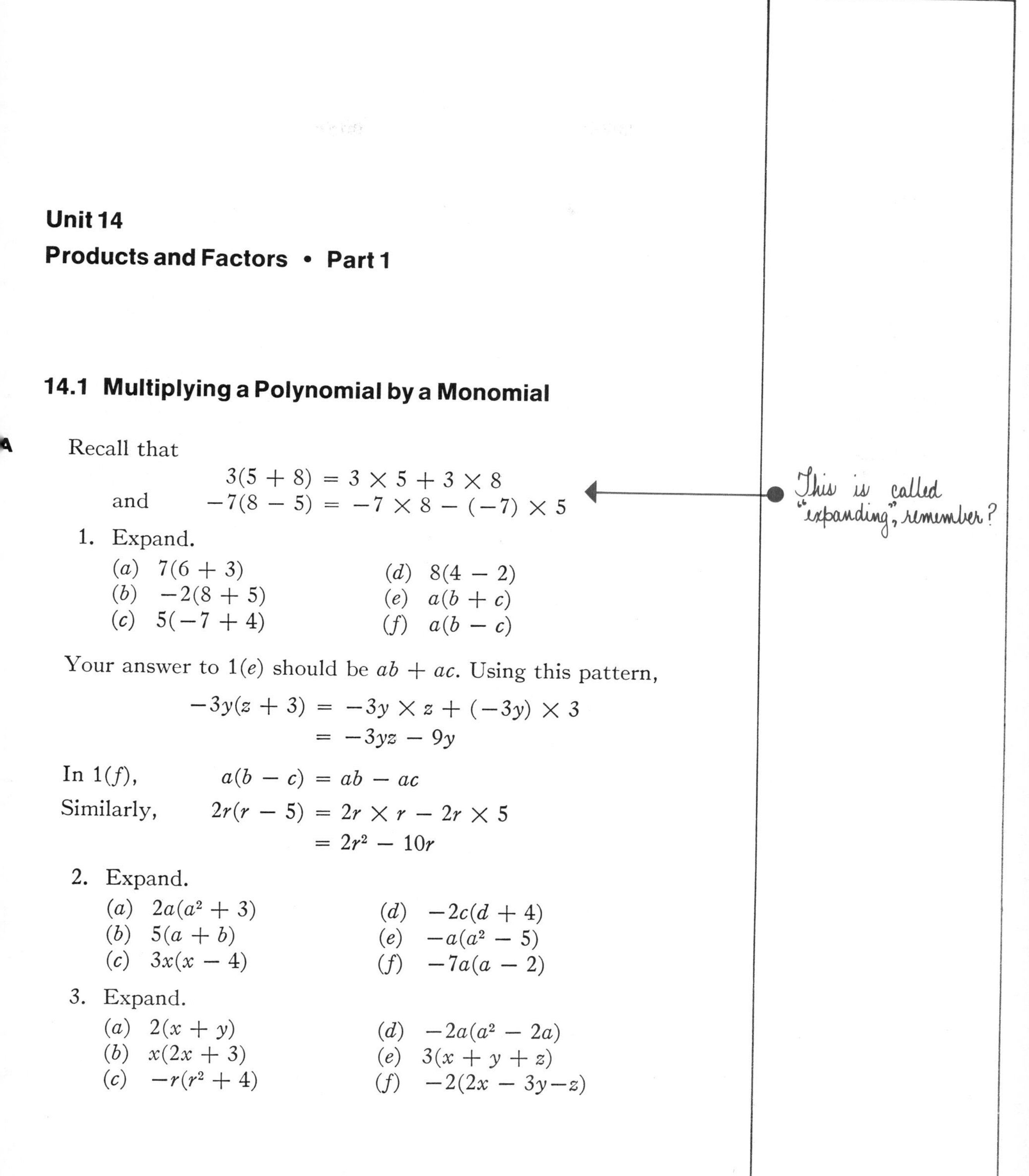

Unit 14

Products and Factors • Part 1

14.1 Multiplying a Polynomial by a Monomial

A Recall that

$$3(5 + 8) = 3 \times 5 + 3 \times 8$$

and

$$-7(8 - 5) = -7 \times 8 - (-7) \times 5$$

This is called "expanding", remember?

1. Expand.

(*a*) $7(6 + 3)$
(*b*) $-2(8 + 5)$
(*c*) $5(-7 + 4)$
(*d*) $8(4 - 2)$
(*e*) $a(b + c)$
(*f*) $a(b - c)$

Your answer to 1(*e*) should be $ab + ac$. Using this pattern,

$$-3y(z + 3) = -3y \times z + (-3y) \times 3$$
$$= -3yz - 9y$$

In 1(*f*), $a(b - c) = ab - ac$

Similarly, $2r(r - 5) = 2r \times r - 2r \times 5$
$$= 2r^2 - 10r$$

2. Expand.

(*a*) $2a(a^2 + 3)$
(*b*) $5(a + b)$
(*c*) $3x(x - 4)$
(*d*) $-2c(d + 4)$
(*e*) $-a(a^2 - 5)$
(*f*) $-7a(a - 2)$

3. Expand.

(*a*) $2(x + y)$
(*b*) $x(2x + 3)$
(*c*) $-r(r^2 + 4)$
(*d*) $-2a(a^2 - 2a)$
(*e*) $3(x + y + z)$
(*f*) $-2(2x - 3y - z)$

In shopping, the cost of 15 items at \$0.99 each is 15(\$1 − 1¢) or \$15 less 15¢.

B Expansion can be used to make multiplication of some numbers easier.

Example

Find the product of 29 and 8; of 503 and 11.

Solution

$$8 \times 29 = 8 \times (30 - 1) = 240 - 8 = 232$$

$$11 \times 503 = 11 \times (500 + 3) = 5500 + 33 = 5533$$

Exercise 14.1

Discussion

1. Expand.
   (*a*) $2(a - b)$
   (*b*) $-3(x + y)$
   (*c*) $-4(p - q)$
   (*d*) $x(x + 2)$
   (*e*) $y(3y - 4)$
   (*f*) $-2x(4x - 5)$

2. Multiply by thinking of the larger number as a sum or a difference.
   (*a*) 5×39
   (*b*) 7×51
   (*c*) 8×48

3. Use the diagram to explain why $a(x + y) = ax + ay$ is reasonable.

	x	y
a	AREA = ?	AREA = ?

4. Expand $(x + y)3$, $(a - b)(-4)$

Written Solutions

5. Expand and simplify.
   (*a*) $3(a + b)$
   (*b*) $-2(x + y)$
   (*c*) $-5(c - d)$
   (*d*) $2x(x + 4)$
   (*e*) $(y - 5)3y$
   (*f*) $5z(3z - 2)$

6. Expand and simplify.
   (*a*) $2(a + b + c)$
   (*b*) $3(x^2 + 2x - 1)$
   (*c*) $-4(m^2 + 3m - 2)$
   (*d*) $(x^2 - 4)2x$
   (*e*) $a^2(a + b)$
   (*f*) $xy(x - 2y)$

5(a) $3a+3b$
(f) $15z^2-10z$
6(a) $2a+2b+2c$
(f) x^2y-2xy^2

7. Multiply by expressing the larger number as a sum or difference.

(*a*) 7×52 (*c*) 21×6 (*e*) 198×7
(*b*) 8×79 (*d*) 5×751 (*f*) 897×8

8. Simplify.

(*a*) $2(x + 2) + 3(x + 4)$ (*d*) $-2(y + 3) - 5(y - 2)$
(*b*) $3(a - 2) + 2(a + 5)$ (*e*) $x(x + 4) + 2(x + 4)$
(*c*) $5(b + 7) - 4(b + 1)$ (*f*) $a(a - 5) - 4(a - 5)$

9. Simplify.

(*a*) $x(x + 2) - 2(x + 2)$ (*d*) $a(a + 6) + 6(a + 6)$
(*b*) $r(r - 5) + 5(r - 5)$ (*e*) $w(w - 4) - 4(w - 4)$
(*c*) $p(p + 4) - 4(p + 4)$ (*f*) $3x(3x - 2) - 2(3x - 2)$

10. Simplify.

(*a*) $7x(3x + 4) + 2(3x + 4)$ (*c*) $-2a(a^2 - b^2) + b(ab - 2)$
(*b*) $3a(2a - 5) - (2a - 5)$ (*d*) $a^2b(a + b) + ab^2(a - b)$

11. Solve.

(*a*) $3(x - 1) - 2(x + 1) = 5$
(*b*) $2(3x + 4) + 4(x - 3) = 7$
(*c*) $x(2x - 3) + 5 = x(2x + 4)$
(*d*) $x(5x - 1) - 3x(x + 2) = x(x - 7) + 9$

7(a) 364 (b) 632 (c) 126 (d) 3755 (e) 1386 (f) 7176
8(a) $5x + 16$ (c) $b + 31$ (e) $x^2 + 6x + 8$
9(a) $x^2 - 4$ (c) $p^2 - 16$ (e) $w^2 - 8w + 16$
10(a) $21x^2 + 34x + 8$ (b) $6a^2 - 17a + 5$ (c) $-2a^3 + 3ab^2 - 2b$ (d) $a^3b + 2a^2b^2 - ab^3$
11(a) $x = 10$ (b) $x = 1.1$ (c) $x = \frac{5}{7}$ (d) $x = 3, x = -3$

14.2 Factors of a Term

1, 2, 3, and 6 divide exactly into 6.
Therefore, {1, 2, 3, 6} is called the *factor set* of 6.

1. State the factor set.

(*a*) 12 (*b*) 20 (*c*) 15 (*d*) 30 (*e*) 24 (*f*) 56

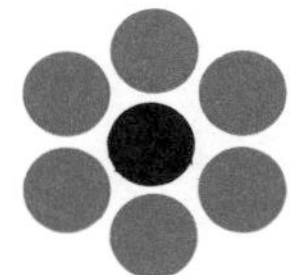

Note that it is also possible to find the *set of variable factors* of a monomial. For instance,

$$\because \frac{a^2b}{a} = ab, \quad \frac{a^2b}{ab} = a, \quad \frac{a^2b}{b} = a^2, \quad \frac{a^2b}{a^2} = b \quad \frac{a^2b}{a^2b} = 1,$$

$\therefore$ $\{a, b, a^2, ab, a^2b\}$ is the set of variable factors of a^2b.

All these divide exactly into a^2b.

2. List the set of variable factors.

(a) x^3 (b) xy^2 (c) x^2y^2

3. $2a$ is one factor of $6ab$. List five other factors that have the coefficients 1, 2, 3 or 6.

4. List as many of the factors as you can that have positive integers as coefficients.

(a) $15x^2$ (b) $18a$ (c) $5xy^2$

hcf

B Two monomials may have factors in common. That is, the same term will divide exactly into each monomial. For example,

(a) $\{1, 2, 3, 6, x, 2x, 3x, 6x, x^2, 2x^2, 3x^2, 6x^2\}$ and (b) $\{1, 3, 9, x, 3x, 9x\}$

are the factor sets of $6x^2$ and $9x$.

The factors that appear in *both* lists are 1, 3, x and $3x$. These are called *common factors* of $9x$ and $6x^2$. $3x$ is called the *highest common factor* (H.C.F.) of $9x$ and $6x^2$. Notice that $3x$ is divisible by all the other common factors.

1. By listing all the factors of each term find the H.C.F.

(a) $5xy$ and $15x$ (b) $4a$ and $8a^2$

Draw a table like the following and complete it.

Terms	*Coefficients*	*H.C.F.*	*Variable Parts*	*H.C.F.*	*H.C.F. of Terms*
$6x^2$, $9x$	6, 9	3	x^2, x	x	$3x$
$5xy$, $15x$					$5x$
$4a$, $8a^2$					$4a$

2. Study the H.C.F.'s of coefficients, variable parts, and terms. How could you find the H.C.F. of two terms by using the H.C.F. of the coefficients and the H.C.F. of the variable parts?

3. State the H.C.F.
   (*a*) 6 and 8
   (*b*) x^2 and x^3
   (*c*) $6x^2$ and $8x^3$
   (*d*) $10a$ and $15a^2$
4. State the H.C.F.
   (*a*) 14 and 21
   (*b*) xy and y^2
   (*c*) $14xy$ and $21y^2$
   (*d*) $12a^2$ and $18b^2$

You know that $6a \times 2b = 12ab$. But there are several pairs of terms whose product is $12ab$, for example, $4a \times 3b$.

1. State the missing factor.
   (*a*) $2a \times \square = 12ab$
   (*b*) $6b \times \square = 12ab$
   (*c*) $12ab \times \square = 12ab$
   (*d*) $5x \times \square = 15x^2$
   (*e*) $3x \times \square = 15x^2$
   (*f*) $3x^2 \times \square = 15x^2$
2. State the missing factor.
   (*a*) $3a \times \square = 6a^2$
   (*b*) $5x \times \square = 5x^2$
   (*c*) $-2a \times \square = -12a$
   (*d*) $3s^2 \times \square = 3s^2$
   (*e*) $-4x \times \square = 4x$
   (*f*) $a^2 \times \square = a^3$

Exercise 14.2

Discussion

1. State the H.C.F.
   (*a*) 3 and 6
   (*b*) 10 and 15
   (*c*) 18 and 24
   (*d*) 21 and 35
2. State the H.C.F.
   (*a*) x^2 and x^3
   (*b*) xy and y
   (*c*) a and a^2
   (*d*) a^2b and a^2b^2
3. State the missing factor.
   (*a*) $3a \times \square = 9a$
   (*b*) $-2b \times \square = -2b^2$
   (*c*) $x^2 \times \square = -3x^3$
   (*d*) $-3r \times \square = 6r^2$
   (*e*) $4x \times \square = -8xy$
   (*f*) $-2a \times \square = 12ab$
   (*g*) $xy \times \square = -xy$
   (*h*) $4a^2 \times \square = 4a^2$
4. How do *you* determine the H.C.F.
   (*a*) of two numbers?
   (*b*) of the variable parts of two terms?
5. What method did *you* use to find the missing factors in Question 3?

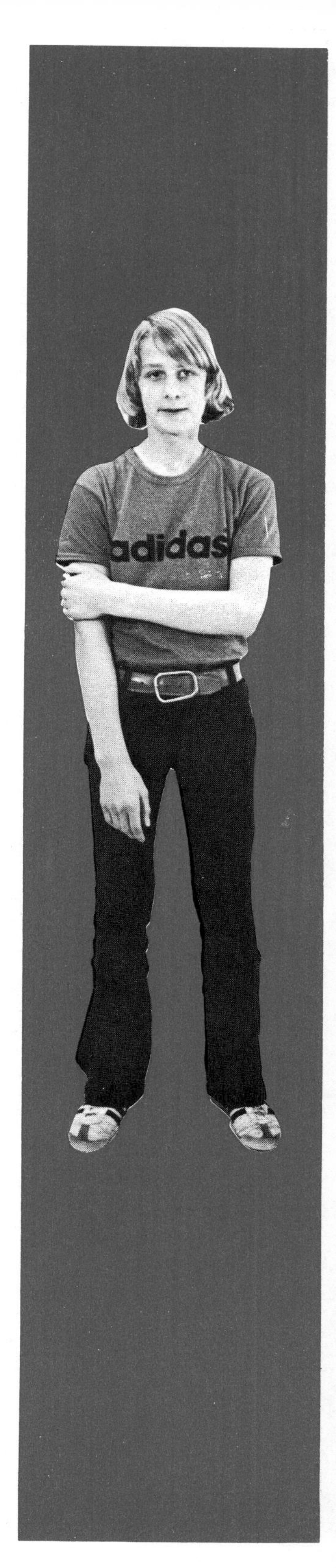

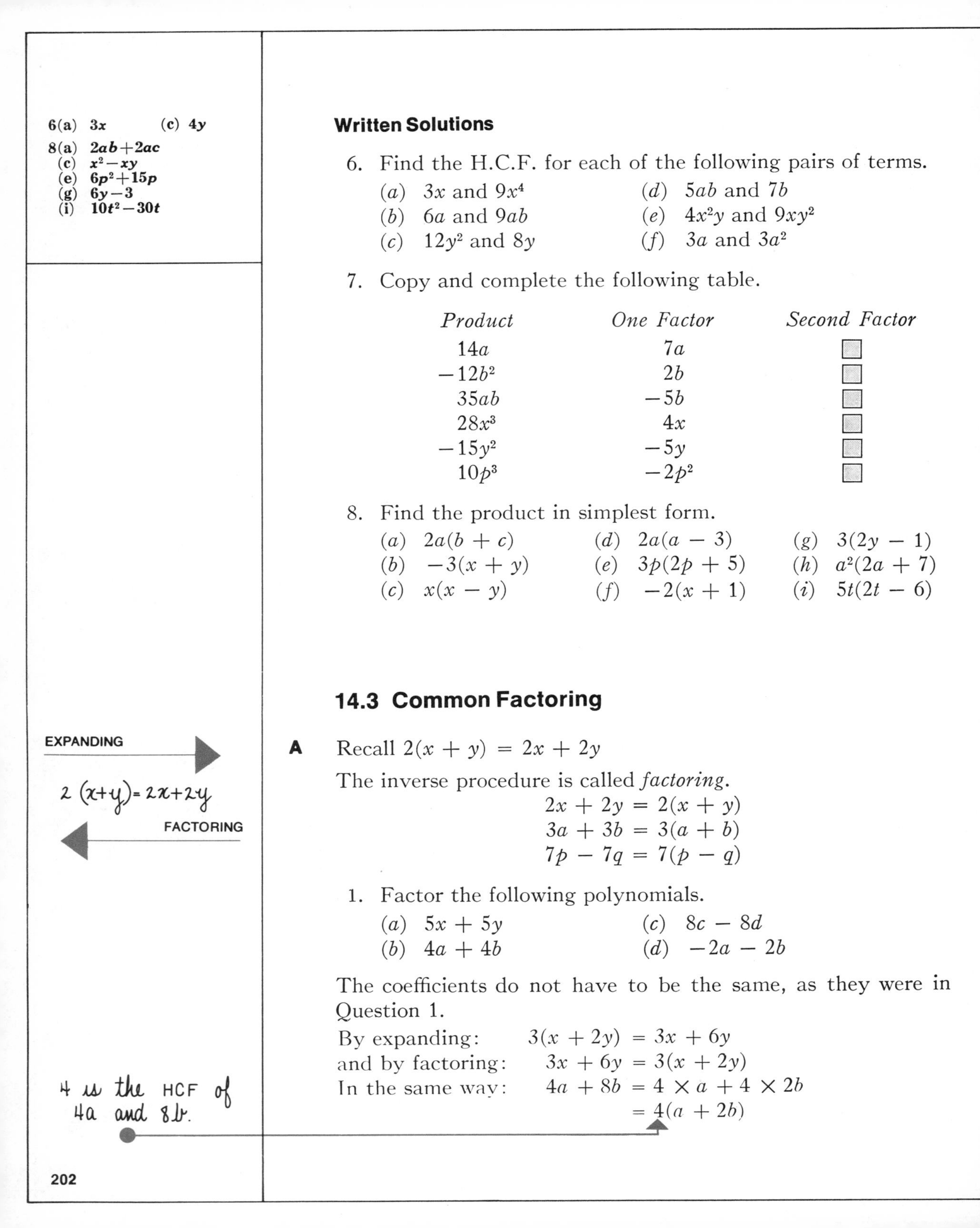

6(a) $3x$ (c) $4y$

8(a) $2ab+2ac$
(c) x^2-xy
(e) $6p^2+15p$
(g) $6y-3$
(i) $10t^2-30t$

Written Solutions

6. Find the H.C.F. for each of the following pairs of terms.
   (*a*) $3x$ and $9x^4$
   (*b*) $6a$ and $9ab$
   (*c*) $12y^2$ and $8y$
   (*d*) $5ab$ and $7b$
   (*e*) $4x^2y$ and $9xy^2$
   (*f*) $3a$ and $3a^2$

7. Copy and complete the following table.

Product	*One Factor*	*Second Factor*
$14a$	$7a$	☐
$-12b^2$	$2b$	☐
$35ab$	$-5b$	☐
$28x^3$	$4x$	☐
$-15y^2$	$-5y$	☐
$10p^3$	$-2p^2$	☐

8. Find the product in simplest form.
   (*a*) $2a(b + c)$
   (*b*) $-3(x + y)$
   (*c*) $x(x - y)$
   (*d*) $2a(a - 3)$
   (*e*) $3p(2p + 5)$
   (*f*) $-2(x + 1)$
   (*g*) $3(2y - 1)$
   (*h*) $a^2(2a + 7)$
   (*i*) $5t(2t - 6)$

14.3 Common Factoring

EXPANDING

$2(x+y) = 2x+2y$

FACTORING

A Recall $2(x + y) = 2x + 2y$

The inverse procedure is called *factoring*.

$$2x + 2y = 2(x + y)$$
$$3a + 3b = 3(a + b)$$
$$7p - 7q = 7(p - q)$$

1. Factor the following polynomials.
   (*a*) $5x + 5y$
   (*b*) $4a + 4b$
   (*c*) $8c - 8d$
   (*d*) $-2a - 2b$

The coefficients do not have to be the same, as they were in Question 1.

By expanding: $3(x + 2y) = 3x + 6y$

and by factoring: $3x + 6y = 3(x + 2y)$

In the same way: $4a + 8b = 4 \times a + 4 \times 2b$
$= 4(a + 2b)$

4 is the HCF of 4a and 8b.

Here's the pattern
a × b + a × c
= a (b + c).
2x is the HCF
of 2x² and 4x.

2. Factor.

(*a*) $2a + 4b$ (*c*) $20c + 4d$

(*b*) $6x + 18y$ (*d*) $7x - 14$

3. Complete the following steps to expand $5(2x + 3y)$.

$$5(2x + 3y) = 5 \times \square + 5 \times \square$$
$$= \square + \square$$

4. Complete the following steps to factor $6a + 9b$.

$$6a + 9b = \square \times 2a + \square \times 3b$$
$$= \square\,(2a + 3b)$$

5. Complete the following steps to factor $12x + 20y$.

$$12x + 20y = 4 \times \square + \square \times \square$$
$$= \square\,(\square + \square)$$

6. Complete the following steps to factor $10x - 25y$.

$$10x - 25y = \square \times \square - 5 \times \square$$
$$= \square(\square - \square)$$

In Questions 4, 5, and 6 there are 2 steps. In the first step, each term is factored so that the terms have a factor in common. This factor is called the *highest common factor* of the 2 terms.

7. Factor.

(*a*) $4x + 6y$ (*c*) $12a + 16b$

(*b*) $10x - 15y$ (*d*) $15x - 9y$

The common factor in the terms of a binomial can also be a variable.

By expanding: $x(x + 1) = x^2 + x$

$\therefore$ by factoring: $x^2 + x = x(x + 1)$

Similarly, $2x^2 + 4x = 2x \times x + 2x \times 2$

$= 2x(x + 2)$

Q1
Q2

Use Question 1 to help you with Question 2.

1. State the H.C.F.
   (*a*) $4a$ and $4ab$
   (*b*) $6xy$ and $9x$
   (*c*) $3x^2$ and $6x$
   (*d*) $10a^2$ and $15a$
   (*e*) $3ab$ and $12b$
   (*f*) $12a^3$ and $20a^2$

2. Factor.
   (*a*) $4a + 4ab$
   (*b*) $6xy + 9x$
   (*c*) $3x^2 - 6x$
   (*d*) $10a^2 - 15a$
   (*e*) $3ab + 12b$
   (*f*) $12a^3 - 20a^2$

Exercise 14.3

Discussion

1. How can you check your answers in factoring?

2. Expand.
   (*a*) $5(x + y)$
   (*b*) $3(a - b)$
   (*c*) $2(x + 1)$
   (*d*) $4(a + 2b)$
   (*e*) $5(2p - q)$
   (*f*) $10(2c + 3d)$

3. State the HCF of the terms in each binomial.
   (*a*) $5x + 5y$
   (*b*) $3a - 3b$
   (*c*) $2x + 2$
   (*d*) $4a + 8b$
   (*e*) $10p - 5q$
   (*f*) $10c + 30d$

Written Solutions

4. Factor.
   (*a*) $3a + 3b$
   (*b*) $5s - 5t$
   (*c*) $10x + 10y$
   (*d*) $23c - 23d$
   (*e*) $38m + 38n$
   (*f*) $-28x - 28y$

5. Factor and check by expanding.
   (*a*) $3a + 6$
   (*b*) $4x - 8$
   (*c*) $5y + 10$
   (*d*) $6m + 9t$
   (*e*) $8c - 12d$
   (*f*) $14x - 21y$

6. Factor and check.
   (*a*) $x^2 + xy$
   (*b*) $p^2 - 2pq$
   (*c*) $3a^2 + ab$
   (*d*) $4a^2 + 6ab$
   (*e*) $10x^2 - 15xy$
   (*f*) $20p^2 - 12pq$

4(a) $3(a+b)$
(c) $10(x+y)$
(e) $38(m+n)$

5(a) $3(a+2)$
(c) $5(y+2)$
(e) $4(2c-3d)$

7. Factor and check.

(*a*) $x^2 + 3x$
(*b*) $2a^2 + 4a$
(*c*) $6y^3 - 9y^2$
(*d*) $12r^4 - 9r^2$
(*e*) $15xy - 10y$
(*f*) $16ab + 24a$

8. Factor.

(*a*) $6a^2 + 6$
(*b*) $4ab - b^2$
(*c*) $5x - 10$
(*d*) $4p^2 - 6pq$
(*e*) $15x^2 - 5x$
(*f*) $-x^2y - xy^2$

9. Factor.

(*a*) $3a + 6ab$
(*b*) $9xy - 18y$
(*c*) $15x^3 + 25x^2$
(*d*) $xy + x$
(*e*) $-7x^2y - 14xy^2$
(*f*) $4abc - 6ac$

10. Factor.

(*a*) $4m^2 - 8mn + 12$
(*b*) $3a^2b^3 + 6ab^2 + 24a^2b^2$
(*c*) $12x^2y - 3xy^2 - 33x^3y + 15x^2y^2 - 3xy$

8(a) $6(a^2+1)$
(c) $5(x-2)$
(e) $5x(3x-1)$
9(a) $3a(1+2b)$
(c) $5x^2(3x+5)$
(e) $-7xy(x+2y)$
10(a) $4(m^2-2mn+3)$
(b) $3ab^2(ab+2+8a)$
(c) $3xy(4x-y-11x^2+5xy-1)$

Puzzlers

1. If 3 cats eat 3 mice in 3 min, how long will it take 50 cats to eat 50 mice?

2. Casey Jones driving a 24-car train along a single track meets Rod Railer driving a train of 30 cars. They stop near a siding that can hold 20 cars. How do they manage to pass?

3. Suppose you know that one of 8 similar coins is counterfeit and heavier than the others. By using an equal-arm balance twice only, how can you determine which one it is?

4. A rope hangs over the side of a ship and is submerged 3 m. If the tide rises 0.5 m/h, how much of the rope is submerged after 3 h?

5. If in your bureau drawer there are 10 blue socks and 16 gray socks and you reach into it in the dark, how many socks must you take out to be sure of getting two that match?

Unit 15
Products and Factors • Part 2

15.1 Multiplying Binomials

1. Recall that

$$b(b + 5) = b^2 + 5b$$
$$\text{and } (b + 5)b = b^2 + 5b$$

Remember the pattern?
$(b + c)a = ba + ca$

2. Expand.

(*a*) $(b + 1)5$
(*b*) $(x - 3)4$
(*c*) $(y + 6)(-1)$
(*d*) $(2r + 3)(-4)$

The more familiar pattern for expanding is $a(b + c) = ab + ac$, which could be written $\square(b + c) = \square \times b + \square \times c$. Thus,

$$\square(x + 3) = \square \times x + \square \times 3$$

Could $\square = (x + 4)$?

$$\begin{aligned}(x + 4)(x + 3) &= (x + 4)x + (x + 4)3 \\ &= x^2 + 4x + 3x + 12 \\ &= x^2 + 7x + 12\end{aligned}$$

3. Complete the following expansions.

(*a*) $(x + 5)(x + 7) = (x + 5) \times \square + (x + 5) \times \square$
(*b*) $(a + 6)(a + 3) = (a + 6) \times \square + (a + 6) \times \square$
(*c*) $(2a + 5)(3a + 1) = \square \times 3a + \square \times 1$
(*d*) $(x - 3)(x - 2) = (x - 3) \times \square + (x - 3) \times \square$

Now you are able to multiply two binomials such as $5x - 4$ and $3x + 7$.

Example

$$\begin{aligned}(5x - 4)(3x + 7) &= (5x - 4)3x + (5x - 4)7\\ &= 15x^2 - 12x + 35x - 28\\ &= 15x^2 + 23x - 28\end{aligned}$$

4. Expand and simplify.

   (*a*) $(x + 3)(x + 4)$
   (*b*) $(a + 2)(a - 7)$
   (*c*) $(x - 2)(x + 4)$
   (*d*) $(2y + 5)(3y + 7)$

Exercise 15.1

Discussion

1. State the product.

   (*a*) $x(x + 4)$
   (*b*) $2y(y + 5)$
   (*c*) $-5(x - 6)$
   (*d*) $3a(a - 5)$
   (*e*) $-2(r + 4)$
   (*f*) $5(6x - 3)$

2. Use the areas of rectangles A, B, C, and D to show that

$$\begin{aligned}(x + 1)(x + 6) &= x(x + 6) + 1(x + 6)\\ &= x^2 + 6x + 1x + 6\end{aligned}$$

2.

$x + 6$

x | 6

$x + 1$

x A | C

1 B | D

3. State the first line you would write when multiplying the following.

   (*a*) $(a + 5)(a - 2)$
   (*b*) $(c - 4)(c + 7)$
   (*c*) $(x - 3)(x - 5)$
   (*d*) $(2y - 4)(5y + 7)$

Written Solutions

4. Expand and simplify.

   (*a*) $(x + 4)(x + 5)$
   (*b*) $(y + 3)(y + 8)$
   (*c*) $(b + 7)(b + 2)$
   (*d*) $(a + 1)(a - 4)$
   (*e*) $(r + 3)(r - 7)$
   (*f*) $(r + 5)(r - 1)$

5. Expand and simplify.

   (*a*) $(p - 2)(p + 4)$
   (*b*) $(t - 3)(t + 7)$
   (*c*) $(h - 5)(h + 2)$
   (*d*) $(a - 4)(a - 3)$
   (*e*) $(x - 10)(x - 5)$
   (*f*) $(y + 7)(y - 7)$

6. Expand and simplify.

   (*a*) $(2x + 5)(x + 3)$
   (*b*) $(y + 4)(3y + 7)$
   (*c*) $(2a + 6)(3a + 5)$
   (*d*) $(t - 4)(3t + 10)$
   (*e*) $(2m - 3)(5m + 6)$
   (*f*) $(3h - 1)(h + 8)$

4(a) $x^2+9x+20$
(c) $b^2+9b+14$
(e) $r^2-4r-21$

5(a) p^2+2p-8
(c) $h^2-3h-10$
(e) $x^2-15x+50$

6(a) $2x^2+11x+15$
(c) $6a^2+28a+30$
(e) $10m^2-3m-18$

7. A rectangular yard measures $(4x - 1)$ metres by $(3x + 2)$ metres. Find its area in square metres.

8. $(x + 4)$ classes contain $(2x - 3)$ students each. How many students are there in all $(x + 4)$ classes?

9. A square measures x metres by x metres. Find the area, in square metres, of the rectangle whose length is 1 m greater than twice the side of the square and whose width is 3 m less than the side of the square.

7. $(12x^2 + 5x - 2)$ m^2
8. $(2x^2 + 5x - 12)$ students
9. $(2x^2 + 5x - 3)$ m^2

9.

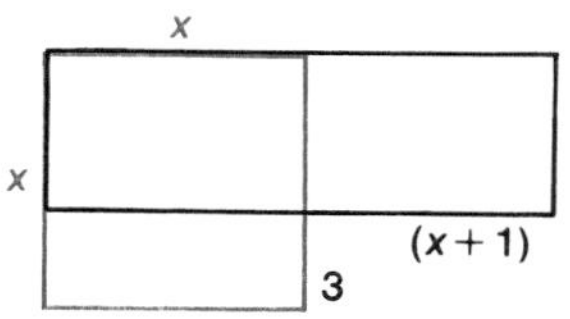

15.2 Shorter Methods for Multiplying Binomials

There are some "thinking steps" that need not be written when multiplying binomials.

$$(y + 3)(y + 5) = y(y + 5) + 3(y + 5)$$

$$= y^2 + 5y + 3y + 15$$

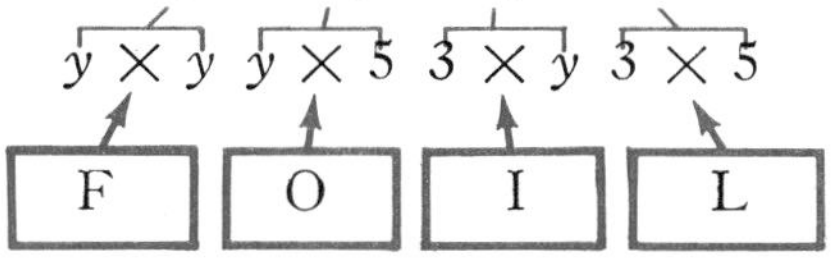

$$y \times y \quad y \times 5 \quad 3 \times y \quad 3 \times 5$$

F O I L

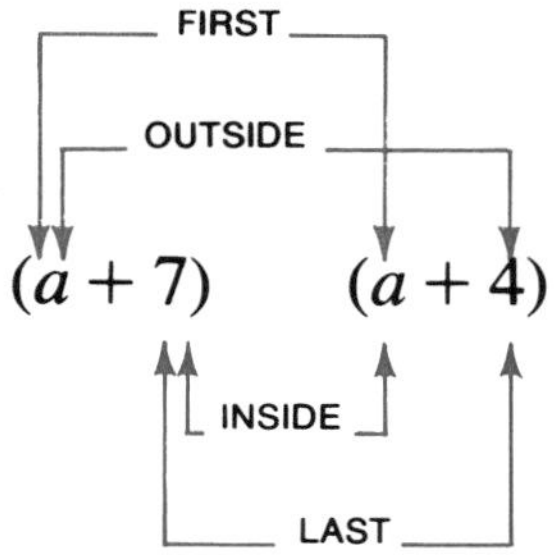

Now try this one.

$$(a + 7)(a + 4) = \overset{F}{a^2} + \overset{O}{4a} + \overset{I}{7a} + \overset{L}{28}$$
$$= a^2 + 11a + 28$$

1. Expand and simplify.
   (*a*) $(x + 2)(x + 3)$
   (*b*) $(a + 6)(a + 2)$
   (*c*) $(r - 2)(r + 5)$
   (*d*) $(c - 5)(c + 8)$

The rule of FOIL may be used in more complicated products.

$$\overset{F}{3x \times 4x} \quad \overset{O}{3x \times 8} \quad \overset{I}{-5 \times 4x} \quad \overset{L}{-5 \times 8}$$

$$(3x - 5)(4x + 8) = 12x^2 + 24x - 20x - 40$$
$$= 12x^2 + 4x - 40$$

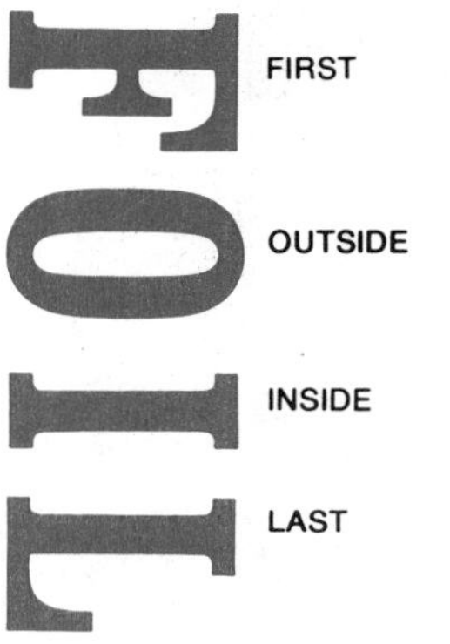

2. Expand and simplify.

(*a*) $(2a + 3)(a + 5)$
(*b*) $(3x + 4)(2x + 7)$
(*c*) $(5b + 2)(b - 1)$
(*d*) $(6y - 3)(5y - 1)$

B Study the following products and see if you can state the final answer without performing middle steps.

$$\begin{aligned}(a + 5)(a + 4) &= a^2 + 4a + 5a + 20 \\ &= a^2 + 9a + 20\end{aligned}$$

$$\begin{aligned}(x + 2)(x + 3) &= x^2 + 3x + 2x + 6 \\ &= x^2 + 5x + 6\end{aligned}$$

1. How do you find the first and last terms in the answer?

2. Do you see a short way of finding these middle terms, $9a$ and $5x$? Read the next two examples. Does your method work?

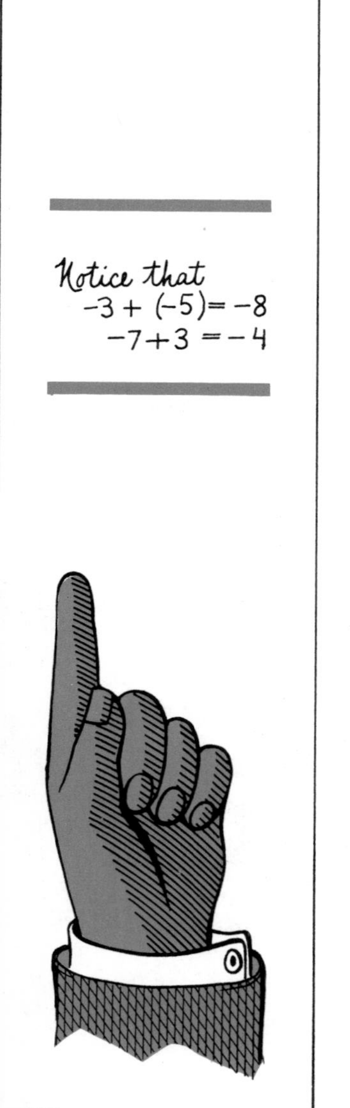

$$\begin{aligned}(y - 3)(y - 5) &= y^2 - 5y - 3y + 15 \\ &= y^2 - 8y + 15\end{aligned}$$

$$\begin{aligned}(r - 7)(r + 3) &= r^2 + 3r - 7r - 21 \\ &= r^2 - 4r - 21\end{aligned}$$

3. State the product.

(*a*) $(x + 2)(x + 6)$
(*b*) $(c + 3)(c + 5)$
(*c*) $(a - 2)(a - 8)$
(*d*) $(d - 1)(d - 4)$

Exercise 15.2

Discussion

1. State the product of $x + 3$ and $x + 5$. What short cuts do *you* use?

2. Will the same short cut work for $(3x + 4)(x + 5)$?

3. State the four terms in the product of $5y - 2$ and $3y + 6$. How do you obtain each term?

4. State the product using the short cut.

(*a*) $(y + 6)(y + 4)$ (*b*) $(x - 4)(x - 5)$ (*c*) $(a + 6)(a - 2)$ (*d*) $(r - 3)(r + 1)$ (*e*) $(p + 3)(p - 7)$ (*f*) $(q - 4)(q + 9)$

5. State the product. (Do not add like terms.)

(*a*) $(2a + 3)(a + 5)$ (*b*) $(x + 4)(3x + 6)$ (*c*) $(2x + 5)(3x + 1)$ (*d*) $(5r - 2)(r - 1)$ (*e*) $(4r - 3)(2r - 5)$ (*f*) $(6p - 4)(2p - 1)$

Written Solutions

6. Multiply the following numbers by first writing them as binomials.

(*a*) 31×42 (*b*) 49×71 (*c*) 34×82 (*d*) 89×29

Like this!

43×82

$= (40 + 3) \times (80 + 2)$

$= (40 \times 80) + (40 \times 2) + (3 \times 80) + (3 \times 2)$

$= 3200 + 80 + 240 + 6$

$= 3526$

7. Expand. (Use the short cut to state the answer.)

(*a*) $(a + 2)(a + 1)$ (*b*) $(x + 5)(x + 7)$ (*c*) $(s + 2)(s + 3)$ (*d*) $(r - 3)(r - 7)$ (*e*) $(p - 5)(p - 2)$ (*f*) $(y - 10)(y - 8)$

8. Expand.

(*a*) $(2x + 3)(x + 1)$ (*b*) $(3x - 5)(x - 4)$ (*c*) $(5a - 2)(5a + 2)$ (*d*) $(3a + 5)(3a + 5)$ (*e*) $(y - 4)(2y + 7)$ (*f*) $(w + 6)(5w - 8)$

After expanding combine like terms.

9. Expand.

(*a*) $(x + 3)(x - 2)$ (*b*) $(a - 4)(a + 7)$ (*c*) $(p - 3)(p + 1)$ (*d*) $(q + 2)(q - 9)$ (*e*) $(c - 3)(c - 8)$ (*f*) $(y - 3)(y + 10)$

10. Expand.

(*a*) $(3a + 5)(3a - 5)$ (*b*) $(y + 4)(y - 12)$ (*c*) $(a + 5)(3a - 1)$ (*d*) $(x + 2y)(x + 5y)$ (*e*) $(2x - 7)(3x + 10)$ (*f*) $(p - 3q)(p - 7q)$

11. Expand.

(*a*) $(3p - 2q)(2p - 5q)$ (*b*) $(2 - 4x)(3 + 5x)$ (*c*) $(3a - 2b)(3a - 2b)$ (*d*) $(1 + 4x)(3 + 7x)$

12. Expand.

(*a*) $(x + 2)(x^2 + 2x + 1)$ (*b*) $(a + b)(x + y + z)$

6(a) 1302 **(b)** 3479 **(c)** 2788 **(d)** 2581
7(a) a^2+3a+2 **(c)** s^2+5s+6 **(e)** $p^2-7p+10$
8(a) $2x^2+5x+3$ **(c)** $25a^2-4$ **(e)** $2y^2-y-28$
9(a) x^2+x-6 **(c)** p^2-2p-3 **(e)** $c^2-11c+24$
10(a) $9a^2-25$ **(c)** $3a^2+14a-5$ **(e)** $6x^2-x-70$
11(a) $6p^2-19pq+10q^2$ **(c)** $9a^2-12ab+4b^2$
12(a) x^3+4x^2+5x+2

Binomial: 2 terms
$x+4$

Trinomial: 3 terms
x^2+5x+4

$(y+1)(y+8)$

$\therefore$ middle term is ▩

15.3 Factors of Trinomials

A When two binomials like $(x + 2)$ and $(x + 3)$ are multiplied, a trinomial results.

$$(x + 2)(x + 3) = x^2 + 5x + 6$$

1. Multiply.
   (*a*) $(a + 3)(a + 5)$
   (*b*) $(y + 4)(y + 2)$
   (*c*) $(5 + t)(4 + t)$
   (*d*) $(x + 2)(x + 7)$

You may reverse this process and factor trinomials into two binomials.

$$x^2 + 5x + 6 = (x + 2)(x + 3)$$
$$a^2 + 8a + 15 = (a + 3)(a + 5)$$

2. State the missing terms in the following.
   (*a*) $x^2 + 7x + 10 = (\square + 2)(\square + 5)$
   (*b*) $a^2 + 3a + 2 = (\square + 1)(\square + 2)$
   (*c*) $y^2 + 6y + 5 = (\square + 1)(\square + 5)$
   (*d*) $4 + 5y + y^2 = (4 + \square)(1 + \square)$
   (*e*) $8 + 6a + a^2 = (2 + \square)(4 + \square)$
   (*f*) $x^2 + 4x + 3 = (x + \square)(x + \square)$
   (*g*) $p^2 + 8p + 7 = (p + \square)(p + \square)$
   (*h*) $r^2 + 8r + 15 = (\square + \square)(r + 3)$
   (*i*) $k^2 - 7k + 12 = (k - 3)(\square - \square)$
   (*j*) $m^2 - 6m - 72 = (m + 6)(\square - \square)$

Example 1

Factor (*a*) $x^2 + 12x + 11$
(*b*) $y^2 + 6y + 8$

Solution

(*a*) $x^2 + 12x + 11 = (x + 1)(x + 11)$

(*b*) Although there appear to be two ways of factoring $y^2 + 6y + 8$, a check by expanding shows that one answer is wrong. Can you find the wrong one?

(i) $y^2 + 6y + 8 = (y + 1)(y + 8)$
(ii) $y^2 + 6y + 8 = (y + 2)(y + 4)$

3. By expansion find which of the following are correct.
   (*a*) $x^2 + 7x + 21 = (x + 3)(x + 7)$
   (*b*) $y^2 + 10y + 16 = (y + 2)(y + 8)$
   (*c*) $a^2 + 5a + 4 = (a + 2)(a + 2)$
   (*d*) $b^2 + 6b + 9 = (b + 3)(b + 3)$

4. The number term in the trinomial helps you to find the numbers in the factors. For example, to factor $x^2 + 9x + 20$ the factors could be $(x + 1)(x + 20)$
   or $(x + 2)(x + 10)$
   or $(x + 4)(x + 5)$
   — Which of these is correct?

5. Factor.
   (*a*) $p^2 + 4p + 3$
   (*b*) $x^2 + 8x + 7$
   (*c*) $q^2 + 10q + 16$
   (*d*) $b^2 + 12b + 20$

So far the trinomials factored have had only positive coefficients. Expand the following products and study the pattern of the signs.

1. Expand.
   (*a*) $(y - 1)(y - 2)$
   (*b*) $(a - 3)(a - 7)$
   (*c*) $(x - 4)(x - 2)$
   (*d*) $(p - 6)(p - 5)$

In each case note the sign of
(a) the middle term,
(b) the last term.

Example 2

Factor $k^2 - 7k + 12$.

Solution

Since the last term, 12, is positive, we know that the two numbers in the factors could be one of the following pairs.

12, 1	−12, −1
6, 2	−6, −2
4, 3	−4, −3

From the middle term −7 the correct pair is −4, −3 since $-4 + (-3) = -7$.

$\therefore\ k^2 - 7k + 12 = (k - 4)(k - 3)$

2. Factor.
   (*a*) $x^2 - 6x + 5$
   (*b*) $a^2 - 4a + 3$
   (*c*) $p^2 - 5p + 6$
   (*d*) $q^2 - 7q + 10$

First Outside Inside Last

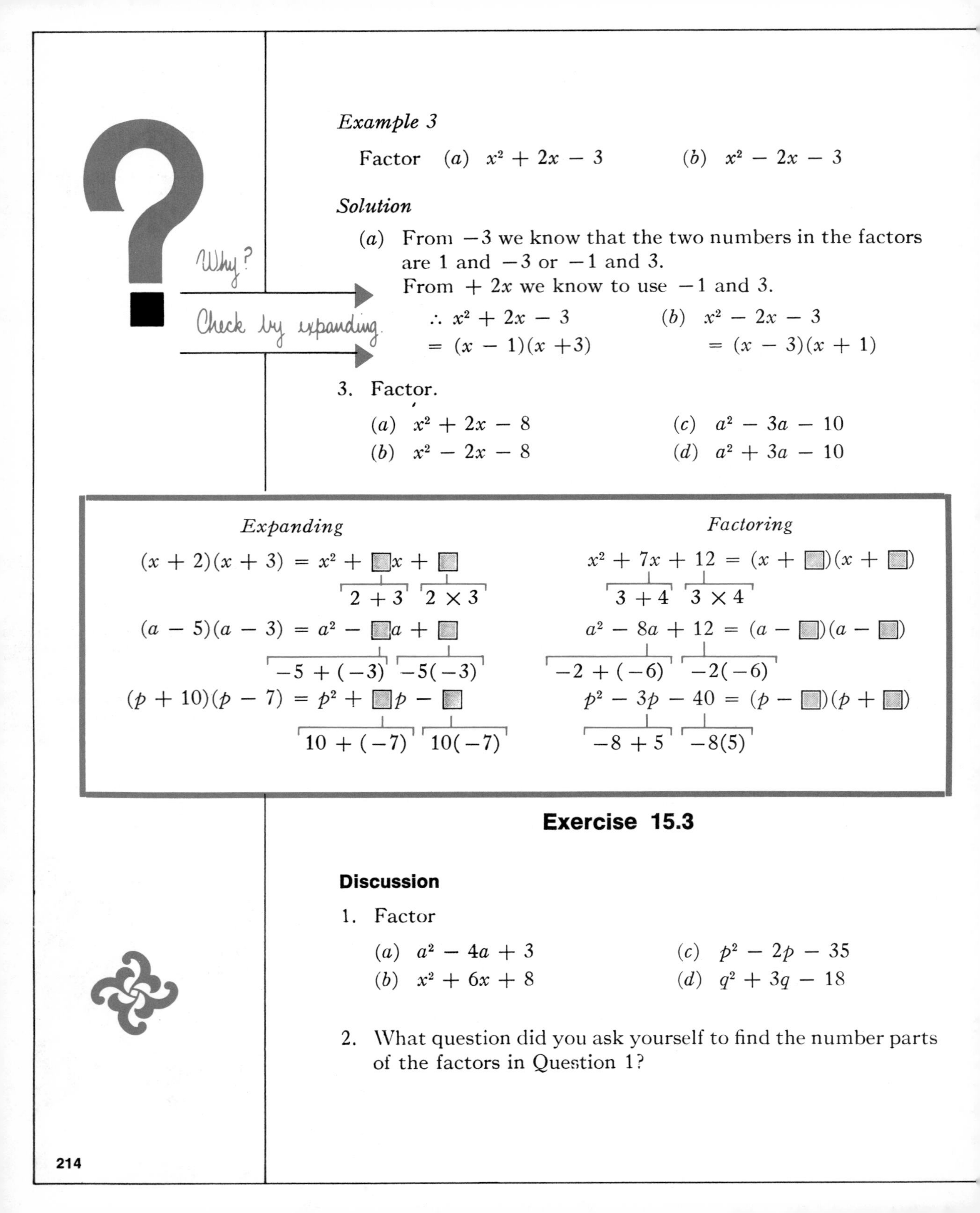

Example 3

Factor (*a*) $x^2 + 2x - 3$ (*b*) $x^2 - 2x - 3$

Solution

(*a*) From -3 we know that the two numbers in the factors are 1 and -3 or -1 and 3.
From $+2x$ we know to use -1 and 3.

Why?

Check by expanding.

$\therefore x^2 + 2x - 3$
$= (x - 1)(x + 3)$

(*b*) $x^2 - 2x - 3$
$= (x - 3)(x + 1)$

3. Factor.

(*a*) $x^2 + 2x - 8$
(*b*) $x^2 - 2x - 8$
(*c*) $a^2 - 3a - 10$
(*d*) $a^2 + 3a - 10$

Expanding	*Factoring*
$(x + 2)(x + 3) = x^2 + \square x + \square$	$x^2 + 7x + 12 = (x + \square)(x + \square)$
$2 + 3$ $\quad 2 \times 3$	$3 + 4$ $\quad 3 \times 4$
$(a - 5)(a - 3) = a^2 - \square a + \square$	$a^2 - 8a + 12 = (a - \square)(a - \square)$
$-5 + (-3)$ $\quad -5(-3)$	$-2 + (-6)$ $\quad -2(-6)$
$(p + 10)(p - 7) = p^2 + \square p - \square$	$p^2 - 3p - 40 = (p - \square)(p + \square)$
$10 + (-7)$ $\quad 10(-7)$	$-8 + 5$ $\quad -8(5)$

Exercise 15.3

Discussion

1. Factor

(*a*) $a^2 - 4a + 3$
(*b*) $x^2 + 6x + 8$
(*c*) $p^2 - 2p - 35$
(*d*) $q^2 + 3q - 18$

2. What question did you ask yourself to find the number parts of the factors in Question 1?

3. For each of the following, state two numbers
   (i) whose product is shown in row A, and
   (ii) whose sum is shown in row B.

A	5	10	20	15	20	−7	−7	−8	−9	−12
B	6	7	−9	−8	21	6	−6	−2	8	1

4. (*a*) Expand.
   $(a + 2b)(a + 5b)$
   $(p - 3q)(p - 4q)$
   $(1 + x)(1 + 4x)$
   $(2 - x)(4 - x)$

   (*b*) Factor.
   $a^2 + 7ab + 12b^2$
   $p^2 - 6pq + 9q^2$
   $1 + 3x + 2x^2$
   $8 - 6x + x^2$

Written Solutions

5. Factor.
   (*a*) $x^2 + 3x + 2$
   (*b*) $a^2 + 10a + 21$
   (*c*) $p^2 + 10p + 25$
   (*d*) $q^2 + 9q + 14$
   (*e*) $m^2 - 4m + 4$
   (*f*) $c^2 - 11c + 28$
   (*g*) $b^2 - 12b + 32$
   (*h*) $y^2 - 13y + 40$

6. Factor.
   (*a*) $x^2 - 8x + 12$
   (*b*) $a^2 + 11a + 30$
   (*c*) $y^2 - 13y + 42$
   (*d*) $b^2 + 15b + 56$
   (*e*) $4 + 5x + x^2$
   (*f*) $10 - 7x + x^2$
   (*g*) $6 + 7x + x^2$
   (*h*) $18 - 9x + x^2$

7. Factor.
   (*a*) $y^2 + 2y - 15$
   (*b*) $y^2 - 2y - 15$
   (*c*) $b^2 + 5b - 50$
   (*d*) $a^2 - 5a - 50$
   (*e*) $x^2 + x - 20$
   (*f*) $x^2 - x - 20$
   (*g*) $m^2 + 7m - 18$
   (*h*) $p^2 - 7p - 18$

8. Factor.
   (*a*) $w^2 + w - 30$
   (*b*) $t^2 - 2t - 35$
   (*c*) $r^2 - 3r - 88$
   (*d*) $x^2 + 4x - 12$
   (*e*) $y^2 + 5y - 6$
   (*f*) $h^2 - 2h - 63$

9. Factor.
   (*a*) $a^2 + 3ab + 2b^2$
   (*b*) $p^2 - 6pq + 8q^2$
   (*c*) $x^2 + 12xy + 35y^2$
   (*d*) $r^2 + 2rt - 15t^2$
   (*e*) $c^2 - 4cd - 5d^2$
   (*f*) $a^2 - 7ab + 10b^2$

Unit 16

Products and Factors • Part 3

In Unit 15 you studied the expansion of 2 binomials and the factoring of trinomials. There are 2 special types of factoring associated with trinomials that we will study in this unit.

F O I L

$(a + b)(c + d)$

16.1 The Pattern $a^2 - b^2$

1. Expand.

(a) $(p + q)(p - q)$

(b) $(x - y)(x + y)$

(c) $(2p + 3)(2p - 3)$

(d) $(c - 5d)(c + 5d)$

How many terms do you get in each answer? Why don't you get three terms?

Example 1

Expand $(6x - 4y)(6x + 4y)$

Solution

$$(6x - 4y)(6x + 4y)$$
$$= 36x^2 + 24xy - 24xy - 16y^2$$
$$= 36x^2 - 16y^2$$

Notice that $(6x)^2 - (4y)^2 = 36x^2 - 16y^2$

How could you find the answer without using the second step?

2. State the product.

(a) $(x + 2)(x - 2)$

(b) $(a + 5)(a - 5)$

(c) $(4t - 1)(4t + 1)$

(d) $(10y + 2z)(10y - 2z)$

B The product of $(a + b)$ and $(a - b)$ is $a^2 - b^2$. Therefore, by factoring, $a^2 - b^2 = (a + b)(a - b)$.

1. Factor.

   (*a*) $x^2 - y^2$
   (*b*) $c^2 - d^2$
   (*c*) $s^2 - t^2$
   (*d*) $a^2 - 9$

In each part of Question 1, how many terms were there? What sign was between the terms? Are these terms special in any way?

Example 2

(*a*) Factor $4x^2 - 9$

(*b*) Factor $25y^2 - 16z^2$

Solution

(*a*)

$$\begin{aligned} & 4x^2 - 9 \\ &= (2x)^2 - (3)^2 \\ &= (2x - 3)(2x + 3) \end{aligned}$$

2x is a square root of $4x^2$
3 is a square root of 9.

(*b*)

$$\begin{aligned} & 25y^2 - 16z^2 \\ &= (5y)^2 - (4z)^2 \\ &= (5y + 4z)(5y - 4z) \end{aligned}$$

2. Factor.

   (*a*) $9a^2 - 16$
   (*b*) $49x^2 - 36y^2$
   (*c*) $64b^2 - 1$
   (*d*) $25 - 81y^2$

Example 3

(*a*) Factor $6x^2 - 54$

(*b*) Factor $a^3 - ab^2$

Solution

(*a*)

$$\begin{aligned} & 6x^2 - 54 \\ &= 6(x^2 - 9) \\ &= 6(x - 3)(x + 3) \end{aligned}$$

It is important to remove any common factor in the first step. Why?

(*b*)

$$\begin{aligned} & a^3 - ab^2 \\ &= a(a^2 - b^2) \\ &= a(a + b)(a - b) \end{aligned}$$

Summary

By expanding,

$$(p + q)(p - q) = p^2 - q^2$$

By factoring,

$$r^2 - s^2 = (r + s)(r - s)$$

Exercise 16.1

Discussion

1. State the square.
   $7, \quad 3a, \quad 5x, \quad 1, \quad 10c, \quad 8y, \quad 2x^2$

2. State a square root of each of the following.
   $36, \quad 4a^2, \quad 81b^2, \quad x^4, \quad 49s^2, \quad 1$

3. Expand: (i) $(a + b)(a - b)$ (ii) $(a + b)(a + b)$
   Can you factor $a^2 + b^2$?

4. Factor.
   (a) $m^2 - n^2$
   (b) $4x^2 - y^2$
   (c) $(3a)^2 - (4b)^2$
   (d) $(a^2)^2 - (b^2)^2$
   (e) $x^4 - y^4$
   (f) $2c^2 - 2d^2$

5. Expand.
   (a) $(x + y)(x - y)$
   (b) $(a + 4)(a - 4)$
   (c) $(c - 3)(c + 3)$
   (d) $(2y - 5)(2y + 5)$
   (e) $(7m - n)(7m + n)$
   (f) $(4p + 3q)(4p - 3q)$

6. Express x^2 in terms of the other sides. Find x.
   (a)

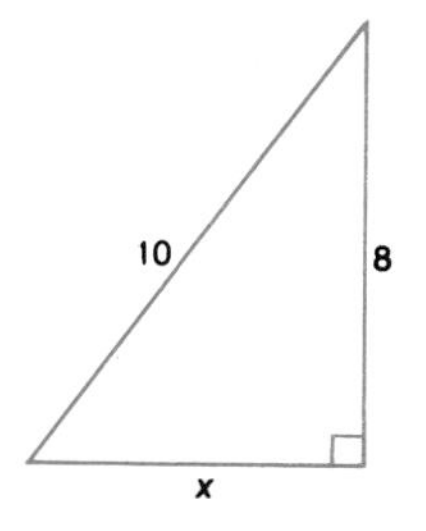

   (b)

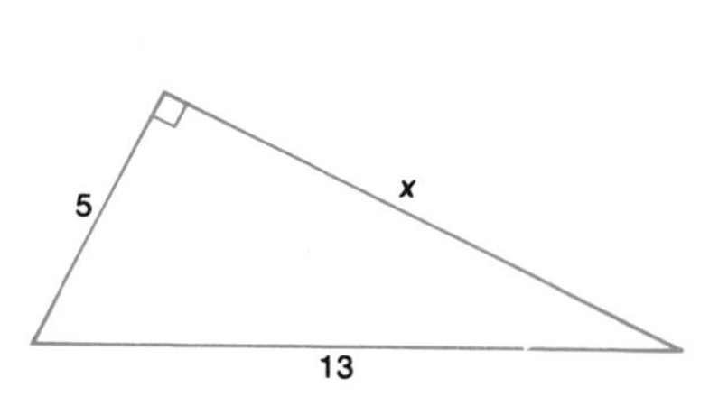

Written Solutions

7. Expand.
   (a) $(5x - y)(5x + y)$
   (b) $(a + 2b)(a - 2b)$
   (c) $(x + 4)(x - 4)$
   (d) $(y - 6)(y + 6)$
   (e) $(2p + 8)(2p - 8)$
   (f) $(3c + 5d)(3c - 5d)$

8. Factor.
   (a) $r^2 - s^2$
   (b) $x^2 - z^2$
   (c) $h^2 - k^2$
   (d) $(2x)^2 - (3y)^2$
   (e) $(5a)^2 - (2b)^2$
   (f) $(7p)^2 - (5q)^2$

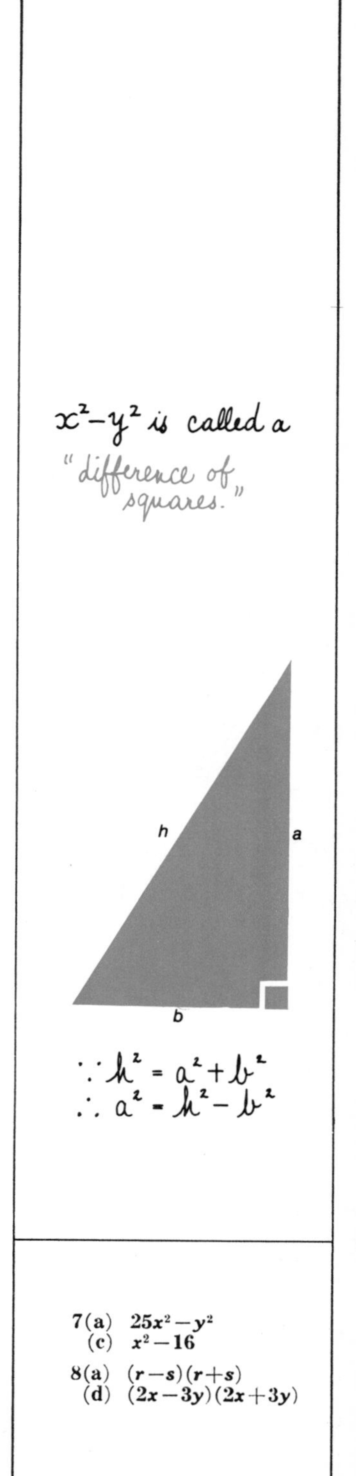

$x^2 - y^2$ is called a "difference of squares."
h
a
b
$\because h^2 = a^2 + b^2$
$\therefore a^2 = h^2 - b^2$

7(a) $25x^2 - y^2$
(c) $x^2 - 16$

8(a) $(r - s)(r + s)$
(d) $(2x - 3y)(2x + 3y)$

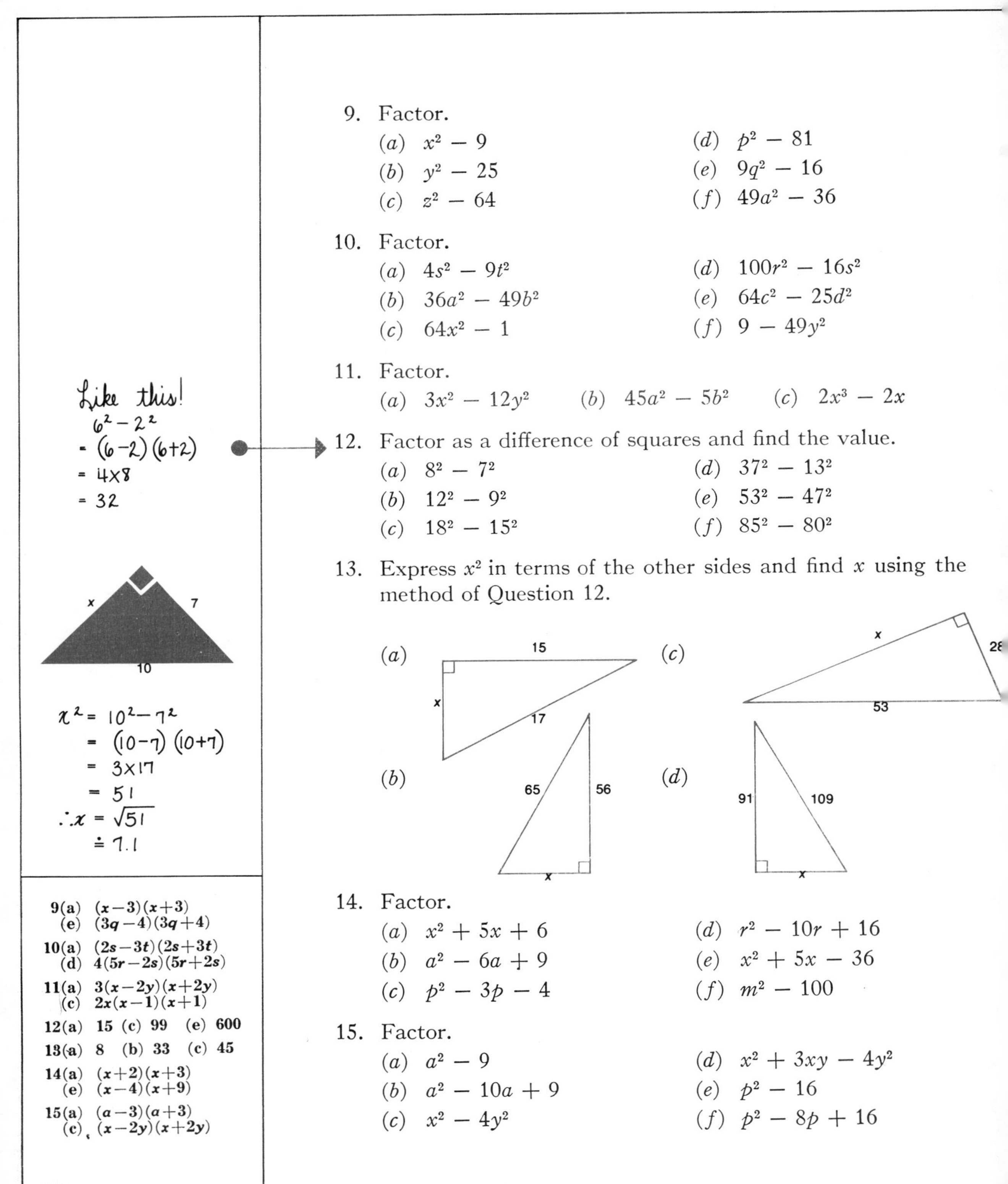

9. Factor.

(*a*) $x^2 - 9$ (*b*) $y^2 - 25$ (*c*) $z^2 - 64$ (*d*) $p^2 - 81$ (*e*) $9q^2 - 16$ (*f*) $49a^2 - 36$

10. Factor.

(*a*) $4s^2 - 9t^2$ (*b*) $36a^2 - 49b^2$ (*c*) $64x^2 - 1$ (*d*) $100r^2 - 16s^2$ (*e*) $64c^2 - 25d^2$ (*f*) $9 - 49y^2$

11. Factor.

(*a*) $3x^2 - 12y^2$ (*b*) $45a^2 - 5b^2$ (*c*) $2x^3 - 2x$

Like this!

$6^2 - 2^2$
$= (6-2)(6+2)$
$= 4 \times 8$
$= 32$

12. Factor as a difference of squares and find the value.

(*a*) $8^2 - 7^2$ (*b*) $12^2 - 9^2$ (*c*) $18^2 - 15^2$ (*d*) $37^2 - 13^2$ (*e*) $53^2 - 47^2$ (*f*) $85^2 - 80^2$

13. Express x^2 in terms of the other sides and find x using the method of Question 12.

$x^2 = 10^2 - 7^2$
$= (10-7)(10+7)$
$= 3 \times 17$
$= 51$
$\therefore x = \sqrt{51}$
$\doteq 7.1$

14. Factor.

(*a*) $x^2 + 5x + 6$ (*b*) $a^2 - 6a + 9$ (*c*) $p^2 - 3p - 4$ (*d*) $r^2 - 10r + 16$ (*e*) $x^2 + 5x - 36$ (*f*) $m^2 - 100$

15. Factor.

(*a*) $a^2 - 9$ (*b*) $a^2 - 10a + 9$ (*c*) $x^2 - 4y^2$ (*d*) $x^2 + 3xy - 4y^2$ (*e*) $p^2 - 16$ (*f*) $p^2 - 8p + 16$

9(a) $(x-3)(x+3)$
(e) $(3q-4)(3q+4)$
10(a) $(2s-3t)(2s+3t)$
(d) $4(5r-2s)(5r+2s)$
11(a) $3(x-2y)(x+2y)$
(c) $2x(x-1)(x+1)$
12(a) 15 **(c)** 99 **(e)** 600
13(a) 8 **(b)** 33 **(c)** 45
14(a) $(x+2)(x+3)$
(e) $(x-4)(x+9)$
15(a) $(a-3)(a+3)$
(c) $(x-2y)(x+2y)$

16.2 The Pattern $a^2 + 2ab + b^2$

Study the following examples carefully.

Example 1

Expand $(3x + 5y)^2$

Solution

$$\begin{aligned}(3x + 5y)^2 &= (3x + 5y)(3x + 5y) \\ &= 9x^2 + 15xy + 15xy + 25y^2 \\ &= 9x^2 + 30xy + 25y^2\end{aligned}$$

$(3x)^2 \quad 2(3x \times 5y) \quad (5y)^2$

Example 2

Expand $(4a + 7b)^2$

Solution

$$\begin{aligned}(4a + 7b)^2 &= (4a)^2 + 2(4a \times 7b) + (7b)^2 \\ &= 16a^2 + 56ab + 49b^2\end{aligned}$$

1. Use FOIL to expand as in Example 1.
   (*a*) $(x + 4)^2$ (*b*) $(a + 3b)^2$ (*c*) $(4p + 5q)^2$

2. Use three steps to expand as in Example 2.
   (*a*) $(y + 5)^2$ * (*b*) $(r + 4s)^2$ (*c*) $(3c + 6d)^2$

Example 3

Expand $(3x - 2y)^2$

Solution

$$\begin{aligned}(3x - 2y)^2 &= (3x - 2y)(3x - 2y) \\ &= 9x^2 - 6xy - 6xy + 4y^2 \\ &= 9x^2 - 12xy + 4y^2\end{aligned}$$

3. Expand (using a short cut if you can!).
   (*a*) $(a - 3)^2$ (*b*) $(x - 4y)^2$ (*c*) $(5x - 3y)^2$

Remember

FOIL?

Notice that the "O" and "I" terms are the same.

1 Square first term.

2 Multiply the terms and double.

3 Square second term.

*

	y	5
y	y^2	5y
5	5y	25

Do you see how this relates to $(y+5)^2$?

B If we expand $(a + b)^2$ and get $(a + b)^2 = a^2 + 2ab + b^2$, then by factoring

$$p^2 + 2pq + q^2 = (p + q)^2$$

1. Factor.
   (*a*) $x^2 + 2xy + y^2$
   (*b*) $r^2 + 2rs + s^2$
   (*c*) $c^2 + 2cd + d^2$
   (*d*) $x^2 + 6x + 9$

Could you factor 1(*d*)? Remember that

$$\begin{aligned}(x + 3)^2 &= x^2 + 2(3x) + (3)^2 \\ &= x^2 + 6x + 9\end{aligned}$$

2. Draw and complete the following table.

Expanding	*Factoring*
$\because\ (a + 2)^2 = a^2 + 4a + 4$	$\therefore\ a^2 + 4a + 4 = (a + 2)^2$
$\because\ (x + 5)^2 = \square + \square + \square$	$\therefore\ x^2 + 10x + 25 = (\square)^2$
$\because\ (b - 3)^2 = b^2 - 6b + 9$	$\therefore\ b^2 - 6b + 9 = (\square)^2$
$\because\ (2x + 5)^2 = 4x^2 + 20x + 25$	$\therefore\ 4x^2 + 20x + 25 = (\square)^2$

When you square a binomial (as in the Expanding section of the table), the first and third terms in the product are squares, like a^2 and 4, x^2 and 25, b^2 and 9, $4x^2$ and 25.

Trinomials that are squares of binomials contain 2 terms that are squares.

Example 4

Factor (*a*) $4a^2 + 28a + 49$
(*b*) $x^2 - 16x + 64$

Solution

(*a*)
$$\begin{aligned}&4a^2 + 28a + 49 \\ &= (2a)^2 + 28a + (7)^2 \\ &= (2a + 7)^2\end{aligned}$$

(*b*)
$$\begin{aligned}&x^2 - 16x + 64 \\ &= (x)^2 - 16x + (8)^2 \\ &= (x - 8)^2\end{aligned}$$

Check on the middle term $28a$
$2(2a)(7) = 28a$.

3. $16a^2 = (4a)^2$. Rewrite each of the following in the same way.
   (*a*) $9x^2$ (*b*) $49b^2$ (*c*) 36 (*d*) $25y^2$

4. Factor using the method of Example 4.

   (*a*) $x^2 + 12x + 36$ (*c*) $y^2 - 8y + 16$
   (*b*) $16a^2 + 24a + 9$ (*d*) $4b^2 - 36b + 81$

   Check each part of Question 4 by expanding.

Make a copy of the chart.

> *Summary*
>
> By expanding, $(a + b)^2 = a^2 + 2ab + b^2$
> $(a - b)^2 = a^2 - 2ab + b^2$
>
> By factoring, $p^2 + 2pq + q^2 = (p + q)^2$
> $y^2 - 2yz + z^2 = (y - z)^2$

Exercise 16.2

Discussion

1. State the square of each monomial.

   (*a*) $3x$ (*c*) $7z$ (*e*) $9a$
   (*b*) $4y$ (*d*) $5b$ (*f*) $6p$

2. State the product of each of the following pairs of terms, and then double your answers.

   (*a*) x, 6 (*c*) $2x$, 3 (*e*) $4x$, $9t$
   (*b*) y, 4 (*d*) $5a$, 7 (*f*) $3p$, $8q$

3. Expand.

   (*a*) $(x + y)^2$ (*c*) $(a + 2)^2$ (*e*) $(y + 7)^2$
   (*b*) $(p + q)^2$ (*d*) $(x - 6)^2$ (*f*) $(3a + 2b)^2$

4. Use the diagram to show that $(a + b)^2 = a^2 + 2ab + b^2$

5. State a square root of each of the following.

   (*a*) $4x^2$ (*c*) 49 (*e*) 100
   (*b*) $9y^2$ (*d*) 64 (*f*) $36a^2$

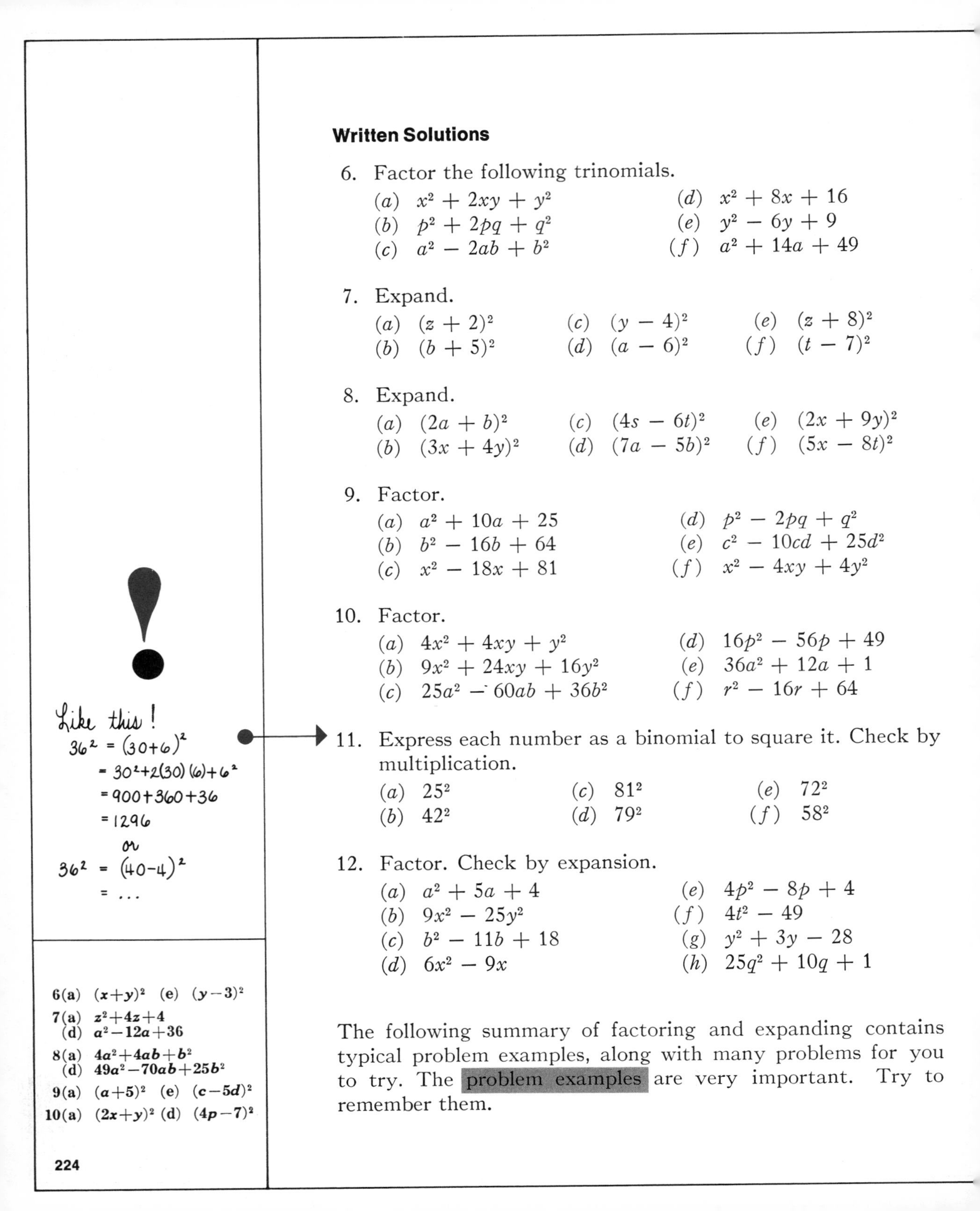

Written Solutions

6. Factor the following trinomials.
   - (a) $x^2 + 2xy + y^2$
   - (b) $p^2 + 2pq + q^2$
   - (c) $a^2 - 2ab + b^2$
   - (d) $x^2 + 8x + 16$
   - (e) $y^2 - 6y + 9$
   - (f) $a^2 + 14a + 49$

7. Expand.
   - (a) $(z + 2)^2$
   - (b) $(b + 5)^2$
   - (c) $(y - 4)^2$
   - (d) $(a - 6)^2$
   - (e) $(z + 8)^2$
   - (f) $(t - 7)^2$

8. Expand.
   - (a) $(2a + b)^2$
   - (b) $(3x + 4y)^2$
   - (c) $(4s - 6t)^2$
   - (d) $(7a - 5b)^2$
   - (e) $(2x + 9y)^2$
   - (f) $(5x - 8t)^2$

9. Factor.
   - (a) $a^2 + 10a + 25$
   - (b) $b^2 - 16b + 64$
   - (c) $x^2 - 18x + 81$
   - (d) $p^2 - 2pq + q^2$
   - (e) $c^2 - 10cd + 25d^2$
   - (f) $x^2 - 4xy + 4y^2$

10. Factor.
    - (a) $4x^2 + 4xy + y^2$
    - (b) $9x^2 + 24xy + 16y^2$
    - (c) $25a^2 - 60ab + 36b^2$
    - (d) $16p^2 - 56p + 49$
    - (e) $36a^2 + 12a + 1$
    - (f) $r^2 - 16r + 64$

Like this!

$36^2 = (30+6)^2$
$= 30^2+2(30)(6)+6^2$
$= 900+360+36$
$= 1296$

or

$36^2 = (40-4)^2$
$= \ldots$

11. Express each number as a binomial to square it. Check by multiplication.
    - (a) 25^2
    - (b) 42^2
    - (c) 81^2
    - (d) 79^2
    - (e) 72^2
    - (f) 58^2

12. Factor. Check by expansion.
    - (a) $a^2 + 5a + 4$
    - (b) $9x^2 - 25y^2$
    - (c) $b^2 - 11b + 18$
    - (d) $6x^2 - 9x$
    - (e) $4p^2 - 8p + 4$
    - (f) $4t^2 - 49$
    - (g) $y^2 + 3y - 28$
    - (h) $25q^2 + 10q + 1$

The following summary of factoring and expanding contains typical problem examples, along with many problems for you to try. The problem examples are very important. Try to remember them.

6(a) $(x+y)^2$ **(e)** $(y-3)^2$
7(a) z^2+4z+4
(d) $a^2-12a+36$
8(a) $4a^2+4ab+b^2$
(d) $49a^2-70ab+25b^2$
9(a) $(a+5)^2$ **(e)** $(c-5d)^2$
10(a) $(2x+y)^2$ **(d)** $(4p-7)^2$

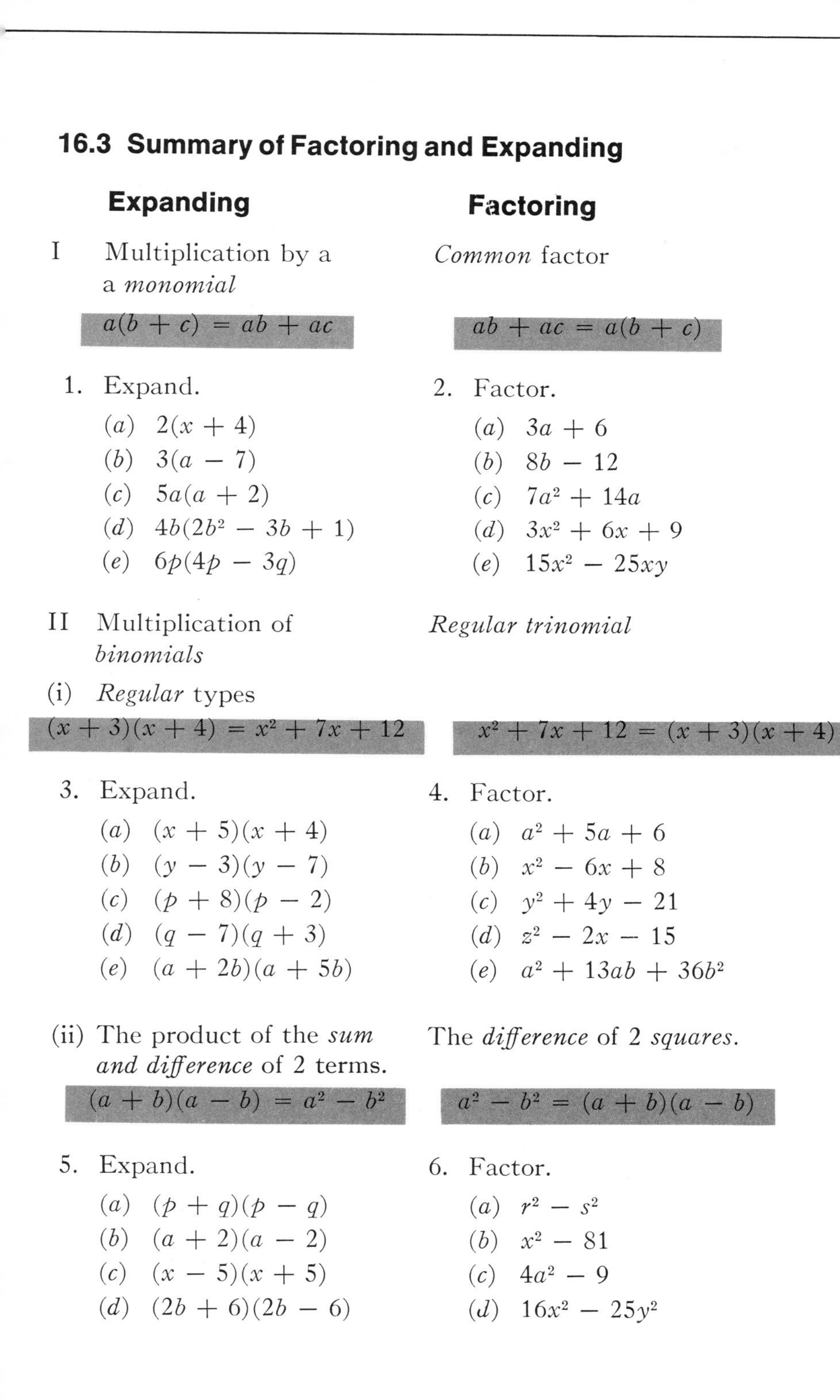

16.3 Summary of Factoring and Expanding

Expanding	**Factoring**
I Multiplication by a a *monomial*	*Common* factor
$a(b + c) = ab + ac$	$ab + ac = a(b + c)$

1. Expand.
   (*a*) $2(x + 4)$
   (*b*) $3(a - 7)$
   (*c*) $5a(a + 2)$
   (*d*) $4b(2b^2 - 3b + 1)$
   (*e*) $6p(4p - 3q)$

2. Factor.
   (*a*) $3a + 6$
   (*b*) $8b - 12$
   (*c*) $7a^2 + 14a$
   (*d*) $3x^2 + 6x + 9$
   (*e*) $15x^2 - 25xy$

Expanding	**Factoring**
II Multiplication of *binomials* (i) *Regular* types	*Regular trinomial*
$(x + 3)(x + 4) = x^2 + 7x + 12$	$x^2 + 7x + 12 = (x + 3)(x + 4)$

3. Expand.
   (*a*) $(x + 5)(x + 4)$
   (*b*) $(y - 3)(y - 7)$
   (*c*) $(p + 8)(p - 2)$
   (*d*) $(q - 7)(q + 3)$
   (*e*) $(a + 2b)(a + 5b)$

4. Factor.
   (*a*) $a^2 + 5a + 6$
   (*b*) $x^2 - 6x + 8$
   (*c*) $y^2 + 4y - 21$
   (*d*) $z^2 - 2x - 15$
   (*e*) $a^2 + 13ab + 36b^2$

Expanding	**Factoring**
(ii) The product of the *sum and difference* of 2 terms.	The *difference* of 2 *squares*.
$(a + b)(a - b) = a^2 - b^2$	$a^2 - b^2 = (a + b)(a - b)$

5. Expand.
   (*a*) $(p + q)(p - q)$
   (*b*) $(a + 2)(a - 2)$
   (*c*) $(x - 5)(x + 5)$
   (*d*) $(2b + 6)(2b - 6)$

6. Factor.
   (*a*) $r^2 - s^2$
   (*b*) $x^2 - 81$
   (*c*) $4a^2 - 9$
   (*d*) $16x^2 - 25y^2$

Always check your factoring by expanding!

(iii) The *square* of a *binomial*

$$(a + b)^2 = a^2 + 2ab + b^2$$

The *perfect square*

$$a^2 + 2ab + b^2 = (a + b)^2$$

7. Expand.
   (*a*) $(x + 5)^2$
   (*b*) $(2x + 7)^2$
   (*c*) $(a - b)^2$

8. Factor.
   (*a*) $x^2 + 2x + 1$
   (*b*) $y^2 - 6y + 9$
   (*c*) $4a^2 + 4a + 1$

Steps in Factoring	*Example*
1. Remove any common factor first.	$3x^2 + 6xy = 3x(x + 2y)$
2. Count the number of terms in the original expression.	i $3x^2 + 12$ $= 3(x^2 + 4)$ Not a difference of squares. Finished. You cannot factor further.
(*a*) If there are 2 terms, they must represent the difference of 2 squares, or you cannot factor further.	ii $3x^2 - 12$ $= 3(x^2 - 4)$ — Difference of squares $= 3(x - 2)(x + 2)$
(*b*) If there are 3 terms, try to factor the expression as a trinomial. (i) Regular trinomial (ii) Perfect square	i $x^2 + 8x + 12$ $= (x + 2)(x + 6)$ ii $x^2 - 6x + 9$ — Perfect square $= (x - 3)^2$

Exercise 16.3

Discussion

1. In each of the following expressions, state the common factor (if there is one!).
   (*a*) $x^2 + 5x$
   (*b*) $3y^2 + 5$
   (*c*) $ab + a^2$
   (*d*) $9x - 15$
   (*e*) $x^2y - xy^2$
   (*f*) $24a^2 - 15$

2. There is no common factor in each of the following. Name the type of factoring required to factor each.

(*a*) $a^2 - b^2$
(*b*) $p^2 + 6p + 9$
(*c*) $x^2 - 8x + 15$
(*d*) $9x^2 - 16$
(*e*) $25x^2 + 10x + 1$
(*f*) $x^2 + 20x + 64$
(*g*) $y^2 - 12y + 35$
(*h*) $a^2 + 8a - 9$
(*i*) $4a^2 - 9$
(*j*) $16a^2 + 40ab + 25b^2$

3. State the correct second term if the following expressions are perfect squares.

(*a*) $p^2 + \square + 16$
(*b*) $q^2 - \square + 25$
(*c*) $x^2 + \square + 36$
(*d*) $y^2 - \square + 49$
(*e*) $a^2 + \square + 64$
(*f*) $16a^2 + \square + 25$
(*g*) $9x^2 - \square + 4$
(*h*) $49b^2 + \square + 16$

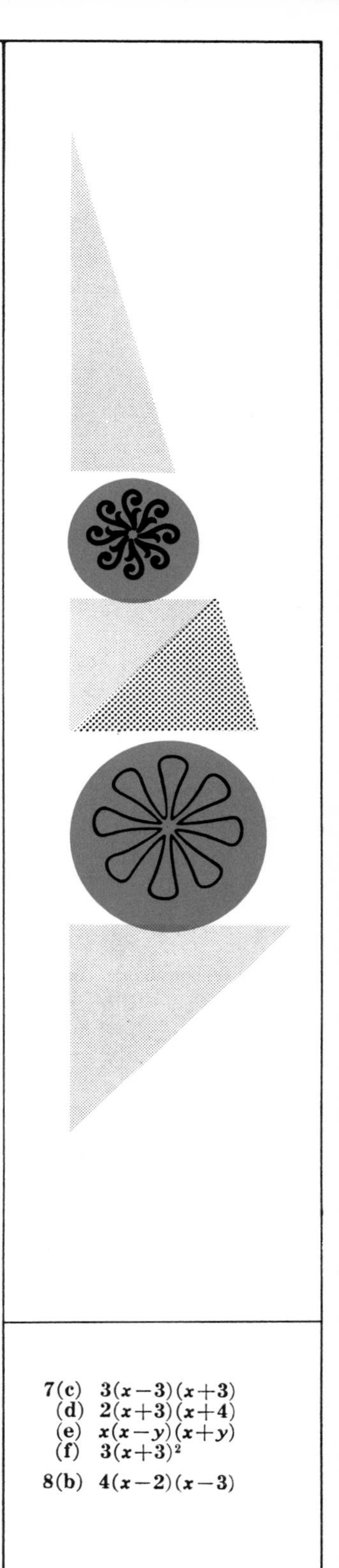

Written Solutions

4. Expand.

(*a*) $(x + 5)(x - 2)$
(*b*) $(x + 6)^2$
(*c*) $(a + 7)(a - 7)$
(*d*) $3x(x^2 + 3x - 2)$
(*e*) $(2a - 3b)^2$
(*f*) $(2x + 5y)(2x - 5y)$

5. Factor.

(*a*) $4p^2 - 9$
(*b*) $a^2 + 3a + 2$
(*c*) $6x^2 + 12$
(*d*) $y^2 - 2y - 15$
(*e*) $16x^2 - y^2$
(*f*) $a^2 - 7a + 10$

6. Factor.

(*a*) $x^2 + 4x + 4$
(*b*) $y^2 + 2y + 1$
(*c*) $a^2 + 4a + 3$
(*d*) $x^2 - 10x + 9$
(*e*) $p^2 + 12p + 36$
(*f*) $q^2 - 17q + 16$

7. Factor.

(*a*) $10p^2 + 15$
(*b*) $9x^2 - 25$
(*c*) $3x^2 - 27$
(*d*) $2x^2 + 14x + 24$
(*e*) $x^3 - xy^2$
(*f*) $3x^2 + 18x + 27$

8. Factor.

(*a*) $2x^2 - 4x + 10$
(*b*) $4x^2 - 20x + 24$
(*c*) $9a^2 - 30a + 25$
(*d*) $9x^2 - 64$
(*e*) $1 - 6x + 9x^2$
(*f*) $4 - y^2$

7(c) $3(x-3)(x+3)$
(d) $2(x+3)(x+4)$
(e) $x(x-y)(x+y)$
(f) $3(x+3)^2$

8(b) $4(x-2)(x-3)$

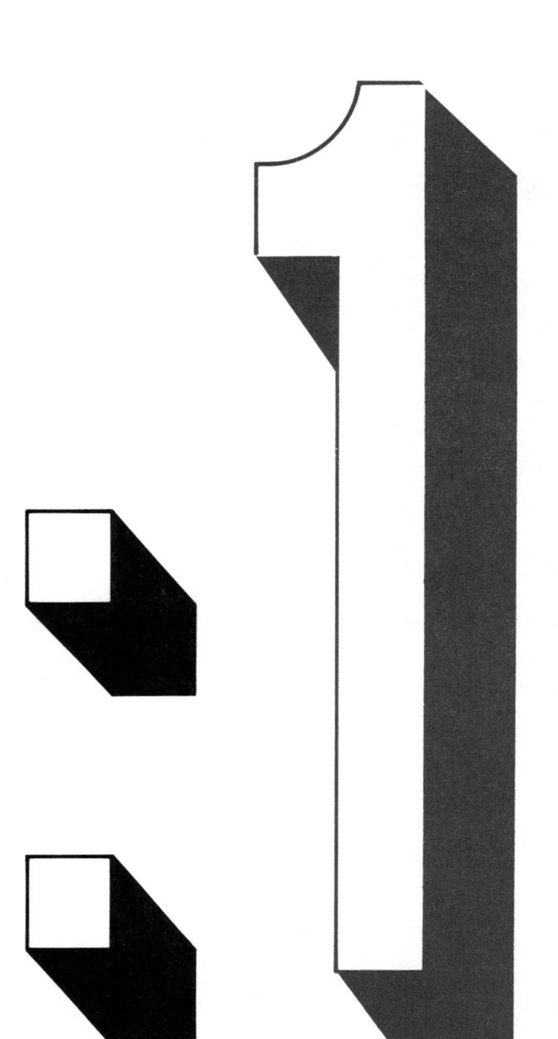
3:1

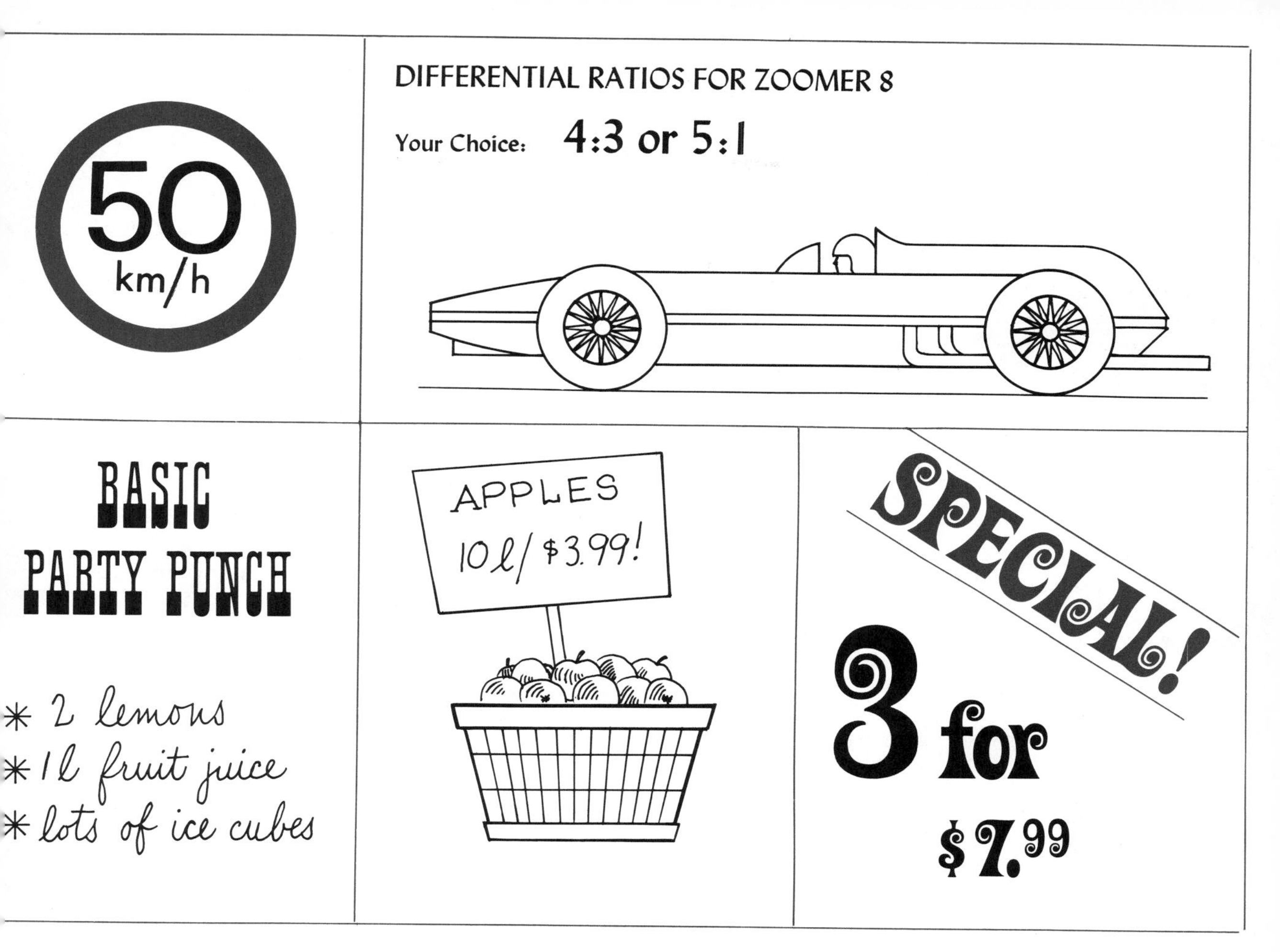

Unit 17
Ratio

At first glance, these situations may appear to have nothing in common. Upon closer inspection, however, we see that all deal with *ratio*.

Generally, we can compare quantities in 2 ways — by subtraction, or by division. The idea of *ratio* is encountered in the second of these, and you will learn more about it in this unit.

These lengths

20 cm, 30 cm
10 km, 15 km
2 mm, 3 mm

are all in the ratio of 2 to 3.

2:3 is called colon notation.

2:3

$\frac{2}{3}$

$\frac{2}{3}$ is called fraction notation.

17.1 Review of Ratio

A

1. Measure the lengths of each of the following line segments.
   (*a*)
   (*b*)
   (*c*)

2. We can compare the lengths of the segments in 1(*a*) in two ways:
   (*a*) by subtraction: the first segment is 3 cm shorter than the second.
   (*b*) by division: the first segment is $\frac{2}{3}$ as long as the second. In this latter case we say that the lengths of the two segments are in the *ratio* of 2 to 3. This is usually written 2:3, although there are cases when we may wish to use the common fraction form $\frac{2}{3}$ to express such a ratio.

3. Using the results of 1(*b*) and (*c*), state the ratio of the length of the first segment to the length of the second segment in each case. Express your results in "colon notation" and also in "fraction notation."

4. Note that although the ratio of 2 to 3 may be written as either 2:3 or $\frac{2}{3}$, it is read as "the ratio of 2 to 3", in each case. Read the following ratios.

   (*a*) 4:7 (*b*) $\frac{5}{9}$ (*c*) $\frac{3}{10}$ (*d*) 6:1 (*e*) 1.5:5

B

1. Measure the lengths of each of the following line segments.
   (*a*)
   (*b*)

2. Express the lengths of the line segments in 1(*a*) as a ratio, in colon notation. Do the same thing for 1(*b*).

3. What difficulty is encountered in expressing these ratios in fraction notation?

4. We see here that when more than two quantities are compared using a ratio, the colon notation must be used. The ratio 2:4:3 is read "2 to 4 to 3". Such a ratio is called a 3-term ratio, since 3 quantities are being compared. A ratio such as 2:3 is called a 2-term ratio.

5. Read the following and classify each as a 2- or 3-term ratio.

(*a*) 5 : 7 (*c*) $\frac{4}{9}$ (*e*) $\frac{3}{7}$

(*b*) 6 : 3 : 2 (*d*) 16 : 2 : 5 (*f*) 3.5:4.25

1. Study the following example.

Example

A piece of plywood is 72 cm long and 54 cm wide. What is the ratio of the length to the width, in lowest terms?

Solution

Since the length of the piece of wood is 72 cm and the width is 54 cm, the ratio of the length to the width is 72:54, or 4:3 in lowest terms. *

2. Using colon notation, write the following as ratios, in lowest terms.

(*a*) 3 kg, 7 kg (*c*) \$2.50, 50¢

(*b*) 2 m, 75 cm (*d*) 3 ℓ, 750 ml

Notice that in a comparison of similar quantities, the units of measurement must be the same!

Rate is very similar to ratio. For example, if a car travels 180 km in 2 h, its average rate of speed is 180 km/2 h, or 90 km/h. Notice that the quantities compared in a *rate* are not the same and, hence, different units are involved.

How does 2:4:3 sound for part (a)?

!

Naturally!

* It is customary to write a ratio in lowest terms.

Use caution when the units are different!

1. Express each of the following rates in lowest terms.
   (*a*) A tree grows 350 cm in 5 years.
   (*b*) A girl spends \$16 in 4 days.
   (*c*) A boy eats 6 eggs in 3 min.
   (*d*) A car travels 200 km in 4 h.

Exercise 17.1

Discussion

1. Is 7:2 the same as 2:7? Explain.
2. Using one ratio in fraction notation, how many quantities can you compare?
3. Is there any limit to the number of items that can be compared using colon notation? Why?
4. Four pieces of pipe have lengths 12 cm, 20 cm, 5 cm, and 15 cm. State the ratio of their lengths, starting with the shortest and ending with the longest.
5. Is the ratio $1\frac{1}{2} : 1\frac{5}{7}$ in lowest terms?
   (*a*) Express $1\frac{1}{2}$ as an improper fraction.
   (*b*) Express $1\frac{5}{7}$ as an improper fraction.
   (*c*) Express the ratio in fraction form.
   (*d*) Using the rule for the division of fractional numbers, simplify the ratio and write it as a fraction in lowest terms.
   (*e*) Express the ratio $1\frac{1}{2} : 1\frac{5}{7}$ in colon notation and in lowest terms.
6. Discuss the difference between "ratio" and "rate." (*Hint*: Numbers *vs.* units)
7. A timber 3 m long is to be divided into 2 parts in the ratio 1:2. Where would you cut it? If the timber were 6 m long, where would you cut it to give the same ratio?

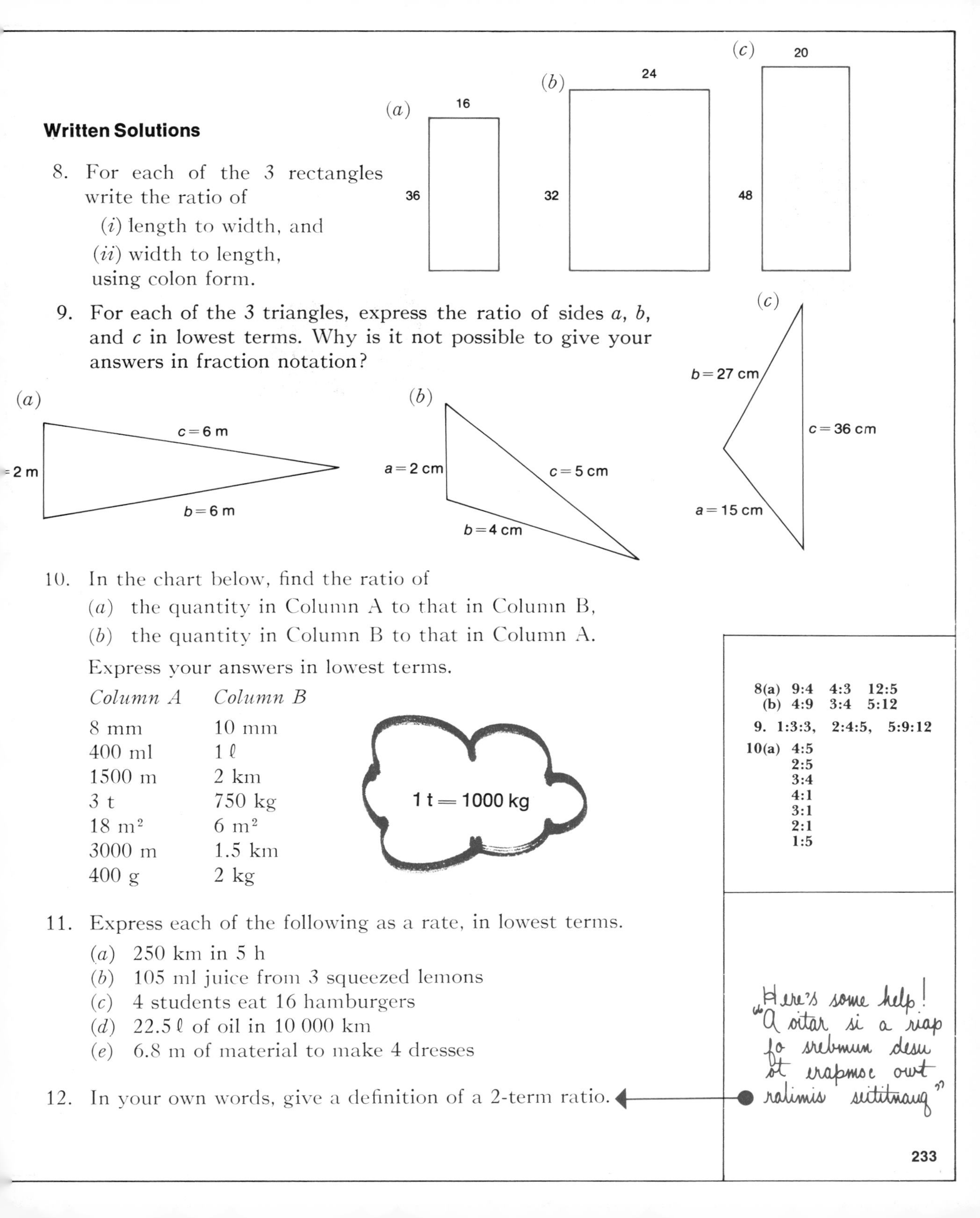

Written Solutions

8. For each of the 3 rectangles write the ratio of
   (*i*) length to width, and
   (*ii*) width to length,
   using colon form.

9. For each of the 3 triangles, express the ratio of sides a, b, and c in lowest terms. Why is it not possible to give your answers in fraction notation?

10. In the chart below, find the ratio of
    (*a*) the quantity in Column A to that in Column B,
    (*b*) the quantity in Column B to that in Column A.

    Express your answers in lowest terms.

Column A	*Column B*
8 mm	10 mm
400 ml	1 ℓ
1500 m	2 km
3 t	750 kg
18 m^2	6 m^2
3000 m	1.5 km
400 g	2 kg

11. Express each of the following as a rate, in lowest terms.
    (*a*) 250 km in 5 h
    (*b*) 105 ml juice from 3 squeezed lemons
    (*c*) 4 students eat 16 hamburgers
    (*d*) 22.5 ℓ of oil in 10 000 km
    (*e*) 6.8 m of material to make 4 dresses

12. In your own words, give a definition of a 2-term ratio.

8(a) 9:4 4:3 12:5
(b) 4:9 3:4 5:12

9. 1:3:3, 2:4:5, 5:9:12

10(a) 4:5
2:5
3:4
4:1
3:1
2:1
1:5

"Here's some help! A oitar si a riap fo srebmun desu ot erapmoc owt ralimis seititnauq"

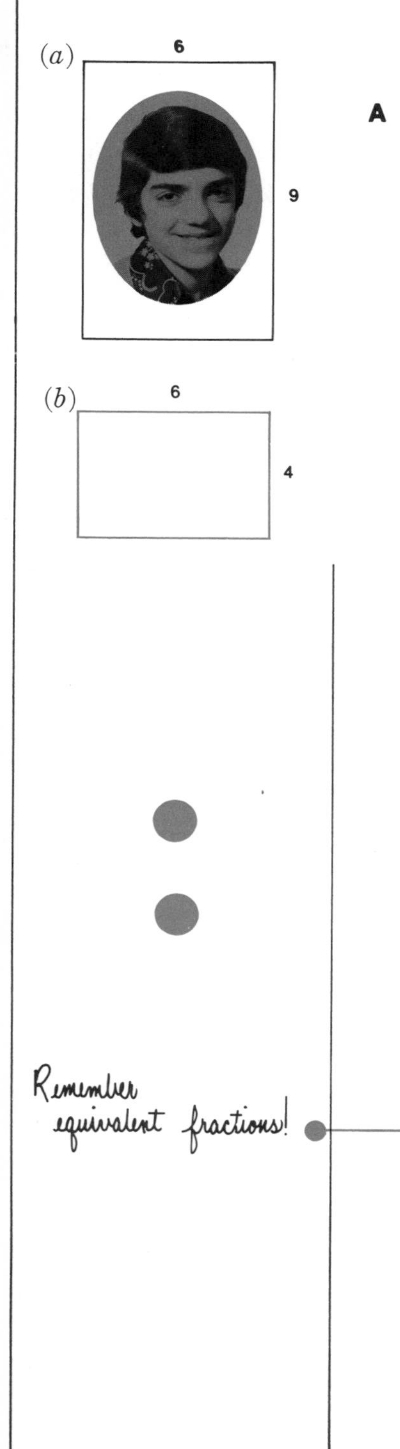

17.2 Equivalent Ratios

A 1. For each of the following rectangles, express the ratio of length to width in lowest terms. What do you notice?

2. Ratios such as 6:4, 9:6, 12:8, 15:10, and 3:2 are said to be *equivalent ratios*. In each of the following, two or more ratios are given. Determine which represent equivalent ratios and which do not.

(*a*) 3:4, 9:12
(*b*) 5:8, 20:36
(*c*) 12:15, 24:30
(*d*) 1:3, 5:15, 7:21
(*e*) 4:7, 8:14, 12:27
(*f*) 1.5:3, 4.5:9

Recall that in Section 17.1 we noted that the ratio 3:4 could also be written as the fraction $\frac{3}{4}$. In many applications, particularly rate problems, it is advantageous to use fraction notation. Hence, equivalent ratios may be expressed either

(*a*) in colon notation

$$3:4 = 6:8 = 9:12 = \ldots \text{ or}$$

(*b*) in fraction notation

$$\frac{3}{4} = \frac{6}{8} = \frac{9}{12} = \ldots$$

In either case, we say "3 is to 4 as 6 is to 8 as 9 is to 12 . . ."

3. Write each of the following in another way.

(*a*) $\frac{1}{2} = \frac{2}{4} = \frac{3}{6}$
(*b*) 2:10 = 1:5
(*c*) $\frac{15}{35} = \frac{3}{7} = \frac{6}{14}$
(*d*) 36:18 = 6:3 = 12:6

4. Fill in the missing number in each of the following.

(a) $\frac{3}{5} = \frac{9}{\square}$

(b) $64:32 = \square:2$

(c) $15:\square = 5:4$

(d) $\square:48 = 4:64$

(e) $\frac{9}{5} = \frac{\square}{45} = \frac{18}{\square}$

(f) $\frac{6}{\square} = \frac{54}{270}$

For (a)

$\frac{3}{5} = \frac{3 \times 3}{5 \times 3} = \frac{9}{15}$

Consider the equivalent ratios $\frac{1}{3}, \frac{2}{6}, \frac{3}{9}, \frac{4}{12}, \frac{5}{15}, \ldots$

1. Select any pair of ratios from this list. Multiply the numerator of the first fraction by the denominator of the second fraction, then multiply the denominator of the first fraction by the numerator of the second fraction. What do you notice?

If $\frac{1}{3} = \frac{4}{12}$
then $1 \times 12 = 12$
and $3 \times 4 = 12$

2. Repeat the steps outlined in Question 1 for two other pairs of ratios from the list.

3. In your own words, make up a rule for testing to see if two ratios are equivalent or not. In future work, we shall refer to this test as the *test for equivalent ratios*.

If $ad = bc$ then $\frac{a}{b} = \frac{c}{d}$,
and
if $\frac{a}{b} = \frac{c}{d}$, then $ad = bc$.

4. Use the test for equivalent ratios to determine which of the following pairs of ratios are equivalent.

(a) $\frac{15}{30}, \frac{2}{4}$ (b) $\frac{1}{2}, \frac{4}{2}$ (c) 3:8, 4:6 *(d) 4:5, 8:10

* Hint: Write (c) and (d) in fraction form first.

The test for equivalent ratios is also helpful in determining missing terms in ratios. For instance, if the ratios $\frac{1}{5}$ and $\frac{x}{30}$ are equivalent, that is, if $\frac{1}{5} = \frac{x}{30}$

then $5x = 30$ (by the test for equivalent ratios)
and $x = 6$

1. Use the test for equivalent ratios to find the number represented by the variable in each of the following.

(a) $\frac{1}{2} = \frac{x}{10}$

(b) $\frac{1}{d} = \frac{2}{38}$

(c) $15:100 = 3:p$

*(d) $5:t = 11:13$

* Hint: Fraction form for (c) and (d).

5(a) 1:4 (g) 7:13
(c) 18:1 (i) 1:20

Exercise 17.2

Discussion

1. Read aloud each of the following.

   (*a*) $2:3 = 4:6 = 6:9 = 8:12 = \ldots$

   (*b*) $\frac{3}{5} = \frac{6}{10} = \frac{9}{15} = \frac{12}{20} = \ldots$

   (*c*) $0.5:3 = 2:12 = 3:18 = \ldots$

2. State an equation in k using the test for equal ratios.

   (*a*) $\frac{k}{2} = \frac{7}{5}$ (*b*) $6:k = 2:8$ (*c*) $3:5 = k:7$ (*d*) $\frac{3}{8} = \frac{7}{k}$

3. State the terms represented by variables in each of the following equations.

   (*a*) $\frac{1}{7} = \frac{x}{21}$

   (*b*) $\frac{7}{2} = \frac{z}{10} = \frac{14}{y}$

   (*c*) $\frac{4}{n} = \frac{8}{6} = \frac{24}{m}$

   (*d*) $\frac{2}{t} = \frac{4}{10} = \frac{10}{k}$

   (*e*) $\frac{4}{6} = \frac{4}{9} = \frac{10}{q}$

   (*f*) $\frac{3}{0.5} = \frac{18}{a} = \frac{b}{2}$

4. Note that if $\frac{2}{3} = \frac{4}{6}$, then

   $\frac{2}{4} = \frac{3}{6}$, $\frac{6}{3} = \frac{4}{2}$, and $\frac{3}{2} = \frac{6}{4}$.

   If $\frac{6}{9} = \frac{10}{15}$, find three other pairs of equivalent ratios using only the numbers 6, 9, 10, and 15.

Written Solutions

5. Express the following ratios in lowest terms.

   (*a*) $18:72$

   (*b*) $\frac{1.2}{3.6}$

   (*c*) $3:\frac{1}{6}$

   (*d*) $\frac{33}{110}$

   (*e*) $0.6:0.8$

   (*f*) $\frac{1}{4}:\frac{5}{8}$

   (*g*) $49:91$

   (*h*) $\frac{2.5}{10}$

   (*i*) $0.7:14$

6. State the value of each variable in each of the following sets of equivalent ratios.

(a) $\frac{7}{8} = \frac{x}{16}$

(b) $5:6 = 25:m$

(c) $2:3 = a:12$

(d) $3:10 = 24:p = q:200$

(e) $\frac{7}{r} = \frac{63}{81} = \frac{s}{45}$

(f) $\frac{5}{12} = \frac{35}{x} = \frac{y}{144} = \frac{150}{z}$

7. Solve for the variable in each of the following.

(a) $\frac{x}{3} = \frac{18}{2}$

(b) $\frac{6}{7} = \frac{y}{4}$

(c) $\frac{1.3}{6.5} = \frac{t}{5}$

(d) $\frac{n}{40} = \frac{0.6}{3}$

(e) $3.2:0.8 = p:0.3$

(f) $\frac{9}{10}:k = \frac{1}{4}:\frac{5}{12}$

8. Express the following ratios with numerator 1.

(a) $\frac{12}{5}$ (b) $\frac{1.2}{6}$ (c) $\frac{0.25}{7}$ (d) $\frac{\frac{2}{9}}{\frac{8}{3}}$

9. Express the following ratios with 1 as the second term.

(a) $2:9$

(b) $0.6:2$

(c) $5:4$

(d) $5:2$

(e) $\frac{7}{2}:\frac{21}{100}$

(f) $1.25:4.5$

10. Use the test for equivalent ratios to find the value of the variable in each of the following equivalent ratios.

(a) $2:3 = r:7$

(b) $\frac{m}{3} = \frac{5}{2}$

(c) $4:1 = 6:c$

(d) $\frac{7}{u} = \frac{6}{10}$

(e) $y:10 = 3:8$

(f) $7:12 = 10:k$

(g) $5:x = 9:5$

(h) $\frac{4}{9} = \frac{t}{20}$

(i) $6:y = 8:3$

(j) $8:13 = p:100$

(k) $\frac{9}{4} = \frac{c}{100}$

(l) $5:8 = m:10$

ratio

6(a) 14 **(c)** 8

7(a) 27 **(e)** 1.2

(c) 1 **(f)** $1\frac{1}{2}$

8(a) $\frac{1}{\frac{5}{12}}$ **(c)** $\frac{1}{28}$

9(a) $\frac{2}{9}:1$ **(c)** $\frac{5}{4}:1$

10(a) $4\frac{2}{3}$ **(g)** $2\frac{7}{9}$

(c) $1\frac{1}{2}$ **(i)** $2\frac{1}{4}$

(e) $3\frac{3}{4}$ **(k)** 225

17.3 Ratio Problems

A Certain types of problems are more easily solved by using ratios than by any other method. In particular, rate problems are quite neatly handled using ratios. Study carefully the following examples.

Example 1

A coffee cake recipe calls for 200 ml of sugar to 300 ml of flour. If an oversize cake is to be made using 1.5 ℓ of sugar, how much flour is required?

Solution

Let the number of litres of flour required be represented by x.

$$\because \quad \frac{200}{300} = \frac{1.5}{x}$$

$$\text{then } 200x = 1.5 \times 300$$

$$\text{and} \quad x = \frac{1.5 \times 300}{200}$$

$$\therefore \quad x = 2.25$$

$\therefore$ 2.25 ℓ of flour are required.

Remember the steps in problem solving?

Example 2

Luella Landluver and Sam Soilseeker together buy a plot of land, agreeing to sell it 3 years later and to share the profit according to the ratio of their investments. If Luella puts up \$6500 and Sam puts up \$3900, how much will each receive from a profit of \$2400?

Solution

Let the portion of the profit received by Luella be k dollars. Now the ratio of Luella's investment (\$6500) to the total investment (\$10 400) is $\frac{6500}{10\,400}$ or $\frac{5}{8}$.

$$\therefore \frac{5}{8} = \frac{k}{2400}$$
$$\therefore 8k = 5 \times 2400$$
$$\therefore k = \frac{5 \times 2400}{8}$$
$$\therefore k = 1500$$

Therefore, Luella will receive \$1500 of the profit, and Sam will receive \$2400 − \$1500 = \$900 of the profit.

Notice that in the above example, the actual ratio used to solve the problem was "hidden" by the wording of the problem.

Example 3

The Crunchy-Munchy Candy Company mixes 20 kg of peanuts, 180 ml of salt, and 24 ℓ of syrup together in a 45 ℓ kettle to make a batch of peanut brittle. They buy a new kettle of 160 ℓ capacity, but still preserve the ratio of peanuts to the amount of salt and syrup. Find how much of each ingredient will be required to produce a batch of peanut brittle in the new kettle.

Solution

The only known ratio in this problem is that of the capacity of the new kettle to the capacity of the old, namely 160:45 or 32:9. Let the new quantities of peanuts, salt, and syrup be x kilograms, y millilitres, and z litres, respectively.

$$\therefore \frac{32}{9} = \frac{x}{20} = \frac{y}{180} = \frac{z}{24}$$

Consider now the first 2 of these.

$$\because \frac{32}{9} = \frac{x}{20}$$
$$\text{then } 9x = 32 \times 20$$
$$\text{and } x = \frac{640}{9}$$
$$\therefore x = 71.1$$

The amount of peanuts required is 71.1 kg.

Similarly, the quantity of salt required is 640 ml, and the quantity of syrup required is 85.3 ℓ.

Newton's Method for Making Peanut Brittle
(It works!)

1 Bring slowly to boil in large skillet: 2 parts sugar, 1 part corn syrup, 1 part water.
2 Boil to "hard crack" stage. (Ask your mother!)
3 Add 2 parts peanuts (shelled, of course), dash of butter and baking soda, and stir to blend.
4 Pour onto greased pan and allow to cool.
5 Devour with relish! (Gusto, that is!)

Guaranteed not to stick to your dentures!

Does this help?

$$\because \frac{32}{9} = \frac{y}{180}$$
$$\text{then } 9y = 32 \times 180$$
$$\text{and } y = \frac{32 \times 180}{9}$$
$$\therefore y = 640$$

$$\because \frac{32}{9} = \frac{z}{24}$$
$$\text{then } 9z = 32 \times 24$$
$$\text{and } z = \frac{32 \times 24}{9}$$
$$\therefore z = \frac{256}{3}$$
$$\text{or } z = 85.3$$

r/min
means "revolutions per minute"
5:8

1. 160 r/min	**6. $22.40**
2. 72 m	**7. 37.5 cm**
3. $150	**8. 154**
4. $7.50	**9. $612**
5. 48, 192	**10. $23.33**

Exercise 17.3

Written Solutions

Read each problem through carefully before you attempt a solution.

1. The ratio of the speeds of 2 pulleys is 4:5. If the speed of the faster is 200 r/min, what is the speed of the slower pulley?

2. The ratio of the heights of 2 trees is 9:2. If the shorter tree is 16 m high, what is the height of the taller tree?

3. A store gives a discount of $8 for each $100 worth of goods purchased. What price was paid for goods on which a discount of $12 was allowed?

4. The prices of a hat and a pair of gloves are in the ratio 7:5. If the hat costs $10.50, find the cost of the gloves.

5. A concrete mix has 3 parts cement to 5 parts sand to 12 parts gravel. How many shovelfuls of cement and gravel are needed if 80 shovelfuls of sand are used?

6. A bank charges $8 interest in one year for each $100 that it lends. What interest will it charge in one year for a loan of $280?

7. Assuming that the most pleasing picture shape is a rectangle with height and width in the ratio 5:8, what should the length of a picture be if it is 60 cm wide?

8. When Marion Kind turns the pedal on her bicycle-built-for-two 9 times, the back wheel turns 22 times. How many times will the back wheel turn if she turns the pedals 63 times?

9. Ethyl and Al Kohall agree to share profits from their partnership in the ratio of 2:3. If Al receives $918, how much does Ethyl receive?

10. The prices of 2 bolts of cloth are in the ratio 7:3. If the less expensive bolt costs $10, what is the price of the other?

11. The waist measurement and the length of a skirt are in the ratio 1.4:1. If a girl's waist measurement is 70 cm, how long is her skirt?

12. The cost price and the selling price of an article are in the ratio of 3.5 to 5.5. What is the selling price of the article if its cost price is $1.40?

13. While waiting for his cookies to bake, Bart Bakalot determined by actual count that 4 spoonfuls of sugar contained 450 grains of sugar. He then declared that, without counting, he could find the approximate number of grains of sugar in 10 spoonfuls. Can you?

14. A 3 m section of pipe has a mass of 20.91 kg. What will be the mass of a 10 m section of the same pipe?

15. Willie Workwell receives $22 for working an 8 h shift. How much will he receive for a 44 h work week at the same rate of pay?

16. Using her automatic drill press, Dierdre Drillwright can drill 3 holes in 1.5 min. Working at the same rate, how many holes could she drill in 6 min?

17. The *mechanical advantage* of a lever or pulley is the ratio

$$\frac{\text{Load lifted}}{\text{Force applied}}$$

If a force of 100 N lifts a load of 250 kg, what load can be lifted by a force of 130 N?

18. Bertie Blockbuster, using a 3-block pulley, can lift a load of 50 kg by pulling with a force of 15 N. What force is needed to lift a load of 125 kg?

19. Hotrod Harriet determines the compression ratio in her car engine by calculating the ratio $V_2:V_1$, where $V_2 = 3.4\ \ell$ and $V_1 = 360$ ml. Express this compression ratio with second term 1.

We measure force in newtons.
N
means "newtons"

11. 50 cm
12. $2.20
13. 1125
14. 69.7 kg
15. $121
16. 12
17. 325 kg
18. 37.5 N
19. 9:4:1

Unit 18
Percent

1. The Toothless Wonder, on TV commercial: " . . . and our group had 49% fewer cavities!"

2. Sales representative to shopper: " . . . yes indeed, that represents a discount of 40% on our regular price!"

3. Car enthusiast to friend: "I tell ya, Kim, milling a hunnert an' twenty thou' off the 'head' will boost the compression ratio by at least 20%!"

4. Mother to business partner: "No wonder you couldn't get through to me! My kids spend 90% of their waking hours on this phone!"

The mathematical idea common to each of these statements is that of *percent*. In this unit you will study this special kind of ratio that is so frequently encountered in living today.

18.1 Working with Percent

A The word "percent" means "in a hundred." Mathematically, we can think of percent as a 2-term ratio in which the second term is 100 (or as a fraction with denominator 100). For instance, 27:100 means the same as $\frac{27}{100}$, and we can write this as 27 per 100, 27 percent, or simply 27%. Usually the symbol % is used to indicate percent.

Remember?

By means of the test for equivalent ratios, we can rewrite *any* 2-term ratio with 100 as the second term, and hence as a percent. Study the example below, in which the ratios $\frac{4}{5}$ and 12:5 are expressed as percents.

(*a*) Let $\frac{4}{5} = \frac{x}{100}$

then $5x = 400$

and $x = 80$

$\therefore \frac{4}{5} = \frac{80}{100} = 80\%$

(*b*) Let $12:5 = \frac{12}{5} = \frac{x}{100}$

then $5x = 1200$

and $x = 240$

$\therefore 12:5 = \frac{240}{100} = 240\%$

1. Convert the following 2-term ratios to percents.

(*a*) $\frac{1}{2}$ (*b*) 5:6 (*c*) 10:6 (*d*) $\frac{21}{8}$

B To change a decimal number to a percent, proceed as follows.

$0.35 = \frac{35}{100} = 35\%$ $0.125 = \frac{12.5}{100} = 12.5\%$

$6.25 = \frac{625}{100} = 625\%$ $0.049 = \frac{4.9}{100} = 4.9\%$

Notice that you use the same method as when converting a decimal fraction to a common fraction.

Look for short cuts!

1. Change the following to percents.

(*a*) 0.25 (*d*) 0.295 (*g*) 7.42
(*b*) 0.94 (*e*) 2.349 (*h*) 16
(*c*) 0.143 (*f*) 0.4 (*i*) 0.025

Given a certain percent, we can reverse the procedure and obtain the ratio or fraction, in lowest terms, from which it came.

Example 1

Change $16\frac{2}{3}\%$ to a ratio in lowest terms.

Solution

$$16\tfrac{2}{3}\% = \frac{16\frac{2}{3}}{100}$$

$$= \frac{\frac{50}{3}}{100}$$

$$= \frac{\cancel{50}}{3} \times \frac{1}{\cancel{100}_{2}}$$

$$= \frac{1}{6}$$

$$\therefore 16\tfrac{2}{3}\% = \frac{1}{6}$$

Recall the division rule?
"Multiply by the reciprocal."
What short cut can you use here?
I can do these in my head!

We can convert any percent to a decimal even more easily.

$$29\% = \frac{29}{100} = 0.29 \quad 162\% = \frac{162}{100} = 1.62 \quad 2.5\% = \frac{2.5}{100} = 0.025$$

1. Change the following percents to decimals.

(*a*) 13% (*c*) 4.4% (*e*) 74.5% (*g*) 95.8%

(*b*) 86% (*d*) 112.5% (*f*) 21.25% (*h*) 610%

2. Draw and complete the following table.

Percent	*Decimal Number*	*Percent*	*Decimal Number*
33%			0.83
72%			0.512
9.25%			1.39
150%			14
61.3%			0.435

9/8
9/8 could be written 1 1/8.
1 1/8
You can also find the solution using ratio.
x/70 = 15/100
∴ x = 10.50

D Sometimes the fraction form is simpler than the decimal form.

Example 2

Express 112.5% as a fraction in lowest terms.

Solution

$$
\begin{aligned}
112.5\% &= \frac{112.5}{100} \\
&= \frac{\cancel{1125}^{9}}{\cancel{1000}_{8}} \\
&= \frac{9}{8} \\
\therefore 112.5\% &= \frac{9}{8}
\end{aligned}
$$

1. Change the following percents to ratios in their lowest terms.

(*a*) 37.5%	(*d*) 0.75%	(*g*) 925%
(*b*) $14\frac{2}{7}\%$	(*e*) $133\frac{1}{3}\%$	(*h*) 6.25%
(*c*) $8\frac{1}{3}\%$	(*f*) 65%	(*i*) 0.5%

E Word problems may also involve percent. Study the following examples carefully.

Example 3

On a cash sale, a discount of 15% is allowed on an article selling for $70. What is the cash price of the article?

Solution

15% of $70 = 0.15 × $70 = $10.50
∴ The discount is $10.50
∴ The cash price is $70 − $10.50 = $59.50

Example 4

A concrete mix is 27% sand and 59% gravel. How many kilograms of each are required for a concrete mix with mass 4.5 t (tonnes)?

Solution

The mass of sand required is 27% of 4.5 t.

$= \frac{27}{100} \times 4500$ kg

$= 1215$ kg

The mass of gravel required is 59% of 4.5 t.

$= \frac{59}{100} \times 4500$ kg

$= 2655$ kg

With ratio:

$\frac{27}{100} = \frac{x}{4500}$

$\frac{59}{100} = \frac{x}{4500}$

Exercise 18.1

Discussion

1. Rename the whole numbers 7, 9, and 13 as percents. State a short-cut for expressing whole numbers as percents.

2. 62.5% of 128 can be found in two ways:
   (*a*) by writing 62.5% as 0.625 and multiplying by 128, and
   (*b*) by expressing 62.5% as the fraction $\frac{5}{8}$ and multiplying by 128.

   Which method is easier? Why?

128
0.625
640
256
768
80.000

$\frac{5}{8} \times 128 = 80$

3. State the correct values to complete the following table.

Decimal Number	*Percent*	*Decimal Number*	*Percent*
0.36	■	2.4	■
■	7.8%	0.125	■
■	40%	■	0.25%
1.63	■	■	78.1%
■	93.9%	0.005	■

Written Solutions

4. Determine the ratio of the number of students in your math class to the total number of students in the school. Write this ratio as a percent.

Don't forget to express each fraction in lowest terms!

5. Draw and complete the following table.

Decimal Number	*Percent*	*Ratio*
0.375		
	$83.\dot{3}\%$	
		$\frac{3}{40}$
1.125		
		15:7
$0.1\dot{6}$		
	62.5%	

6. When you have finished this problem, what percent of the problems requiring written solutions will you have completed?

7. Very often a *discount* is given as a reduction in the *marked price* of goods. The actual price at which the goods are sold is called the *selling price*. For instance, a discount of 10% on a marked price of \$60 would give a selling price of \$54.

   Construct and complete the following table.

Hint: Use the test for equivalent ratios in part (e).

$\frac{16}{100} = \frac{32}{x}$ (marked price)

Problem	(*a*)	(*b*)	(*c*)	(*d*)	(*e*)
Marked Price	\$100	\$80	\$48		
Discount		\$20		\$18	\$32
Rate of Discount	30%				16%
Selling Price			\$36	\$72	

rate of profit = $\frac{\text{profit}}{\text{cost price}}$

8. If the merchant in a dry goods store purchases a bolt of cloth from the manufacturer for \$50 and sells it to a customer for \$60, he makes a *profit* of \$10 on the transaction. Here, \$50 is the *cost price* to the merchant and \$60 is the *selling price* of the cloth. The *rate of profit* is the ratio of profit to cost price. The rate of profit on the bolt of cloth is 10:50 or $\frac{10}{50}$ or 20%.

Construct and complete the following table.

Problem	(a)	(b)	(c)	(d)	(e)
Cost Price	$150	$96	■	$128	■
Profit	■	■	$15	■	$42
Rate of Profit	■	12.5%	■	37.5%	14%
Selling Price	$180	■	$90	■	■

Same hint as for Question 7.

9. A rubber band 7 cm long is stretched until the increase in length is 2.8 cm. What is the percent increase in length?

10. A piece of cast metal contains 20% iron, 35% magnesium, and the rest is nickel. How many kilograms of each metal are there in a 0.75 t casting?

11. Find the mass that is $83\frac{1}{3}\%$ greater than 216 kg.

12. Taking advantage of a discount, Jane bought a transistor radio for $32. If this was 80% of the marked price, find the marked price. What was the value of the discount Jane received on the radio?

13. In an assorted package of candies *exactly* 14% are red. How many packages would have to be purchased to get 70 red candies if a package has no more than 60 candies in it?

14. In one 8 h shift on an assembly line, 3% of all the parts inspected were rejected because of defects. If 291 parts were accepted as free from defects, how many parts were inspected?

6. **27.3%**
9. **40%**
10. **150 kg iron**
262.5 kg magnesium
337.5 kg nickel
11. **396 kg**
12. **$40, $8**
13. **10**
14. **300**

A toughie!

A sneaky one!

18.2 Simple Interest

Simple interest? Sounds easy!

One of the most common applications of percent is found in calculations involving *interest.* Interest is money you pay for the use of another person's money, or money you receive for letting someone use your money.

The sum of money borrowed is called the *principal* of the loan. The sum of money paid back (principal + interest) is called the *amount* of the loan.

per annum

means "per year." Did you know that?

Interest is related to principal, rate, and time by the following formula, called the *interest formula*

$I = Prt$

where I is the interest, in dollars
P is the principal, in dollars
r is the interest rate (% per annum)
t is the time of the loan, in years.

It is important that you always use the proper units in this formula, as given above.

Principal, interest, and amount are related by the formula

$A = P + I$

where A is the amount, in dollars
P is the principal, in dollars
I is the interest, in dollars

Using these formulas, along with the rules for solving equations from Unit 13, we can solve interest problems as shown in the following examples.

Example 1

Find the interest on \$80 at 6% per annum for 2 years.

Solution

$\because I = Prt$

$\therefore I = 80 \times \frac{6}{100} \times 2$

$= \frac{960}{100}$

$= 9.60$

$\therefore$ The interest is \$9.60.

P	= \$80
r	= 6% per year
t	= 2 years

Example 2

Find the annual rate of interest that will earn \$3.50 on \$150 in 4 months.

Solution

$\because \quad I = Prt$

$\therefore \; 3.50 = \overset{50}{\cancel{150}} \times r \times \frac{1}{\cancel{3}}$

then $3.50 = 50r$

and $\quad r = \frac{3.50}{50} = 0.070 = 7.0\%$

$\therefore$ The interest rate is 7.0%.

$I = \$3.50$
$P = \$150$
$t = \frac{1}{3}$ year

4 months $= \frac{4}{12}$ year
$\frac{1}{3}$ year

Example 3

How much money would have to be loaned out from June 12 to July 22 at 10% per annum in order to earn $8 interest?

Solution

$\because \; I = Prt$

$\therefore \; 8 = P \times \frac{\cancel{10}}{\underset{10}{\cancel{100}}} \times \frac{\cancel{40}^{4}}{365}$

or $\; 8 = P \times \frac{4}{365}$

and $P = {}^{2}\cancel{8} \times \frac{365}{\cancel{4}}$

$= 730$

$\therefore$ $730 would have to be loaned out.

$I = \$8$
$r = 10\%$
$t = \frac{40}{365}$ year

Number of days remaining in June 18
in July 22
40

Notice that the first day is not included but that the last day is!

40 days $= \frac{40}{365}$ year.

Example 4

How many days will it take to earn $12.10 interest on $365 at 10% per annum?

Solution

$\because \quad I = Prt$

$\therefore \; 12.10 = 365 \times \frac{\cancel{10}}{\underset{10}{\cancel{100}}} \times t$

then $12.10 = 36.5t$

and $\quad t = \frac{12.10}{36.5}$

$\therefore$ The time is $\frac{12.10}{36.5}$ years.

$\therefore$ The number of days is $\frac{12.10}{36.5} \times 365$ or 121 days.

$I = \$12.10$
$P = \$365$
$r = 10\%$

Remember that t in the formula $I = Prt$ must be in years.

Example 5

Find the amount of a loan of \$5000 for 1.5 years at 11.5% per annum.

Solution

$P = \$500$
$r = 11.5\%$
$t = 1.5$ years

$\because\ I = Prt$

$\therefore\ I = \overset{\cancel{50}\ 25}{\cancel{5000}} \times \frac{11.5}{\cancel{100}} \times \frac{3}{\cancel{2}}$

$= 862.50$

$\therefore$ Interest is \$862.50.

$\because\ A = P + I$

$\therefore\ A = \$5000 + \$862.50$

$= \$5862.50$

$\therefore$ The amount is \$5862.50.

Exercise 18.2

Note: Unless otherwise stated, all interest rates are per annum.

Discussion

1. State the interest for 1 year.
   (*a*) \$500 at 5% (*b*) \$300 at 4% (*c*) \$1000 at 6% (*d*) \$350 at 10% (*e*) \$230 at 11% (*f*) \$100 at 12.5%

2. State the interest on \$8000 for one year at these rates.
   (*a*) 4% (*b*) 5% (*c*) 8% (*d*) 10% (*e*) 12.5% (*f*) 9.5%

\$500

3. State the interest on \$500 at 6% for these times.
   (*a*) 1 year (*b*) $\frac{1}{3}$ year (*c*) 6 months (*d*) 2 months (*e*) 1 month (*f*) 0.8 year

4. State the number of days in the following loan periods.
   (*a*) March 10 to March 28
   (*b*) Oct. 7 to Nov. 12
   (*c*) July 8 to Aug. 14
   (*d*) Jan. 3 to Feb. 19
   (*e*) May 29 to June 30
   (*f*) Sept. 10 to Nov. 3

Written Solutions

5. Draw and complete the table using the formula $I = Prt$.

Problem	(*a*)	(*b*)	(*c*)	(*d*)	(*e*)	(*f*)	(*g*)	(*h*)	(*i*)	(*j*)
Interest			\$1.50	\$1.75	\$2.50	\$45	\$1.20	\$4.50		\$4
Principal	\$50	\$300	\$150	\$75		\$1000		\$150	\$4000	\$400
Rate	6%	5%	4%	7%	6%		12%		14%	
Time (months)	12	6			2	12	3	4	6	2

6. Find the amount of a loan for \$9850 for 2.5 years at 12%.
7. How much money will earn \$216 interest at 6% in 8 months?
8. In how many months at 5% would \$3360 amount to \$3402?
9. Draw and complete the following table.

Problem	(*a*)	(*b*)	(*c*)	(*d*)	(*e*)
Interest	\$256.50	\$93	\$500	\$35	\$87.50
Principal	\$4275	\$6200	\$50 000	\$4200	\$8400
Rate					
Time	1 year	120 days	1 month	30 days	75 days
Amount					

Here's a short cut to help you find r.

$\because I = Prt$

$\therefore \frac{I}{Pt} = r$

or $r = \frac{I}{Pt}$

$r = \frac{I}{Pt} \times 100\%$

10. Determine the amount of a \$1200 loan at 13.5% made on May 3 and paid on September 26.
11. A loan for \$2450 is made on October 18 at 5%. Find the date on which \$2465.10 will pay off the loan.

Here's a toughie!

12. \$1000 is loaned out at 10% for 1 year.
    (*a*) Calculate the amount needed to settle the loan.
    (*b*) If this new sum of money is then loaned out, again at 10% for 1 year, find the new amount that will be paid to settle the loan at the end of the second year.
    (*c*) What is the total interest earned on the original \$1000 over the 2-year period?

5(a) \$3 (b) \$7.50 (c) 3 (d) 4 (e) \$250 (f) 4.5% (g) \$40 (h) 9% (i) \$280 (j) 6%
6. \$12 805
7. \$5400
8. 3 months
9(a) 6% \$4531.50 (b) 4.56% \$6293 (c) 12% \$50 500 (d) 10.1% \$4235 (e) 5.07% \$8487.50
10. \$1264.80
11. Dec. 2
12(a) \$1100 (b) \$1210 (c) \$210

18.3 Compound Interest and Instalment Buying

$A = P + I$

A

1. Using an interest rate of 5% per annum and a time of 1 year, find the interest and amount on principals of
   (*a*) \$100 (*b*) \$105 (*c*) \$110.25

2. How is the amount in each part of Question 1 related to the principal in the next part?

B The calculations carried out in Question 1, for five interest periods, could be shown in a table.

Interest Period	1	2	3	4	5
Principal	\$100	\$110	\$121	\$133.10	\$146.41
Rate	10%	10%	10%	10%	10%
Time (years)	1	1	1	1	1
Interest	\$10	\$11	\$ 12.10	\$ 13.31	\$ 14.64
Amount	\$110	\$121	\$133.10	\$146.41	\$161.05

This is an example of *compound interest*. We say that \$100 bearing interest at 10%, and *compounded annually*, amounts to \$161.05 in 5 years.

$I = Prt$

$A = P + I$

1. A sum of \$500 is invested at an interest rate of 6%, compounded annually. Find the amount after 3 years, by drawing and completing the following table.

Interest Period	1	2	3
Principal	\$500	\$530	
Rate	6%	6%	6%
Time (years)	1	1	1
Interest			\$33.71
Amount			

2. Suppose that \$1000 earns interest at the rate of 5%, compounded semi-annually.
   (*a*) How many interest periods occur each year?
   (*b*) How many interest calculations will have to be made in a 2-year period?
   (*c*) Find the amount after 2 years by completing the table.

Interest Period	1	2	3	4
Principal	\$1000	\$1025		\$1078.90
Rate	5%	5%	5%	5%
Time (years)	0.5	0.5	0.5	0.5
Interest				
Amount				

It is not uncommon for people to buy items "on time." Indeed, merchants will arrange "friendly payment terms" on just about anything! Such phrases as

"Fly now, pay later!"
"Only \$6 down, . . ."
"Easy weekly payments of only . . . ."

are read in every newspaper, and heard over every television channel.

It is therefore most important that you be aware of the *true interest rate* when you buy under an instalment plan. Compound interest is the only way to determine the true interest rate, but the methods involved are complex and difficult. The following formula, however, gives a very close approximation to the true interest rate on an instalment purchase.

$$r = \frac{2NC}{P(n+1)}$$ where
r is the true interest rate per annum
N is the number of payment intervals in a year
C is the carrying charge (C = total instalment price − cash price)
P is the principal (P = cash price − down payment)
n is the number of payments made

Example 1

The cash price of an article is \$160, and the "time" payment price is \$175 if payment is made in 10 equal monthly instalments. Find the interest rate charged.

Solution

$r = \dfrac{2NC}{P(n+1)}$ where N = 12 payments per year
C = \$175 − \$160 = \$15
P = \$160
n = 10 payments made

$$\therefore r = \frac{2 \times 12 \times 15}{160 \times (10+1)} = \frac{\overset{3}{\cancel{24}} \times \overset{3}{\cancel{15}}}{\underset{4}{\cancel{\underset{\cancel{20}}{160}}} \times 11} = \frac{9}{44} = 0.2045 \text{ or } 20.45\%$$

∴ The true interest rate is approximately 20.5% per annum.

1
12
1 payment a month
= 12 payments a year

Example 2

Mr. N. Stalment buys a TV set for \$50 down and agrees to pay \$5/week for 40 weeks. If he had been able to pay cash, Mr. Stalment could have purchased the set for \$225. Find the rate of interest charged.

Solution

$r = \dfrac{2NC}{P(n+1)}$ where N = 52 payments per year
C = \$250 − \$225 = \$25
P = \$225 − \$50 = \$175
n = 40 payments made

\$50 down + \$5 per week for 40 weeks = \$250.
One each week for 40 weeks.

$$\therefore r = \frac{2 \times 52 \times \cancel{25}}{\underset{7}{\cancel{175}} \times 41} \doteq 0.362 = 36.2\%$$

∴ The interest rate is approximately 36.2% per annum.

Exercise 18.3

Discussion

1. If you had the choice of investing your money with interest compounded annually, semi-annually, or quarterly, which would you choose? Why?

Semi-annually means twice a year.

Quarterly means 4 times a year.

2. Which would be more work:
   (*a*) to calculate the amount of $800 at 5% for 3 years by the "simple interest" method, or
   (*b*) to calculate the amount of $800 at 5%, compounded annually, for 3 years? Explain.

That is, $I = Prt$ where $t = 3$ years.

Written Solutions

3. By completing a table like the following, show that $1200 will amount to $1429.22 after 3 years, if interest is at 6% compounded annually.

Interest Period	1	2	3
Principal	$1200		
Rate	6%	6%	6%
Time (years)	1	1	1
Interest			
Amount			$1429.22

4. Determine the interest that will be earned on $800 in 2 years, if the interest is at 6% compounded semi-annually.

5. An investment of $5000 is to be made at a rate of 5%. Find the total interest that will be earned after 3 years:
   (*a*) by simple interest methods,
   (*b*) by compounding the interest annually.

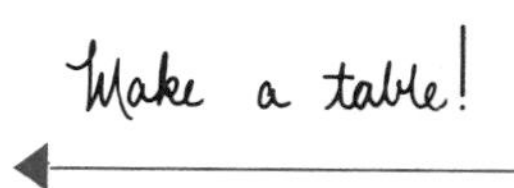

6. Which is the better investment, and by how much:
   (*a*) $800 at 6.5% for 1 year, or
   (*b*) $800 at 6% compounded quarterly, for one year?

4. $100.41
5(a) $750 (b) $788.13
6(a) is better by $2.91

7. 25.3%
8. 33.8%
9. 26.4%
Can you think of other kinds of insurance?

7. Dawn Paiment buys a used car priced at \$725 cash. However, she pays \$200 down, and agrees to 18 monthly payments of \$35 each. Find the rate of interest Dawn is being charged.

8. The Sonny Celsius Loan Company will loan out \$300 cash in return for an agreement to make 40 weekly payments of just \$8.50 each. Determine the rate of interest the company is charging.

9. Dora Digit finds an electronic calculator advertised at a local department store for just \$89. Instead of paying cash, she agrees to pay only \$5 down and \$8/month for the next year. Find the interest rate Dora is being charged on her purchase.

10. In your local newspaper, find two advertisements that give details concerning instalment buying. Calculate the true interest rate in each case.

18.4 Insurance and Taxes

Two common applications of percent are found in insurance and taxes. Simply stated, *insurance* is protection against some unexpected financial loss. There are several types of insurance available, the most common being fire, automobile, and life insurance. In any type of insurance, the money you pay for the protection is called the *premium*. The ratio of the premium to the amount of protection desired is called the *premium rate* and may be expressed in several ways. For example, if someone is paying a \$90 premium each year for \$30 000 worth of fire protection on a house, the premium rate could be expressed as follows.

\$30 per \$10 000	\$0.30 per \$100
\$3 per \$1000	30¢ per \$100
\$1.50 per \$500	0.3%

and so on.

That is, $\frac{30}{10\,000} = \frac{3}{1000} = \frac{1.5}{500} = \frac{0.3}{100} = 0.3\%$

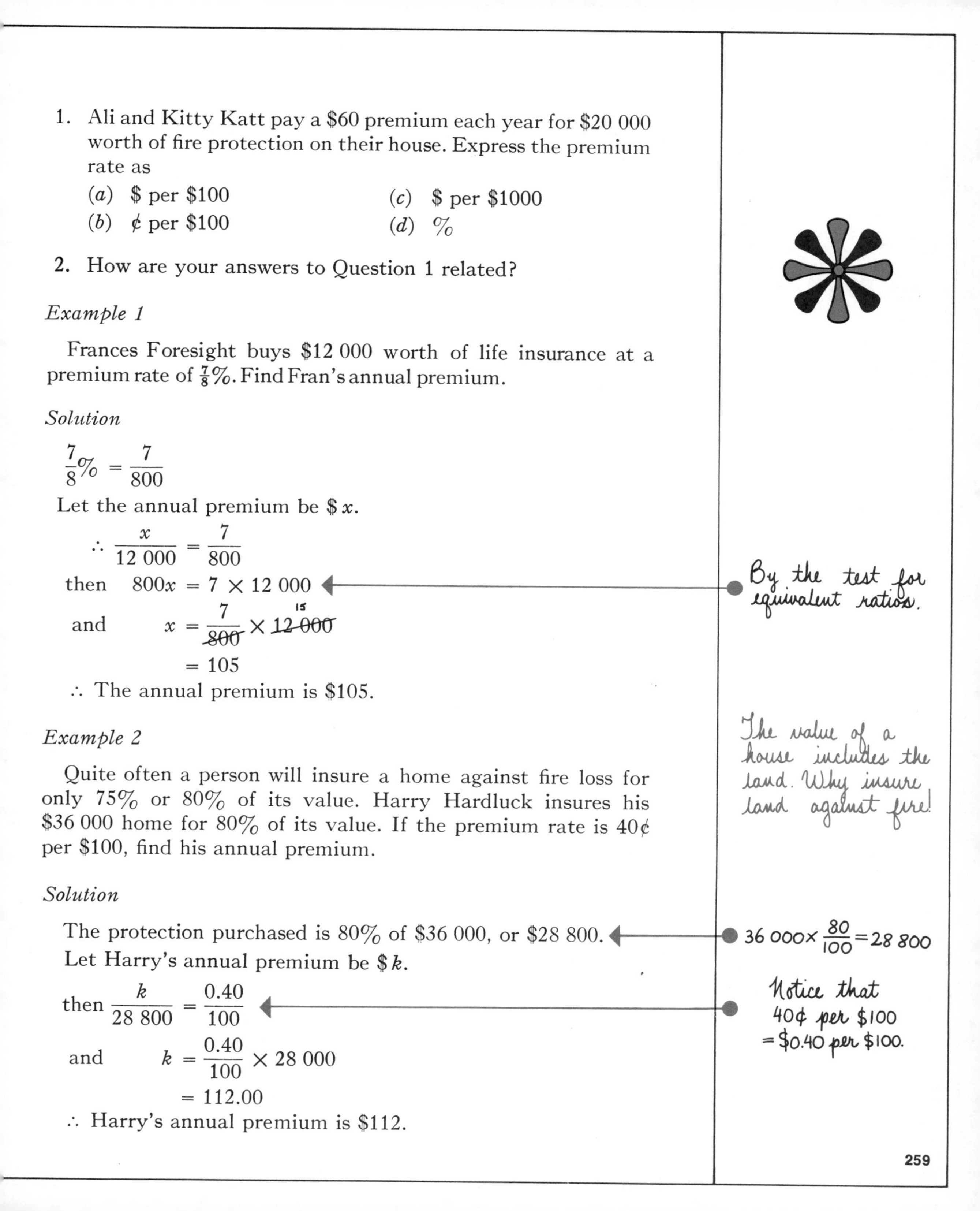

1. Ali and Kitty Katt pay a $60 premium each year for $20 000 worth of fire protection on their house. Express the premium rate as

   (a) $ per $100
   (b) ¢ per $100
   (c) $ per $1000
   (d) %

2. How are your answers to Question 1 related?

Example 1

Frances Foresight buys $12 000 worth of life insurance at a premium rate of $\frac{7}{8}$%. Find Fran's annual premium.

Solution

$$\frac{7}{8}\% = \frac{7}{800}$$

Let the annual premium be $ x.

$$\therefore \frac{x}{12\,000} = \frac{7}{800}$$

then $800x = 7 \times 12\,000$ ◄── By the test for equivalent ratios.

and $x = \frac{7}{\cancel{800}} \times \overset{15}{\cancel{12\,000}}$

$= 105$

∴ The annual premium is $105.

Example 2

Quite often a person will insure a home against fire loss for only 75% or 80% of its value. Harry Hardluck insures his $36 000 home for 80% of its value. If the premium rate is 40¢ per $100, find his annual premium.

The value of a house includes the land. Why insure land against fire!

Solution

The protection purchased is 80% of $36 000, or $28 800. ◄── $36\,000 \times \frac{80}{100} = 28\,800$

Let Harry's annual premium be $ k.

then $\frac{k}{28\,800} = \frac{0.40}{100}$ ◄── Notice that 40¢ per $100 = $0.40 per $100.

and $k = \frac{0.40}{100} \times 28\,000$

$= 112.00$

∴ Harry's annual premium is $112.

B "Only two things are certain: death and taxes!"

Sales tax, income tax, property tax, corporation profit tax, and so on, affect all of us to some degree. We shall discuss property taxes, which pay for essential services within the community, such as education, sewage disposal, and road repair.

As with an insurance rate, tax rate could be given as a ratio or percent, but it is more often expressed as a *mill rate*. For instance, the tax rate might be 43 mills per dollar, which is the same as the ratio 43:1000 or 4.3%.

1000 mills = \$1
10 mills = 1¢
1 mill = 0.1¢

"60 mills per dollar" is often shortened to "60 mills."

1. Express a tax rate of 60 mills as follows.
   (*a*) ¢ per 1000¢ (*b*) \$ per \$1 (*c*) ¢ per \$1 (*d*) %

C The amount of the tax is based on the assessed value of the property, called the *assessment*.

Example 3

Find the taxes Reg Ister pays. His property is assessed at \$8000 when the mill rate is 40 mills.

Solution

Let the taxes be represented by t dollars.

$t = \frac{40}{1000} \times 8000$

$$\therefore \frac{t}{8000} = \frac{40}{1000}$$

$$\therefore t = 320$$

∴ The taxes are \$320.

Example 4

If Marj Innol pays \$420 in taxes and the mill rate is 50 mills, find the assessed value of her property.

Solution

Let the assessed value be represented by v dollars.

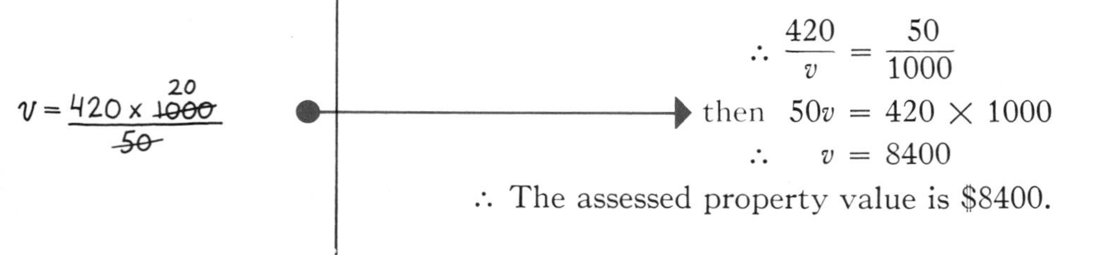

$$\therefore \frac{420}{v} = \frac{50}{1000}$$

$$\text{then } 50v = 420 \times 1000$$

$$\therefore v = 8400$$

∴ The assessed property value is \$8400.

Exercise 18.4

Discussion

1. What conditions might affect premium rates for fire insurance? Automobile insurance? Life insurance?
2. Determine the various types of insurance your parents consider in protecting your family against unforeseen future events.
3. Why might a person insure his property (buildings and land) for only a certain portion of its value against financial loss due to fire?
4. Ask your parents to show you the most recent tax bill on your property, so that you can see how your local council spends the taxes it collects.
5. When a person purchases gasoline, part of the price of each litre goes to the government as taxes. This is a "hidden" tax that is included in the price of the gasoline. How many other instances of "hidden" taxes can you find?

Are there hidden taxes on clothing?

6. State each of the following premium rates in three other ways, as indicated in the following table.

	\$ per \$100	*\$ per \$1000*	*¢ per \$100*	*%*
(a)	0.30			
(b)		1.50		
(c)				0.25
(d)			20	

7. Express each of the following tax rates in three other ways, as indicated in the table.

	Mills per \$1	*¢ per \$1*	*\$ per \$1*	*%*
(a)	40			
(b)				5.5
(c)		6.2		
(d)			0.045	

Written Solutions

8. Draw and complete the following table.

House	A	B	C	D
Assessed Value	\$7000	\$8000		\$11 200
Tax Rate	66 mills		44 mills	
Taxes		\$480	\$528	\$459.20

9. Draw and complete the following table.

House	A	B	C	D
Amount of Protection	\$24 000		\$45 000	\$43 200
Premium Rate	0.3%	25¢ per \$100		\$2.80 per \$1000
Premium		\$72	\$90	

10. If there is a 5% sales tax on an article costing \$29.40, what is the total amount the customer must pay?

11. Before leaving on an air trip, Hi Flyer pays \$3 for \$50 000 worth of insurance on his life. Find the premium rate as a percent.

12. What amount of home fire protection could you purchase for \$28.80 if the premium rate is 0.18%?

13. Anna Lyze insures her \$55 500 house against fire loss for 70% of its value. If the premium rate is 24¢ per \$100, find the annual premium.

14. If a homeowner pays \$377.20 in taxes and the tax rate is 41 mills, find the assessed value of the property.

15. A property is assessed at \$8650 in a community in which the tax rate is 59 mills. If 47% of the taxes raised goes toward education, how much money does this property contribute toward education expenses?

8(a) \$462
(b) 60 mills
(c) \$12 000
(d) 41 mills

9(a) \$72
(b) \$28 800
(c) 0.2%
(d) \$120.96

10. \$30.87
11. 0.006%
12. \$16 000
13. \$93.24
14. \$9200
15. \$239.86

More Puzzles and Problems

1. To draw a figure *unicursally* is to draw the figure with one continuous line and no line is passed over more than once.

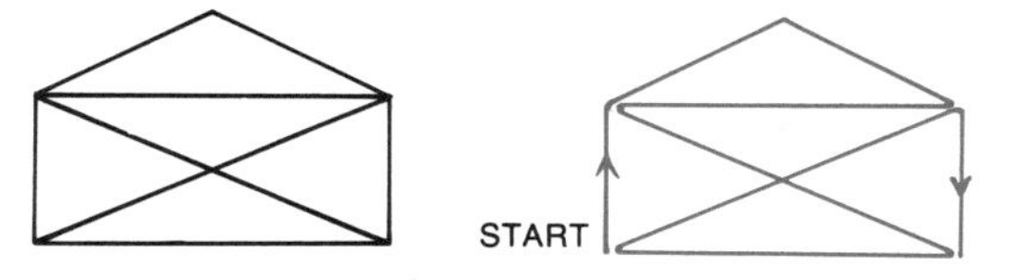

Make copies of the following figures unicursally.

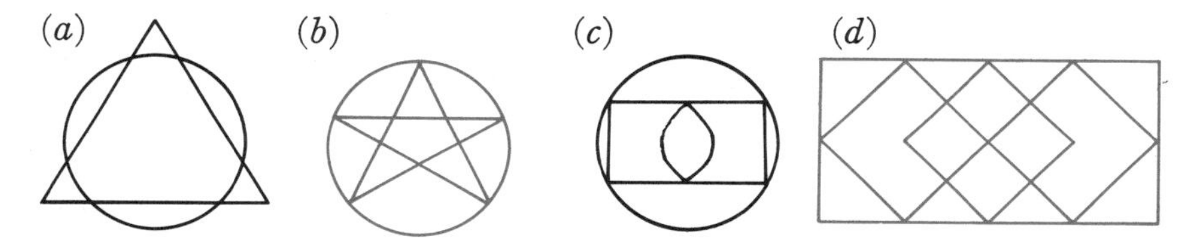

2. The margin figure consists of 12 toothpicks. Remove 2 toothpicks, leaving two squares.

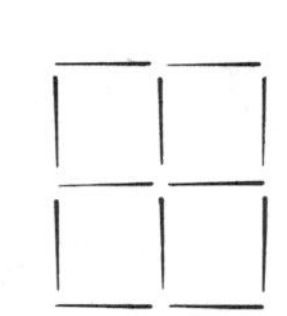

3. Remove 4 toothpicks to leave 5 squares.

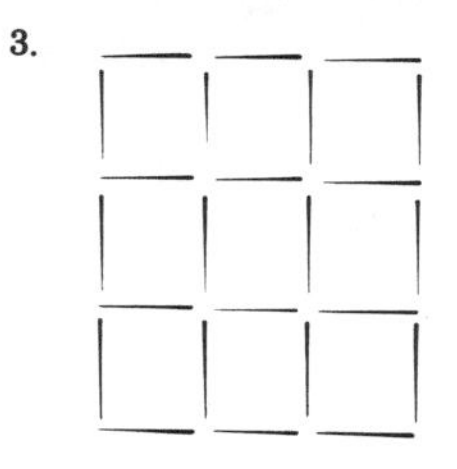

4. A cube is made of smaller cubes. The large cube is painted, dried, and taken apart.

   How many faces (of small cubes) are not painted?

5. Place two 5¢ coins side by side. Hold one fixed and roll the other around the fixed one. Which way is the head facing when the coin is halfway around?

6 A car is driven up one side of a 1 km long hill at 50 km/h. How fast must it travel 1 km down the other side to average 100 km/h for the whole trip?

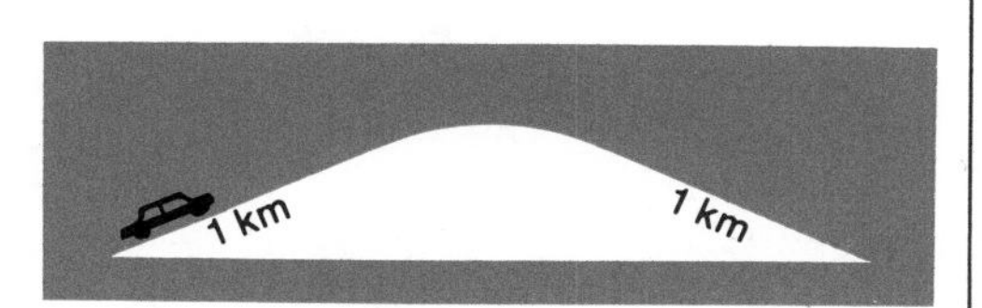

Maintaining Basic Skills

Exercise 4

1. Find the following sum or difference.

(*a*) $3 + (-2)$ (*d*) $5 - (-2)$ (*g*) $6 - 8$
(*b*) $-5 + 1$ (*e*) $4 + (-8)$ (*h*) $-2 + (-7)$
(*c*) $-2 - 5$ (*f*) $-1 - (-3)$ (*i*) $3 - (-5)$

2. State the product or quotient.

(*a*) $5 \times (-3)$ (*d*) $\frac{25}{-5}$ (*g*) $(-2)(-3)(-4)$
(*b*) $-2(6)$ (*e*) $\frac{-4}{12}$ (*h*) $-10 \div (-1)$
(*c*) $(-1)(-4)$ (*f*) $\frac{-10}{-15}$ (*i*) $(-1)^7$

3. Simplify.

(*a*) $4 \times 3 + 5$ (*d*) $(-2)^3 - 1$ (*g*) $1\frac{3}{5} \div \frac{4}{15}$
(*b*) $4 + 3 \times 5$ (*e*) $3(-1)^2 + 4$ (*h*) $-\frac{2}{3} \times 1\frac{7}{8}$
(*c*) $1\frac{3}{4} - 2\frac{1}{8}$ (*f*) $1 - 2(-3)^2$ (*i*) $(\frac{2}{3})^2 - \frac{5}{6}$

4. Calculate the following.

(*a*) 2.31×0.057 (*d*) $0.0493 \div 0.0016$
(*b*) 1.05^2 (*e*) $6.8 \times 0.5 \times 9.6$
(*c*) $26.8 \div 540$ (*f*) $58.7 \div 0.015$

5. Combine like terms to simplify.

(*a*) $3x + y + 5x + 2y$ (*c*) $3x^2 - 5x + 8x - 4$
(*b*) $8a - 4b - 3a + 7b$ (*d*) $-6y^2 + 5y - y + 1$

6. Solve the following equations.

(*a*) $3x + 2 = x + 8$ (*d*) $4 - 2x = 3x - 6$
(*b*) $4a - 3 = 2a - 5$ (*e*) $3 + 7y = 15 - y$
(*c*) $2b + 1 = 7b + 11$ (*f*) $1 + 3x = 1 + 2x$

7. State the product or quotient.

(*a*) $(2x)(3x)$ (*f*) $-35xy \div (-5x)$
(*b*) $(-3a)(2b)$ (*g*) $(2x^3)^2$
(*c*) $(15a^2)(-\frac{1}{3}a)$ (*h*) $-6x^5 \div 2x^2$
(*d*) $28a^2 \div 4a$ (*i*) $(-3a^2b)(-5ab^2)$
(*e*) $-15ab \div 5b$ (*j*) $-24xy^2 \div (-4x^2y)$

8. Find the value.

(*a*) $\sqrt{30}$ (*b*) $\sqrt{450}$ (*c*) $\sqrt{6.25}$ (*d*) $\sqrt{2209}$

1(a)	**1**	**(e)**	**−4**
(c)	**−7**	**(g)**	**−2**
2(a)	**−15**	**(g)**	**−24**
(d)	**−5**	**(i)**	**−1**
3(a)	**17**	**(f)**	**−17**
(d)	**−9**	**(g)**	**6**
4(a)	**0.131 67**	**(e)**	**32.64**
5(a)	$8x + 3y$	**(b)**	$5a + 3b$
6(b)	$a = -1$	**(d)**	$x = 2$
7(a)	$6x^2$	**(g)**	$4x^6$
(d)	$7a$	**(i)**	$15a^3b^3$
8(a)	**5.477**	**(c)**	**2.5**

9. Simplify.

(a) $\frac{2}{3} - \frac{3}{5}$
(b) $2.375 \div 7.6$
(c) $\frac{3}{4} + \frac{2}{3} \times \frac{3}{5}$
(d) $1\frac{2}{3} + 3(1\frac{3}{4})$
(e) $\frac{5}{8} \times \frac{2}{3} - \frac{1}{3}$
(f) $2.75(0.3 - 0.4)$
(g) $2(1.3) - 3(2.6)$
(h) $-\frac{5}{6} + 2(1\frac{1}{3})$
(i) $(\frac{2}{3})^2 - \frac{5}{12}$

10. Expand.

(a) $2(x + 3)$
(b) $3(a - 5)$
(c) $-2(y - 1)$
(d) $x(4x + 2)$
(e) $2y(y - 4)$
(f) $-3a(a^2 + 1)$
(g) $-5x(3x - 6)$
(h) $2(a + b + c)$
(i) $x(x^2 + 2x + 1)$

11. Factor.

(a) $ab + ac$
(b) $2x + 4$
(c) $6y - 12$
(d) $x^2 + 3x$
(e) $6a - 9$
(f) $104 + 15$
(g) $a^2 - 4a$
(h) $4c - 6$
(i) $8x^2 + 12x$

12. Expand.

(a) $(x + 1)(x + 2)$
(b) $(a - 4)(a - 5)$
(c) $(z + 3)(z - 2)$
(d) $(t - 4)(t + 7)$
(e) $(p + 6)(p - 9)$
(f) $(c - 10)(c + 8)$
(g) $(2x + 5)(3x + 4)$
(h) $(5x + 1)(4x + 7)$
(i) $(3a - 5)(8a + 12)$
(j) $(7a - 10)(5a + 2)$

13. Factor.

(a) $y^2 + 8y + 15$
(b) $r^2 - 3r + 2$
(c) $s^2 - 7s + 12$
(d) $x^2 + 10x + 16$
(e) $a^2 + 2a - 15$
(f) $z^2 - 3z - 10$
(g) $p^2 + 5p - 14$
(h) $r^2 - 4r - 12$
(i) $y^2 + y - 20$

14. Expand.

(a) $(x + 3)(x - 3)$
(b) $(y - 5)(y + 5)$
(c) $(5a - 4)(5a + 4)$
(d) $(6x + 2)^2$
(e) $(5b - 4)^2$
(f) $(3y - 5z)^2$

15. Factor.

(a) $r^2 - 16$
(b) $9a^2 - 25$
(c) $49t^2 - 1$
(d) $x^2 + 8x + 16$
(e) $25a^2 + 70a + 49$
(f) $36p^2 - 12p + 1$

16. Find the value of the following expressions.

(a) $3x - 5y$; $x = 1$, $y = -2$
(b) $2a^2 - 4a$; $a = 5$
(c) $(a + b)^2$; $a = -1$, $b = 2$
(d) $\frac{3a + b}{a - b}$; $a = 4$, $b = -3$
(e) $x^2 - 3y^2$; $x = -3$, $y = -2$
(f) $r^2 - 3r + 2$; $r = 7$
(g) $2(p + q) - 5$; $p = 7$, $q = -4$
(h) $\frac{3}{x} - \frac{4}{y}$; $x = 5$, $y = -2$

9(a) $\frac{1}{15}$ **(e)** $\frac{1}{12}$
(c) $\frac{23}{20}$ **(g)** -5.2

10(a) $2x + 6$
(d) $4x^2 + 2x$
(g) $-15x^2 + 30x$
(i) $x^3 + 2x^2 + x$

11(b) $2(x + 2)$
(d) $x(x + 3)$
(g) $a(a - 4)$
(i) $4x(2x + 3)$

12(a) $x^2 + 3x + 2$
(d) $t^2 + 3t - 28$
(g) $6x^2 + 23x + 20$
(i) $24a^2 - 4a - 60$

13(b) $(r - 2)(r - 1)$
(d) $(x + 2)(x + 8)$
(f) $(z + 2)(z - 5)$
(h) $(r - 6)(r + 2)$

14(a) $x^2 - 9$
(c) $25a^2 - 16$
(e) $25b^2 - 40b + 16$

15(a) $(r - 4)(r + 4)$
(c) $(7t - 1)(7t + 1)$
(e) $(5a + 7)^2$

16(a) 13 **(e)** -3
(c) 1 **(g)** 1

Summary of Units 10 to 18

Unit 10

Square Root, Part 1

	Do you understand...?	*Can you...?*
10.1 Square Root by Inspection	square root of a number perfect square prime factors	list the squares of 1, 2, 3,. . ., 24, 25 find the prime factors of a number
10.2 Square Root from Tables	square root table	find the square root of a number using square root tables
10.3 The Right-Angled Triangle	right angle hypotenuse Law of Pythagoras	determine the length of one side of a right-angled triangle, given the other 2 sides

Unit 11

Square Root, Part 2

	Do you understand...?	*Can you...?*
11.1 Calculating Square Root—Newton's Method	estimating a square root the average of 2 numbers first, second, ... approximations	approximate a square root using Newton's Method
11.2 Calculating Square Root—The Formal Method	the use of a diagram to find square root "pairing off" finding a trial divisor	calculate the square root of a perfect square using the Formal Method
11.3 Calculating Approximate Square Roots—The Formal Method	how to check the answer to a square root problem	calculate the square root of any decimal number to the required number of decimal places
11.4 Applications of Square Root		solve problems involving square roc

	Do you understand...?	*Can you...?*
Unit 12		
Operations with Polynomials		
12.1 Adding and Subtracting Terms	term coefficient like terms	add and subtract like terms
12.2 Adding and Subtracting Polynomials	monomial binomial trinomial polynomial	add and subtract polynomials
12.3 Multiplying and Dividing Monomials	exponent base	multiply and divide terms
Unit 13		
Equations and Inequations Revisited		
13.1 Equations and Inequations With Variables on Both Sides	root of an equation	solve an equation or inequation by adding or subtracting
13.2 Formulas	that a formula is a special type of equation isolation of a variable	substitute values into a formula manipulate a formula to isolate a variable
13.3 Strategy of Solving Equations		expand to eliminate brackets list the steps in solving an equation

	Do you understand...?	*Can you...?*
Unit 14 **Products and Factors, Part 1**		
14.1 Multiplying a Polynomial by a Monomial	expanding	expand the product of a monomial and a polynomial
14.2 Factors of a Term	factor set of variable factors common factor highest common factor (HCF)	find the factor set of a number find the set of variable factors of a term find the HCF of 2 terms
14.3 Common Factoring	factoring common factor	find the HCF of the terms of a binomial
Unit 15 **Products and Factors, Part 2**		
15.1 Multiplying Binomials		multiply 2 binomials
15.2 Shorter Methods for Multiplying Binomials	FOIL	use FOIL to multiply 2 binomials
15.3 Factors of Trinomials		factor a trinomial check factoring by expanding
Unit 16 **Products and Factors, Part 3**		
16.1 The Pattern $a^2 - b^2$	difference of squares	factor a difference of 2 squares
16.2 The Pattern $a^2 + 2ab + b^2$	perfect square	square a binomial in 2 ways factor a perfect square
16.3 Summary of Factoring and Expanding		list (in order) the 4 types of factoring

	Do you understand...?	*Can you...?*
Unit 17 **Ratio**		
17.1 Review of Ratio	colon notation fraction notation 2-term ratio 3-term ratio rate	write a ratio in lowest terms, using either colon notation or fraction notation
17.2 Equivalent Ratios	equivalent ratios test for equivalent ratios	find a ratio that is equivalent to a given ratio find the missing term in a pair of equivalent ratios
17.3 Ratio Problems		recall the main steps in solving problems
Unit 18 **Percent**		
18.1 Working with Percent	percent	change a 2-term ratio to a percent change a decimal to a percent change a percent to a ratio change a percent to a decimal solve problems involving percent
18.2 Simple Interest	interest principal interest rate amount	use the interest formula correctly
18.3 Compound Interest and Instalment Buying	compound interest true interest rate carrying charge	calculate interest compounded annually or semi-annually determine true interest rate for instalment buying
18.4 Insurance and Taxes	insurance premium premium rate property taxes mill rate assessment	calculate insurance premiums and rates calculate taxes, mill rates, and assessments

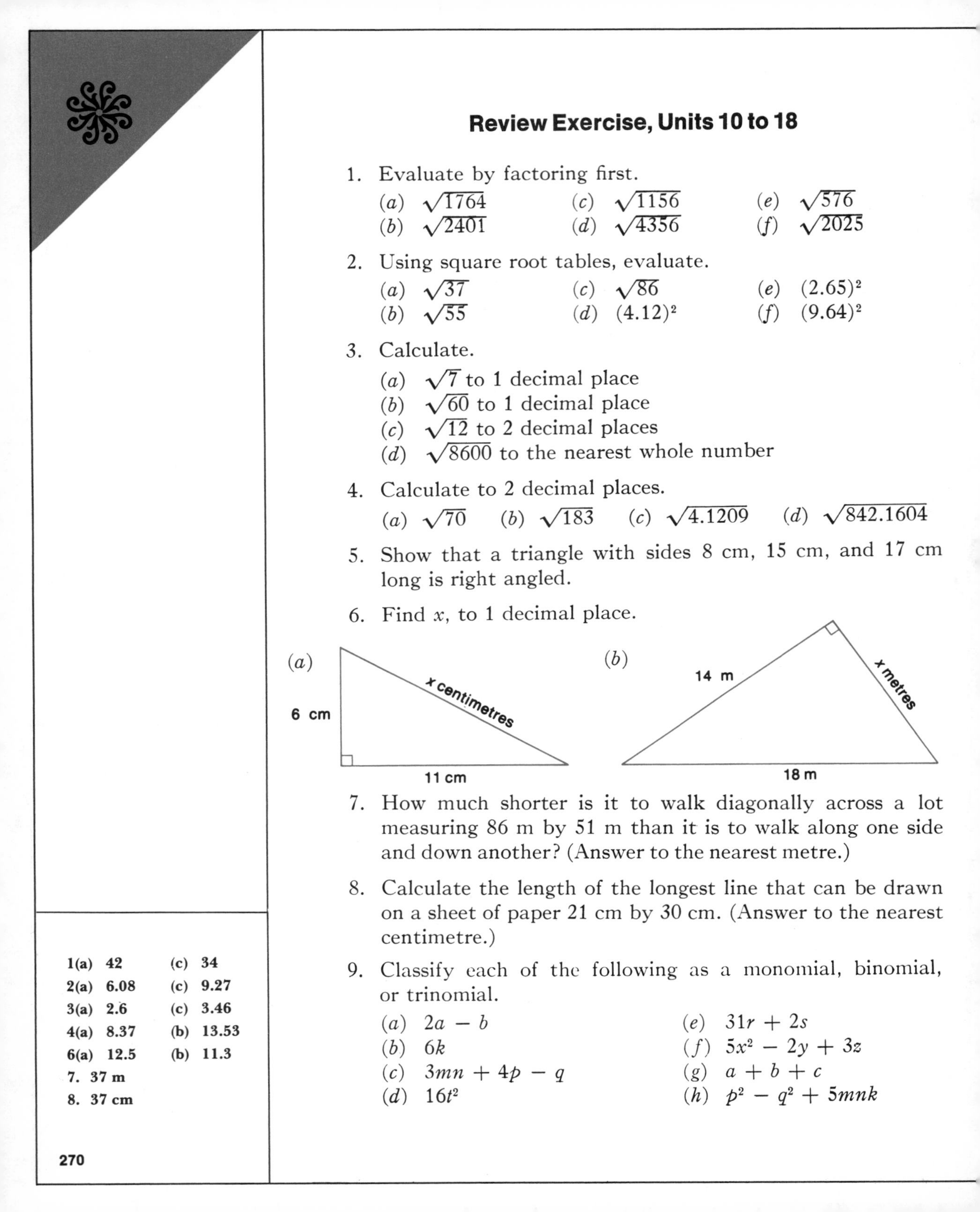

Review Exercise, Units 10 to 18

1. Evaluate by factoring first.
   (*a*) $\sqrt{1764}$ (*c*) $\sqrt{1156}$ (*e*) $\sqrt{576}$
   (*b*) $\sqrt{2401}$ (*d*) $\sqrt{4356}$ (*f*) $\sqrt{2025}$

2. Using square root tables, evaluate.
   (*a*) $\sqrt{37}$ (*c*) $\sqrt{86}$ (*e*) $(2.65)^2$
   (*b*) $\sqrt{55}$ (*d*) $(4.12)^2$ (*f*) $(9.64)^2$

3. Calculate.
   (*a*) $\sqrt{7}$ to 1 decimal place
   (*b*) $\sqrt{60}$ to 1 decimal place
   (*c*) $\sqrt{12}$ to 2 decimal places
   (*d*) $\sqrt{8600}$ to the nearest whole number

4. Calculate to 2 decimal places.
   (*a*) $\sqrt{70}$ (*b*) $\sqrt{183}$ (*c*) $\sqrt{4.1209}$ (*d*) $\sqrt{842.1604}$

5. Show that a triangle with sides 8 cm, 15 cm, and 17 cm long is right angled.

6. Find x, to 1 decimal place.

   (*a*) (*b*)

7. How much shorter is it to walk diagonally across a lot measuring 86 m by 51 m than it is to walk along one side and down another? (Answer to the nearest metre.)

8. Calculate the length of the longest line that can be drawn on a sheet of paper 21 cm by 30 cm. (Answer to the nearest centimetre.)

9. Classify each of the following as a monomial, binomial, or trinomial.
   (*a*) $2a - b$ (*e*) $31r + 2s$
   (*b*) $6k$ (*f*) $5x^2 - 2y + 3z$
   (*c*) $3mn + 4p - q$ (*g*) $a + b + c$
   (*d*) $16t^2$ (*h*) $p^2 - q^2 + 5mnk$

1(a) 42 **(c) 34**
2(a) 6.08 **(c) 9.27**
3(a) 2.6 **(c) 3.46**
4(a) 8.37 **(b) 13.53**
6(a) 12.5 **(b) 11.3**
7. 37 m
8. 37 cm

10. In the expression $5a - 2b^2 + 3ab - 12d$, state
   (*a*) the variables used in the expression,
   (*b*) the number of terms, and
   (*c*) the coefficient of each term.

11. Simplify.
   (*a*) $4x - 7x$
   (*b*) $2ab + 9ab$
   (*c*) $3y - 2y - 6y$
   (*d*) $-2m^2 + 6m^2$
   (*e*) $(2a - b) + (6a + 3b)$
   (*f*) $4x^2 - (2x^2 + 3y^2)$
   (*g*) $(4a - 9b + c) - (2a + b - c)$
   (*h*) $(-3p + 7q) - (-8p - 5q)$

12. Find the product.
   (*a*) $4m \times 8m$
   (*b*) $3ab \times 2a^2$
   (*c*) $-5xy^2 \times 2xy$
   (*d*) $(-2k)(-3k) \times 6$
   (*e*) $4w^3(-3v)$
   (*f*) $-8(-5ab)(-2a)$
   (*g*) $-32m^2n \times (-3mn^3)$
   (*h*) $4xy \times 13z \times 2$

13. Find the quotient.
   (*a*) $x^5 \div x^2$
   (*b*) $4m^3n \div 2mn$
   (*c*) $\dfrac{-12a^2b^3}{4ab}$
   (*d*) $39t^2v^3 \div (-13tv)$
   (*e*) $25xy \div 5xy$
   (*f*) $\dfrac{105r^2st^3}{-21rt^2}$
   (*g*) $\dfrac{-14ab^3}{-7ab}$
   (*h*) $40x^2y^2 \div (-8xy^2)$

14. Expand.
   (*a*) $a(b + c)$
   (*b*) $m(2m + n)$
   (*c*) $3a(2a - b)$
   (*d*) $-6(x - 4y)$
   (*e*) $-5a(a + 2b - c)$
   (*f*) $-4p^2(-7p + 3q - 2r)$

15. Factor and check by expanding.
   (*a*) $3a + 6b$
   (*b*) $4m^2 - 8m$
   (*c*) $10a^3 - 15a^2$
   (*d*) $-16x^2y + 2xy$
   (*e*) $2a^2 + 6ab - 10a^2b^2$
   (*f*) $32k^2 - 48k^5$

16. Expand.
   (*a*) $(x + 3)(x + 2)$
   (*b*) $(a - 6)(a + 5)$
   (*c*) $(2m - 3)(m - 7)$
   (*d*) $(2p - q)(4p + 3q)$
   (*e*) $(3x - 7)(5x - 1)$
   (*f*) $(6a^2 - 3)(2a^2 + 5)$
   (*g*) $(7 - 4x)(9 + 2x)$
   (*h*) $(a - 2b)(3a + 6)$
   (*i*) $(5m - n)(5m + n)$
   (*j*) $(3 - 2x)(3 + 2x)$

11(g) $2a - 10b + 2c$
(h) $5p + 12q$

12(a) $32m^2$
(c) $-10x^2y^3$
(g) $96m^3n^4$

13(a) x^3
(c) $-3ab^2$
(e) 5
(g) $2b^2$

14(a) $ab + ac$
(f) $28p^3 - 12p^2q + 8p^2r$

16(a) $x^2 + 5x + 6$
(c) $2m^2 - 17m + 21$
(e) $15x^2 - 38x + 7$
(g) $63 - 22x - 8x^2$
(i) $25m^2 - n^2$

17. Factor.

(a) $a^2 + 5a + 6$
(b) $m^2 + 2m - 3$
(c) $p^2 - 4p - 12$
(d) $w^2 - w - 20$
(e) $y^2 - 7y + 10$
(f) $x^2 - 14x - 72$

18. Expand and simplify.

(a) $3x(x + 4) + 2x(x - 5)$
(b) $7m(m - 3) + m(m + 6)$
(c) $6x(x - 2) + 3x(2x + 1)$
(d) $(k + 4)(k - 3) - 2k(k + 1)$
(e) $(a - 2b)(3a + b) + (5a + b)(a - 2b)$
(f) $(p - 3q)(2p + 5q) - (6p + q)$

19. Expand and simplify.

(a) $(x - 3)(x + 3)$
(b) $(5r - s)(5r + s)$
(c) $(a - 3c)(a + 3c)$
(d) $(x + 3)^2$
(e) $(2x - 5)^2$
(f) $(3m + 7)^2$

20. Factor.

(a) $a^2 - 25$
(b) $4q^2 - 1$
(c) $16m^2 - 36n^2$
(d) $4x^2 - 12xy + 9y^2$
(e) $25r^2 + 70rs + 49s^2$
(f) $9a^2 - 36ab + 36b^2$

21. Find the HCF of each of the following.

(a) $3x^2$, $6x^3$
(b) $2mn$, $5m^2$
(c) $5ab$, $15ab^3$
(d) $16c^2d^3$, $12cd^4$

22. Factor.

(a) $10r^2 + 25$
(b) $2x^2 - 10x + 8$
(c) $m^2 + 10m - 39$
(d) $49 - 25a^2$
(e) $36a^2 + 60ab + 25b^2$
(f) $9x - 12y + 18z + 6v$
(g) $7 - 28p^2$
(h) $t^2 - 6t - 91$

23. Solve.

(a) $2m = m - 5$
(b) $a + 4 = 5a$
(c) $2x - 7 = 3x$
(d) $x + 9 = 3$
(e) $6y - 4 = 8y$
(f) $3g = 16 - 5g$
(g) $-4x - 12 = 2x$
(h) $-7 - x = 0$
(i) $3t - 8 = -t$
(j) $3p = 6p + 9$

17(a) $(a + 3)(a + 2)$
(c) $(p - 6)(p + 2)$
(e) $(y - 2)(y - 5)$

18(a) $5x^2 + 2x$
(c) $12x^2 - 9x$

19(a) $x^2 - 9$
(c) $a^2 - 9c^2$
(e) $4x^2 - 20x + 25$

21(a) $3x^2$

22(a) $(2r^2 + 5)$
(c) $(m + 13)(m - 3)$
(e) $(6a + 5b)^2$
(g) $7(1 - 2p)(1 + 2p)$
(h) $(t - 13)(t + 7)$

23(a) $m = -5$
(c) $x = -7$
(e) $y = -2$
(f) $g = 2$
(h) $x = -7$
(j) $p = -3$

24. By substitution, check to see if the given value for x is a root of the given equation.
   (a) $3x - 4 = 5x, \quad x = 2$
   (b) $-17 + x = 3x + 9, \quad x = -13$
   (c) $2x - 1 = x + 8, \quad x = 9$
   (d) $24x + 2 = -9 + 13x, \quad x = -1$

25. Isolate m in each of the following.
   (a) $m - 3x = 2$
   (b) $4a + m = 12$
   (c) $-6 = 3k + m$
   (d) $2b = 3c - m$
   (e) $2p - m + q = 0$
   (f) $-m + 5 = 6r$
   (g) $2x + 3y + m = 0$
   (h) $-m - 6z + t = 5s$

26. Solve and check.
   (a) $5k - 2 = 4k + 3$
   (b) $6m + 3 - 2m + 1 = 0$
   (c) $-14 + x = 8 + 3x$
   (d) $1 = 5y + 10 - 2y$
   (e) $-18 + p + 12 = -2p$
   (f) $a - 20 = 5a + 4$
   (g) $9t = 7t - (20 - 8)$
   (h) $4(t + 1) = -17 - 3t$

27. Adding 4 to 2 times a number gives the same answer as multiplying the number by 5 and subtracting 11. Find the number.

28. Solve.
   (a) $0.375 = 3.75y$
   (b) $6y = 7$
   (c) $-3y = \frac{2}{5}$
   (d) $4y - 2 = 3$
   (e) $16 - 3y = 12$
   (f) $4 - 2y = 7$

29. Solve for the variable indicated.
   (a) $V = IR; \quad R$
   (b) $x - y = 3; \quad y$
   (c) $P = C + nk; \quad k$
   (d) $Q = \frac{cv}{t}; \quad v$

30. Solve.
   (a) $-3(t - 1) = 15$
   (b) $7(y - 2) = 2(3 + y)$
   (c) $\frac{a - 1}{4} = \frac{17 + a}{6}$
   (d) $6 - \frac{1}{3}m = \frac{5}{6} + m$

31. Using colon notation, write the following as ratios, in lowest terms.
   (a) 1.875 kg, 625 g
   (b) 16 m, 64 mm
   (c) 3.5 m, 70 cm, 560 mm
   (d) 500 kg, 2.5 t

25(a) $m = 2 + 3x$
(c) $m = -3k - 6$
(e) $m = 2p + q$
(g) $m = -2x - 3y$

27. 5

28(a) $y = 0.1$
(c) $y = -\frac{2}{15}$
(e) $y = \frac{4}{3}$

29(a) $R = \frac{V}{I}$
(c) $k = \frac{P - C}{n}$

30(a) $t = -4$
(c) $a = 37$

31(a) 3:1

32. Use the test for equivalent ratios to determine which of the following represent true statements.

(*a*) $5 : 4 = 11 : 9$

(*b*) $\frac{5}{8} = \frac{17.5}{28}$

(*c*) $6 : 0.625 = 48 : 5$

(*d*) $12 : 16 = 39 : 52$

33. Find the value of each variable in each of the following sets of equivalent ratios.

(*a*) $5 : x = 1 : 9$

(*b*) $7 : 18 = m : 2$

(*c*) $3 : 20 = a : 80 = 24 : k$

(*d*) $\frac{7}{p} = \frac{49}{21} = \frac{s}{30}$

(*e*) $0.2 : 0.3 = a : 1.2$

(*f*) $\frac{4}{5} : t = \frac{1}{8} : \frac{5}{6}$

34. The ratio of the heights of 2 children is 7:5. If the taller one is 154 cm tall, determine the height of the shorter one.

35. The prices of 2 dresses are in the ratio 11:14. If the less expensive dress costs $14.30, find the price of the other.

36. Melba Toast types a 440-word essay in 5.5 min. At this same rate, how long would it take her to type a 10 000-word report?

37. Change to percent.

(*a*) 0.93
(*b*) 1.67
(*c*) 0.025
(*d*) 0.06
(*e*) 0.275
(*f*) 3

38. Express as a percent.

(*a*) $\frac{4}{5}$
(*b*) $\frac{3}{8}$
(*c*) $5 : 3$
(*d*) $5 : 6$

39. Express as decimal numbers.

(*a*) 47%
(*b*) 7.5%
(*c*) 235%
(*d*) $3 : 4$
(*e*) $3.75 : 7.5$
(*f*) $6.75 : 3$

40. On a cash sale, a discount of 20% is allowed on an article selling for $160. What is the cash price of the article?

41. If 25% of a number is 32, what is the number?

42. What is the rate of profit on an article costing $56 that sells for $77?

33(a) $x = 45$ **(e)** $a = 0.8$
(c) $a = 12$, $k = 160$
34. 110 cm
35. $18.20
36. 2 h 5 min
37(a) 93% **(e)** 27.5%
(c) 2.5%
38(a) 80% **(c)** $166\frac{2}{3}$%
39(a) 0.47 **(e)** 0.5
(c) 2.35
40. $128
41. 128
42. 37.5%

43. Calculate the interest on \$730 at 6% for

(*a*) 5 years (*b*) 2 months (*c*) 40 days

44. Determine the amount of the loan in each part of Question 43.

45. Use the following table to determine the amount of \$300 compounded annually at 10%, after 3 years.

Interest period	1	2	3
Principal	\$300		
Rate	10%		
Time (years)	1		
Interest			
Amount			

46. Mr. and Mrs. Koolmore buy a refrigerator by paying \$32.25/month for 8 months. If they had been able to pay cash, they could have purchased it for \$240. Find the rate of interest charged.

47. F. N. Brimstone insures his \$32 000 home for 80% of its value against fire loss. His premium rate is \$0.15 per \$100.

(*a*) Calculate the protection purchased.

(*b*) Determine his annual premium.

48. Calculate the taxes Claire Voyant pays. Her property is assessed at \$8700 when the mill rate is 50 mills.

49. Find the assessed value of a property on which the taxes are \$220 and the mill rate is 4.4%.

43(a) \$219 (b) \$7.30 (c) \$4.80

44(a) \$949 (b) \$737.30 (c) \$734.80

45. \$399.30

46. 20%

47(a) \$25 600 (b) \$38.40

48. \$435

49. \$5000

Unit 19

Perimeter and Area of Plane Figures

Panelling a recreation room, wallpapering a bedroom, roofing a cottage, tiling a floor, . . . any of these projects involve measurement of a flat surface. In calculations like these there are many formulas you may use, such as $A = lw$, $P = 2l + 2w$, and $c = \pi d$.

In the next 2 units you will study the basic formulas involved in finding perimeter, area, and volume.

19.1 Perimeter and Linear Measure

A The perimeter of a plane figure is the distance around it. For example, the perimeter of the figure shown below can be found as follows.

$$P = 14 + 5 + 9 + 6 + 4 + 4 + 8$$
$$= 50$$

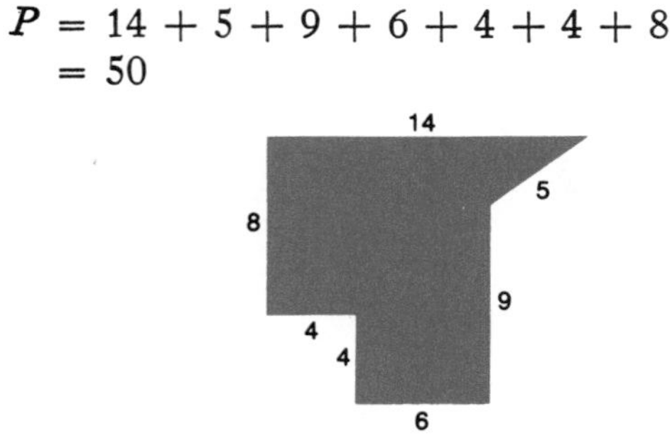

1. Determine the perimeter of each of the following plane figures.

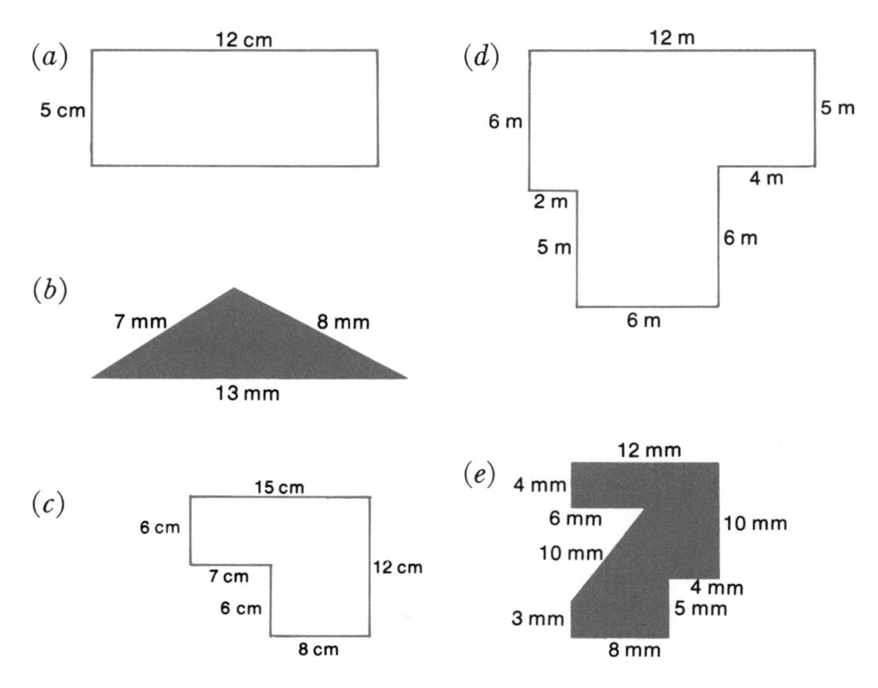

2. Note that linear units (metres, for example) are used in measuring perimeter. List as many other common units for linear measure as you can.

SHAPE	PERIMETER FORMULA
Square with sides l, l, l, l	$P = l + l + l + l$ $= 4l$
Rectangle with sides l, w, l, w	$P = l + w + l + w$ $= 2l + 2w$ $= 2(l + w)$
Triangle with sides a, b, c	$P = a + b + c$
Circle with diameter d and circumference C	$\because \frac{C}{d} = \pi$ $\therefore C = \pi d$

The perimeter of some geometric figures can be expressed by a simple formula.

1. Using the formulas shown, determine the perimeter of each of the following plane figures.

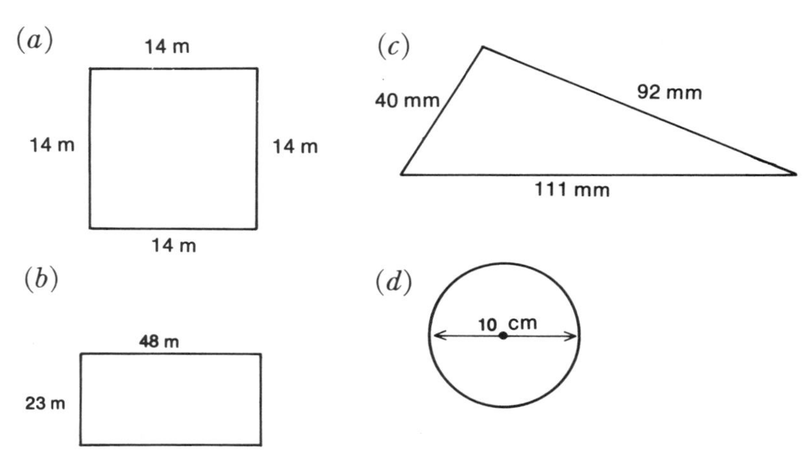

Study carefully the following examples involving perimeters.

Example 1

Find the perimeter of the semicircle (to 1 decimal place).

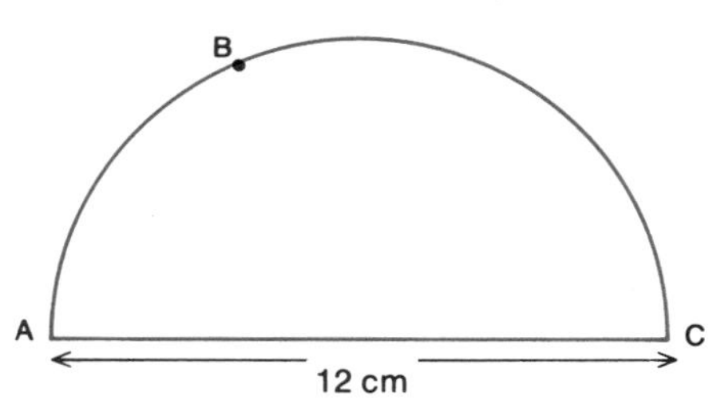

Note that perimeter of a circle is usually called circumference.

$\pi \doteq 3.14$

Solution

$$
\begin{aligned}
P &= AC + \text{arc } ABC \\
&= 12 + \tfrac{1}{2} \times (\text{circumference of circle, diameter } 12) \\
&= 12 + \tfrac{1}{2}(\pi \times 12) \\
&= 12 + 6\pi \\
\therefore \quad P &\doteq 12 + 6(3.14) \\
&= 12 + 18.84 \\
&= 30.84
\end{aligned}
$$

Recall that arc means a part of a circle.

Why $\frac{1}{2}$?

∴ The perimeter of the semicircle is 30.8 cm, to 1 decimal place.

Example 2

The slant height (s) of a cone is determined by the formula $s = \sqrt{h^2 + r^2}$, where h and r represent the height of the cone and the radius of its base, respectively. (See diagram.)

A load of grain is dumped onto a platform and forms a cone 12 m high with a radius of 16 m. Find the slant height of the pile of grain.

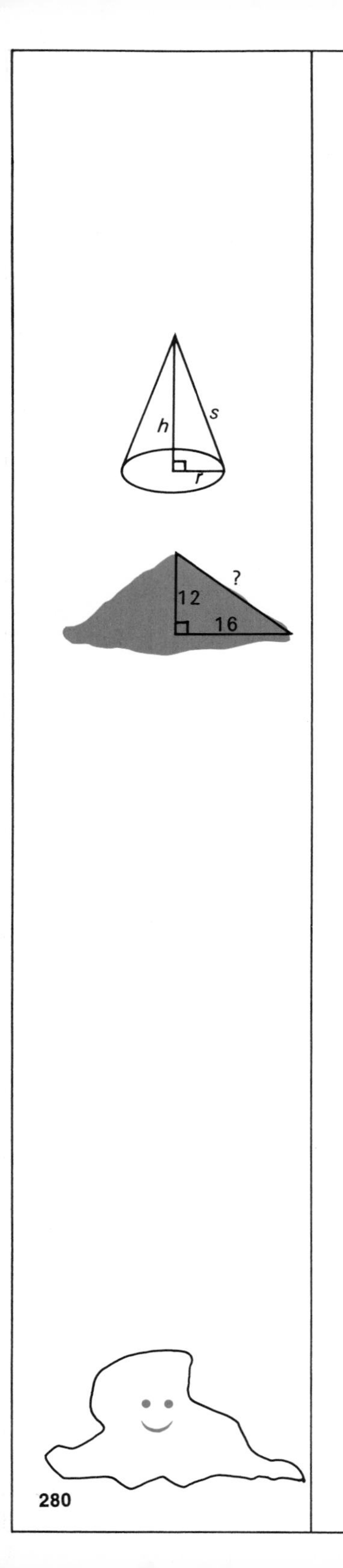

Solution

$$\begin{aligned} s &= \sqrt{h^2 + r^2} \\ &= \sqrt{12^2 + 16^2} \\ &= \sqrt{144 + 256} \\ &= \sqrt{400} \\ &= 20 \end{aligned}$$

∴ The slant height of the grain pile is 20 m.

Exercise 19.1

Discussion

1. In your own words, state the meaning of each of the following terms.
   (*a*) perimeter
   (*b*) linear measure
   (*c*) circumference
   (*d*) plane figure

2. Find an expression for the perimeter of each figure.

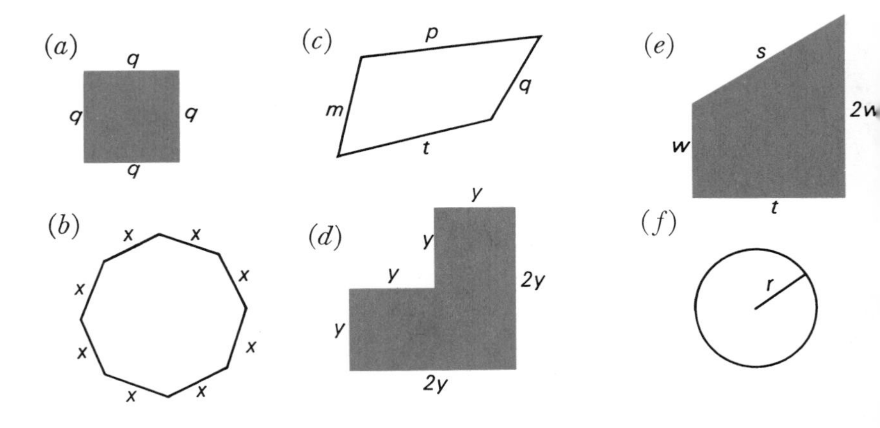

3. Given a piece of thread and a ruler, how might you find the perimeter of the figure shown in the margin?

Written Solutions

4. Carl Cooker has just shaped his pie dough into a 25 cm pie plate and trims off the excess with a knife. What length is the strip of dough that he trims off? (Use $\pi = 3.14$.)

5. Harriet Handiwon prepares a large box for shipping by fastening 3 steel straps around it, as shown. Allowing an extra 10 cm for fastening each strap, what total length of strapping does Harriet need?

6. When preparing its newspapers for delivery to distribution centers within the city, the *Hometown News* ties each bundle of 50 papers with a piece of string. If a bundle is in the form of a cylinder, as shown, find the length of string required for each bundle, allowing an extra 20 cm for the knot. (Use $\pi = 3.14$.)

7. How much lace is required to put a border on a rectangular tablecloth measuring 90 cm by 175 cm, allowing 5 cm at each corner for a loop?

8. Find the length of strapping required to support the heating pipe as shown in the diagram. (Use $\pi = 3.14$)

9. During the framing of a garage, a diagonal brace is used temporarily on a side wall, as shown. Determine the length of the brace, correct to 1 decimal place.

10. Calculate the length of weather stripping necessary to fit around the edge of a door whose measurements are as given in the diagram. (Use $\pi = 3.14$)

11. A recreation room measuring 8.2 m by 4.3 m has its floor partly covered by a rug so that a border of 50 cm is left between the wall and the edge of the rug on all sides. Find the perimeter of the rug.

12. The ratio of the length of a rectangular lot to its width is 2:1. If the perimeter of the lot is 420 m, find its dimensions.

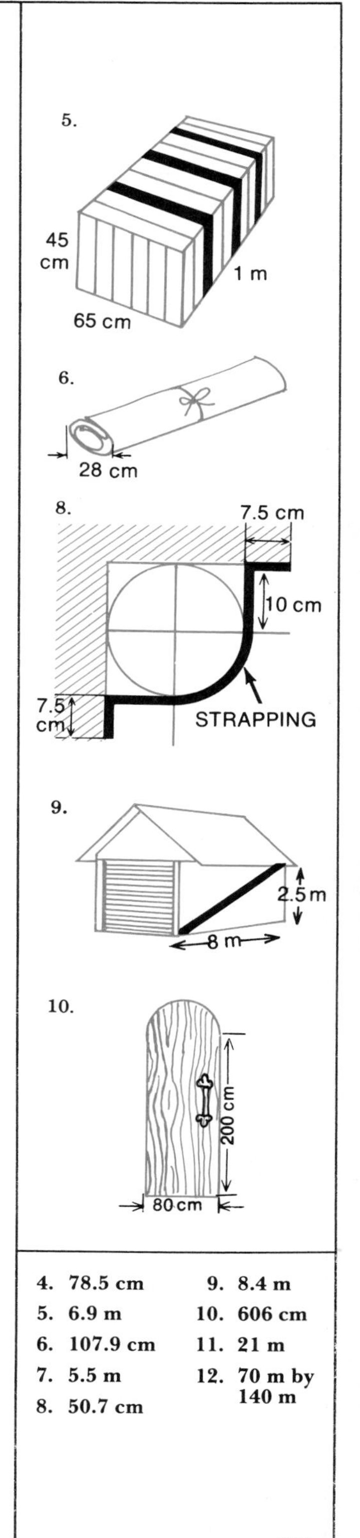

4. 78.5 cm	9. 8.4 m
5. 6.9 m	10. 606 cm
6. 107.9 cm	11. 21 m
7. 5.5 m	12. 70 m by 140 m
8. 50.7 cm	

13. 170 pearls
14. 350 km

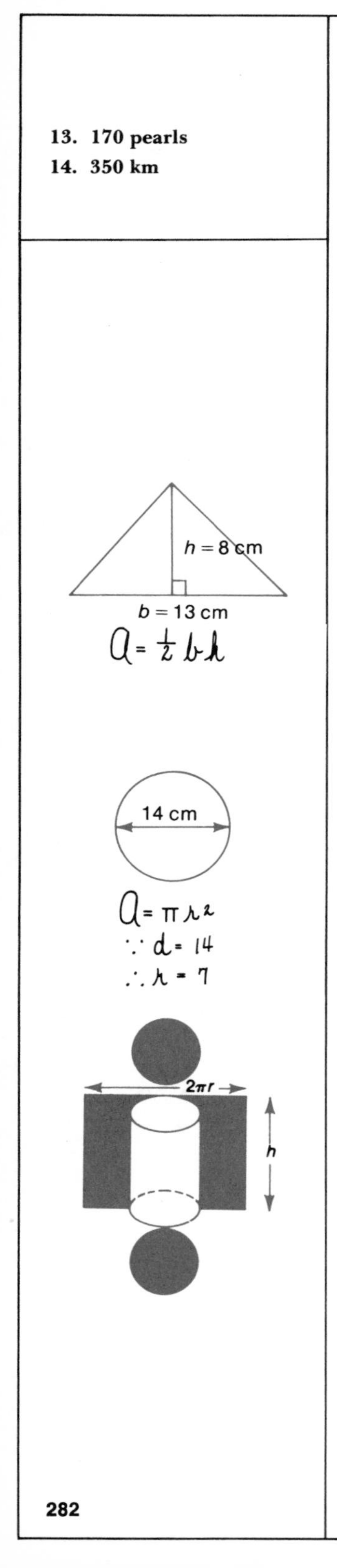

13. Betty wears a pearl necklace "choker" 18 cm in diameter. If the average number of pearls per centimetre is 3, determine the number of pearls on the necklace.

14. A communications satellite has a circular orbit about the earth and travels 42 200 km in each orbit. If the radius of the earth is approximately 6370 km, how far is the satellite above the earth's surface? (Use $\pi = 3.14$.)

19.2 Areas and Square Measure

Study carefully the following examples.

Example 1 Calculate the area of the triangle.

Solution

$$\begin{aligned} A &= \tfrac{1}{2}bh \\ &= \tfrac{1}{2}(13)(8) \\ &= 52 \end{aligned}$$

∴ The area is 52 cm².

Example 2 Find the area of a circle whose diameter is 14 cm.

Solution

$$\begin{aligned} A &= \pi r^2 \\ &\doteq 3.14(7)^2 \\ &= 3.14(49) \\ &\doteq 154 \end{aligned}$$

∴ The area is approximately 154 cm².

Example 3

Find the total surface area of an unopened tin can 10 cm in diameter and 15 cm high.

Solution

$$\begin{aligned} \text{Total surface area} &= (\text{Area of curved portion}) + (\text{Top area}) \\ &\quad + (\text{Bottom area}) \\ &= 2\pi rh + 2(\pi r^2) \\ &\doteq 2(3.14)(5)(15) + 2(3.14)(5)^2 \\ &= 471 + 157 \\ &= 628 \end{aligned}$$

∴ The total surface area is approximately 628 cm².

Example 4

Find the total surface area of a ball with a radius of 3.8 cm.

Solution

$$\begin{aligned} A &= 4\pi r^2 \\ &\doteq 4(3.14)\ (3.8)^2 \\ &= 181.37 \end{aligned}$$

∴ The area is approximately 181 cm².

Example 5

Determine the lateral surface area (sides only) of a square pyramid whose base measures 4 m by 4 m, and whose slant height is 9 m.

Solution

Each face is a triangle. There are 4 triangles of equal area.

$$\begin{aligned} A &= 4 \times (\tfrac{1}{2}bh) \\ &= 4 \times \tfrac{1}{2} \times 4 \times 9 \\ &= 72 \end{aligned}$$

∴ The lateral surface area is 72 m².

Example 6

Calculate the lateral surface area of a cone whose base has radius 2 m and whose slant height is 10 m.

Solution

$$\begin{aligned} A &= \pi rs \\ &\doteq 3.14(2)(10) \\ &= 62.8 \end{aligned}$$

∴ The area is approximately 62.8 m².

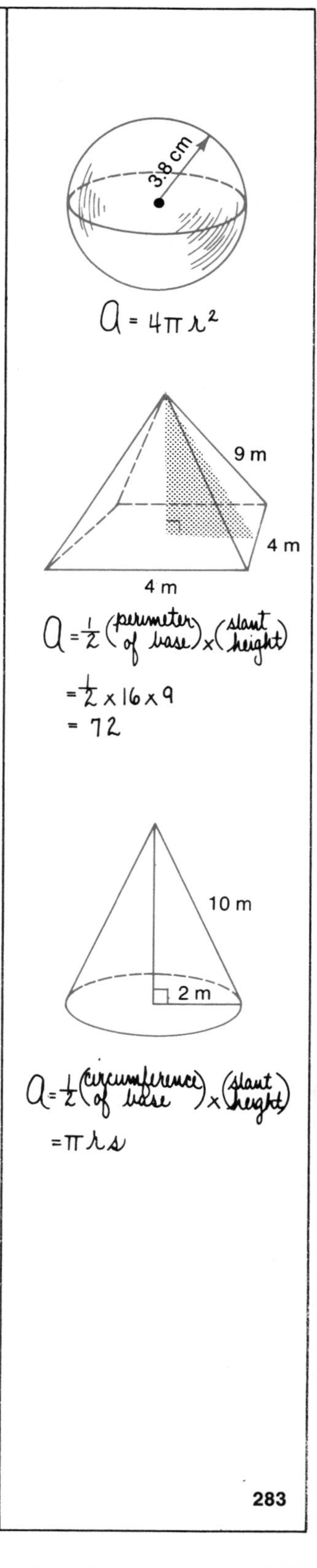

Exercise 19.2

Discussion

1. What is incorrect about each of the following statements?
   (*a*) The surface area of the ball is 28.2 cm.
   (*b*) The area to be painted is about 75 m.
   (*c*) This sheet of paper covers 0.6 m.

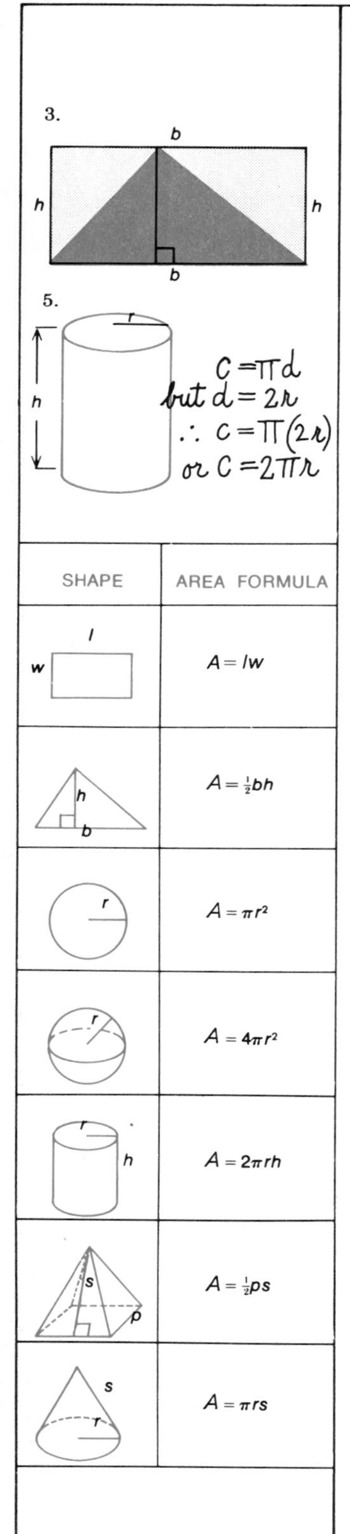

2. In your own words, tell what is meant by "surface area."

3. With reference to the diagram, explain where the formula for the area of a triangle, $A = \frac{1}{2}bh$, comes from.

4. What do you notice about the formula for the surface area of a sphere, $A = 4\pi r^2$? Where have you encountered the expression πr^2 before?

5. Can you explain why the formula for the circumference of a circle ($c = 2\pi r$) occurs in the formula for the area of the curved surface of a cylinder ($A = 2\pi rh$)?

6. By referring back to Example 5, can you guess what might be meant by a "triangular" pyramid?

Written Solutions

(Use $\pi = 3.14$)

7. Find the surface area of the outer surface of an ice cream cone, if the radius of the open end is 2.5 cm, and the slant height is 12 cm.

8. What is the surface area of a basketball 25 cm in diameter?

9. U.N. Rapid pulls the paper label from a tin of orange juice that measures 11.5 cm across the top and 23 cm high. What is the area of the label?

10. Determine the area of Bea Franklin's kite, if its dimensions are as shown.

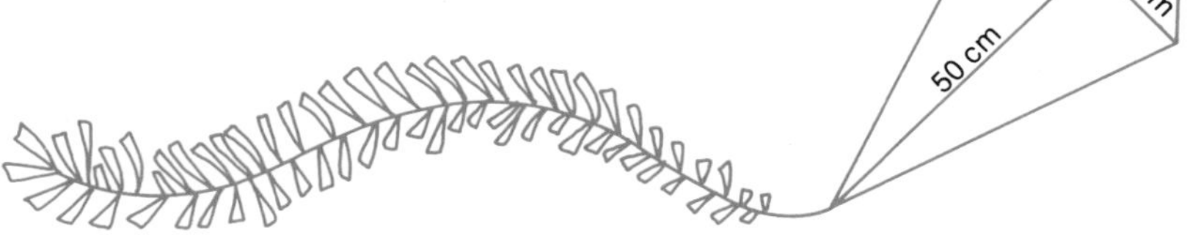

11. Calculate the lateral surface area of a pyramid whose base is a square measuring 10.5 m to the side and whose slant height is 13 m.

12. Cathy Cutmore had completed cutting a 2 m border around the front lawn when she stubbed her toe on a rock, and her sister had to finish the job. How many square metres of lawn did her sister have to cut?

13. How much larger is a circle of radius 3 cm than a triangle with base 9.6 cm and height 4.8 cm?

14. Hydraulic Jack squeezes a circular metal pipe 6 cm in diameter into a square pipe of the same area. Find the length of the side of the square pipe, to 1 decimal place.

15. Which is larger and by how much: a rectangular lot 36 cm by 12 m, or a square lot with the same perimeter?

16. As part of a store window display, a styrofoam ball 10 cm in diameter is cut into 4 identical quarter-spheres as shown. Calculate
    (*a*) the surface area of one part, and
    (*b*) the increased surface area of styrofoam due to the cutting.

17. An inflated spherical weather balloon 8 m in diameter is to be painted for easy visibility. If 1 spray can of paint costs \$1.98 and covers 6 m^2, find the cost of painting the balloon.

18. A wooden salad bowl is in the shape of a hemispherical shell 1 cm thick with measurements as shown. Calculate the surface area of the wood that contacts water when the bowl is washed.

19. A rectangular sheet of metal measures 72 cm by 30 cm. From the sheet, circular pieces are to be stamped out that are 4 cm in diameter. Determine for 1 sheet
    (*a*) the maximum number of pieces that can be stamped,
    (*b*) the amount of scrap metal, and
    (*c*) whether the waste increases if the diameter is changed to 2 cm.

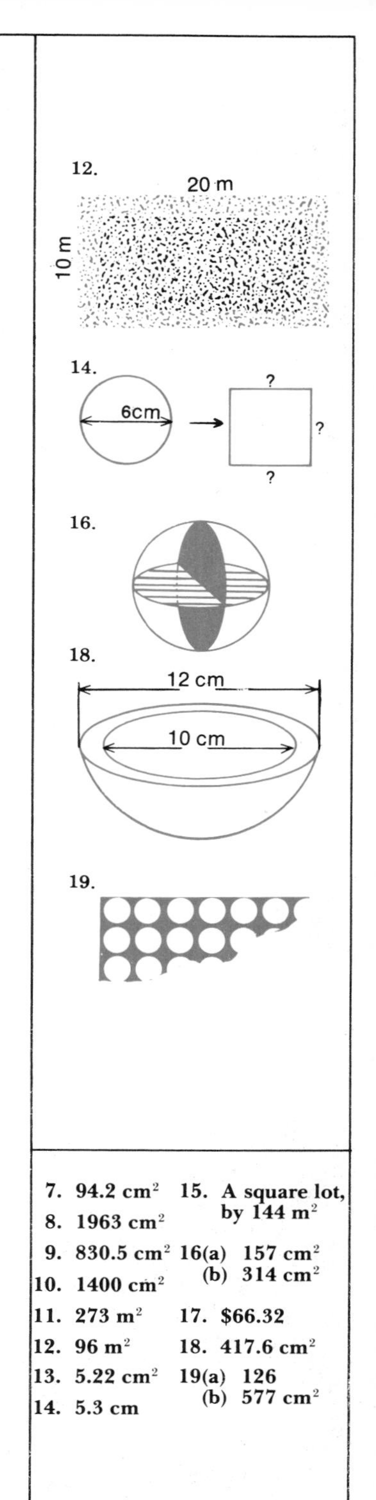

Unit 20
Volume of Solid Figures

Now that you have studied linear and square measure, we will consider the measure of volume.

When we encounter such things as the number of litres of gasoline we must buy, the amount of space inside a suitcase, the capacity of a container, or the amount of earth in a truckload, then we are dealing with *volume* .

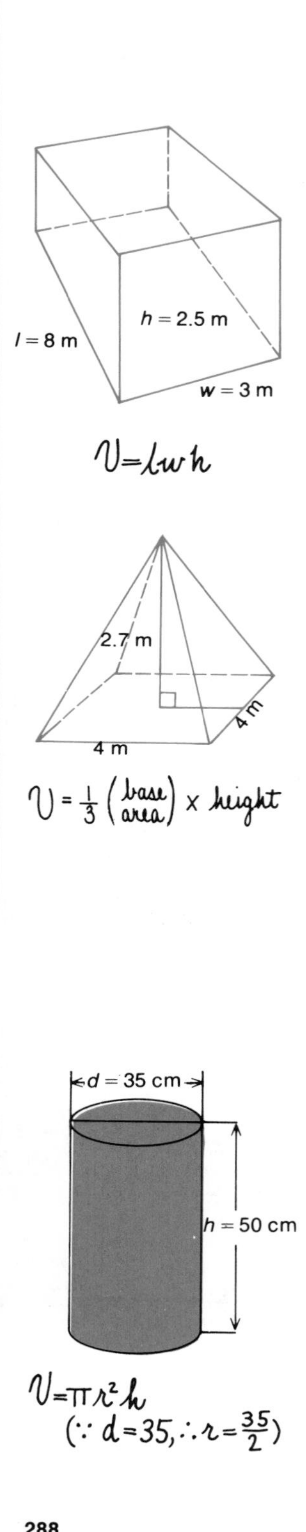

20.1 Volume

You will become successful in solving volume problems as you learn to identify the shape of the figure involved and then use the correct formula.

Example 1

Determine the number of cubic metres of air in a room measuring 2.5 m by 3 m by 8 m.

Solution

$$\begin{aligned} V &= lwh \\ &= 8 \times 3 \times 2.5 \\ &= 60 \end{aligned}$$

∴ The volume of the room is 60 m^3.

Example 2

A tent is in the form of a pyramid 2.7 m high with a base 4 m square. Determine the number of cubic metres of air forced out of the tent when it collapses flat on the ground.

Solution

$$\begin{aligned} V &= \tfrac{1}{3}(\text{Base area}) \times (\text{Height}) \\ &= \tfrac{1}{3}(4 \times 4) \times \overset{0.9}{2.7} \\ &= 14.4 \end{aligned}$$

∴ The quantity of air forced out is 14.4 m^3.

Example 3

An ice cream container is cylindrical in shape, with a diameter of 35 cm and a height of 50 cm. Determine the capacity, in litres, of the container. (Use $\pi = \frac{22}{7}$.)

Solution

$$V = \pi r^2 h$$

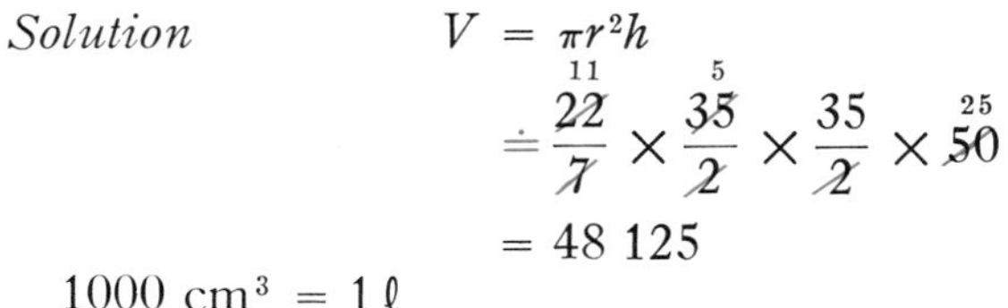

$$\doteq \frac{\overset{11}{22}}{7} \times \frac{\overset{5}{35}}{2} \times \frac{35}{2} \times \overset{25}{50}$$

$$= 48\ 125$$

1000 cm^3 = 1 ℓ

∴ The capacity of the container is 48.125 ℓ.

Example 4

Determine the quantity of air required to inflate a beach ball to a diameter of 42 cm. If a person can supply 3 ℓ of air with each breath, how many breaths are required to inflate the ball? (Use $\pi = \frac{22}{7}$, and ignore the fact that air is compressible.)

$V = \frac{4}{3}\pi r^3$

$(\because d = 42, \therefore r = 21)$

Solution

$$V = \frac{4}{3}\pi r^3$$
$$\doteq \frac{4}{3} \times \frac{22}{7} \times \overset{7}{21} \times 21 \times 21$$
$$= 38\,808$$

$\therefore$ The volume of the beach ball is 38.808 ℓ.

$1000\ cm^3 = 1$ ℓ

If one breath supplies 3 ℓ of air, then the number of breaths required to fill the ball is

$$38.808 \div 3 \doteq 12.9$$

Hence, 13 breaths are required.

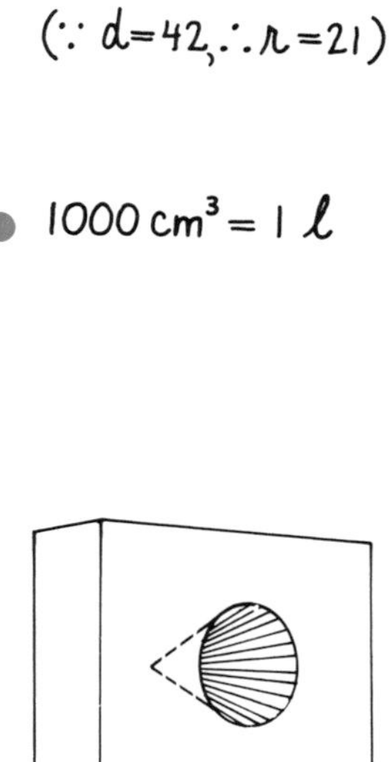

Example 5

The speaker on a hi-fi set is conical in shape with a diameter of 20 cm and a height of 7.5 cm. Determine the volume of air vibrating within the cone of the speaker. (Use $\pi = 3.14$.)

$V = \frac{1}{3}\pi r^2 h$

Solution

$$V = \frac{1}{3}\pi r^2 h$$
$$\doteq \frac{1}{\cancel{3}} \times 3.14 \times 10 \times 10 \times \overset{2.5}{\cancel{7.5}}$$
$$= 785$$

$\therefore$ The volume of air vibrating within the cone is 785 cm^3.

Notice the difference between these.

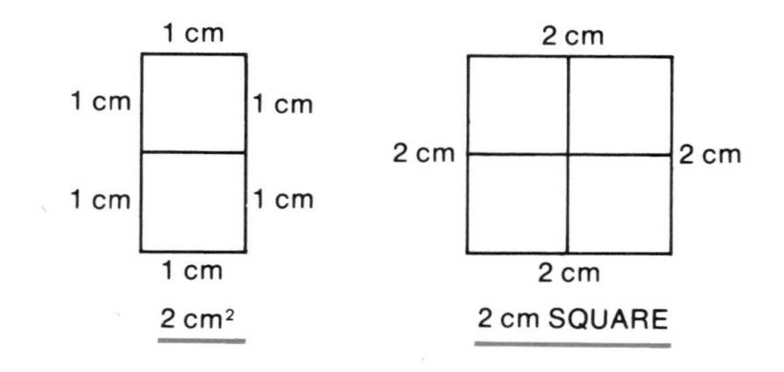

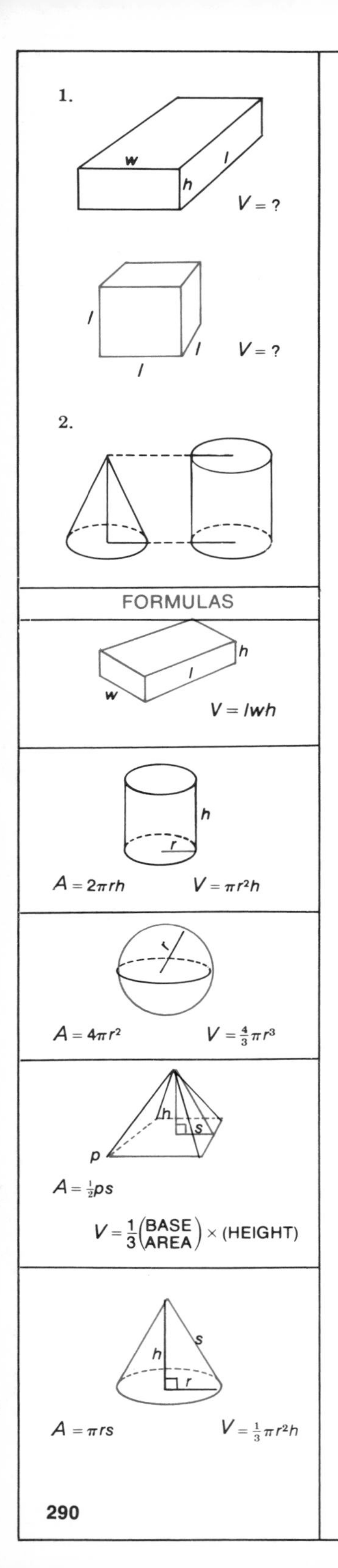

Exercise 20.1

Discussion

1. Use the volume of a rectangular solid to determine the formula for the volume of a cube with length of side l.

2. By studying the respective formulas, determine the relationship between the volume of a cone and the volume of a cylinder having the same base.

3. Recall that the area of a circle is given by the formula $A = \pi r^2$. Using the formula for the volume of a pyramid, determine a formula for the volume of a pyramid of height h whose base is a circle of radius r. What other name can we give to such a pyramid?

4. Classify the problems in the "Written Solutions" part of this exercise according to geometric shapes. State also the proper formula to be used in finding the required volume.

Written Solutions

Use $\pi = 3.14$, unless otherwise stated.

5. Calculate the volume of air in a shoe box measuring 15 cm by 12 cm by 33 cm.

6. How many cubic centimetres of sugar will a cylindrical canister 25 cm high and 15 cm in diameter hold?

7. Determine the volume of a cone 7 m in diameter and 14 m high. (Use $\pi = \frac{22}{7}$.)

8. Find the volume of a pyramid 8 m high, with a rectangular base measuring 6 m by 4 m.

9. Calculate the volume, in litres, of a basketball whose diameter is 24 cm.

10. A cylindrical oil storage tank measures 10 m high and 15 m in diameter. How many kilolitres of oil can be stored in the tank? ($1 \text{ m}^3 = 1 \text{ kl}$)

11. How many litres of water are required to fill a cylindrical canning kettle of radius 20 cm and height 30 cm, to $\frac{2}{3}$ of its total volume?

12. If 1 student in a classroom requires 4 m³ of air space, what is the maximum number of students that can be assigned to a room measuring 10 m by 7 m by 3 m?

13. The Rollem Flat Mfg. Co. recommends that its lawn rollers should be $\frac{1}{3}$ full for best results. How much water should be placed in the roller if it is 1 m wide and 60 cm in diameter?

14. A wooden bowl in the shape of a hemisphere has measurements as shown. Calculate the volume of water the bowl will hold.

15. If 1 cm³ of steel has mass 6.9 g, find the total mass of a solid steel hemispherical paper weight 8 cm in diameter. (The handle has mass 30 g.)

16. A research rocket consists of a cylindrical body for fuel storage, and a conical nose section for instrumentation. Using the measurements given in the diagram, determine the total volume in the rocket for fuel and instrumentation.

17. A liquid oxygen storage tank for a moon rocket is in the shape of a cylinder 30 cm in diameter and 1.2 m long, with hemispherical ends, as shown. How much liquid oxygen will the tank hold?

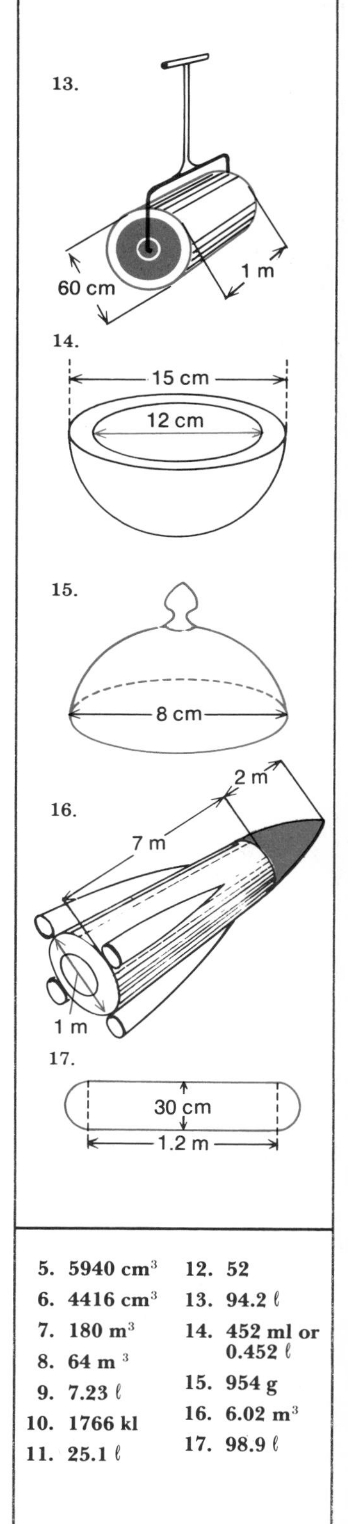

5. 5940 cm³
6. 4416 cm³
7. 180 m³
8. 64 m³
9. 7.23 ℓ
10. 1766 kl
11. 25.1 ℓ
12. 52
13. 94.2 ℓ
14. 452 ml or 0.452 ℓ
15. 954 g
16. 6.02 m³
17. 98.9 ℓ

20.2 Measurement Problems

Now that you have formulas for perimeter, area, and volume, try your hand at this mixture of measurement problems. Remember to ask yourself these three basic questions in each problem:

(1) Does the question ask for perimeter, or area, or volume?
(2) What geometric shape is involved?
(3) What formula will I use?

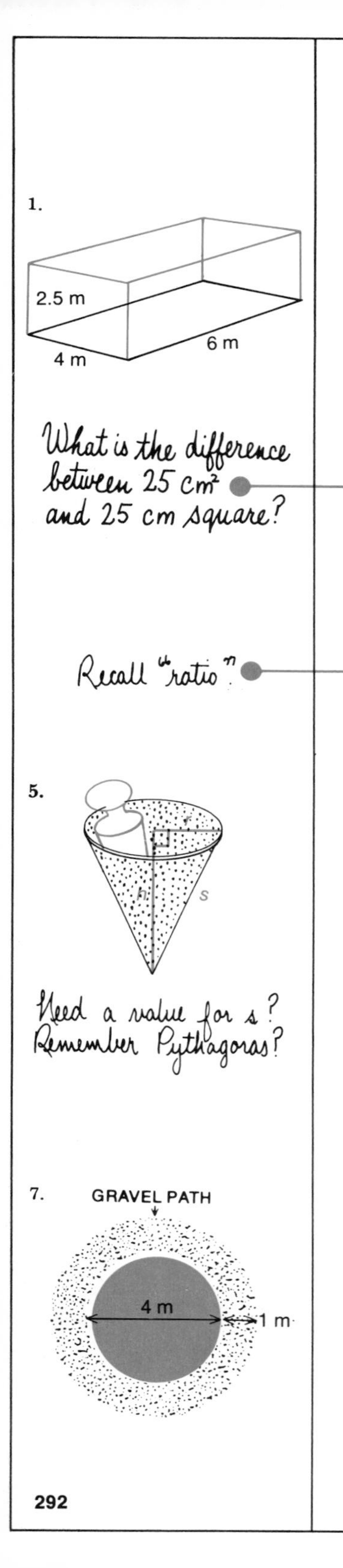
1.
2.5 m
4 m
6 m
What is the difference between 25 cm² and 25 cm square?
Recall "ratio".
5.
h
s
Need a value for s? Remember Pythagoras?
7.
GRAVEL PATH
4 m
1 m

Exercise 20.2

Written Solutions

Use $\pi = 3.14$, unless otherwise stated.

1. Will Retire wishes to put a strip of moulding around the edge of the ceiling and down the 4 corners of his recreation room, as shown. How many metres of moulding does he require?

2. Calculate the number of ceiling tiles required to cover the ceiling of the room in Question 1, if each tile is 25 cm square.

3. Referring again to Question 1, find the number of 1000 W electric heaters required to heat the room, if 35 W will heat 1 m^3 of air.

4. The ratio of the surface areas of 2 spheres is 2.5:1. If the diameter of the smaller sphere is 2 cm, find the surface area of the larger sphere.

5. A colander is used to mash cooked apples into applesauce. The colander itself is a perforated metal cone with a conical wooden "grinder" which forces the apples out through the small holes and into a bowl below. If the metal cone is 30 cm high and 20 cm in diameter, calculate the following.
   (*a*) The total area over which the mashing action takes place.
   (*b*) The capacity of the colander, in litres (with the wooden grinder removed).

6. A 12-cup muffin pan has holes that are cylindrical in shape, each cup being 6 cm across and 4 cm deep. If each cup is to be filled $\frac{3}{4}$ full with batter, determine the total amount of muffin batter required to make 36 muffins.

7. Greta Growmore wishes to surround her circular flower bed with a gravel walk 1 m wide, as shown.
   (*a*) Calculate the area of the walk, in square metres.
   (*b*) If the depth of gravel in the walk is 10 cm, determine the amount of gravel required for the walk.

8. The speed of a point on the surface of a grinding wheel is given by the formula $s = \dfrac{\pi d n}{100}$,
where s is the speed in metres per minute,
d is the diameter in centimetres, and
n is the number of revolutions per minute.
   (*a*) Calculate the surface speed on a 35 cm diameter grinding wheel turning at 1200 r/min. (Use $\pi = \frac{22}{7}$.)
   (*b*) Determine the diameter of a grinding wheel turning at 280 r/min if the surface speed is 176 m/min.

9. Harold Handyman builds a summer cottage in the shape of a pyramid with base 10 m square, height 12 m, and slant height 13 m.
   (*a*) Determine the surface area of the exterior of the cottage.
   (*b*) If the building code specifies 20 m³ of air per sleeper for this type of cottage, how many people can sleep in Harold's cottage?

10. A roll of movie film fits into a container 28 cm in diameter and 2.5 cm high. Determine both the volume and the surface area of the container. (Use $\pi = \frac{22}{7}$.)

11. Penelope Pennybrite goes to the local Malt Shop for her favorite drink, a double-rich chocolate malted milk shake. She finds that, in addition to the old standard size (a cylinder measuring 10 cm in diameter and 15 cm high) at 60¢, there is now a new jumbo size (a cone 16 cm in diameter and 30 cm high) at 90¢. By finding the cost per millilitre, determine which size milk shake is the better buy.

12. A sporting goods firm manufactures solid rubber balls, 6 cm in diameter, and ships them to retail stores in cartons, with 45 balls to the carton.
   (*a*) Calculate the surface area of 1 ball.
   (*b*) Determine the mass, in kilograms, of a carton of balls if 1 cm³ of rubber has a mass of 3 g.

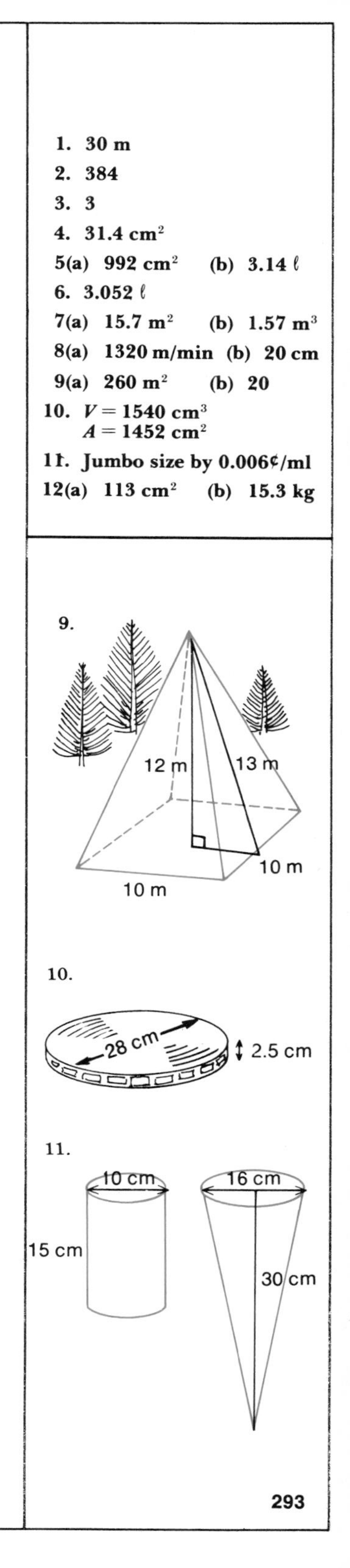

1. 30 m
2. 384
3. 3
4. 31.4 cm²
5(a) 992 cm² (b) 3.14 ℓ
6. 3.052 ℓ
7(a) 15.7 m² (b) 1.57 m³
8(a) 1320 m/min (b) 20 cm
9(a) 260 m² (b) 20
10. V = 1540 cm³ A = 1452 cm²
11. Jumbo size by 0.006¢/ml
12(a) 113 cm² (b) 15.3 kg
9.
12 m
13 m
10 m
10 m
10.
28 cm
2.5 cm
11.
10 cm
15 cm
16 cm
30 cm

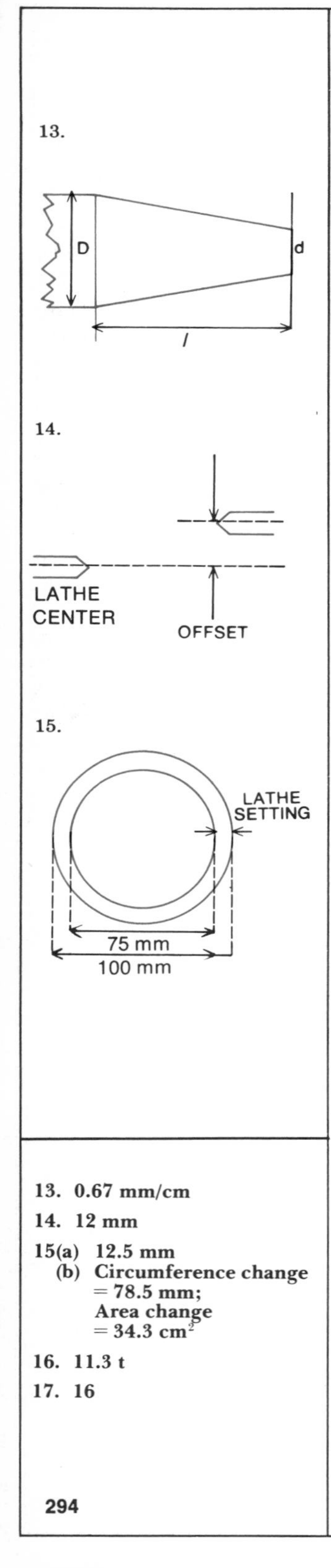

13. A piece of metal is to be tapered on a lathe. Calculate the taper when $D = 2.2$ cm, $d = 1.4.$ cm, and $l = 12$ cm.

$$T = \frac{(D - d) \times 10}{l},$$

where T is the taper, in millimetres per centimetre
D is the large diameter, in centimetres
d is the small diameter, in centimetres
l is the length of the taper, in centimetres

14. In setting the lathe to cut a taper, it is necessary to know the offset. Find the offset required when the taper is 0.6 mm/cm and the length of the work is 40 cm.

$$O = \frac{TL}{2},$$

where O is the offset, in millimetres
T is the taper, in millimetres per centimetre
L is the length of the work, in centimetres

15. A piece of circular stock 100 mm in diameter is to be reduced to 75 mm in diameter by turning it down on a lathe.
   (*a*) Determine the lathe setting to the nearest 0.1 mm.
   (*b*) Calculate the change in circumference and the change in the area of the cross section.

16. A pile of sand dumped on to a platform is in the shape of a cone 2 m high and 4 m in diameter. If the density of sand is 1.35 t/m³, find the mass of the pile of sand.

17. How many tennis balls 7.5 cm in diameter can be packaged in a box 15 cm by 15 cm by 30 cm?

13. 0.67 mm/cm
14. 12 mm
15(a) 12.5 mm
(b) Circumference change = 78.5 mm; Area change = 34.3 cm²
16. 11.3 t
17. 16

18. Using the dimensions shown, determine the area of each of the following figures.

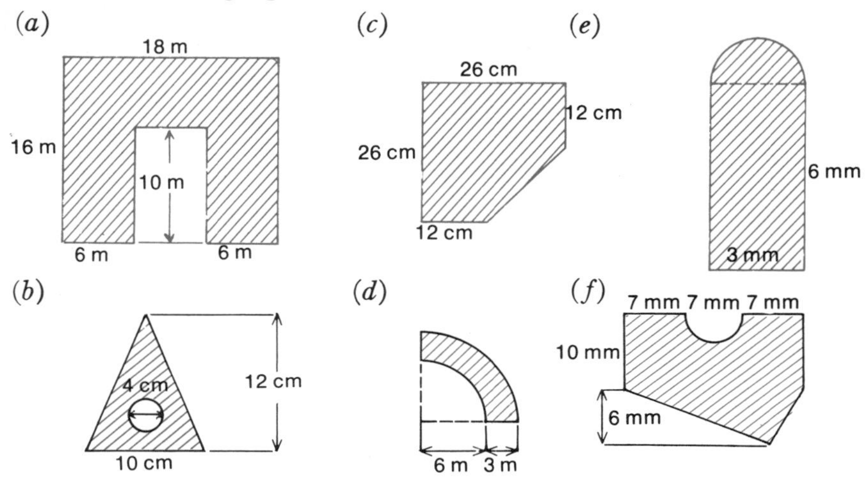

19. Using the dimensions shown, calculate the volume of each of the articles shown.

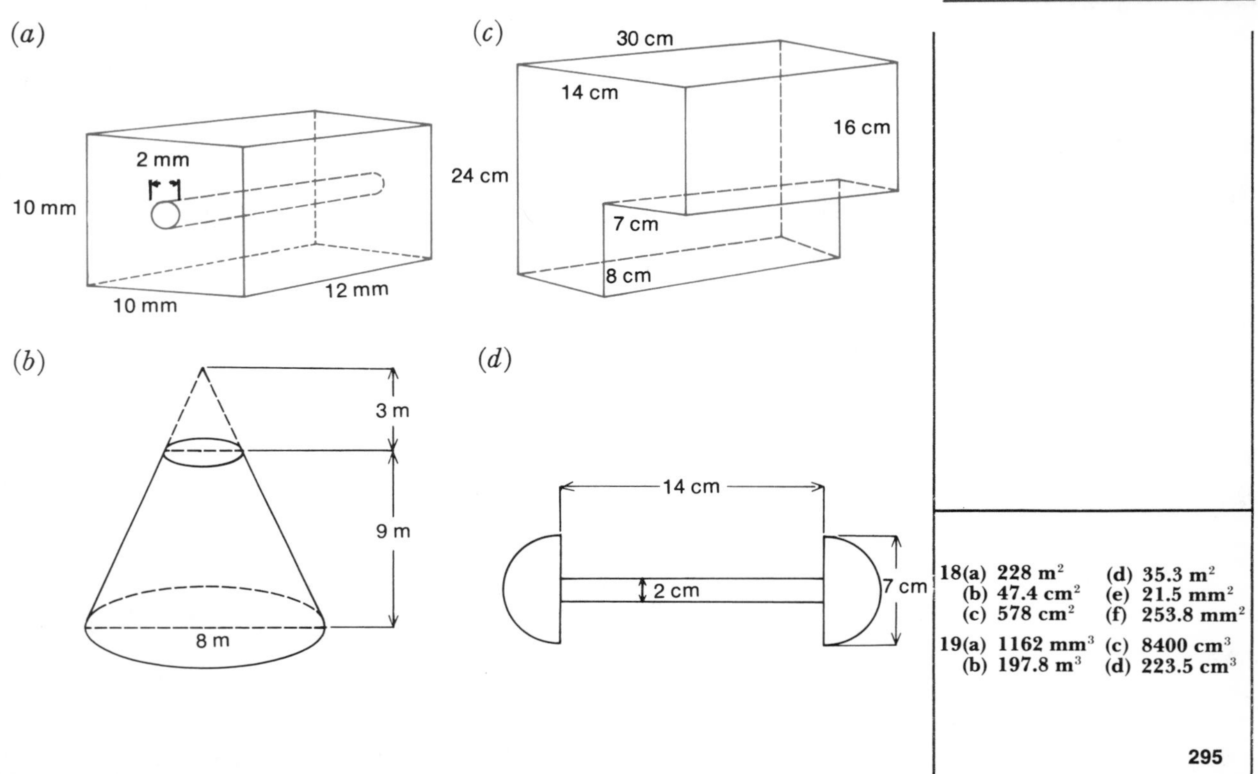

18(a) 228 m^2 (b) 47.4 cm^2 (c) 578 cm^2 (d) 35.3 m^2 (e) 21.5 mm^2 (f) 253.8 mm^2

19(a) 1162 mm^3 (b) 197.8 m^3 (c) 8400 cm^3 (d) 223.5 cm^3

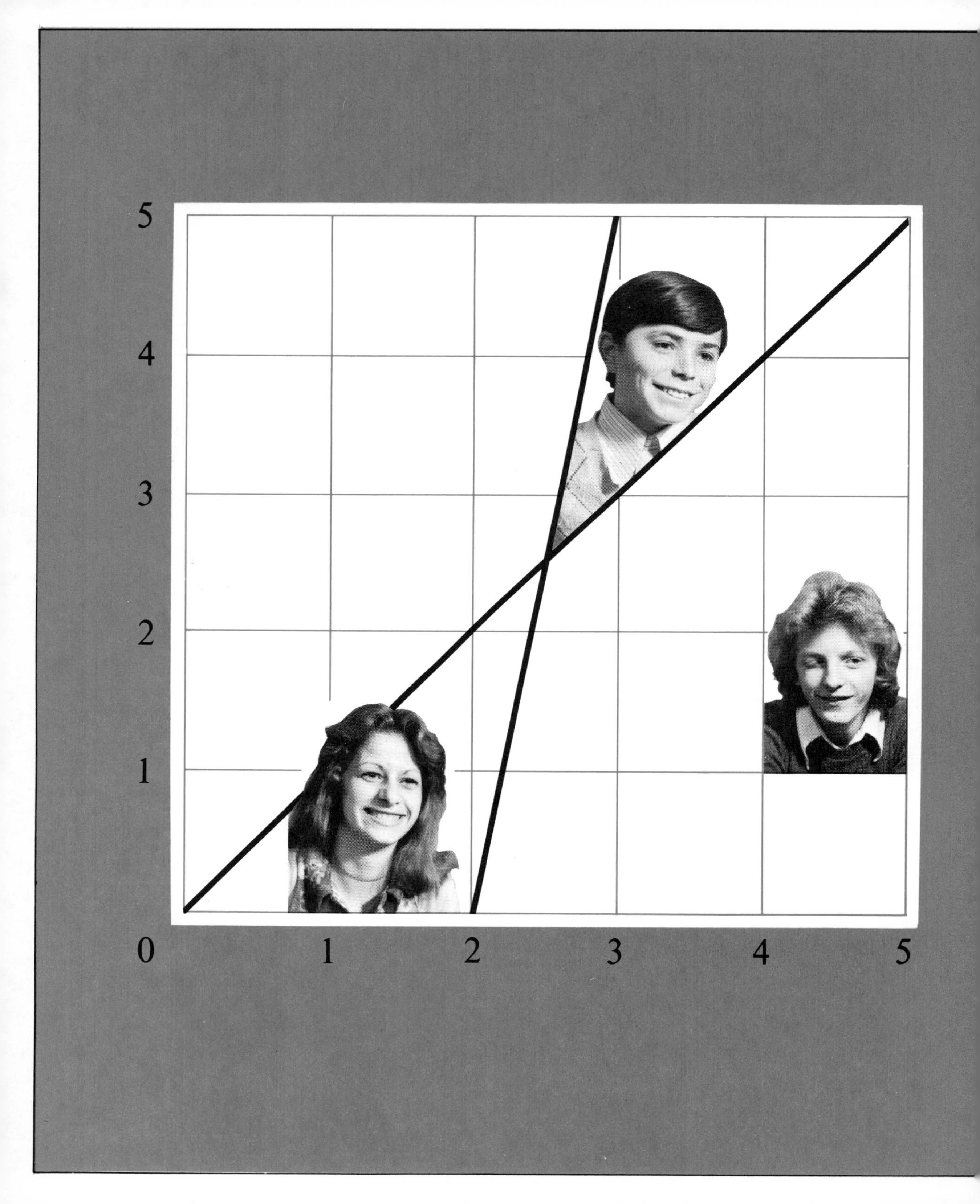
5
4
3
2
1
0
1
2
3
4
5

Unit 21

Graphs • Part 1

(*a*) *Table of values*

Distance (km)	20	40	60	80	100	120	140
Speed (km/h)	10	20	30	40	50	60	70

(*b*) *Set of pairs of values*
The first number is the speed and the second is the distance.
{(10, 20), (20, 40), (30, 60), . . ., (70, 140)}

(*c*) *Graph*

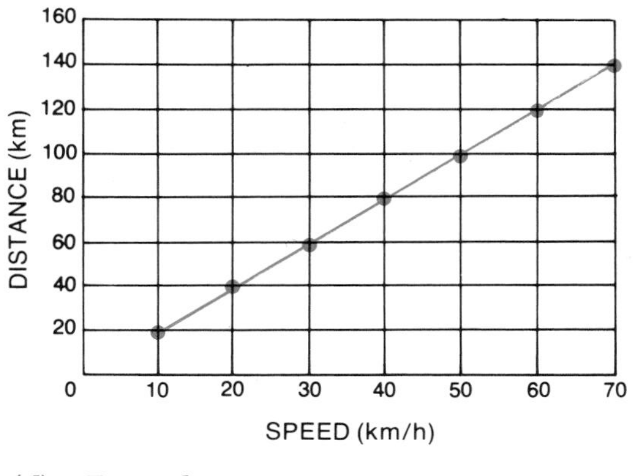

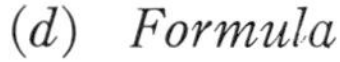
(*d*) *Formula*

$$d = 2v$$

Each of these 4 methods shows the relationship between distance and speed for a 2 h trip by car. In this unit you will learn to use each method to solve problems that deal with relationships between 2 variables.

Remember?
d = distance
v = velocity, or speed

"Variables" are things that change!

21.1 Ordered Pairs and Their Graphs

A

1. Suppose that gasoline costs 18¢/ℓ at the local service station. Draw a table to show the total cost of several different amounts of gas.

Cost (dollars)	$1.80						
Amount (litres)	10	15	20	25	30	35	40

2. Another way to show this information is by ordered pairs.

   $\{(10, 1.80), (15, 2.70), (20, 3.60), \ldots, (40, 7.20)\}$

   Which numbers show the amount?
   Which show the cost?

Since the first number in each pair shows the amount of gas and the second the cost, the *order* of writing these numbers is important. We call them *ordered pairs* of numbers.

3. $P = 4l$ is a formula that gives the perimeter, P, of a square whose side has length l. Construct a set of ordered pairs (l, P) that shows the sides and perimeters of squares measuring 1, 2, 3, . . ., 8 along one side.

   $\{(1, 4), (2, \square), \ldots, (8, \square)\}$

B Ordered pairs of numbers can be shown in a diagram in which 2 lines are drawn to meet at a 90° angle. These lines are called the *horizontal axis* and the *vertical axis* and they meet at the *origin*. Mark off equal lengths along the axes and name the points 1, 2, 3, 4, . . . as shown in Figure 1.

By drawing vertical lines 1, 2, 3, 4, 5 and horizontal lines 1, 2, 3, 4, 5, ordered pairs can be shown by positions on the diagram. (Squared paper like this is called *graph paper*.)

VERTICAL AXIS
HORIZONTAL AXIS
ORIGIN

FIGURE 1

In Figure 2, point A lies where vertical line 2 meets horizontal line 1.

∴ The position of A is given by the ordered pair (2, 1).

Note the order: (right, up)

1. To which line does the 2 refer?
2. Keeping the order (right, up) name the position of B, C, and D in Figure 2.
3. In Figure 3 name the position of each point using an ordered pair of numbers. (Notice the scale on the axes.)
4. Scale a sheet of graph paper as shown in Figure 4, and mark the points (1, 6), (3, 1), (4, 3), (5, 1), (7, 6). Join the first point to the second, the second to the third, and so on. What letter of the alphabet have you formed?

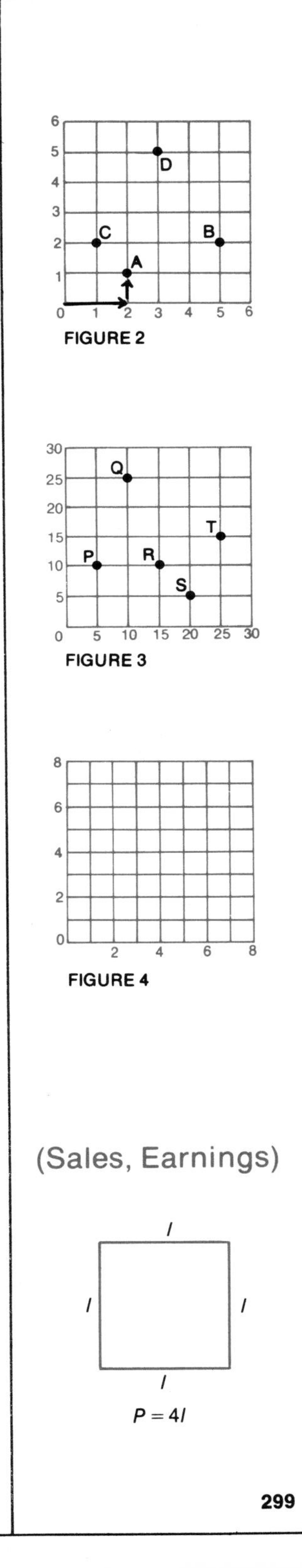

A sales representative is frequently paid a basic salary plus a *commission* that depends on sales. Suppose the basic salary is \$600/month and the commission is 5% of sales. Then the following formula can be used to calculate the sales representative's earnings.

$$E = 600 + 0.05S$$

where E = earnings
S = sales

For example, if sales are \$20 000, then

$$\begin{aligned} E &= 600 + 0.05S \\ &= 600 + 0.05(20\,000) \\ &= 600 + 1000 \\ &= 1600 \end{aligned}$$

∴ (20 000, 1600) is an ordered pair obtained from this formula.

1. Substitute S = 5000, 7500, 10 000, 12 500, 15 000 to find 5 more ordered pairs.
2. Graph the following set of ordered pairs that results from the formula for the perimeter of a square.

$$\{(1, 4), (2, 8), (3, 12), (4, 16), \ldots, (8, 32)\}$$

What pattern do you see in the position of these points?

Exercise 21.1

Discussion

1. Name the ordered pairs corresponding to A, B, C, D, E, F.

2. Which letter names each of the following points?
   (4, 4) (0, 2) (5, 0) (7, 7) (1, 5) (2, 1)

3. (*a*) Where do the points (0, 0), (3, 0), (8, 0) all lie?
   (*b*) Where do the points (0, 0), (0, 3), (0, 7) all lie?

4. List 4 ordered pairs (v, C) of the relationship $C = 10v$.

5. List three ordered pairs (x, y) of each relationship.
   (*a*) $y = x + 3$ (*b*) $y = 2x$

6. In drawing the graph of (10, 6), (15, 8), (25, 12), (40, 18), what scale would you show along each axis?

Written Solutions

7. Graph the following points on the same diagram.
   (3, 1), (3, 6), (5, 4), (7, 6), (7, 1)
   Join the points in order. What letter have you formed?

8. For the points (50, 10), (75, 20), (80, 40), (100, 60), what scales should you show on the vertical and horizontal axes? Graph these ordered pairs on the same diagram.

9. Graph the following sets of ordered pairs.
   (*a*) {(1, 3), (2, 6), (3, 9), (4, 12)}
   (*b*) {(0, 0), (2, 0), (2, 3), (4, 3), (5, 2)}
   (*c*) {(0, 5), (1, 4), (2, 3), (3, 2), (4, 1), (5, 0)}
   (*d*) {(1, 3), (2, 3), (3, 3), (4, 3), (5, 3)}

10. (*a*) Water is poured into a container so that the water level rises 1 cm each second. Using the vertical axis to show the height of the water and the horizontal axis to show the time passed, draw a graph of the height of the water after 1 s, 2 s, and so on, to 10 s.

(*b*) Draw a straight line through the points in the graph of part (*a*). State the height of the water after 2.5 s, 5.5 s, and 7.5 s.

11. (*a*) The height of water in a storage tank is 30 m. During a hot spell, the level drops 1.5 m each day for 8 days. Draw a graph that shows the height at the end of each of the 8 days.
    (*b*) Join the points of your graph in part (*a*) with a straight line and state the height of the water after $4\frac{1}{2}$ days and $6\frac{1}{2}$ days.

12. (*a*) Find a set of ordered pairs (a, b) for the formula $b = a + 3$ for $a = 0, 1, 2, \ldots, 8$.
    (*b*) Draw the graph of the relationship in part (*a*).

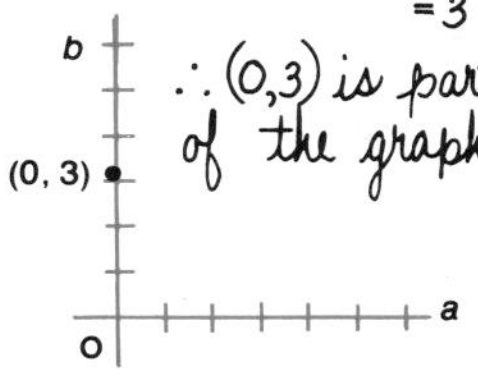

13. (*a*) Find a set of ordered pairs (x, y) for the formula $y = 2x + 1$ for $x = 0, 1, 2, 3, 4, 5$.
    (*b*) Draw the graph of the ordered pairs in (*a*).
    (*c*) Join the points in the graph, and from the graph find y when $x = 2.5$. Check your value of y by substituting 2.5 for x in the formula $y = 2x + 1$.

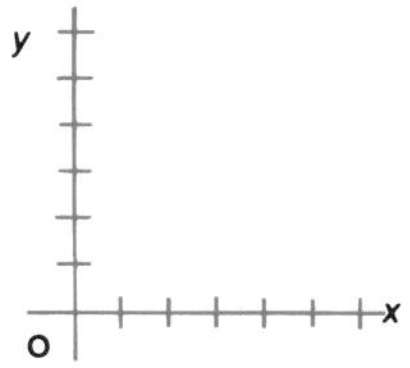

14. Two cars accelerate from 0 km/h, as shown.
    (*a*) Which car has the greater acceleration?
    (*b*) How fast is each car travelling after 5 s?
    (*c*) What is the difference in the time it takes the cars to reach a speed of 60 km/h?

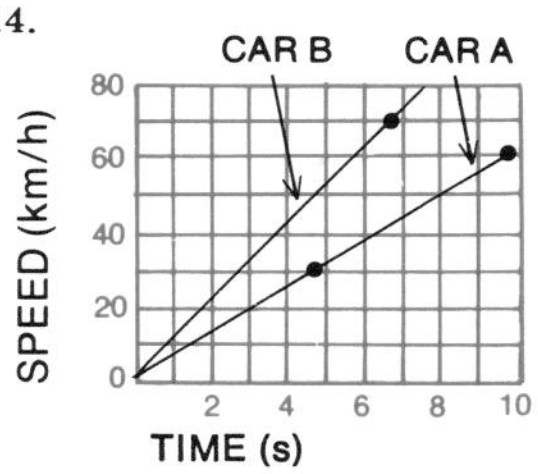

21.2 Solving Problems by Graphs

Relationships in the last section were used to form sets of ordered pairs and then a graph of this set was drawn. Here we will reverse these steps and start with a graph.

1. Name the ordered pairs for A, B, C, D, E.
2. What ordered pair names the origin?
3. Using these points as a graph, what is the distance when the time is 2? What is the time when the distance is 3?

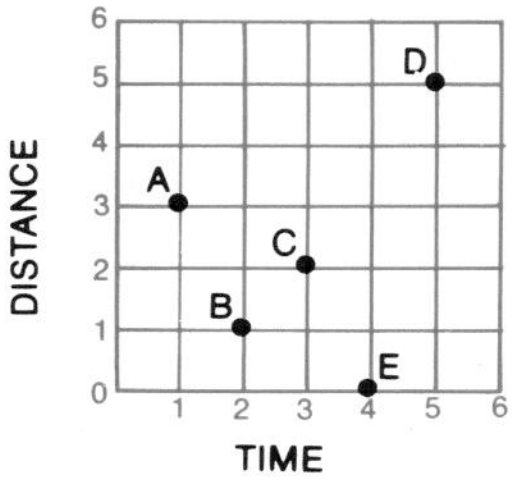

10(b) 2.5 cm, 5.5 cm, 7.5 cm
11(b) 23.25 m, 20.25 m

After 1 day the height is 30 m − 1.5 m or 28.5 m.

12. If $a = 0$, $b = 0 + 3 = 3$
∴ (0, 3) is part of the graph.

13.

14.

Notice the scales used on each axis.

Recall that a line consists of a set of points. Often graphs appear as straight lines.

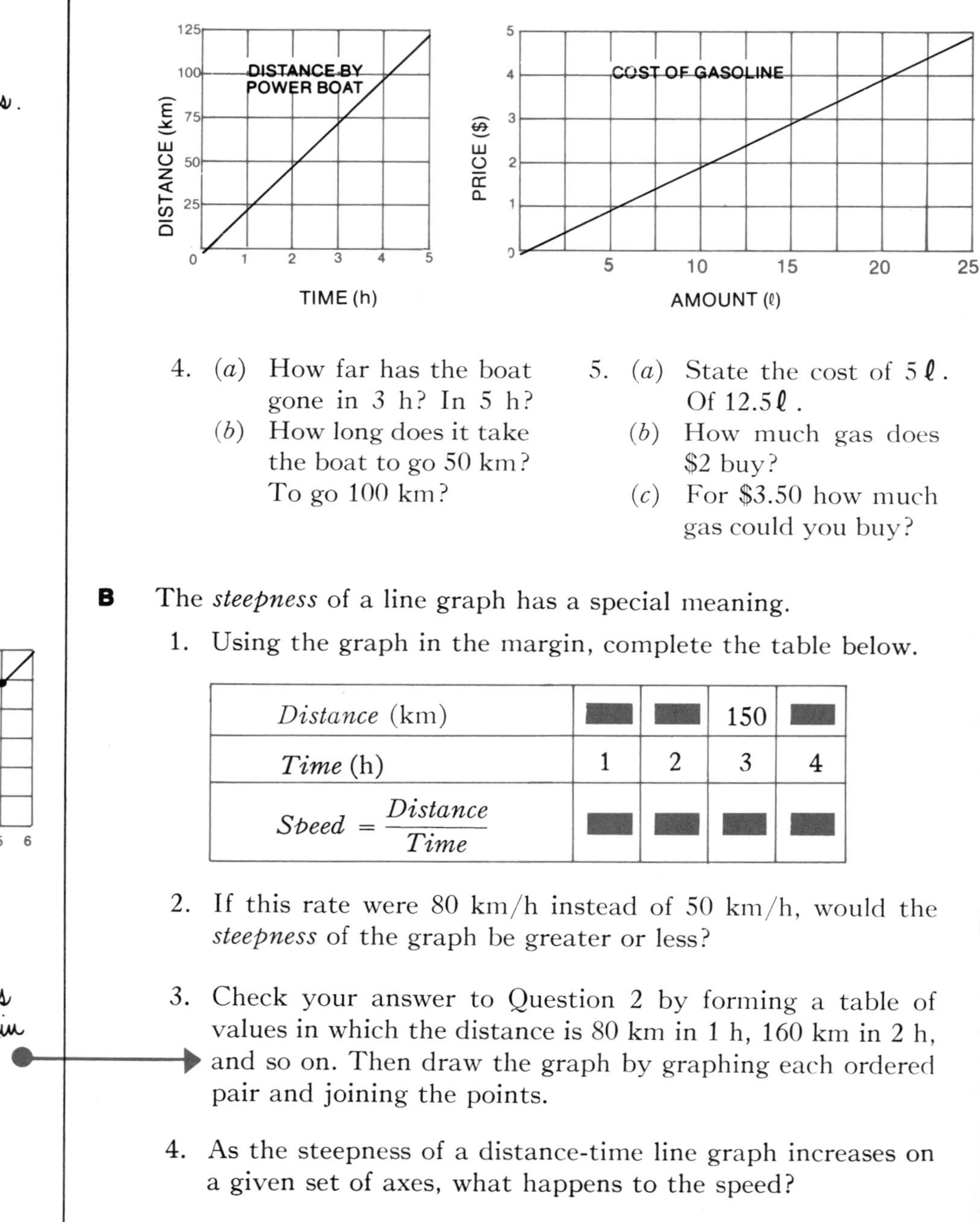

4. (*a*) How far has the boat gone in 3 h? In 5 h?
   (*b*) How long does it take the boat to go 50 km? To go 100 km?

5. (*a*) State the cost of 5 ℓ. Of 12.5 ℓ.
   (*b*) How much gas does $2 buy?
   (*c*) For $3.50 how much gas could you buy?

B The *steepness* of a line graph has a special meaning.

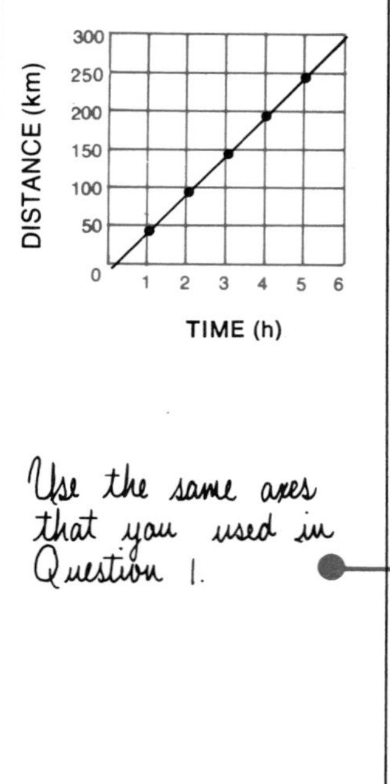

1. Using the graph in the margin, complete the table below.

Distance (km)	▬	▬	150	▬
Time (h)	1	2	3	4
Speed = $\frac{Distance}{Time}$	▬	▬	▬	▬

2. If this rate were 80 km/h instead of 50 km/h, would the *steepness* of the graph be greater or less?

Use the same axes that you used in Question 1.

3. Check your answer to Question 2 by forming a table of values in which the distance is 80 km in 1 h, 160 km in 2 h, and so on. Then draw the graph by graphing each ordered pair and joining the points.

4. As the steepness of a distance-time line graph increases on a given set of axes, what happens to the speed?

5. Car A and Car B are travelling at 60 km/h and the graph shows their speeds as they slow down to a stop.

   (*a*) How long does it take each car to stop?

   (*b*) Which car slows down at a faster rate?

   (*c*) Does the steepness of the graph tell you which car slows down more rapidly? Explain.

6. X and Y each make a trip of 24 km along the same road, but X walks and Y rides a bicycle. However, Y leaves later than X. Use the graph to answer the following questions.

   (*a*) How long had X been walking when Y started to ride?

   (*b*) How long had X been walking when Y caught up to him? How far had they both gone at that time?

   (*c*) Compare X's walking rate to Y's riding rate.

   (*d*) Find the average rate of speed for X and Y during the trip.

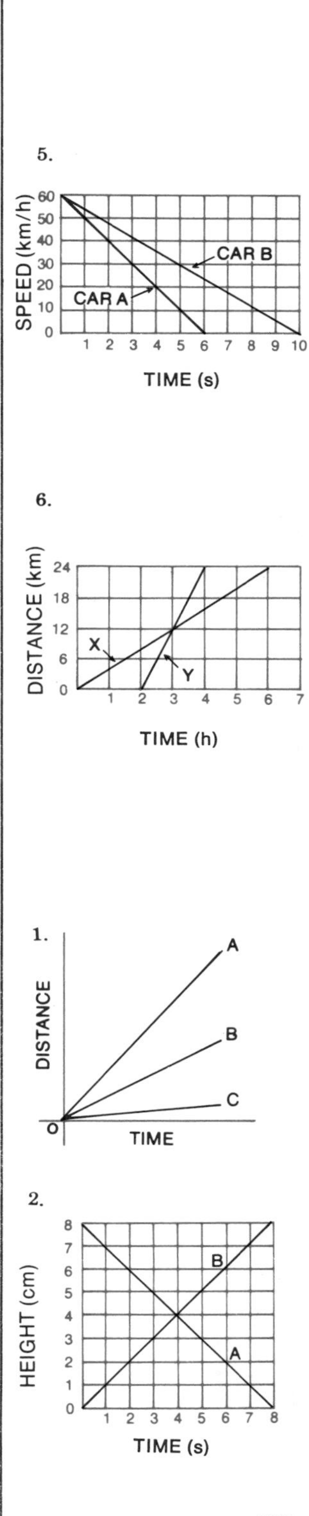

Exercise 21.2

Discussion

1. The distance-time graphs of A, B, and C are in the diagram. Whose speed is greatest? Whose speed is least?

2. The height of water in containers A and B, for different times, is shown on the graph.

   (*a*) What are the water heights in containers A and B at 0 s?

   (*b*) As time passes, what is happening to the height in each container?

   (*c*) When are the heights the same? What is the height at this time?

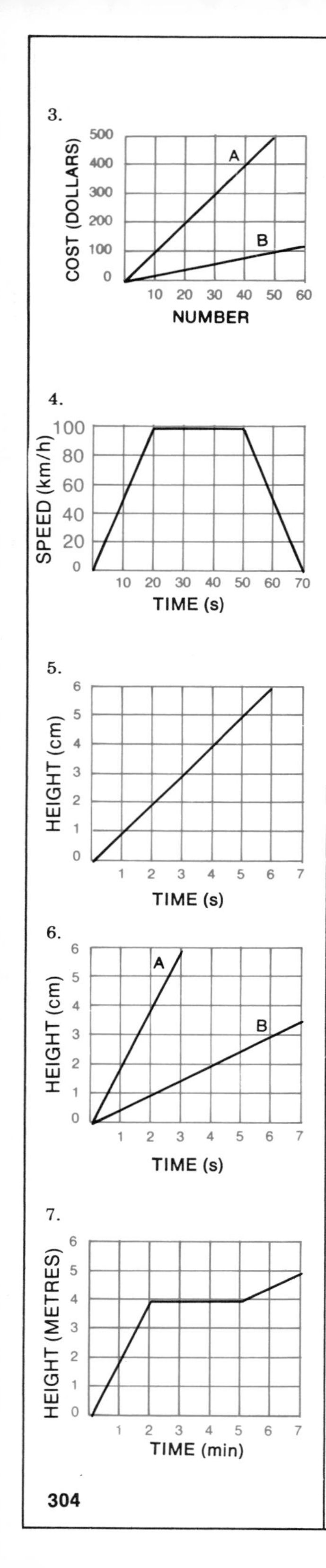

3. Graph A shows the cost of buying a quantity of sweaters and B shows the cost of a quantity of socks.
   (*a*) State the cost of 10, 20, and 30 sweaters.
   (*b*) State the cost of 50 pairs of socks. Of one pair.
   (*c*) By a construction on the graph how could you find the number of sweaters you could buy for $175?

4. The graph shows the speed of a car at various times.
   (*a*) How long does it take to accelerate from 0 km/h to 100 km/h?
   (*b*) Explain the flat part of the graph.
   (*c*) How long does it take to stop the car?

Written Solutions

5. The graph shows the height of water in a container at various times as it is being filled.
   (*a*) State the height after 3 s. After 5 s.
   (*b*) When is the height 2 cm? When is it 4 cm?
   (*c*) At what rate is the water level rising?

6. Water is poured at different rates into two containers A and B.
   (*a*) For A, state the height of the water after 1 s and after 2 s.
   (*b*) For B, state the height after 2 s and after 4 s.
   (*c*) At what rate is the water rising in each container?

7. An ocean freighter is filled from a grain elevator and the height of the grain at various times is shown by the graph.
   (*a*) State the height after 2 min and after 5 min.
   (*b*) What happened to the flow of grain between the second and fifth minutes?
   (*c*) During what time is the grain level rising most rapidly?

8. The graph illustrates the fuel loading rates of two jet aircraft.

(*a*) State the quantity of fuel in each jet after 2 min.

(*b*) When do the jets contain the same quantity of fuel?

(*c*) Which jet is being filled more rapidly?

9. The following table shows the distance travelled by hikers on the Bruce Trail in Southern Ontario and the time they have taken up to this point.

Distance (km)	5	8	8	12	15	15
Time (hours)	1	2	3	4	5	6

(*a*) Graph the ordered pairs shown in the table.

(*b*) Join the points with straight line segments.

(*c*) How far did the hikers walk in the first hour? What was their rate of walking?

(*d*) During the second hour how far did they walk? State their rate during the second hour. State their average rate for the first 2 h.

(*e*) During the third hour, what did the hikers do? How does this show on the graph?

10. The heights (in centimetres) of 3 children in a family, at several different ages, are shown in the table.

Child \ *Age*	0	1	5	10	12	15
John	50	90	125	140	150	180
Judy	40	75	100	125	145	155
Wendy	45	85	120	135	150	165

(*a*) Graph each (Age, Height) ordered pair on the same set of axes.

(*b*) Join the set of points for each child with line segments.

(*c*) When is the growth most rapid for each child?

Unit 22

Graphs • Part 2

22.1 Graphing Points in a Plane

You learned in Unit 21 that the points on a graph are associated with ordered pairs of numbers. The members of these ordered pairs are called *coordinates* of the point.

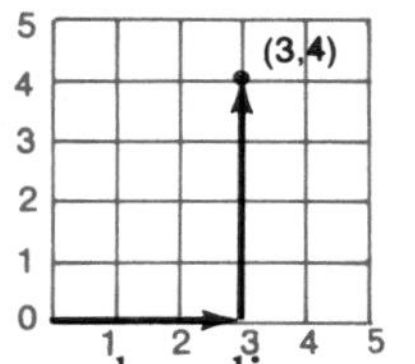

If the axes are number lines, negative numbers as well as positive numbers can be used in graphing. The method for naming the point remains the same.

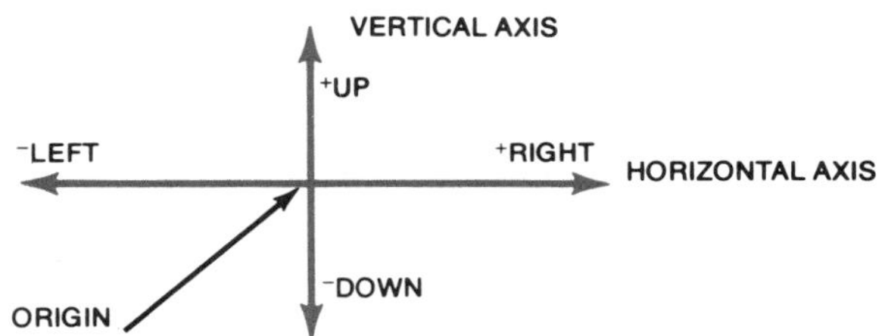

The first number represents the distance to the *right or left* of the origin along the horizontal axis. The second number represents the distance *above or below* the origin along the vertical axis.

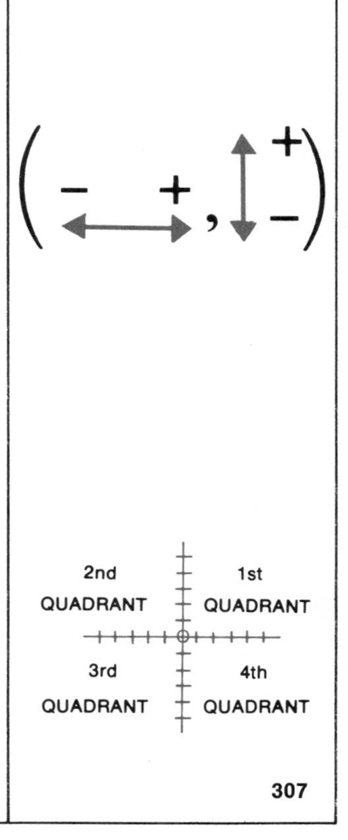

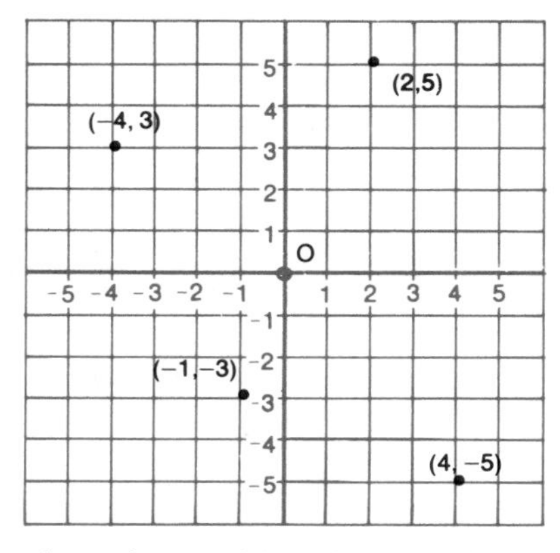

Each of the four regions formed by the axes is called a *quadrant*.

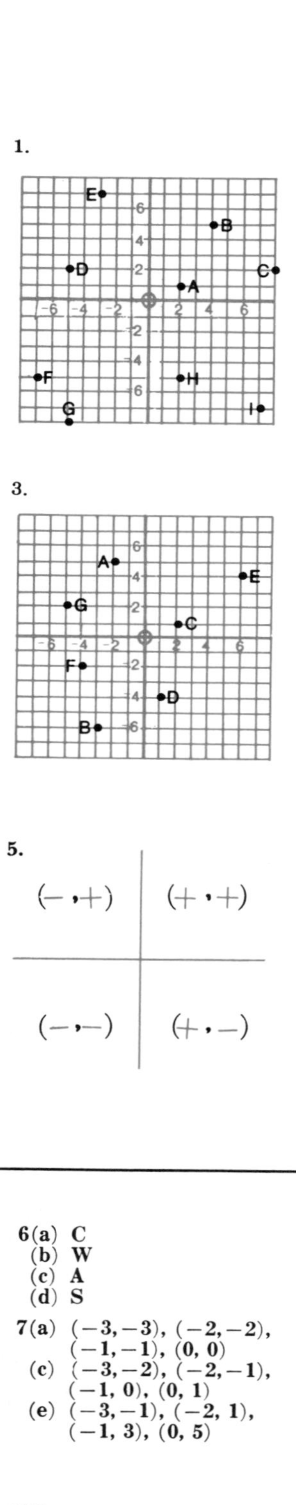

6(a) C
(b) W
(c) A
(d) S

7(a) (−3, −3), (−2, −2), (−1, −1), (0, 0)
(c) (−3, −2), (−2, −1), (−1, 0), (0, 1)
(e) (−3, −1), (−2, 1), (−1, 3), (0, 5)

Exercise 22.1

Discussion

1. (*a*) What are the coordinates of the points A, B, C, . . ., I?
   (*b*) Which points lie in quadrant 1? 2? 3? 4?

2. (*a*) Describe the position of each of the following points using the terms *left* or *right*, and *up* or *down*.
   (2, −1), (−5, 4), (1, 6), (−3, −2), (4, −1), (−6, 5)
   (*b*) State the quadrant in which each point of part (*a*) lies.

3. The following points are named by letters in the diagram. Match the letters to the ordered pairs.
   (−4, −2), (2, 1), (−2, 5), (1, −4), (−3, −6), (6, 4), (−5, 2).

4. (*a*) What do the following pairs of points have in common?
   (i) (5, 0), (−2, 0) (ii) (0, −4), (0, 6)
   (*b*) Where does each lie from the origin?

5. (*a*) Which quadrant consists of points whose coordinates are both negative?
   (*b*) State a similar condition on the coordinates of all points in the 2nd quadrant and in the 4th quadrant.

Written Solutions

6. Graph the following sets, each on a separate diagram.
   (*a*) {(3, 3), (3, 4), (−4, 4), (−4, −5), (3, −5), (3, −4)}
   (*b*) {(−5, 6), (−2, −3), (0, 0), (2, −3), (5, 6)}
   (*c*) {(−4, −4), (−3, 0), (0, 6), (3, 0), (4, −4)}
   (*d*) {(3, 3), (2, 4), (−2, 4), (−3, 3), (−3, 1), (−2, 0), (2, 0), (3, −1), (3, −3), (2, −4), (−2, −4), (−3, −3)}
   (*e*) {(7, 0), (2, 1), (3, 3), (1, 2), (0, 7), (−1, 2), (−3, 3), (−2, 1), (−7, 0), (−2, −1), (−3, −3), (−1, −2), (0, −7), (1, −2), (3, −3), (2, −1)}

   Check by joining the points in the order given. You should form a letter of the alphabet in each case except (*e*).

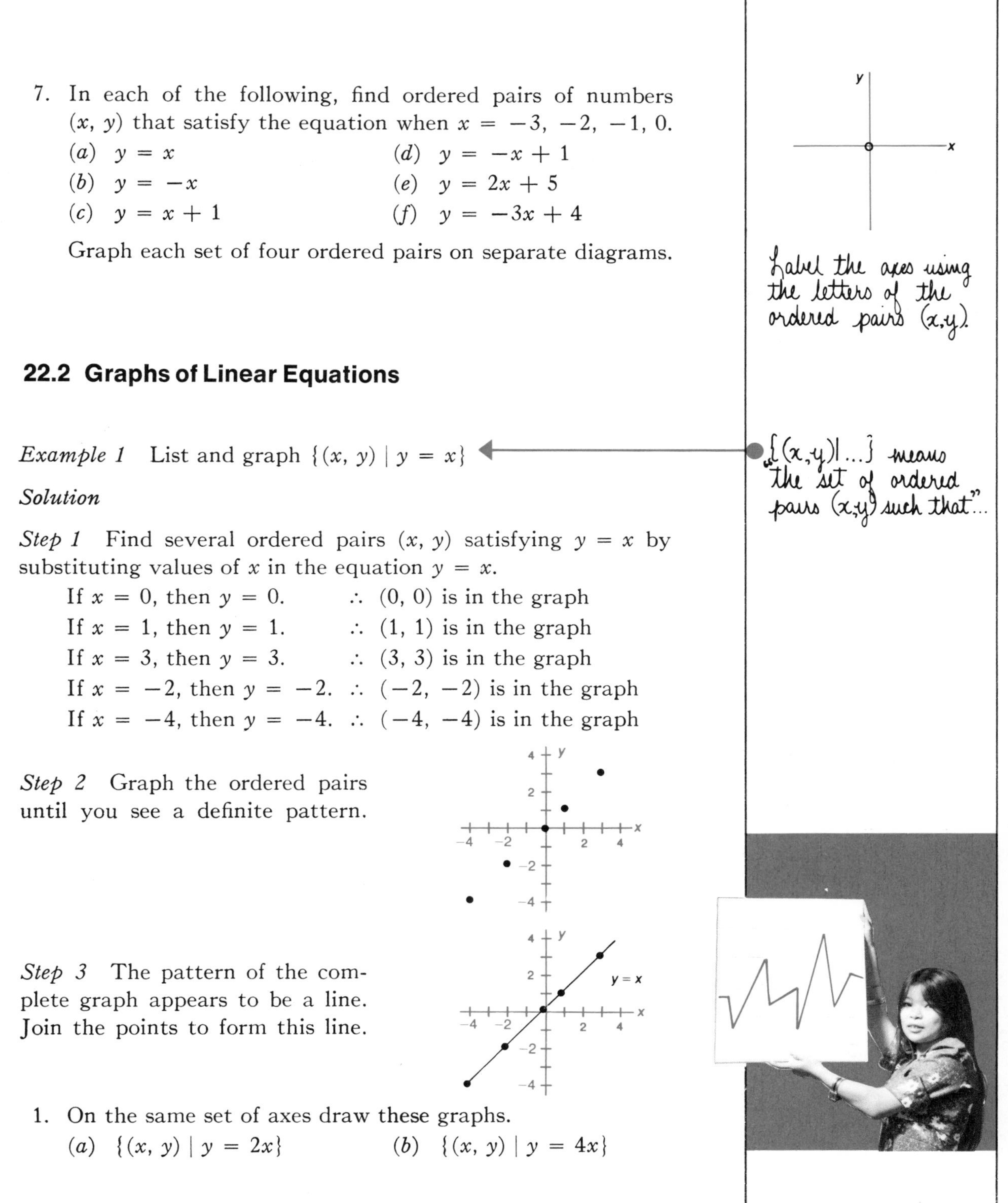

7. In each of the following, find ordered pairs of numbers (x, y) that satisfy the equation when $x = -3, -2, -1, 0$.
   (*a*) $y = x$ (*d*) $y = -x + 1$
   (*b*) $y = -x$ (*e*) $y = 2x + 5$
   (*c*) $y = x + 1$ (*f*) $y = -3x + 4$

   Graph each set of four ordered pairs on separate diagrams.

Label the axes using the letters of the ordered pairs (x,y).

22.2 Graphs of Linear Equations

Example 1 List and graph $\{(x, y) \mid y = x\}$

"$\{(x,y) \mid \ldots\}$ means "the set of ordered pairs (x,y) such that"...

Solution

Step 1 Find several ordered pairs (x, y) satisfying $y = x$ by substituting values of x in the equation $y = x$.

If $x = 0$, then $y = 0$. $\therefore$ $(0, 0)$ is in the graph
If $x = 1$, then $y = 1$. $\therefore$ $(1, 1)$ is in the graph
If $x = 3$, then $y = 3$. $\therefore$ $(3, 3)$ is in the graph
If $x = -2$, then $y = -2$. $\therefore$ $(-2, -2)$ is in the graph
If $x = -4$, then $y = -4$. $\therefore$ $(-4, -4)$ is in the graph

Step 2 Graph the ordered pairs until you see a definite pattern.

Step 3 The pattern of the complete graph appears to be a line. Join the points to form this line.

1. On the same set of axes draw these graphs.
   (*a*) $\{(x, y) \mid y = 2x\}$ (*b*) $\{(x, y) \mid y = 4x\}$

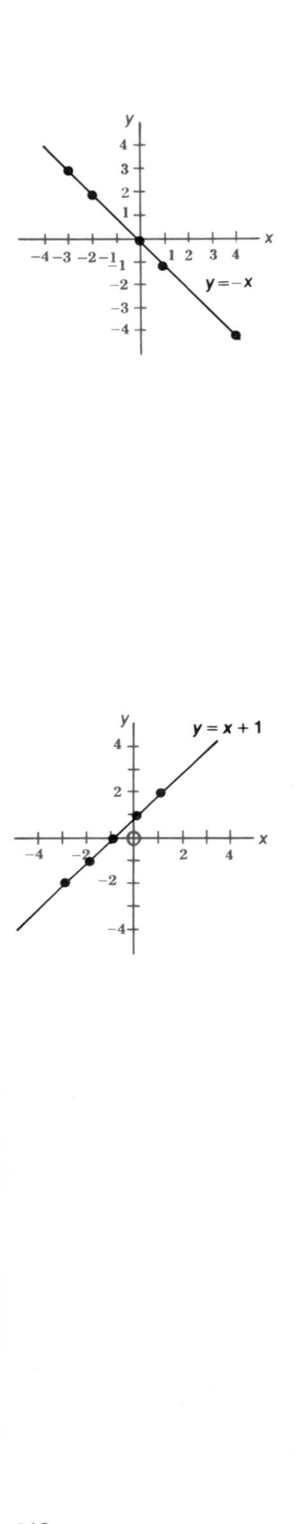

Example 2 List and graph $\{(x, y) \mid y = -x\}$

Solution

If $x = -3$,	$y = -(-3)$	
	$= 3$	$\therefore (-3, 3)$ is in the graph
If $x = -2$,	$y = -(-2)$	
	$= 2$	$\therefore (-2, 2)$ is in the graph
If $x = 0$,	$y = -0$	
	$= 0$	$\therefore (0, 0)$ is in the graph
If $x = 1$,	$y = -1$	$\therefore (1, -1)$ is in the graph
If $x = 4$,	$y = -4$	$\therefore (4, -4)$ is in the graph

2. Copy the graph of $y = -x$ on your own diagram from Example 2. Then list and graph on the same set of axes the following sets.

   (*a*) $\{(x, y) \mid y = -2x\}$ (*b*) $\{(x, y) \mid y = -4x\}$

   How are these 3 lines related to each other?

Example 3 Graph $\{(x, y) \mid y = x + 1\}$

Solution Substitute values of x in $y = x + 1$

If $x = -3$,	$y = -3 + 1$	
	$= -2$	$\therefore (-3, -2)$ is in the graph
If $x = -2$,	$y = -2 + 1$	
	$= -1$	$\therefore (-2, -1)$ is in the graph
If $x = -1$,	$y = -1 + 1$	
	$= 0$	$\therefore (-1, 0)$ is in the graph
If $x = 0$,	$y = 0 + 1$	
	$= 1$	$\therefore (0, 1)$ is in the graph
If $x = 1$,	$y = 1 + 1$	
	$= 2$	$\therefore (1, 2)$ is in the graph

3. Copy the graph of $\{(x, y) \mid y = x + 1\}$ from Example 3 and then graph on the same axes the following.

   (*a*) $\{(x, y) \mid y = x + 2\}$ (*c*) $\{(x, y) \mid y = x - 1\}$
   (*b*) $\{(x, y) \mid y = x + 4\}$ (*d*) $\{(x, y) \mid y = x - 3\}$

Note that in each case we substitute integers until the pattern of the graph is clear, then we connect the points with a line. Since the graph is a straight line, we call the equation a *linear equation*.

Exercise 22.2

Discussion

1. Which equation has the steepest graph?

   (*a*) $y = 2x$ (*b*) $y = 5x$ (*c*) $y = x$

2. Choose the equations whose graphs would slant upward to the right.

   (*a*) $y = -x$ (*c*) $y = -3x + 2$

   (*b*) $y = 2x$ (*d*) $y = 5x - 4$

3. Choose sets whose graphs are parallel.

   (*a*) $\{(x, y) \mid y = x\}$ (*c*) $\{(x, y) \mid y = x + 2\}$

   (*b*) $\{(x, y) \mid y = 2x + 1\}$ (*d*) $\{(x, y) \mid y = 2x - 3\}$

4. (*a*) What is the x coordinate of the point where any graph crosses the y axis?

   (*b*) State the point where the graph of each of the following equations crosses the y axis.

   (i) $y = x$ (iii) $y = 2x - 3$

   (ii) $y = x + 4$ (iv) $y = -2x + 5$

Written Solutions

5. By listing a sufficient number of ordered pairs draw the graph of each of the following. Draw (*a*), (*b*) on the same diagram; (*c*), (*d*) on another diagram; and (*e*), (*f*) on a third diagram.

   (*a*) $\{(x, y) \mid y = x + 3\}$ (*d*) $\{(x, y) \mid y = 2x - 3\}$

   (*b*) $\{(x, y) \mid y = -2x\}$ (*e*) $\{(x, y) \mid y = -5x + 4\}$

   (*c*) $\{(x, y) \mid y = x - 5\}$ (*f*) $\{(x, y) \mid y = 4 + 2x\}$

   State the coordinates of the point where the two graphs meet on each diagram.

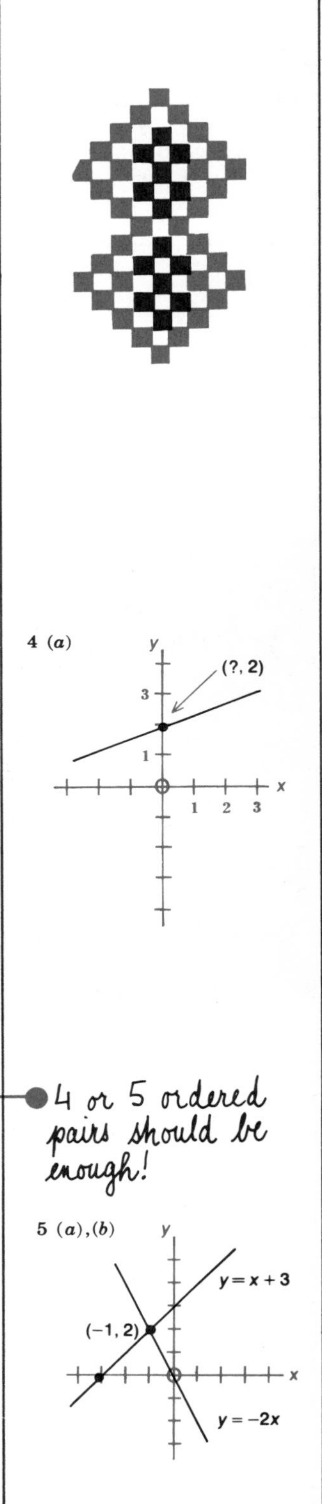

6(b) (*i*) 8 s (*ii*) 10 s (*iii*) 65 km/h

7(b) (*i*) $2000 (*ii*) 650 (*iii*) $500

6. A car is proceeding at 100 km/h and slows down by 10 km/h each second. Its speed, v, after t seconds is found from the formula $v = 100 - 10t$.

   (*a*) Construct the graph of the set of ordered pairs (t, v) from this formula. Use positive values of t.

   (*b*) By drawing lines on your graph, determine

   (*i*) how many seconds were required to slow to a speed of 20 km/h,

   (*ii*) how long it took the car to stop, and

   (*iii*) what speed the car was going after 3.5 s.

7. The cost, C dollars, of producing n yearbooks is found using the formula

$$C = 2n + 500$$

   (*a*) Construct the graph of the set of ordered pairs (n, C) from this formula. Use $n = 100, 200, \ldots, 1000$.

   (*b*) From your graph determine

   (i) the cost of producing 750 yearbooks,

   (ii) the number of yearbooks you could produce for $1800, and

   (iii) the minimum amount required before the first copy is produced.

22.3 Graphs of Non-Linear Equations

A In the previous section each set of ordered pairs studied resulted in a straight line graph. Other types of graphs often occur.

1. Using $x = -3, -2, -1, 0, 1, 2, 3$ find a set of ordered pairs satisfying the equation $y = x^2$.

   If $x = -3$, then $y = (-3)^2$

   $= 9 \quad \therefore (-3, 9)$ is in the graph

   In the same way find six more ordered pairs.

I'll help with the easy ones.
If $x=3$, $y=3^2=9$
$\therefore (3,9)$ is in the graph.
If $x=2$, $y=2^2=4$
$\therefore (2,4)$ is in the graph.
If $x=1$, $y=1^2=1$
$\therefore (1,1)$ is in the graph.
If $x=0$, $y=0^2=0$
$\therefore (0,0)$ is in the graph.

2. Graph carefully each ordered pair in Question 1. Do the points of the graph lie in a straight line?

3. To gain a better idea of the shape of this graph, find more ordered pairs using $x = 1.5, -0.5, 0.5, 1.5$.

4. Now draw a smooth curve through the points.

5. On the same set of axes repeat steps 1 to 4 using the equation $y = 2x^2$.

6. Using the same set of axes again, graph $\{(x, y) \mid y = -x^2\}$ and $\{(x, y) \mid y = -2x^2\}$.

3 Consider the equation $y = \frac{1}{x}$.

1. Find a set of ordered pairs (x, y) for this equation using $x = 4, 3, 2, 1, \frac{1}{2}, \frac{1}{3}, \frac{1}{4}$. For example, if $x = 4$, then $y = \frac{1}{4}$. $\therefore$ $(4, \frac{1}{4})$ is in the graph.

If $x = \frac{1}{4}$, $\therefore y = 4$ $\therefore (\frac{1}{4}, 4)$ is a point in the graph.

2. Plot these ordered pairs. In what quadrant do they lie?

To "plot a point" means to draw a point in position.

3. As x increases beyond 4, what is happening to the value of $\frac{1}{x}$? By substituting large numbers for x can $\frac{1}{x}$ ever equal 0?

4. For small values of x ($\frac{1}{10}, \frac{1}{100}, \frac{1}{1000}$, for example), what is the value of $\frac{1}{x}$?

5. Sketch the graph in quadrant 1. Your graph should not touch either axis.

6. Now consider ordered pairs found by using negative values for x. If x is a negative number, what kind of number will $\frac{1}{x}$ be?

7. Find a set of ordered pairs (x, y) using $x = -4, -3, -2, -1, -\frac{1}{2}, -\frac{1}{3}, -\frac{1}{4}$, in the equation $y = \frac{1}{x}$. Plot these on your graph.

8. Sketch the graph in quadrant 3. How is this part of the graph related to the part in quadrant 1?

5,8.

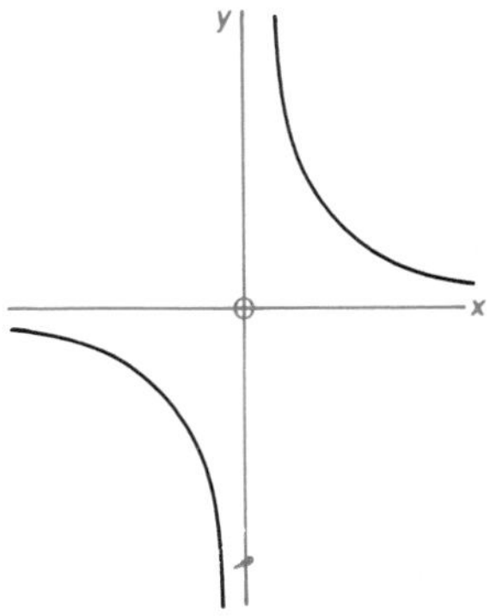

y

x

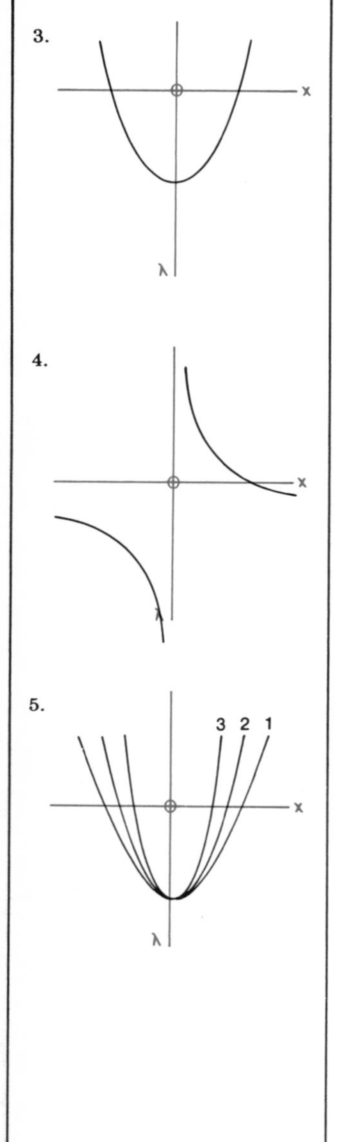

Exercise 22.3

Discussion

1. From the following equations choose those whose graphs are straight lines.

   (*a*) $y = x$ (*c*) $y = x^2$ (*e*) $y = \frac{2}{x}$

   (*b*) $y = x + 1$ (*d*) $y = -2x^2$ (*f*) $y = 2x + 1$

2. What do the graphs of the following equations have in common?

   (*a*) $y = -x^2$ (*b*) $y = -2x^2$ (*c*) $y = -4x^2$

3. Choose the equations whose graphs open upward.

   (*a*) $y = 2x^2$ (*b*) $y = -x^2$ (*c*) $y = -4x^2$ (*d*) $y = 3x^2$

4. Which of the following equations have graphs that are in two separate parts?

   (*a*) $y = x + 3$ (*b*) $y = \frac{6}{x}$ (*c*) $y = -\frac{1}{x}$ (*d*) $y = 6x^2$

5. Match the graphs in the margin with the equations that follow.

   (*a*) $y = x^2$ (*b*) $y = 2x^2$ (*c*) $y = 3x^2$

Written Solutions

6. List and graph the following sets. Use at least ten ordered pairs in each case.

   (*a*) $\{(x, y) \mid y = 0.5x^2\}$ (*c*) $\left\{(x, y) \mid y = \frac{12}{x}\right\}$

   (*b*) $\{(x, y) \mid y = -2x^2\}$ (*d*) $\left\{(x, y) \mid y = -\frac{1}{x}\right\}$

7. If an object is dropped from an airplane and we ignore air resistance, the distance *d* metres it falls in *t* seconds is found from the formula

   $$d = 4.9t^2$$

   (*a*) Construct the graph of the set of ordered pairs (t, d) for this formula. Use $t = 0, 2, 4, 6, \ldots, 20$.

(*b*) From your graph find

(*i*) the distance the object falls in 8.5 s, and

(*ii*) how long it takes the object to fall to the ground if released from a height of 1000 m.

8. The surface area, A, of a sphere with a radius r is found approximately from the formula

$$A = 12.6r^2$$

(*a*) Construct the graph of the set of ordered pairs (r, A) for this formula. Use $r = 0, 0.5, 1, 1.5, 2, 2.5, 3$.

(*b*) By drawing lines on this graph, find

(*i*) the area of the surface of a sphere whose radius is 1.75 cm, and

(*ii*) the radius required to produce a sphere with a surface area of 100 cm^2.

9. The resistance, R (ohms), in a 120 V electrical circuit with a current flow of I (amperes) can be found using the formula in the margin.

(*a*) Construct a graph of the set of ordered pairs (I, R) for $I = 2, 3, 4, 5, 6, 8, 10, 12, 15, 20, 24, 30, 40, 60$.

(*b*) Using your graph find

(*i*) the resistance in an electric kettle where the current is 12.5 A,

(*ii*) the resistance in a toaster drawing an 8.75 A current, and

(*iii*) the current in an electric frying pan in which the resistance is 12.5Ω.

10. Try this some Thursday! Plot the following points and join those in each line.

(−6, 4)(−6, 2)
(−3, 7)(−3, 3)(0, 3)(0, 7)
(2, 3)(2, 7)
(4, 7)(7, 7)(4, 3)(7, 3)
(−11, −6)(−11, −2)(−8, −2)
(−11, −4)(−9, −4)
(−11, −2)(−8, −2)
(−9, 7)(−5, 7)(−5, 3)(−9, 3)(−9, 7)
(−6, −6)(−6, −2)(−3, −2)(−3, −4)(−6, −4)
(1, −6)(1, −2)(3, −2)(4, −3)(4, −5)(3, −6)(1, −6)
(−5, −4)(−3, −6)
(−1, −2)(−1, −6)
(5, −6)(7, −2)(9, −6)
(6, −4)(8, −4)
(9, −2)(11, −4)(13, −2)
(11, −4)(11, −6)

7(b) (*i*) **about 350 m**
(*ii*) **about 14.3 s**

8(b) (*i*) **about 39 cm^2**
(*ii*) **about 2.8 cm**

9(b) (*i*) **about 10 Ω**
(*ii*) **about 14 Ω**
(*iii*) **about 10 A**

$$R = \frac{120}{I}$$

V means "volts"
A means "amperes"
Ω means "ohms"

Maintaining Basic Skills

Exercise 5

1. Perform the following operations.
   (*a*) 23.4×16.9
   (*b*) $4.2 \times 0.68 \times 5.1$
   (*c*) $(3.7 \times 10^2) \times 4.9$
   (*d*) $4.83 \div 0.051$
   (*e*) $0.0634 \div 8.5$
   (*f*) $1.28 \div (7.2 \times 10^3)$

2. Simplify.
   (*a*) $1\frac{2}{3} + 3\frac{5}{6} - 2\frac{1}{5}$
   (*b*) $\frac{2}{5} \times \frac{7}{10} \times \frac{15}{14}$
   (*c*) $6\frac{1}{8} \div 1\frac{3}{4}$
   (*d*) $\frac{7}{10} - \frac{2}{15} + 1\frac{5}{6}$
   (*e*) $\frac{3}{8} + \frac{5}{8} \times \frac{11}{15}$
   (*f*) $\frac{2}{3} \times \frac{6}{7} - \frac{5}{14}$

3. Simplify.
   (*a*) $-1 + (-2) + (-3)$
   (*b*) $(-1)(-2)(-3)$
   (*c*) $3(-4)^2$
   (*d*) $(-2 + 5)^2$
   (*e*) $-35 \div 5$
   (*f*) $4 - (-5)$
   (*g*) $-2 + (-3)(6)$
   (*h*) $3^2 - 4(-1)^2$

4. Reduce to simplest form.
   (*a*) $\frac{14}{21}$ (*b*) $10 : 15 : 25$ (*c*) $\frac{24}{28}$ (*d*) $0.5 : 0.75$

5. Change to a decimal.
   (*a*) $\frac{5}{8}$ (*b*) $\frac{3}{5}$ (*c*) 75% (*d*) $\frac{7}{200}$ (*e*) 25% (*f*) 1.5%

6. Change to a percent.
   (*a*) 0.55 (*b*) $\frac{3}{4}$ (*c*) 1.25 (*d*) 0.045 (*e*) $\frac{3}{8}$ (*f*) 2.2

7. Change to a common fraction.
   (*a*) 15% (*b*) 95% (*c*) 0.48 (*d*) 0.075 (*e*) 2.5% (*f*) 0.009 (*g*) 7.75% (*h*) $6\frac{3}{8}$%

8. Collect like terms and simplify.
   (*a*) $3x + 2x + 4y - y$
   (*b*) $5a - 3b - 2a + 4b$
   (*c*) $7x - 3 + 5 - 8x$
   (*d*) $3a^2 - 2a - 4a + 1$

9. State the product.
   (*a*) $x^2 \times x^3$
   (*b*) $3x \times 4y$
   (*c*) $(-3a^5)(5a^3)$
   (*d*) $x(x + 4)$
   (*e*) $2a(a + 1)$
   (*f*) $-3y(2y + 5)$

10. State the quotient.
   (*a*) $r^8 \div r^3$
   (*b*) $6y^4 \div 2y^3$
   (*c*) $21x^3 \div (-7x)$
   (*d*) $-15xy \div (-5y)$

1(a) 395.46
(c) 1813
(e) 0.007 458 82
2(a) $\frac{33}{10}$ **(c)** $\frac{7}{2}$ **(e)** $\frac{5}{6}$
3(c) 48 **(g)** −20
5(a) 0.625 **(e)** 0.25
(c) 0.75
6(a) 55% **(e)** 37.5%
(c) 125%
7(a) $\frac{3}{20}$ **(e)** $\frac{1}{40}$
(c) $\frac{12}{25}$ **(g)** $\frac{31}{400}$
9(c) $-15a^8$ **(d)** $x^2 + 4x$

11. Expand.

(a) $(x + 3)(x + 5)$
(b) $(y + 6)(y - 6)$
(c) $(a - 4)(a + 1)$
(d) $(x - 2)^2$
(e) $(3r + 5)(3r - 5)$
(f) $(5c - 6)(4c + 5)$

12. Solve the following equations.

(a) $x + 5 = 8$
(b) $m - 3 = -2$
(c) $5t - 1 = 14$
(d) $3y = 4 - 2y$
(e) $4h - 2 = 6h + 8$
(f) $5m + 1 = 11 - 3m$
(g) $1 - 2y = 5y - 13$
(h) $3p + 5 = 5 - 4p$

13. Solve the following equations.

(a) $0.5x + 0.6 = 3$
(b) $0.5a - 3.6 = 5.9$
(c) $4(y - 3) = 6$
(d) $2(r + 3) = -4$
(e) $\frac{a + 1}{3} = \frac{a - 5}{4}$
(f) $\frac{3s + 2}{5} = \frac{2s - 1}{1.0}$
(g) $\frac{3}{4}(p + 1) = \frac{5}{6}(p - 2)$
(h) $3.6(h - 3) = 5.4$

14. Isolate the variable indicated in the following.

(a) $a + b = 2$; a
(b) $3y + z = 1$; z
(c) $I = \frac{E}{R}$; E
(d) $x + 2y + 1 = 0$; x

15. Find the area (A) or the volume (V). Use $\pi = 3.14$.

(a) $A = \pi r^2$, $r = 2.6$ cm
(b) $A = 4\pi r^2$, $r = 6.5$ mm
(c) $A = \frac{1}{2}bh$, $b = 4.2$ mm, $h = 6.8$ mm
(d) $V = \frac{1}{3}\pi r^2 h$, $r = 5$ m, $h = 8$ m

16. Find the interest earned on the following.

(a) \$200 deposited for 6 months at 5%
(b) \$1500 loaned for 3 years at 7%

17. Find the following amounts.

(a) 5% of \$80
(b) $33\frac{1}{3}$% of \$1.24
(c) 7.5% of \$12 000
(d) 0.25% of \$800

18. By substitution of the known values find the value of the resulting variable.

(a) $I = Prt$, $I = \$250$, $r = 5\%$, $t = 2$ years
(b) $r = \frac{2NC}{P(n + 1)}$, $N = 12$, $C = \$60$, $P = \$300$, $n = 18$

11(a) $x^2 + 8x + 15$
(c) $a^2 - 3a - 4$
(e) $9r^2 - 25$

12(a) $x = 3$ **(e)** $h = -5$
(c) $t = 3$ **(g)** $y = 2$

13(a) $x = 4.8$ **(e)** $a = -19$
(c) $y = 4.5$ **(g)** $p = 29$

15(a) 21.23 cm²
(b) 530.66 mm²
(c) 14.28 mm²
(d) 209.33 m³

16(a) \$5 **(b)** \$315

17(a) 84 **(c)** \$900

18(a) \$2500 **(b)** 25.25%

Unit 23

Basic Geometric Constructions

Long before people used the word "geometry," Nature was at work constructing geometrical wonders. The lacy symmetry of a snowflake, the delicate lines of a spider's silken web, the gentle curve of a flower's petal, . . . the list of Nature's works of art is endless.

Although humans cannot compete with much of Nature's work, there are some fields of endeavor in which our imagination and ingenuity are unique. In any one of Canada's large cities you will find distinctive architectural style and beauty.

In both the wonders of Nature and human endeavor there are basic elements of geometry.

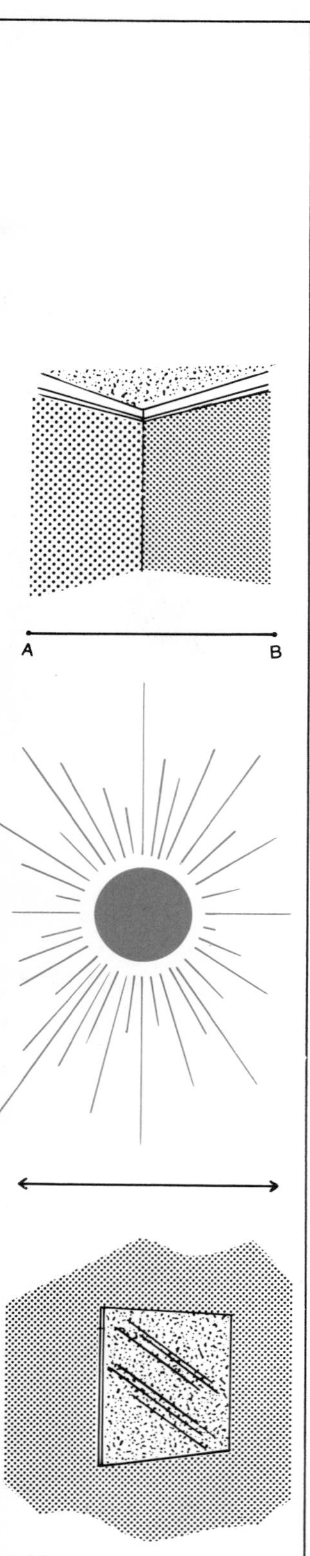

Some Basic Geometric Facts

If you are unfamiliar with the following terms, take time to read the list over carefully.

Point

We cannot measure a point in any way, but it does have the property of position. For example, the corner of a room at the floor or ceiling is a point. A point is a mathematical idea and is not defined.

Line Segment

We can measure the length of a line segment by using a ruler or a measuring tape. You can think that a line segment consists of the two end points (such as A and B) and all the points between them. A line segment has the property of straightness. For instance, the edge of this page is a line segment.

Ray

We say that the sun gives off rays of light. These light rays have a beginning but no ending (unless they strike an object in space!) A ray is similar to a line segment but it has only one end point.

Line

A line is similar to a line segment, but it has no end points. To indicate this, arrows are used, as shown. Can you think of any examples of lines?

Plane

A plane is a geometrical figure that possesses the property of flatness. For example, a window pane is part of a plane.

Angle

An angle is a figure formed from 2 rays with a common end point, called the *vertex*. It can also be thought of as the "amount of rotation" of a ray about a fixed point. We refer to the angle shown as ∠DEB or ∠BED. There are numerous examples of angles — the angle the roof of a house makes with one wall, for instance.

D
E
B
VERTEX (THE MIDDLE LETTER IN NAMING AN ANGLE)

Opposite Angles

Opposite angles are the equal angles lying on opposite sides of a vertex formed by two crossing lines.

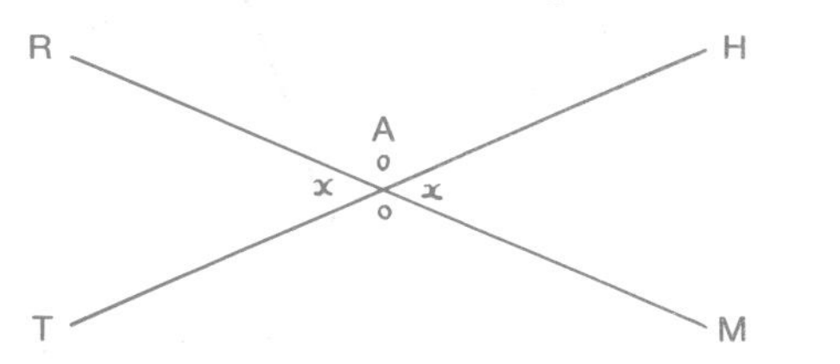

Note that equal angles have identical markings.
∠RAH = ∠TAM
∠RAT = ∠HAM

Complementary angles are any two angles whose sum is 90°.

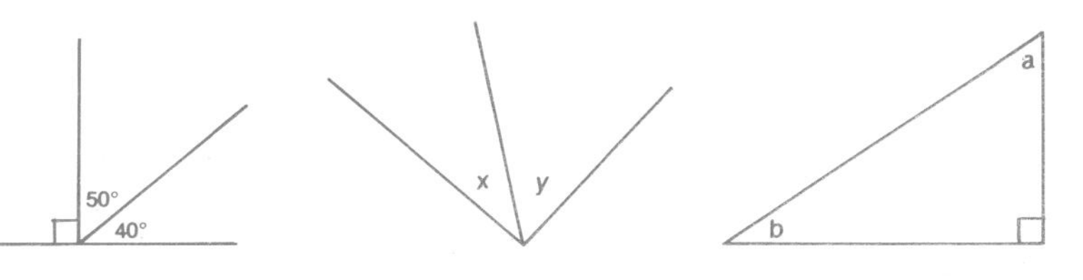

Supplementary angles are any two angles whose sum is 180°.

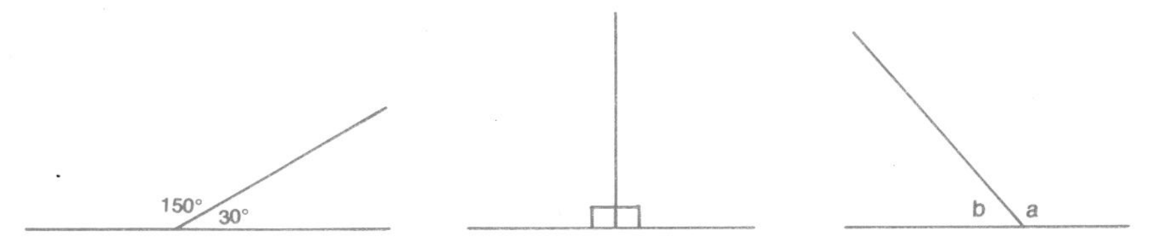

Collinear Points

Three or more points on the same line are collinear.

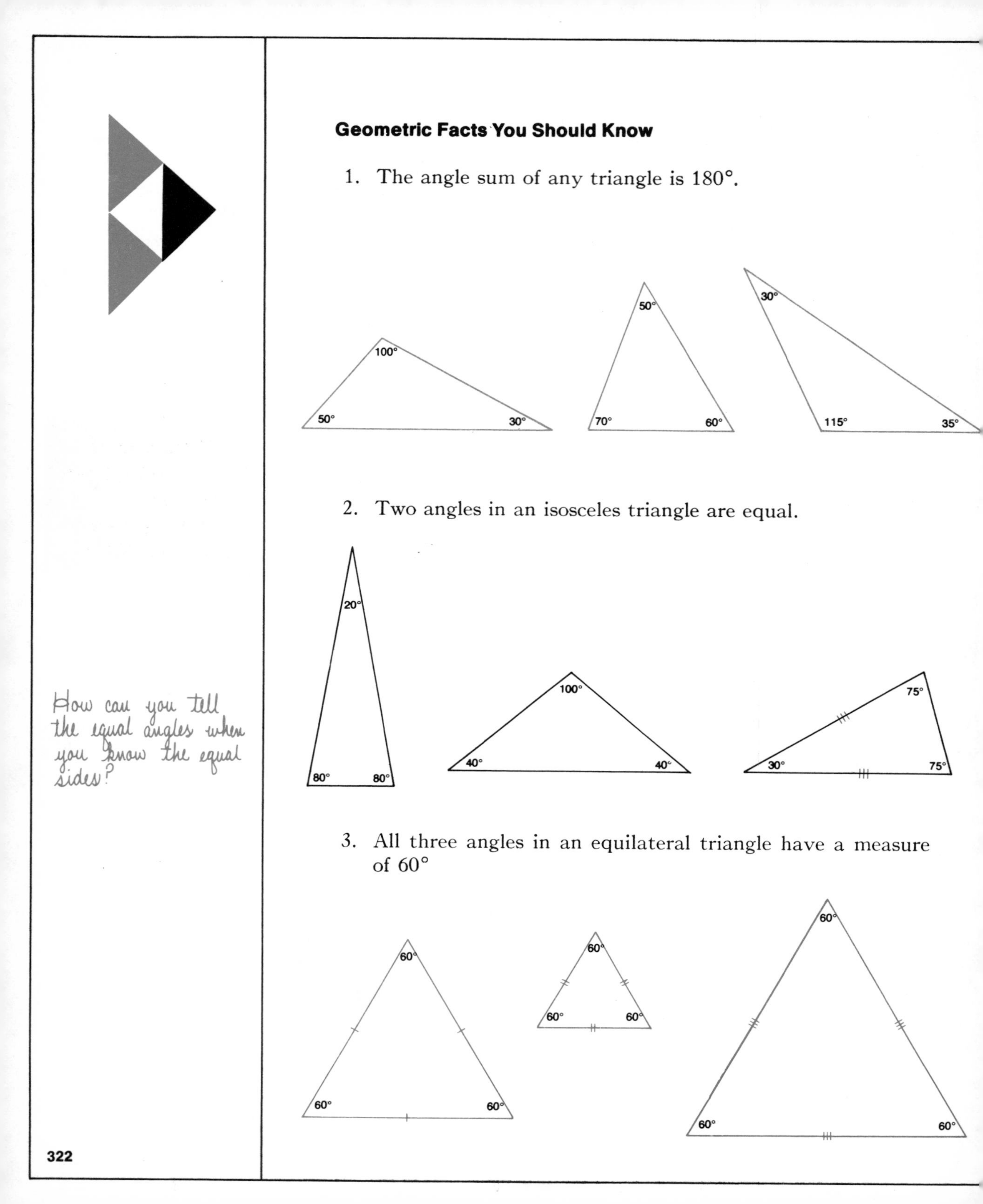

Geometric Facts You Should Know

1. The angle sum of any triangle is 180°.

2. Two angles in an isosceles triangle are equal.

How can you tell the equal angles when you know the equal sides?

3. All three angles in an equilateral triangle have a measure of 60°

Some Common Geometric Terms

Polygon—a simple closed figure formed from line segments

Triangle—a polygon of 3 sides.

Quadrilateral—a polygon of 4 sides.

Pentagon—a polygon of 5 sides.

Hexagon—a polygon of 6 sides.

Octagon—a polygon of 8 sides.

Decagon—a polygon of 10 sides.

Regular polygon—a polygon in which all sides are equal and all angles are equal.

Square—a regular quadrilateral.

Rectangle—a quadrilateral with opposite sides equal and interior angles of 90°.

Parallelogram—a quadrilateral with opposite sides parallel.

Some Geometric Instruments

1. Ruler—for drawing straight line segments.
2. Compasses—for drawing arcs or circles.
3. Protractor—for measuring angles.
4. A sharp pencil.
5. Set squares—for drawing angles of 30°, 45°, 60°, 90°.

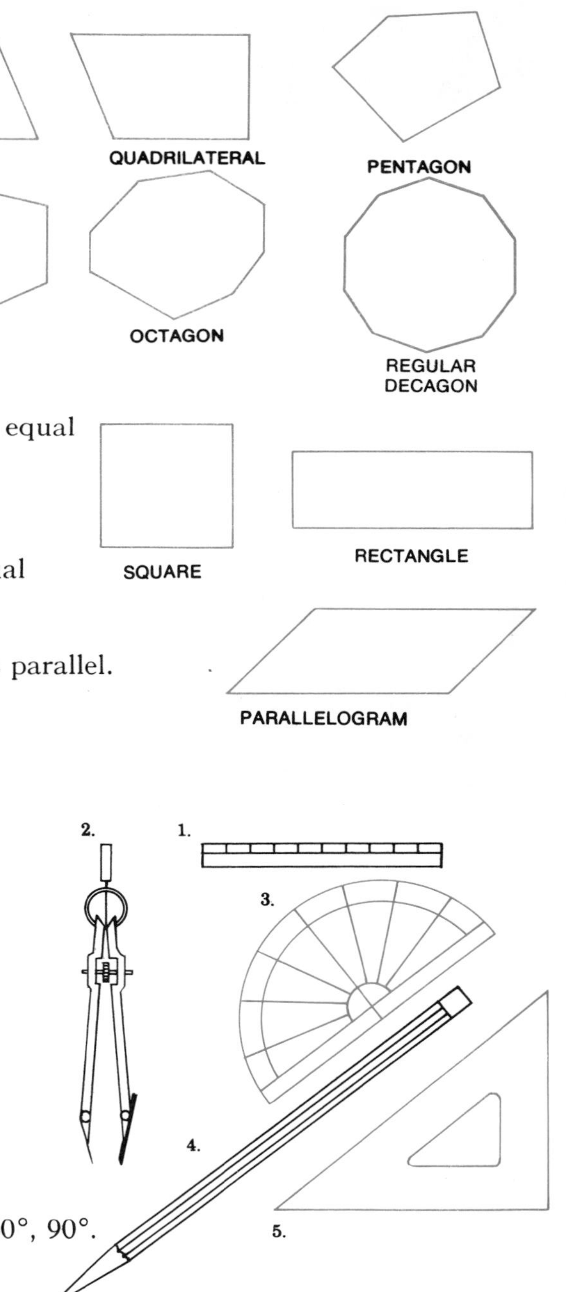

23.1 The 6 Basic Ruler-and-Compasses Constructions

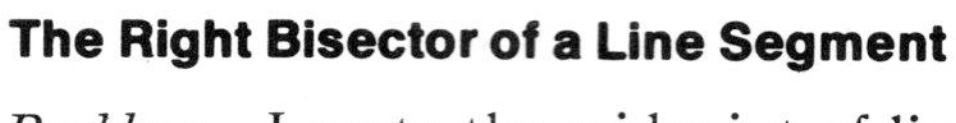

The Right Bisector of a Line Segment

Problem Locate the midpoint of line segment AB.

Step 1 With center A, draw an arc as shown.

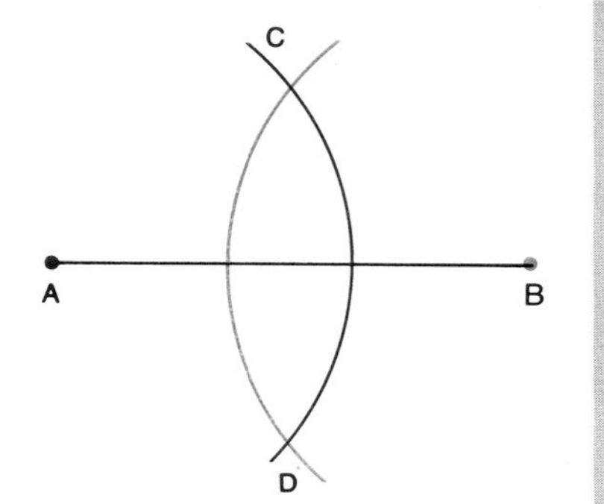

Step 2 With center B and the same radius, draw an arc to cut the first arc at C and D.

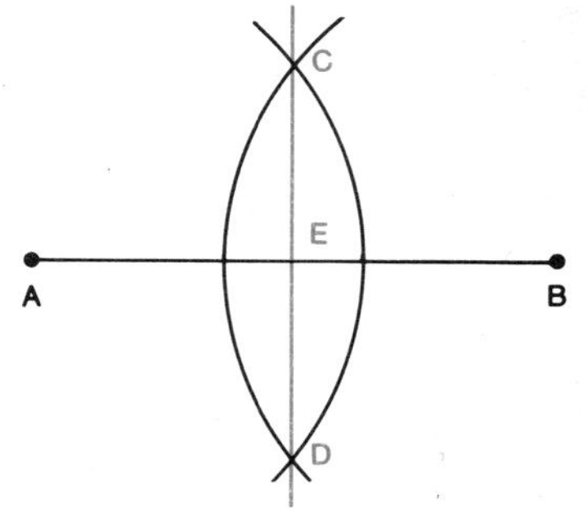

Step 3 Join C to D with a line segment cutting AB at E. CD is the required bisector, and E is the midpoint of AB.

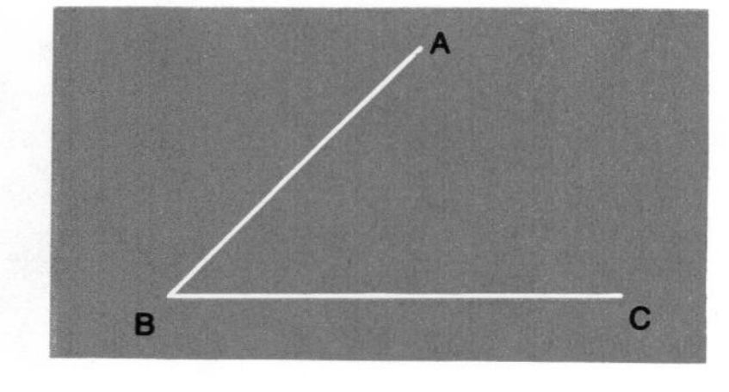

The Bisector of an Angle

Problem Draw the bisector of ∠ABC.

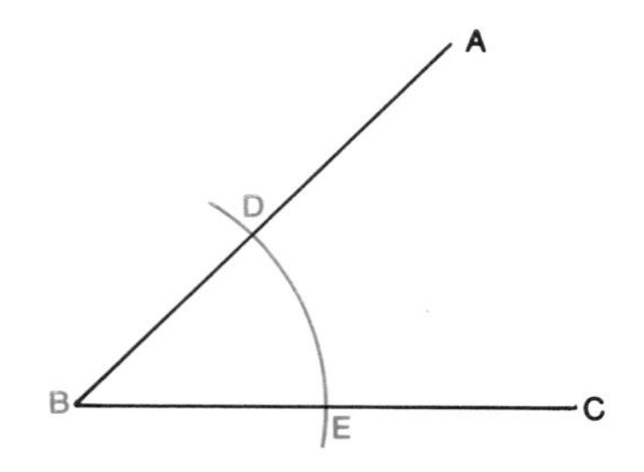

Step 1 With center B, draw an arc to cut AB at D and BC at E.

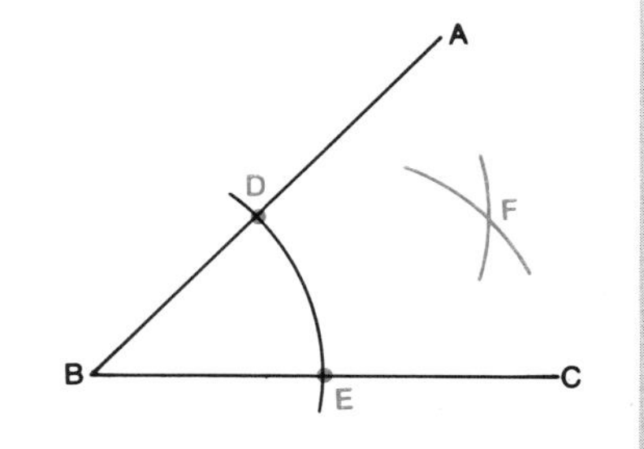

Step 2 With centers D and E and equal radii, draw arcs to intersect at F.

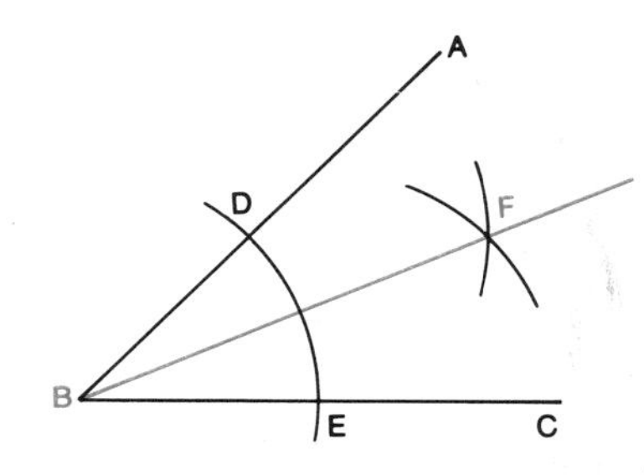

Step 3 Join B to F. BF is the required angle bisector.

The Perpendicular to a Line at a Point

Problem Draw a line segment through C perpendicular to AB.

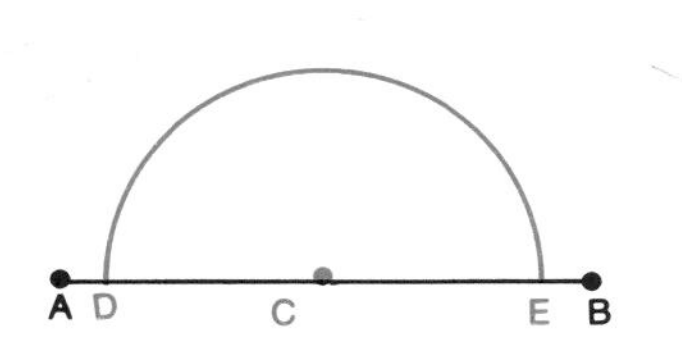

Step 1 With center C and a suitable radius, draw a semicircle to cut AC at D and CB at E.

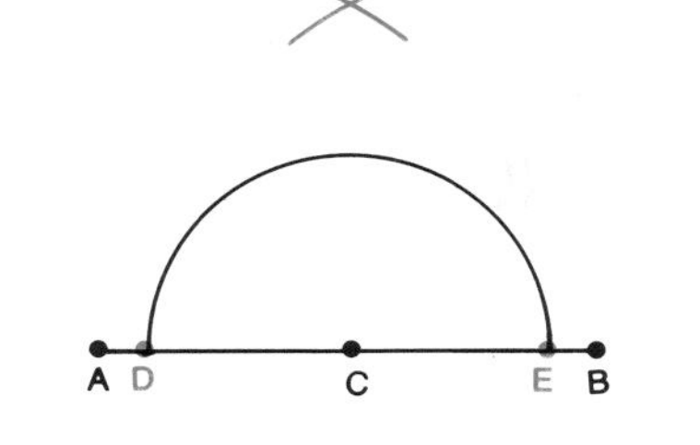

Step 2 With centers D and E and equal radii, draw arcs to intersect at P.

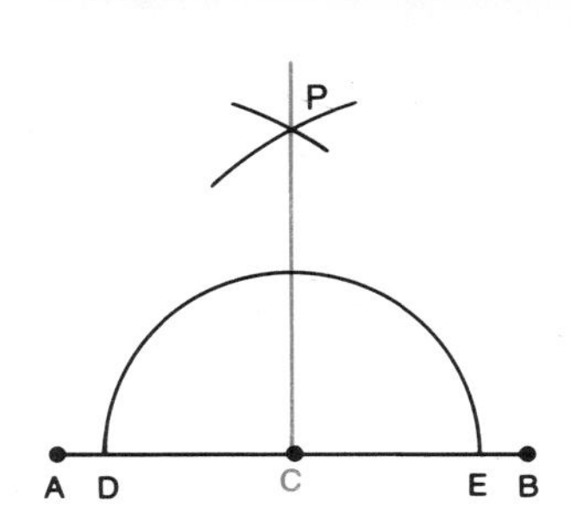

Step 3 Join C to P. CP is the required perpendicular.

The Perpendicular to a Line from a Point

Problem Draw a perpendicular from point Q to a line MN.

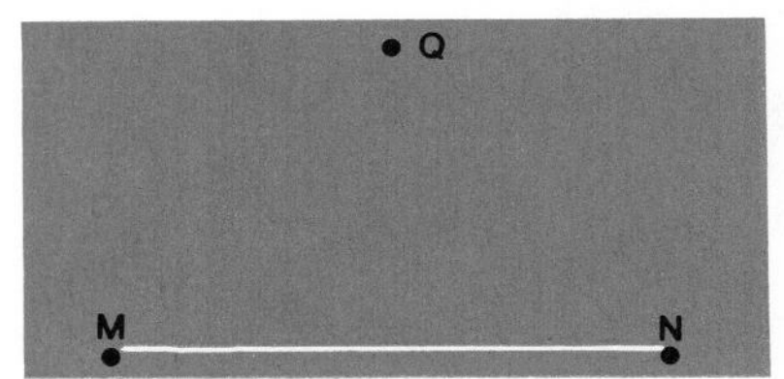

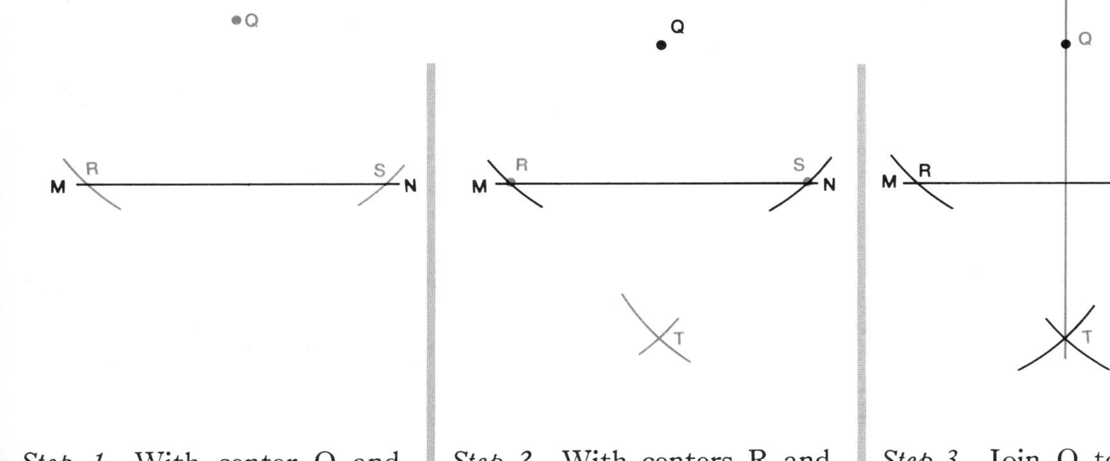

Step 1 With center Q and suitable radius, draw an arc to cut MN at R and S.

Step 2 With centers R and S and equal radii, draw arcs to intersect at T.

Step 3 Join Q to T. QT is the required perpendicular.

A Line Parallel to a Given Line

Problem Draw a line parallel to AB through point P.

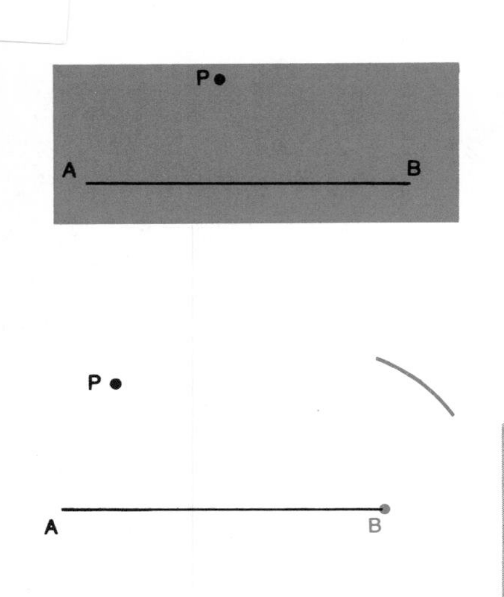

Step 1 With center B and radius AP, draw an arc.

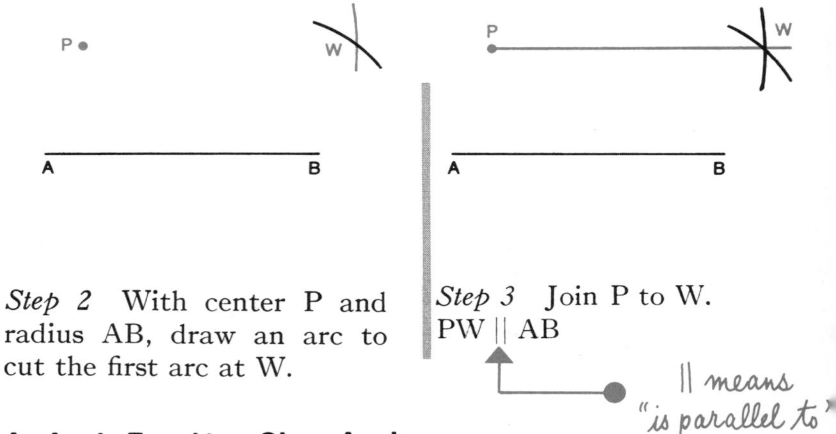

Step 2 With center P and radius AB, draw an arc to cut the first arc at W.

Step 3 Join P to W.
PW || AB

An Angle Equal to a Given Angle

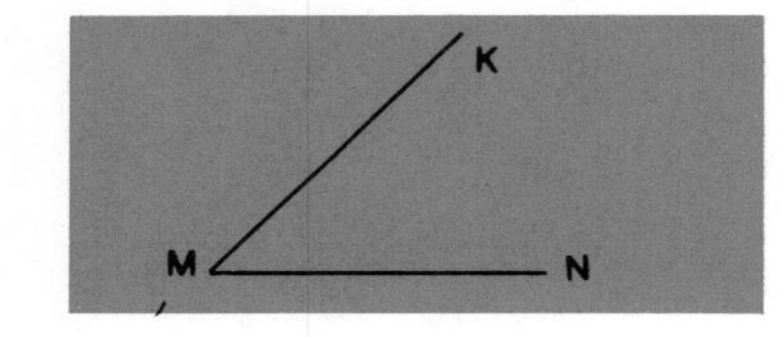

Problem Construct ∠ABC equal to a given ∠KMN.

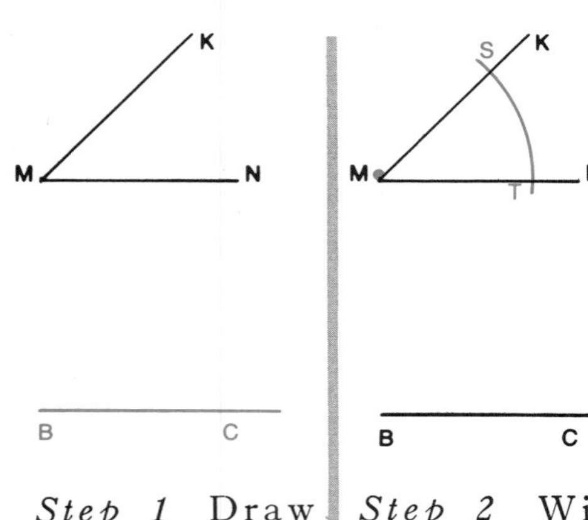

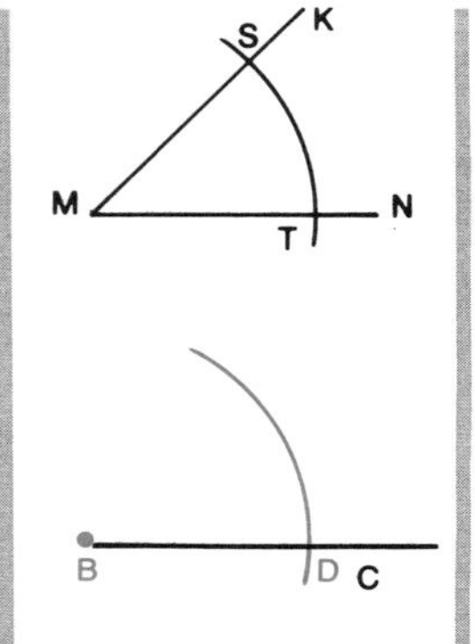

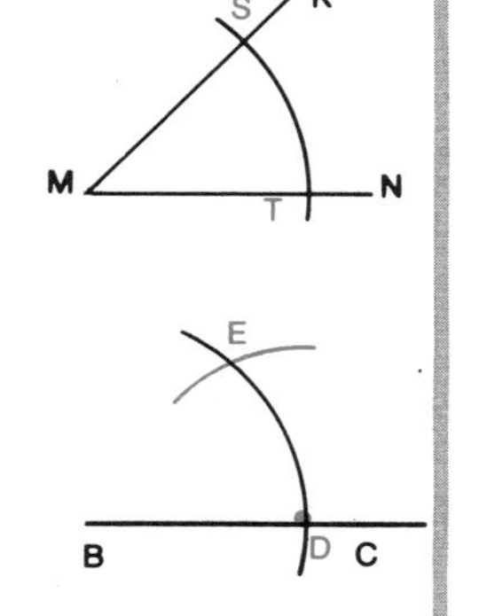

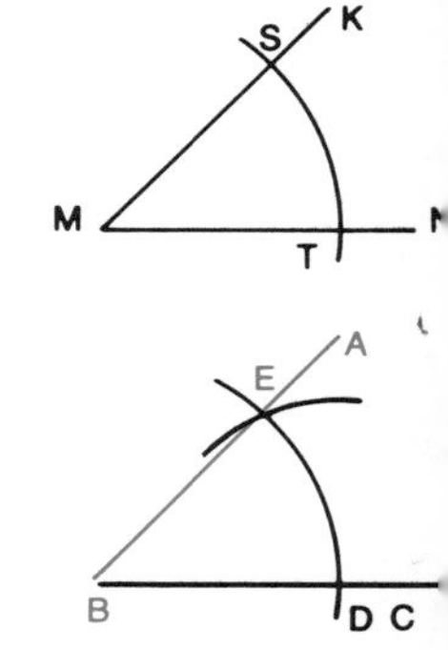

Step 1 Draw base line BC longer than MN.

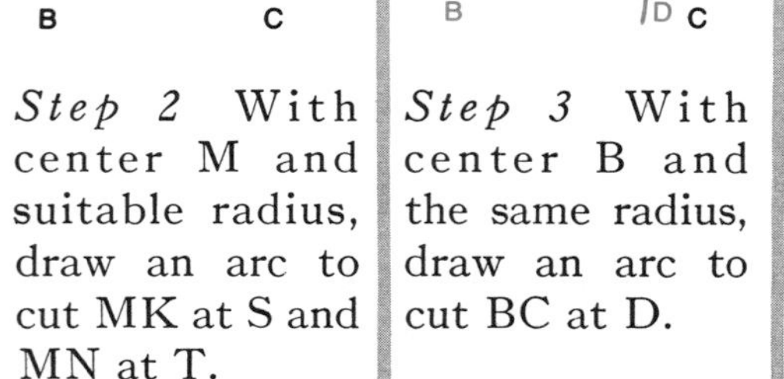

Step 2 With center M and suitable radius, draw an arc to cut MK at S and MN at T.

Step 3 With center B and the same radius, draw an arc to cut BC at D.

Step 4 With center D and radius TS, draw an arc to cut the first arc at E.

Step 5 Join B to E and extend to A.
∠ABC = ∠KMN

Exercise 23.1

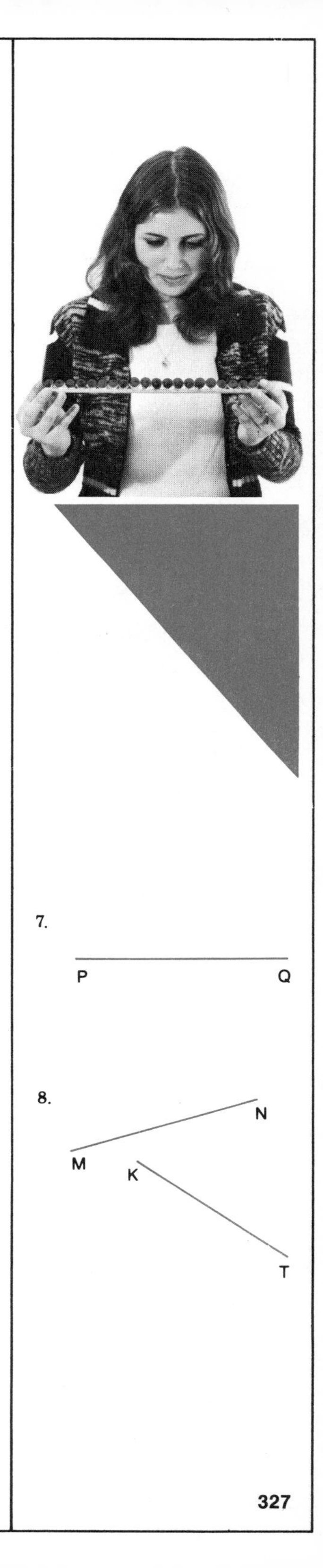

Discussion

1. How many points are there in a line? A ray? A line segment?
2. What is the least number of points required to fix the position of a line?
3. Give physical examples of a line segment, a plane surface, and a three-dimensional object.
4. What is the *greatest* number of points of intersection of 2 lines? 3 lines? 4 lines? 5 lines?
5. Is it possible for 2 lines in a plane to have no points in common? Explain.
6. Name the geometrical figure formed by joining 3 non-collinear points.

Written Solutions

Use ruler and compasses only.

7. Draw a segment PQ and construct the right bisector of the segment. Using a protractor, measure the angles formed between the bisector and the line segment PQ. What do you notice?
8. Draw segments MN and KT and construct the right bisector of the segments. Check by measurement.
9. Draw angles SAM, PEG, and JIL. Construct the angle bisectors for each angle. Check using a protractor.

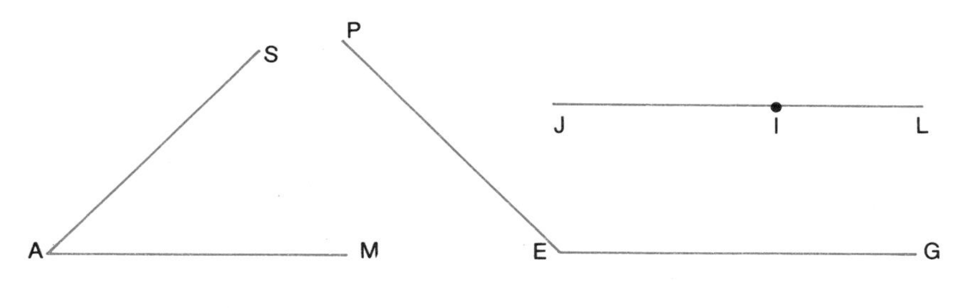

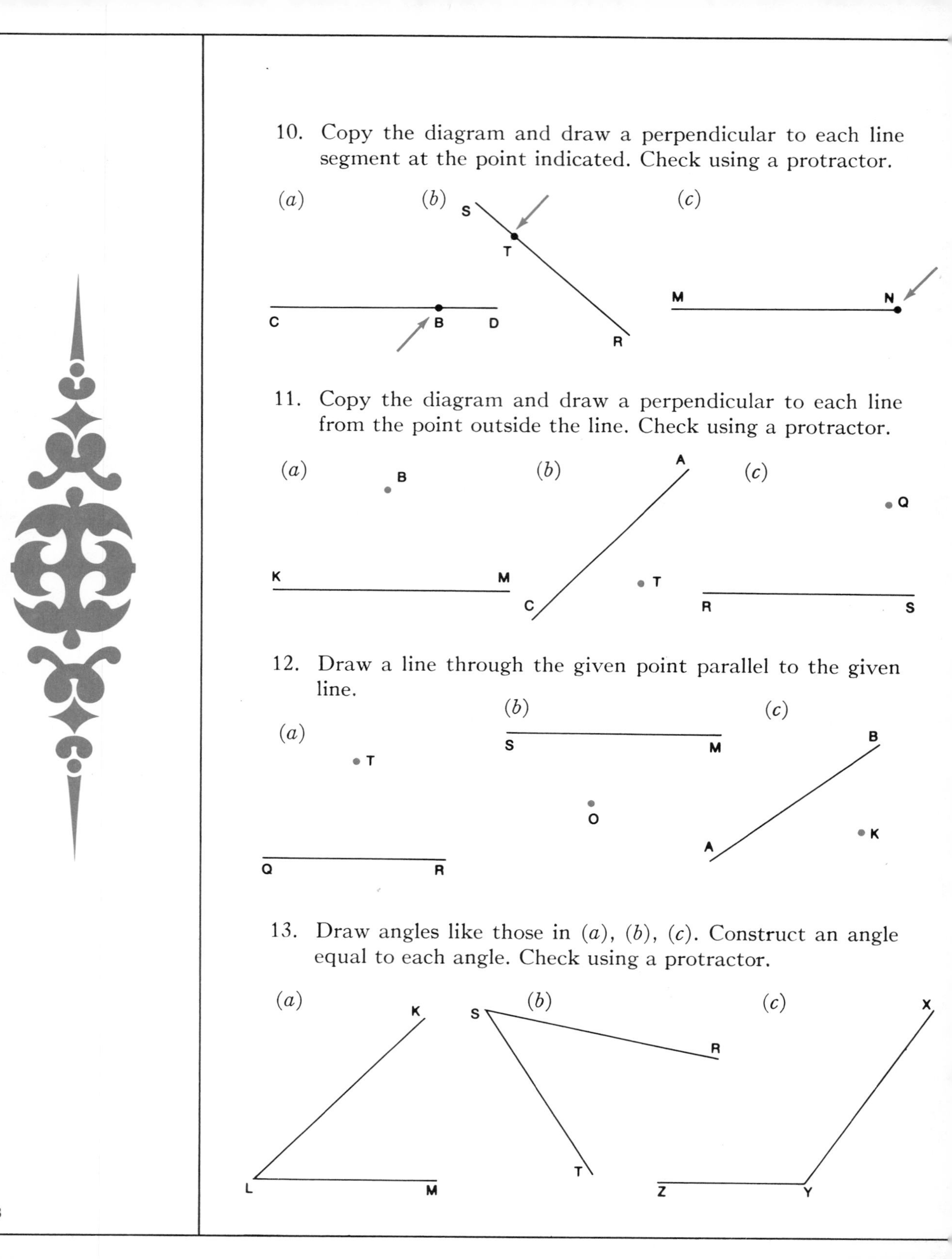

10. Copy the diagram and draw a perpendicular to each line segment at the point indicated. Check using a protractor.

(*a*) (*b*) (*c*)

11. Copy the diagram and draw a perpendicular to each line from the point outside the line. Check using a protractor.

(*a*) (*b*) (*c*)

12. Draw a line through the given point parallel to the given line.

(*a*) (*b*) (*c*)

13. Draw angles like those in (*a*), (*b*), (*c*). Construct an angle equal to each angle. Check using a protractor.

(*a*) (*b*) (*c*)

14. Draw angles like those in (*a*) and (*b*). Construct an angle equal to the *sum* of the two angles. Check by measurement.

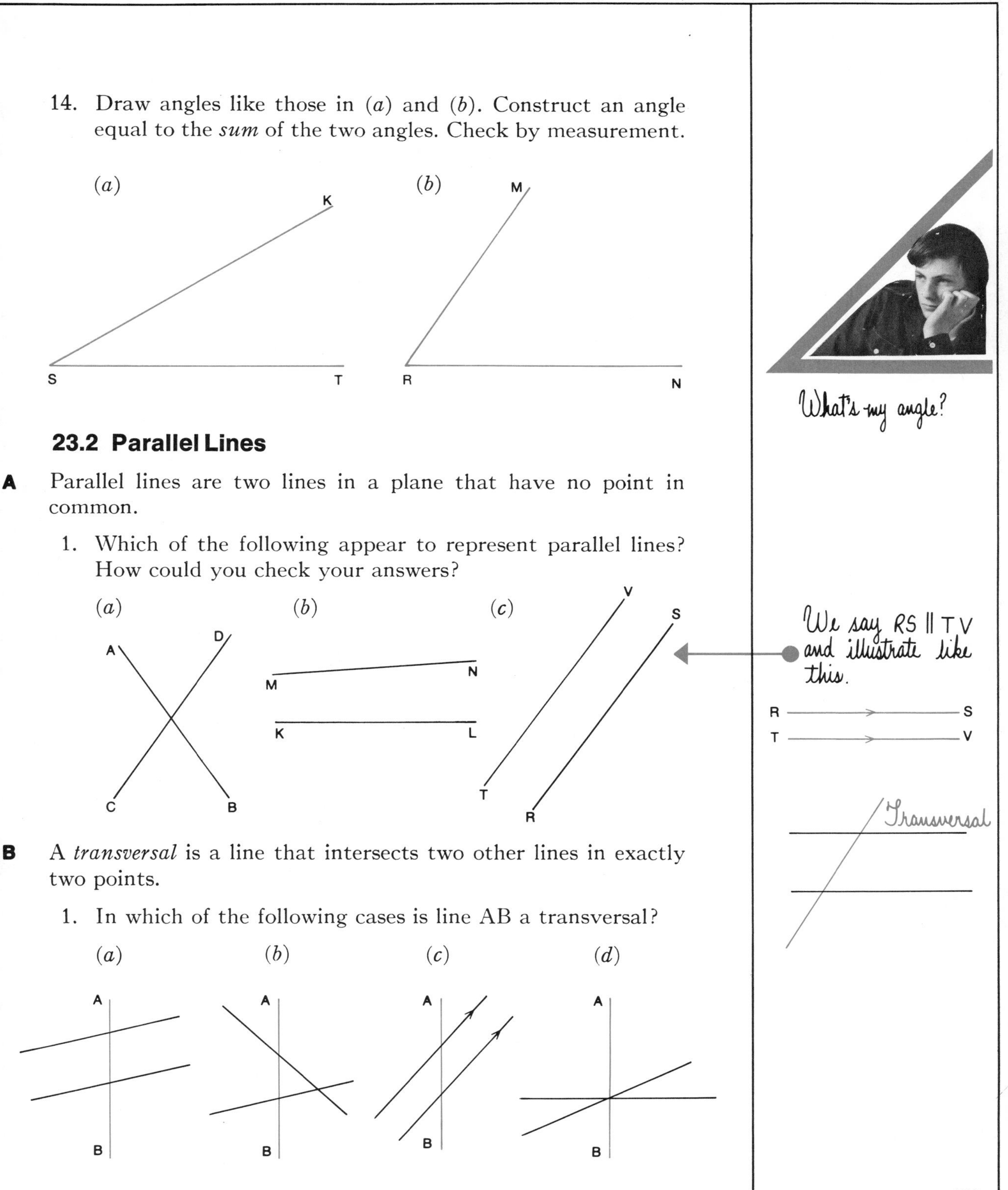

23.2 Parallel Lines

A Parallel lines are two lines in a plane that have no point in common.

1. Which of the following appear to represent parallel lines? How could you check your answers?

B A *transversal* is a line that intersects two other lines in exactly two points.

1. In which of the following cases is line AB a transversal?

C In each of the following diagrams, PQ is a transversal for a pair of parallel lines.

1. Measure and record the measure of the angles indicated.

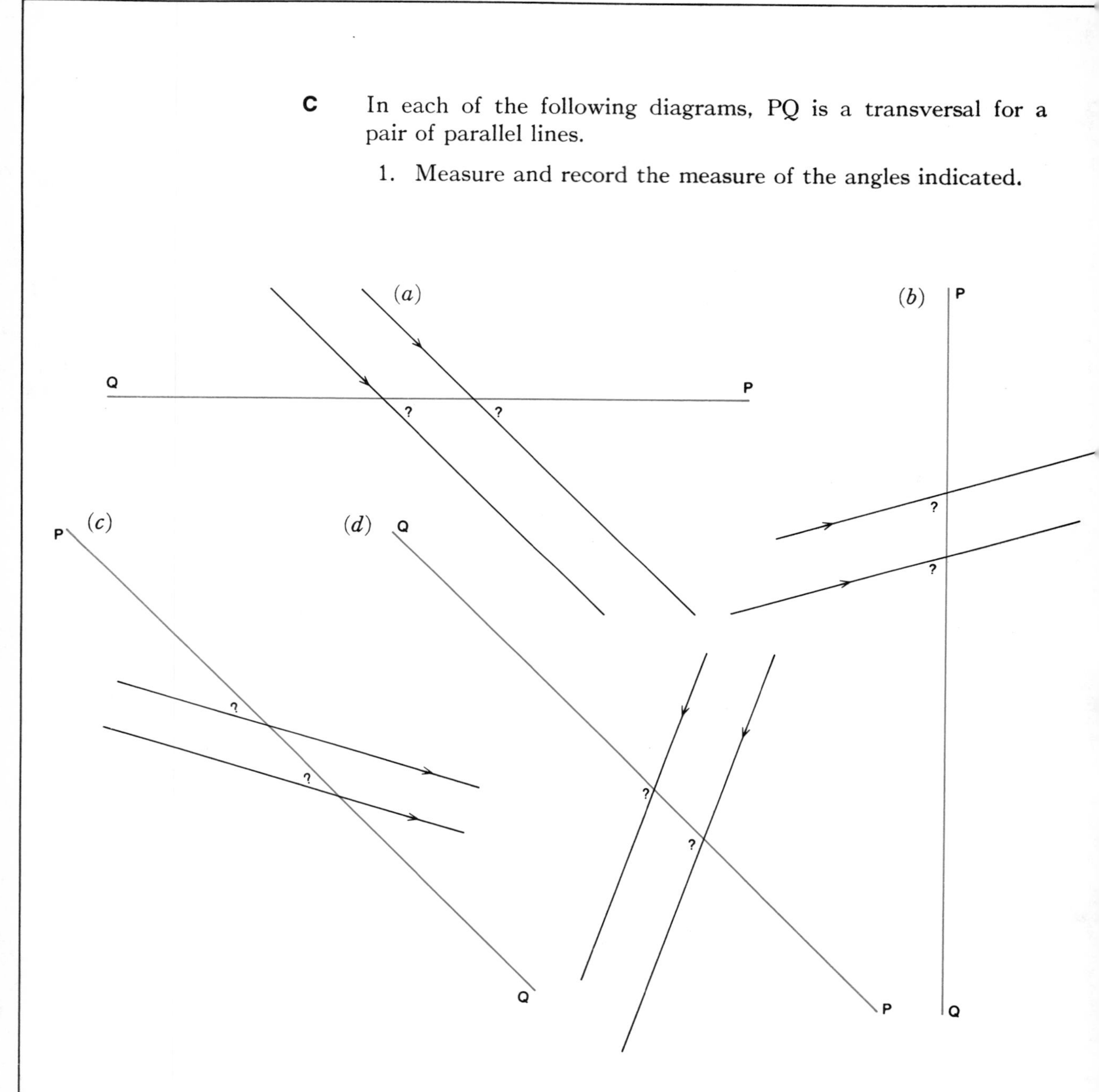

2. What do you notice about the angles measured in each case? Such pairs of angles are called *corresponding angles*. Can you explain why this is a suitable name?

D In each of the following diagrams, MN is a transversal for a pair of parallel lines.

1. Measure and record the degree measure of the angles indicated.

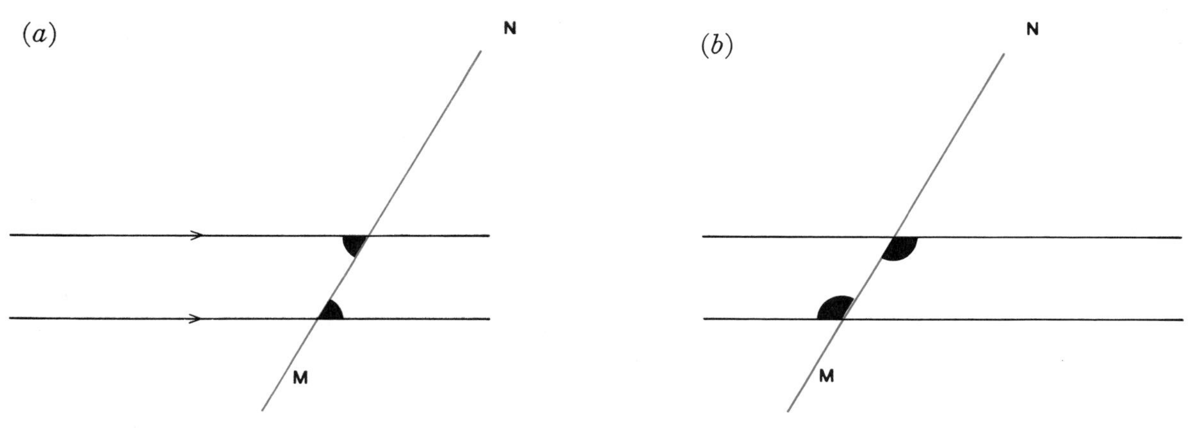

2. What do you notice about the angles measured in each case? Such pairs of angles are called *alternate angles*. Why is this a suitable name?

E In the following diagrams, CB is a transversal.

1. Consider the case in which CB meets the parallel lines at right angles at points A and R.
   What is the sum of $\angle MAR$ and $\angle ART$?
   $\angle MAR + \angle ART = ▤°$

2. Now suppose we rotate AB so that $\angle MAR$ is increased by 20°.
   What is the measure of $\angle MAR$ now? Would you expect $\angle ART$ to increase also, or to decrease? By how much?
   Check your answers by measurement with a protractor.

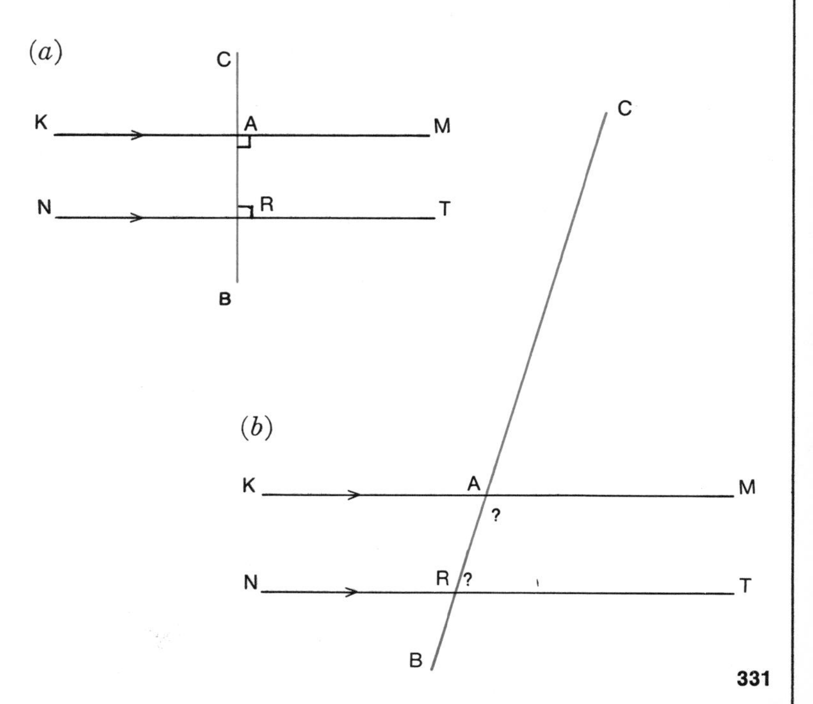

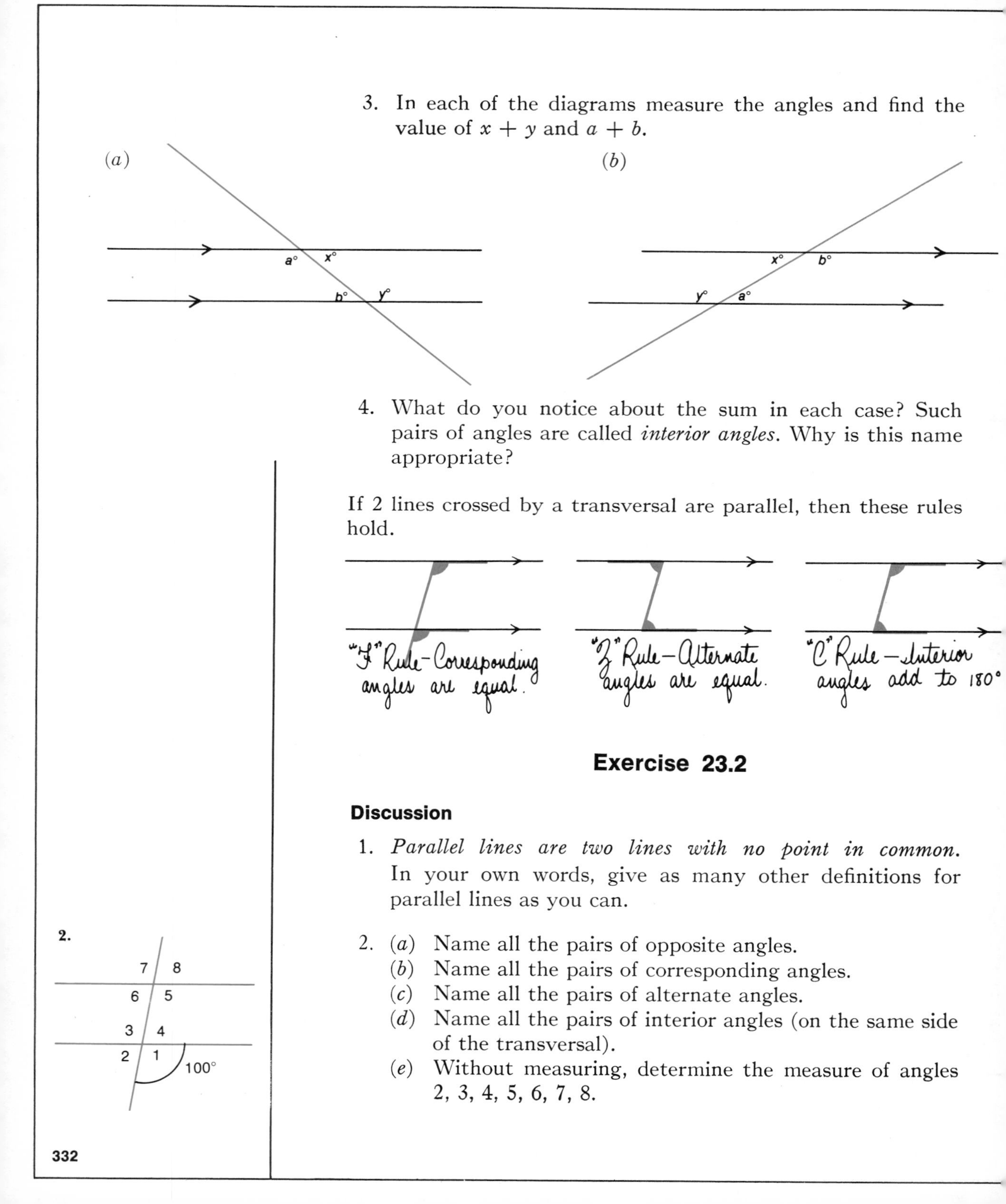

3. In each of the diagrams measure the angles and find the value of $x + y$ and $a + b$.

4. What do you notice about the sum in each case? Such pairs of angles are called *interior angles*. Why is this name appropriate?

If 2 lines crossed by a transversal are parallel, then these rules hold.

"F" Rule–Corresponding angles are equal.
"Z" Rule–Alternate angles are equal.
"C" Rule–Interior angles add to 180°

Exercise 23.2

Discussion

1. *Parallel lines are two lines with no point in common.* In your own words, give as many other definitions for parallel lines as you can.

2. (*a*) Name all the pairs of opposite angles.
   (*b*) Name all the pairs of corresponding angles.
   (*c*) Name all the pairs of alternate angles.
   (*d*) Name all the pairs of interior angles (on the same side of the transversal).
   (*e*) Without measuring, determine the measure of angles 2, 3, 4, 5, 6, 7, 8.

2.

3. A parallelogram is a quadrilateral with opposite sides parallel. Using the information in the diagram, and without measurement, determine the measure of angles 1, 2, 3, 4, 5, 6, 7, 8, 9 in parallelogram ABCD.

Written Solutions

4. Without measurement determine the measure of each angle in the following diagrams.

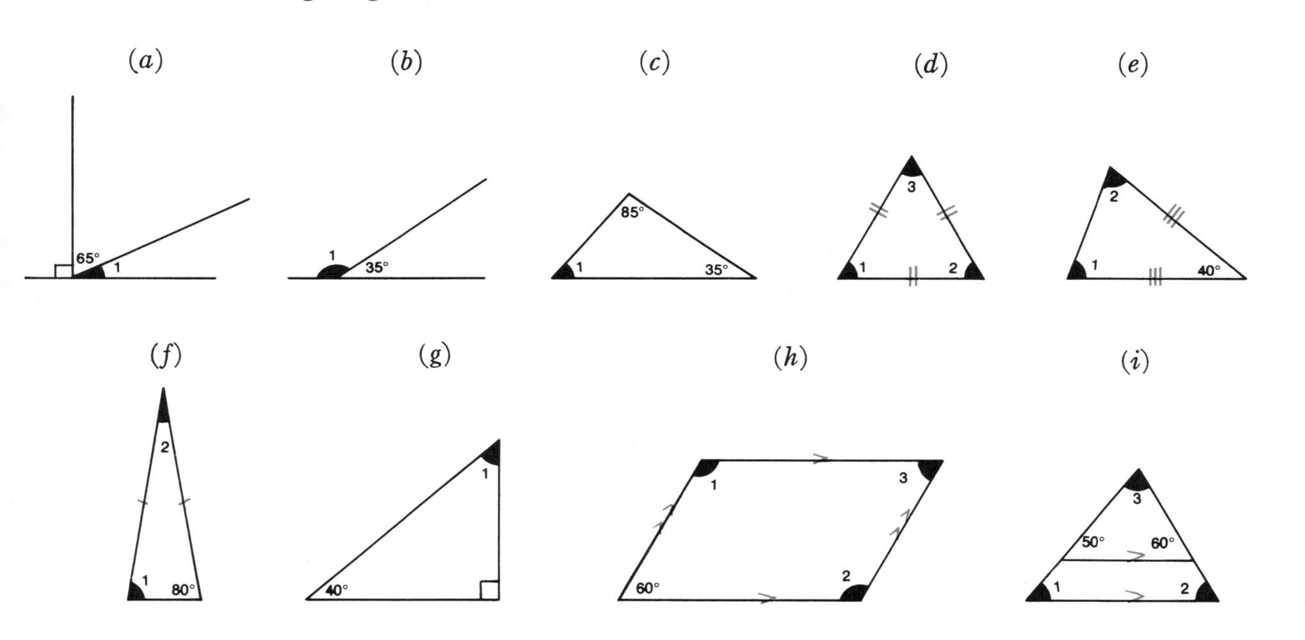

5. Without measurement, determine the measure of each numbered angle in the following diagrams.

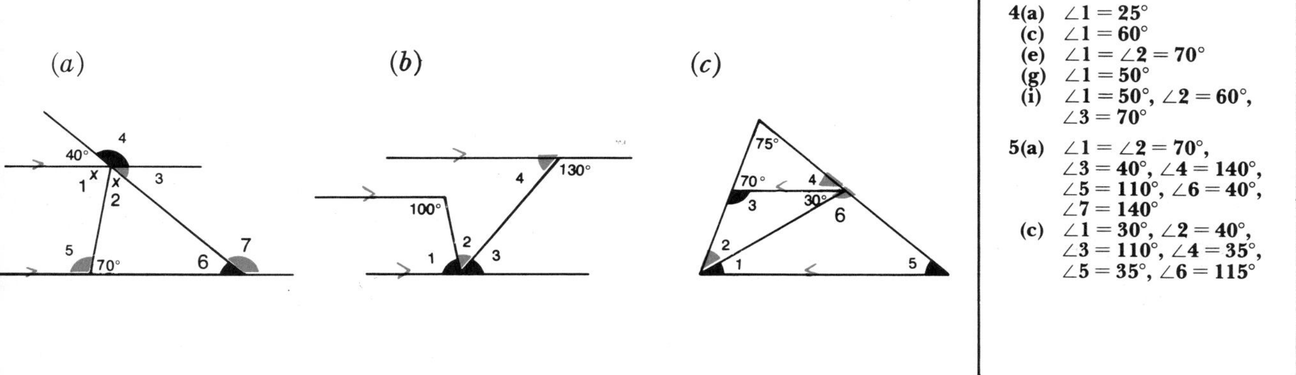

4(a) $\angle 1 = 25°$
(c) $\angle 1 = 60°$
(e) $\angle 1 = \angle 2 = 70°$
(g) $\angle 1 = 50°$
(i) $\angle 1 = 50°$, $\angle 2 = 60°$, $\angle 3 = 70°$

5(a) $\angle 1 = \angle 2 = 70°$, $\angle 3 = 40°$, $\angle 4 = 140°$, $\angle 5 = 110°$, $\angle 6 = 40°$, $\angle 7 = 140°$
(c) $\angle 1 = 30°$, $\angle 2 = 40°$, $\angle 3 = 110°$, $\angle 4 = 35°$, $\angle 5 = 35°$, $\angle 6 = 115°$

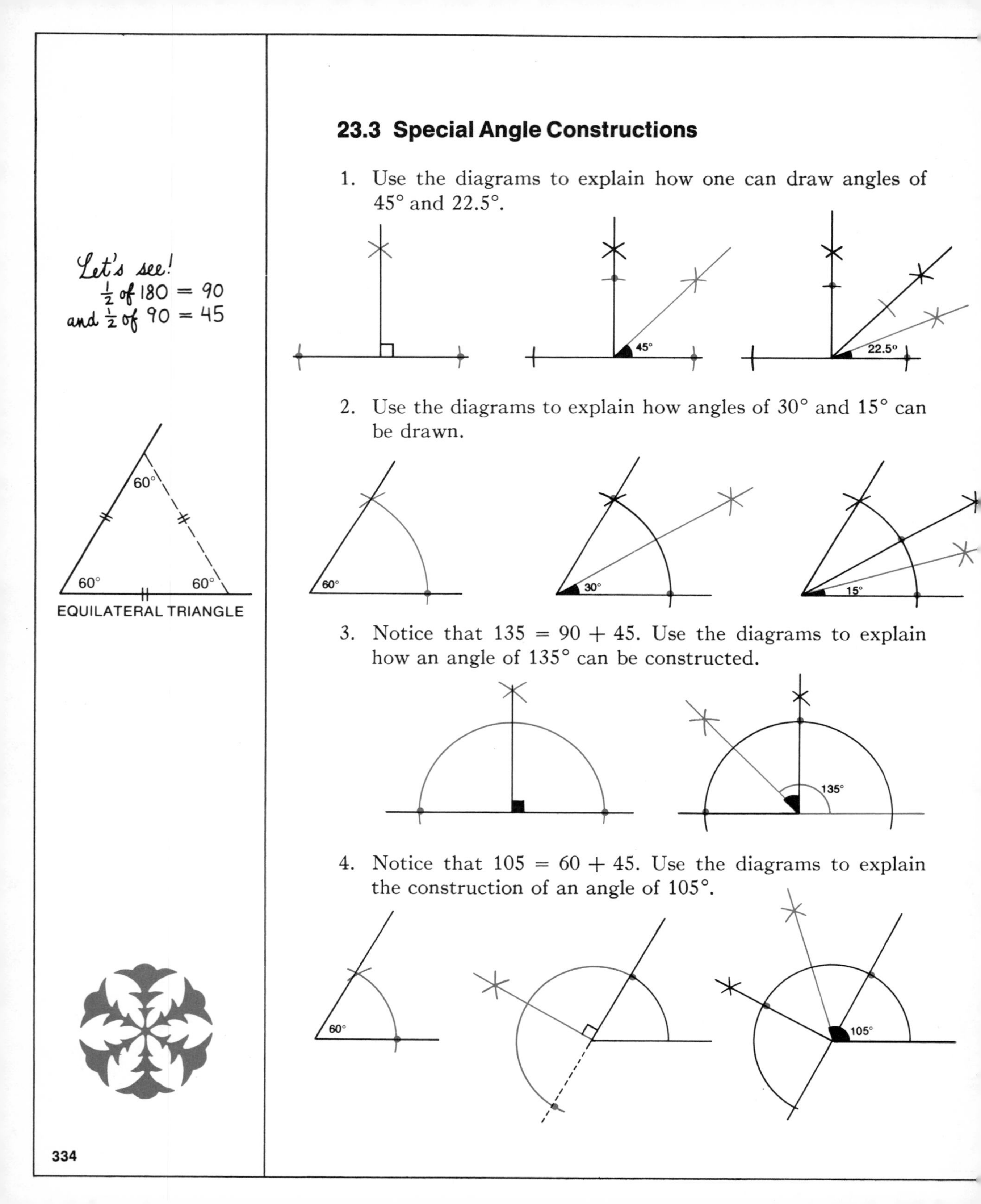

23.3 Special Angle Constructions

1. Use the diagrams to explain how one can draw angles of 45° and 22.5°.

2. Use the diagrams to explain how angles of 30° and 15° can be drawn.

3. Notice that $135 = 90 + 45$. Use the diagrams to explain how an angle of 135° can be constructed.

4. Notice that $105 = 60 + 45$. Use the diagrams to explain the construction of an angle of 105°.

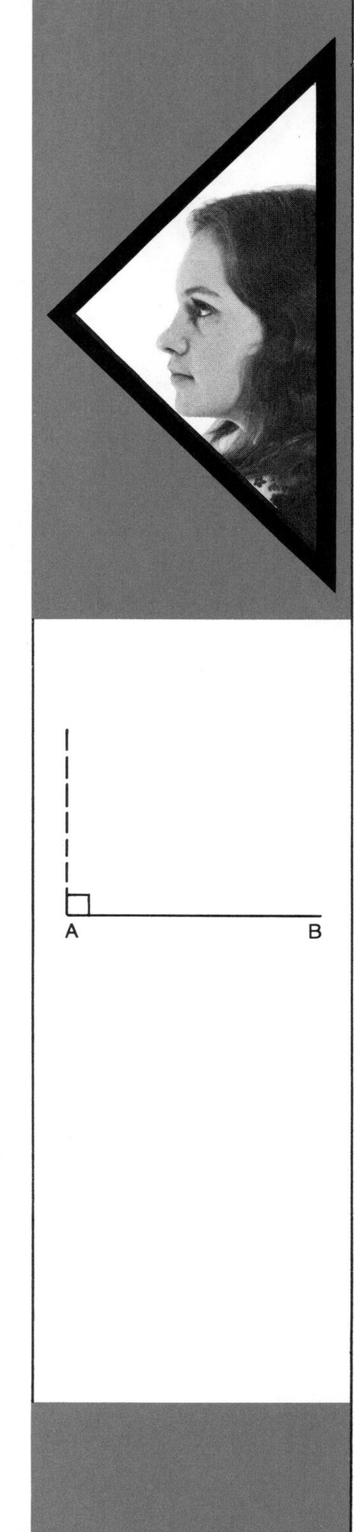

Exercise 23.3

Discussion

1. Express each of the following special angles as the sum or difference of the basic angles of 22.5°, 45°, 90°, 15°, 30°, 60°.

   For example, 82.5° = 60° + 22.5°

(*a*) 150°	(*d*) 52.5°	(*g*) 97.5°
(*b*) 67.5°	(*e*) 75°	(*h*) 142.5°
(*c*) 120°	(*f*) 165°	(*i*) 112.5°

Written Solutions

Use ruler and compasses only for the following constructions.

2. Construct accurately the angles given in Question 1. Check your accuracy by measuring with a protractor.

3. By first constructing a 60° angle and using the bisection principle, construct a perpendicular to line AB at point A *without extending the line!* Solve this problem in as many different ways as you can.

23.4 Construction of Triangles

A Recall that triangles may be classified according to either sides or angles.

Classification by Sides

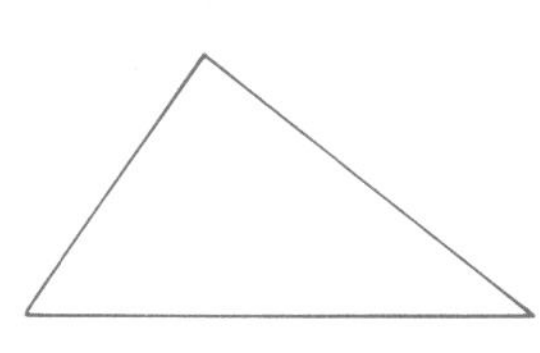

Scalene
no sides equal

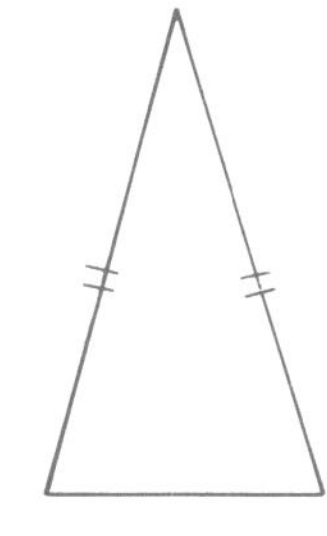

Isosceles
two sides equal

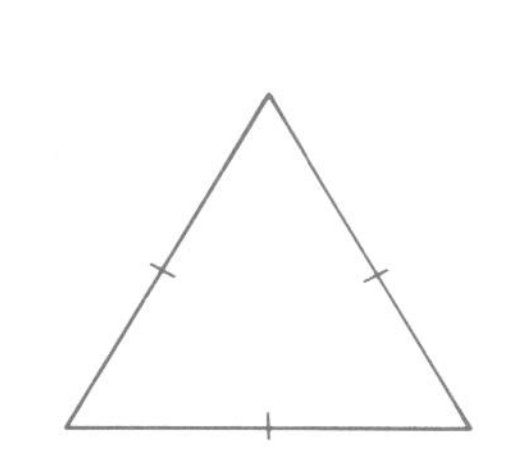

Equilateral
three sides equal

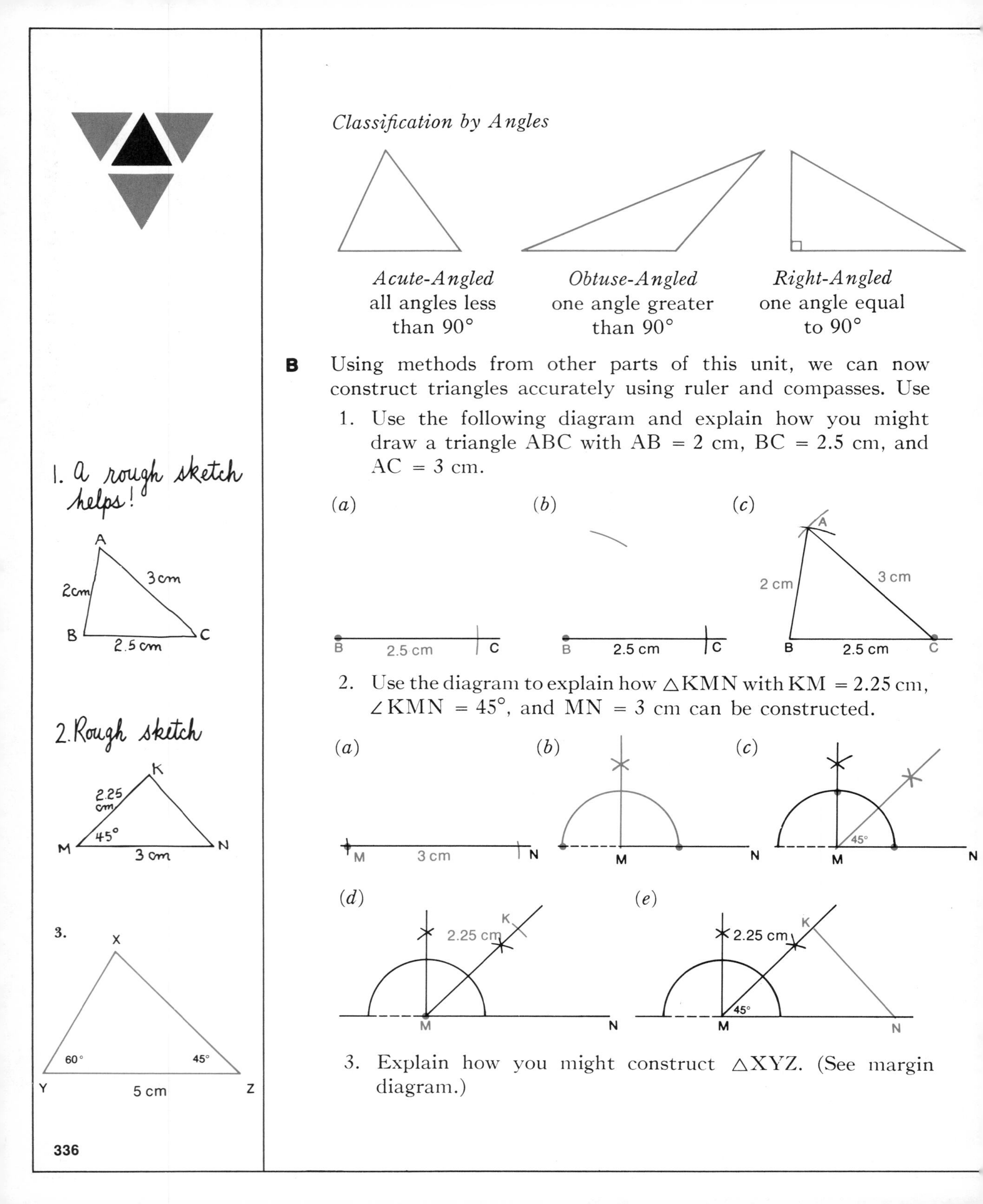

Classification by Angles

B Using methods from other parts of this unit, we can now construct triangles accurately using ruler and compasses. Use

1. Use the following diagram and explain how you might draw a triangle ABC with AB = 2 cm, BC = 2.5 cm, and AC = 3 cm.

2. Use the diagram to explain how $\triangle$KMN with KM = 2.25 cm, $\angle$KMN = 45°, and MN = 3 cm can be constructed.

3. Explain how you might construct $\triangle$XYZ. (See margin diagram.)

Exercise 23.4

Discussion

1. Classify the triangles shown below according to both sides and angles.

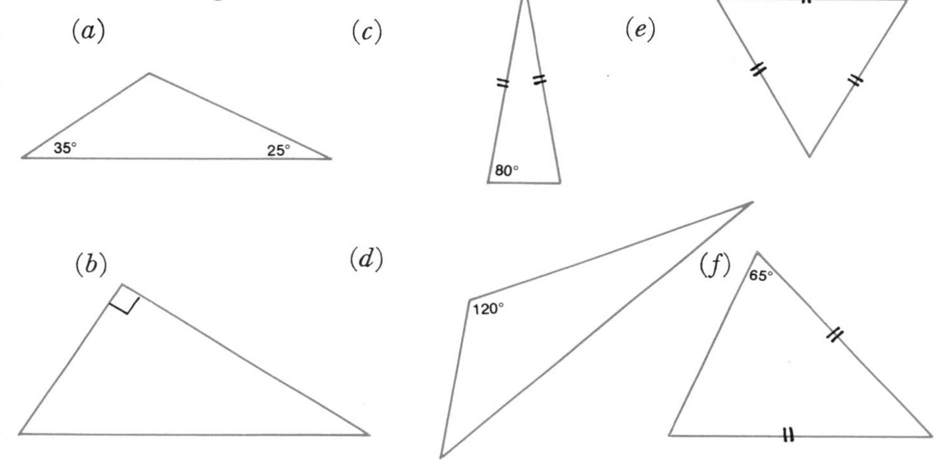

Written Solutions

2. The following triangles are not drawn to scale. Explain how each is constructed and draw each accurately using ruler and compasses.

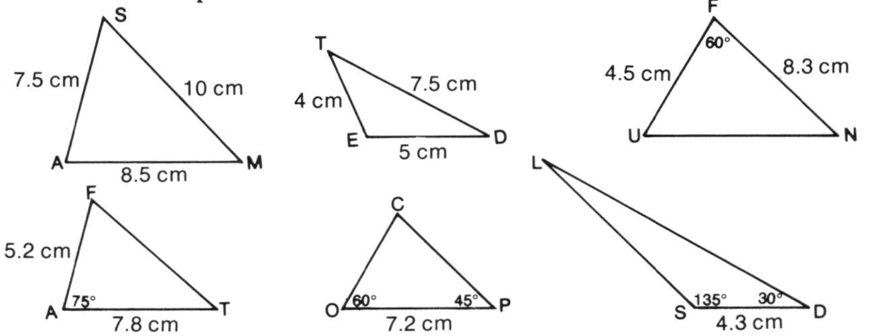

3. Construct $\triangle UFO$ with $\angle OUF = 105°$, $\angle UFO = 30°$, and $OF = 6.5$ cm.

4. Construct a right-angled isosceles triangle whose equal sides are 5.4 cm long.

5. Explain why it is impossible to construct $\triangle KEN$ with $EN = 5$ cm, $KE = 2.1$ cm, and $KN = 2.5$ cm.

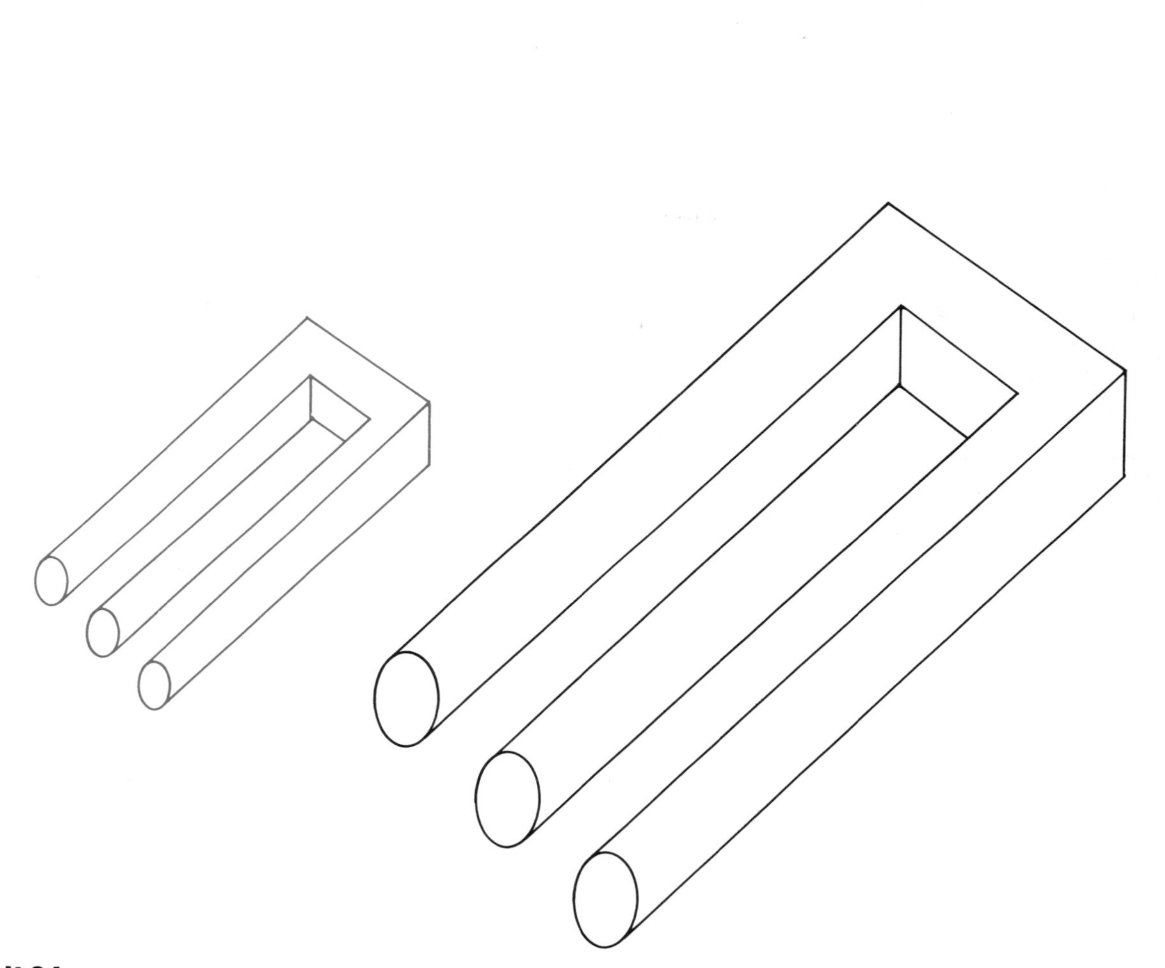

Unit 24
Similar Triangles

The idea of *similar figures* is a very common one. A model of a ship or automobile is similar to the real thing, but of course is "scaled down." A photograph may be "blown-up" to produce an enlargement that is similar to the original picture.

In geometry too, we encounter similar figures. Two squares may be of different sizes, yet are similar figures. Any pair of circles, though of different diameter, are similar.

In this unit we shall study only similar triangles, although the properties of similarity discovered here may be applied to many other geometric shapes.

24.1 Basic Properties of Similar Triangles

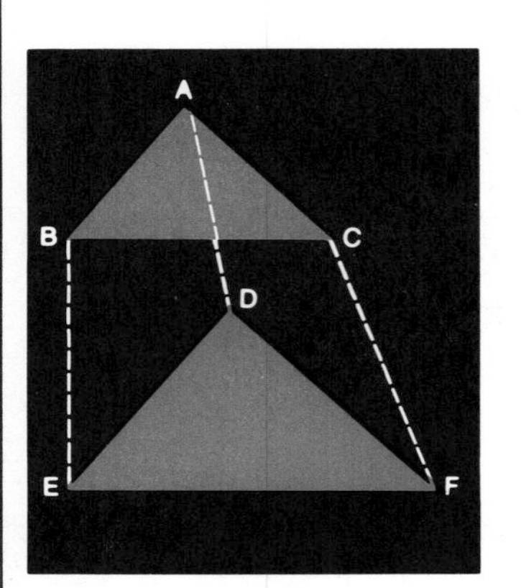

A Think of △DEF as a photographic enlargement of △ABC where

1. D corresponds to A,
   E corresponds to B, and
   F corresponds to C.

   AB and DE are called *corresponding sides*. Name two other pairs of corresponding sides.

2. Also, ∠ABC and ∠DEF are *corresponding angles*. Name two other pairs of corresponding angles.

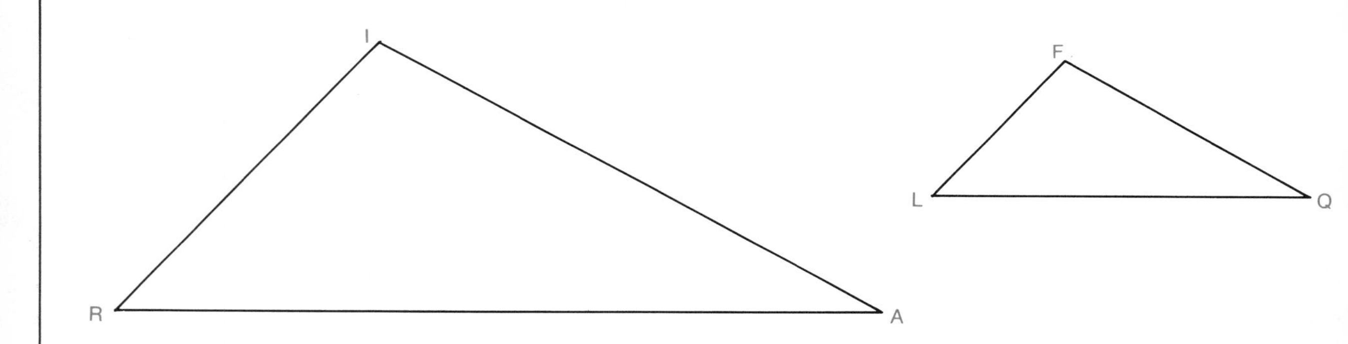

3. Consider triangles IRA and FLQ. Copy and complete the following table. Use a protractor to measure angles, and give ratios in lowest terms.

Ratio of Corresponding Sides	*Comparison of Corresponding Angles*
$\frac{IR}{FL}$ = ▤	∠RIA = ▤°, ∠LFQ = ▤°
$\frac{RA}{LQ}$ = ▤	∠IRA = ▤°, ∠FLQ = ▤°
$\frac{IA}{▤}$ = ▤	∠IAR = ▤°, ∠▤ = ▤°

B It appears that triangles having the same shape have equal corresponding angles. Also, the ratios of corresponding sides are the same.

1. In triangles PQR and KMN, corresponding pairs of angles are equal as shown. Measure the sides of each triangle and find the ratio of each pair of corresponding sides.

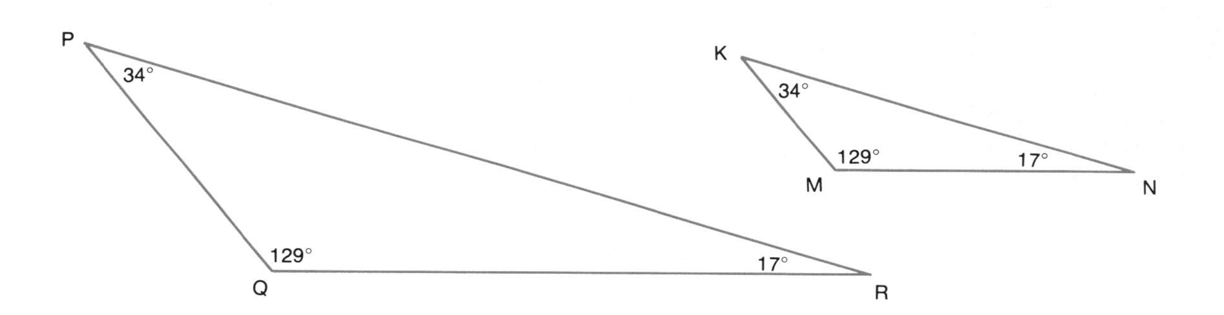

Notice that when all pairs of corresponding angles are equal, then the ratios of corresponding sides are equal and the triangles have the same shape.

2. In triangles JAN and FEB, corresponding sides are in the same ratio.

$$\frac{JA}{FE} = \frac{6}{12} = \frac{1}{2} \qquad \frac{AN}{EB} = \frac{5}{10} = \frac{1}{2} \qquad \frac{JN}{FB} = \frac{5.5}{11} = \frac{1}{2}$$

J
A
N
6 UNITS
5.5 UNITS
5 UNITS
F
E
B
12 UNITS
11 UNITS
10 UNITS

Measure the angles of each triangle. What relationship is there between corresponding angles?

Notice that when the ratios of corresponding sides are equal, then all pairs of corresponding angles are equal and the triangles have the same shape.

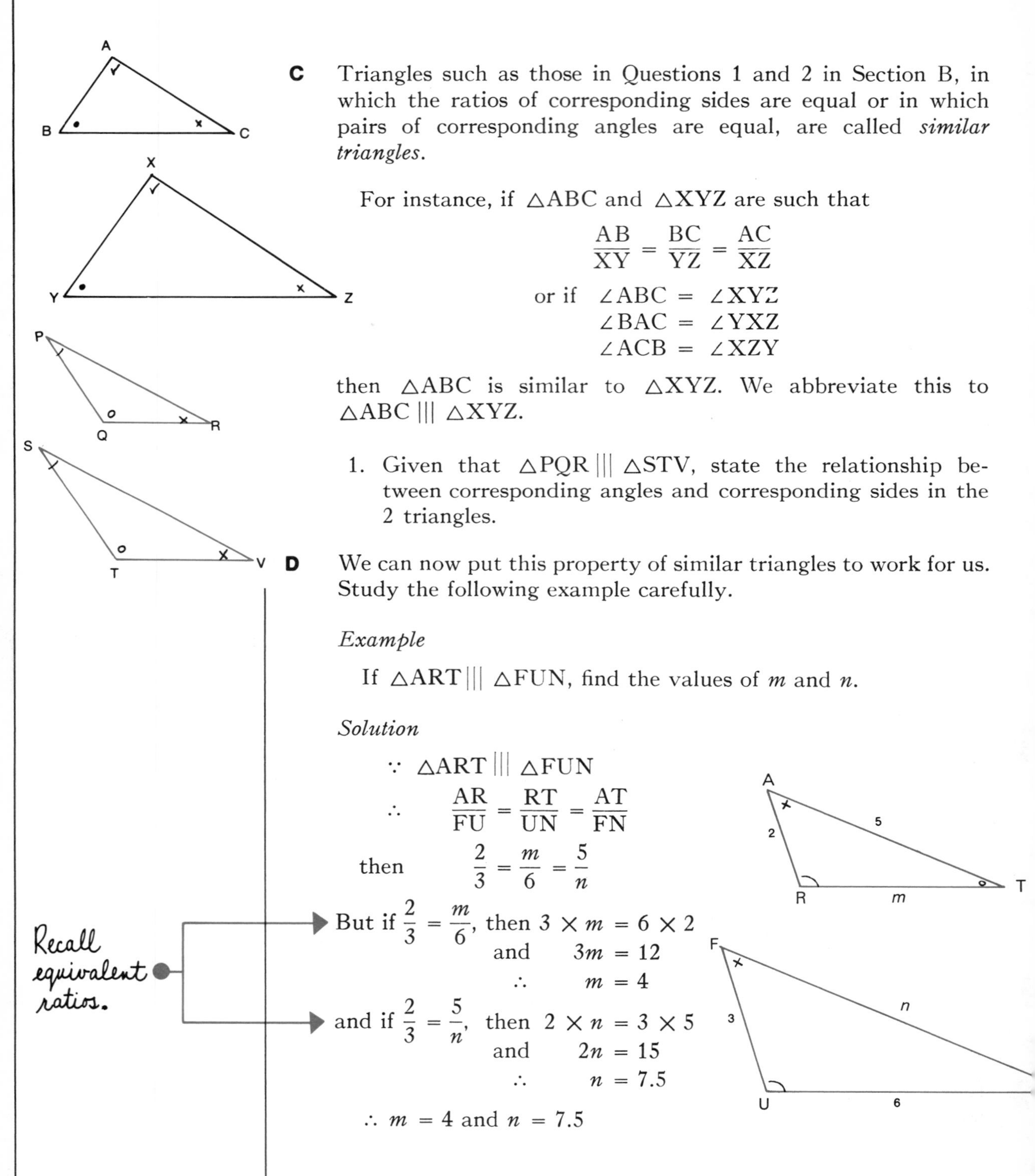

C Triangles such as those in Questions 1 and 2 in Section B, in which the ratios of corresponding sides are equal or in which pairs of corresponding angles are equal, are called *similar triangles*.

For instance, if $\triangle ABC$ and $\triangle XYZ$ are such that

$$\frac{AB}{XY} = \frac{BC}{YZ} = \frac{AC}{XZ}$$

or if

$$\angle ABC = \angle XYZ$$
$$\angle BAC = \angle YXZ$$
$$\angle ACB = \angle XZY$$

then $\triangle ABC$ is similar to $\triangle XYZ$. We abbreviate this to $\triangle ABC \,|||\, \triangle XYZ$.

1. Given that $\triangle PQR \,|||\, \triangle STV$, state the relationship between corresponding angles and corresponding sides in the 2 triangles.

D We can now put this property of similar triangles to work for us. Study the following example carefully.

Example

If $\triangle ART \,|||\, \triangle FUN$, find the values of m and n.

Solution

$\because \triangle ART \,|||\, \triangle FUN$

$\therefore \quad \frac{AR}{FU} = \frac{RT}{UN} = \frac{AT}{FN}$

then $\quad \frac{2}{3} = \frac{m}{6} = \frac{5}{n}$

But if $\frac{2}{3} = \frac{m}{6}$, then $3 \times m = 6 \times 2$
and $3m = 12$
$\therefore \quad m = 4$

and if $\frac{2}{3} = \frac{5}{n}$, then $2 \times n = 3 \times 5$
and $2n = 15$
$\therefore \quad n = 7.5$

$\therefore m = 4$ and $n = 7.5$

Exercise 24.1

Discussion

1. Name the pairs of corresponding sides and corresponding angles in the following pairs of similar triangles.

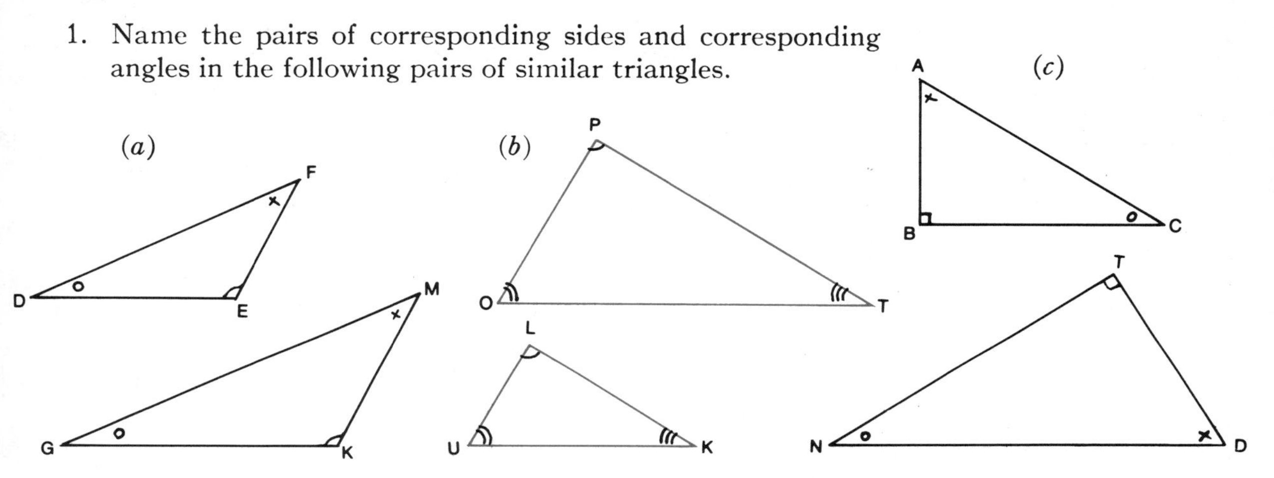

2. Discuss the following statement: *If two angles in one triangle are equal to two corresponding angles in another triangle, then the two triangles are similar.*

3. Many everyday objects are similar. Check your kitchen or garage at home to see how many examples of similarity you can find.

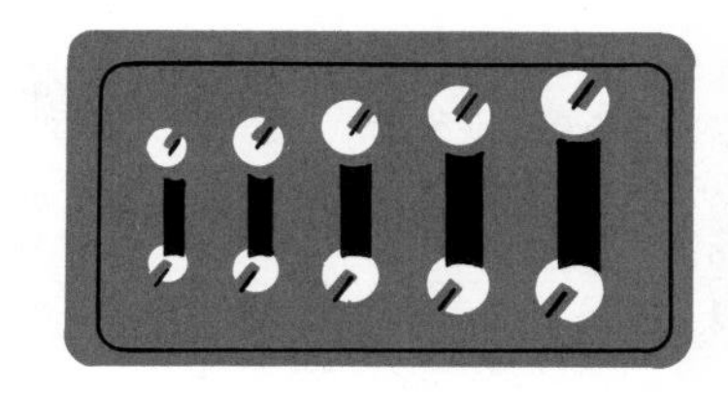

Written Solutions

4. Find x and y.

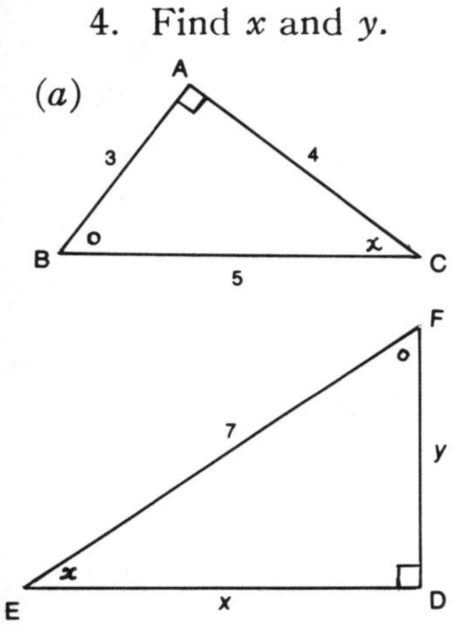

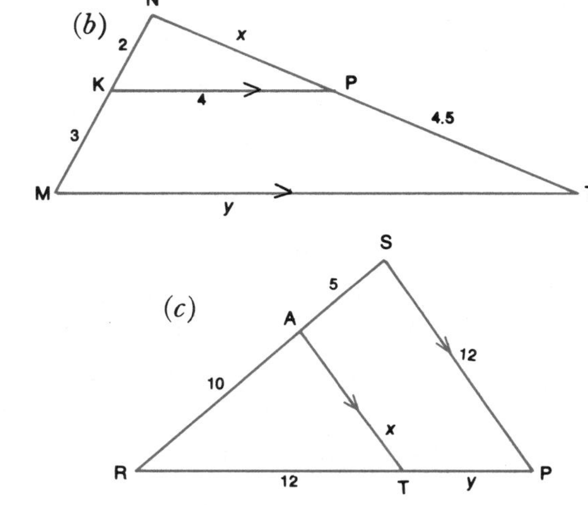

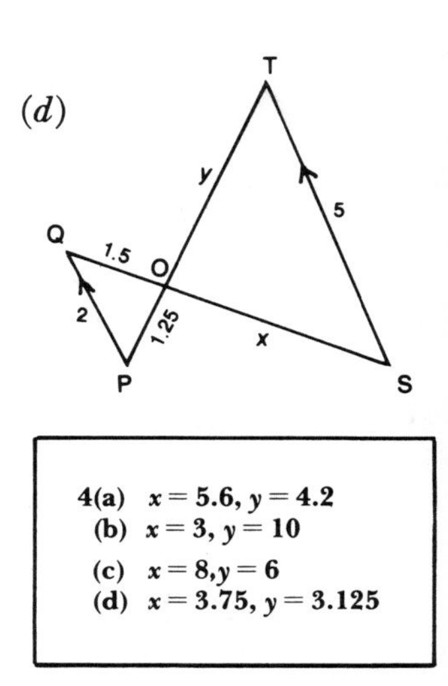

4(a) $x = 5.6$, $y = 4.2$
(b) $x = 3$, $y = 10$
(c) $x = 8$, $y = 6$
(d) $x = 3.75$, $y = 3.125$

24.2 Problems Involving Similar Triangles

Recall
1. Diagram
2. "Let" statement (units!)
3. Form equation.
4. Solve equation.
5. Final statement (units!)

The methods involved in solving problems with similar triangles are not new to you. The same basic steps are followed as for any problem.

Example

Determine the height of a tree whose shadow is 8 m long when a model 2 m tall has a shadow 1.5 m long.

Solution

Notice that the model, her shadow, and part of the sun's ray form a triangle.

Let x metres represent the height of the tree. Since the triangles are similar,

$$\therefore \quad \frac{x}{2} = \frac{8}{1.5}$$

$$\text{then } 1.5x = 8 \times 2$$

$$\text{and} \quad x = \frac{16}{1.5}$$

$$\therefore \quad x = 10.7$$

$\therefore$ The tree is 10.7 m high.

2 m

x metres

1.5 m

8 m

Exercise 24.2

Written Solutions

1. When the shadow of a building is 15 m long, a fence post 2 m high casts a shadow 3 m long. How high is the building?
2. A factory needs a sloping ramp that rises 25 cm for each metre travelled along the ramp. If the ramp will end at a platform 1.5 m above ground level, how long will the ramp be?
3. A basketball player 2.1 m tall casts a shadow 3.5 m long at the same time the shadow of a telephone pole is 10 m long. What is the height of the pole?
4. A tent is in the form of a cone with height 3 m and diameter 2.5 m. Inside the tent, how close to the edge of the tent can a 140 cm tall child stand?

1. 10 m **3. 6 m**
2. 6 m **4. 58 cm**

4.

?

3 m

2.5 m

5. A ladder placed with its foot 4 m from a vertical wall just touches the top of a 1.5 m fence that is 3 m from the wall. How high up the wall does the ladder reach?

6. The shadow of a metre-stick is 1.2 m long when a woman's shadow is 2 m long. How tall is the woman?

7. A Boy Scout lying on the ground lines up the head of a friend with the top of a nearby tree, as shown. Using the given measurements, find the height of the tree.

8. Given the problem of finding the distance between 2 trees at opposite ends of a lake, a hiker takes measurements as shown and calculates the distance between the trees. What should the answer be?

9. To find the distance across a river, a Girl Guide sets up stakes at A, B, C, and D, so that stakes D and B line up with a large tree at T on the other side of the river. Using the measurements shown, calculate the distance across the river.

10. The shadows of a flagpole and a tree are 25 m and 20 m long, respectively, at 09:00. At 14:00, the pole's shadow is 10 m long. How long is the tree's shadow at 14:00?

11. Hal O'Leg comes out of a movie eating a bag of popcorn. He then crosses the street to get some peanuts, moves down a few doors to buy some chocolate bars, and recrosses the street to have a double-rich chocolate malted milk shake to quench his thirst. Using the measurements shown in the diagram, and allowing a total of 10 m for walking within the nut shop and the candy store, determine how far Hal walked from the movie to the soda fountain.

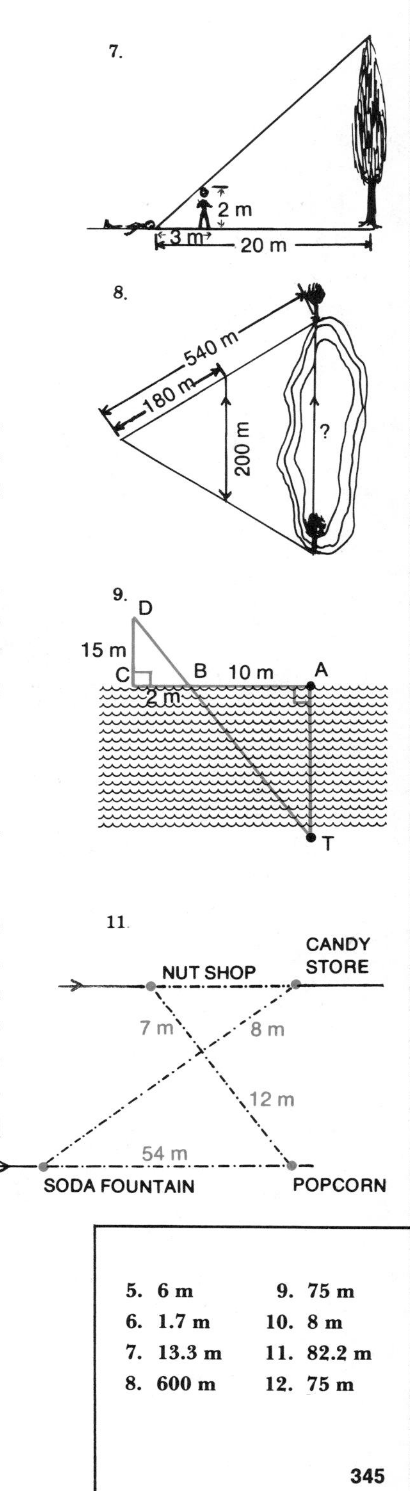

12. A spherical boulder of diameter 4 m falls into a narrow V-shaped ravine that is 20 m wide at the top, as shown. Using the given measurements, calculate the depth of the ravine.

20 m

?

15 m

5. 6 m	9. 75 m
6. 1.7 m	10. 8 m
7. 13.3 m	11. 82.2 m
8. 600 m	12. 75 m

Unit 25
Probability

"There is a 60% chance of rain."

"The odds in favor of that race horse winning on Saturday are 5 to 2."

"Today, a 15-year-old female may expect to live to be 72 years old."

Statements like these appear daily in our local newspapers or are broadcast over radio or television. What is the precise meaning of each statement? How are these numbers determined? You will find the beginning of an answer to these questions in this unit.

Unlike many mathematical topics which have been studied for centuries, most of the ideas in *probability* have been developed in the 20th Century. The applications of this field today go far beyond forecasting the likelihood of rain or the chances of winning a lottery. Did you ever win a prize in a game of chance at a fair or exhibition? The amount of the prize is calculated using probability. Have you ever picked up the telephone and found that no line is available to a certain exchange? The telephone company uses probability theory to decide on the number of trunk lines to install.

It is not important for you to have a detailed understanding of this topic now, but you should be familiar with some of the basic ideas involved.

CANADA
1975
Could I toss
10 coins at once?
Sure would
save time!
TALLY
2 //
3 ##/ /
4
5
6
7
8

25.1 Experiments with Chance Events

Most of us have called "heads" or "tails" on the toss of a coin. This is a simple chance event with which we are familiar. The experiments in this section are of a similar nature and involve cards, dice, and colored marbles in situations that may be new to you.

A Toss a coin 10 times and record the number of heads you get. Repeat the procedure 4 more times and record your results in a table.

Trial	*Number of Heads* (H)	*Number of Tosses*	$\frac{H}{10}$
1		10	
2		10	
3		10	
4		10	
5		10	

1. How many heads would you expect to get in 10 tosses?
2. What average number of heads did you obtain?
3. What fraction do you obtain if you divide the total number of heads by the total number of tosses (50)?
4. What fraction would you have expected to get?

B This next experiment involves rolling a pair of dice 60 times and tallying the times you get each of the possible sums 2, 3, . . . , 12. Note also the number of "doubles" you get.

1. How many "doubles" do you expect to get?
2. Do you think that any sum(s) will appear more frequently than the others? Which one(s)?
3. Now do the experiment and answer the following questions.
   (*a*) Which sums appeared most often?
   (*b*) Do you have any explanation for this?
   (*c*) Did you get more "doubles" than you expected?

Check your results with those obtained by other members of your class.

C Place 2 red marbles, 3 white marbles, and 5 black marbles in a container in which they can be easily mixed. Without looking in the container, draw a marble, note its color, replace it, and mix the marbles again. Do this 10 times and record the number of marbles of each color drawn.

Follow this procedure 5 times and record the results in a table like the one below.

If you don't have marbles, use buttons!

How many of each color do you expect to get in 10 draws?

Trial	RED		WHITE		BLACK	
	Number drawn	*Number drawn* ÷ 10	*Number drawn*	*Number drawn* ÷ 10	*Number drawn*	*Number drawn* ÷ 10
1						
2						
3						
4						
5						
Totals						

1. Calculate the average number of times each color was drawn per trial.
2. What decimal fractions do you form when you divide your answers for Question 1 by 10?
3. What fraction of the marbles in the container were red? White? Black?
4. Compare the fractions formed in Questions 2 and 3.

Average no. of reds $= \frac{\text{Total reds}}{5}$

Summary

Let's review the results of the 3 experiments. In tossing a fair coin, we would expect that a head would occur as often as a tail and, therefore, the chance or *probability* of obtaining a head is 1 in 2.

In rolling a pair of dice, the outcomes are not equally likely, as certain sums appear more often than others.

In drawing marbles from a container you had a reasonable chance to guess how often you would draw each type of marble. Frequently your *intuition* helps you determine the probability of the occurrence of such an event.

Would this
'spinner'
change your
answer to
Question 2?

Exercise 25.1

Discussion

1. A die has the numbers 1 to 6 on its faces. If you tossed the die 6 times, how many times would you expect to get an even number? An odd number?

2. 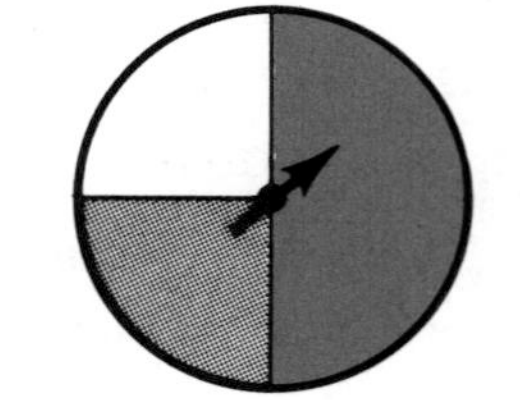
When you spin the pointer, it will come to rest pointing to a colored, grey, or white region. What are the chances of its pointing to colored? To grey? To white? Why?

3. On a true–false test of 20 questions, how many should you be able to get correct by pure guessing? What is the likelihood of getting any one question correct?

4. In a multiple-choice test, there are 5 answers possible for each of 10 questions. By guessing, how many could you expect to answer correctly? What are your chances of being correct on any one question?

5. A deck of 52 playing cards has 13 black clubs, 13 red diamonds, 13 red hearts, and 13 black spades. What are your chances of drawing
   (*a*) a black card?
   (*b*) a diamond?
   (*c*) an ace of any suit?
   (*d*) the Queen of hearts?
   (*e*) a 2 or 3 of any suit?
   (*f*) a spade lower than the 10 of spades?

6. In tossing a coin we have allowed for 2 outcomes — heads or tails. Is there a third possibility?

7. In repeated tosses of a coin, what are the chances of getting a head on each toss? Is this true after you have already tossed 3 heads in a row?

8. In 100 tosses of a coin, how many heads would you expect to get? In practice, would this actually happen? As you increase the number of tosses, what happens to the fraction

$$\frac{\text{Number of heads}}{\text{Number of tosses}}?$$

25.2 Finding Probabilities

The experiments of Section 25.1 led us to a rough idea of the likelihood of certain events. Intuitively, it is often possible to make statements of probability as you did in Exercise 25.1. In this section, we want to study in greater detail the method of finding the probability of events.

When we say that there is 1 chance in 2 of getting a "head" when we flip a coin, we also mean that

the probability of a head is $\frac{1}{2}$

In short,

$$P(\text{head}) = \tfrac{1}{2}$$

A What probability should we assign to an impossible event, such as rolling a sum of 13 with a pair of dice?

1. How many times will an impossible event occur in 10 trials? 100 trials? 1000 trials? What is the probability of such an event?

What probability should we assign to an event that is certain to occur, like drawing a red marble from a jar containing only red marbles?

2. If an event is certain to happen, how many times will it occur in 10 trials? 100 trials? 1000 trials? What is the probability of an event that is certain to happen?

Summary

$$P(\text{impossible event}) = 0$$
$$P(\text{certain event}) = 1$$

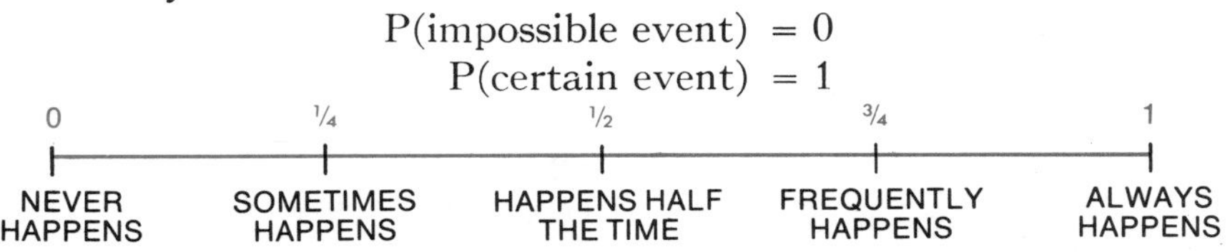

B When you roll a fair die the chances of any one number turning face up are the same. That is, the outcomes of the throw are *equally likely*.

1. List the 6 possible outcomes from rolling a die.
2. How many of these numbers are even?
3. State the probability of obtaining an even number.

$P(red) = \frac{3}{10} = 0.3$

C A jar contains 3 red marbles, 4 blue marbles, 2 yellow marbles, and 1 green marble.

1. Find
   (*a*) P(drawing a red marble)
   (*b*) P(drawing a blue marble)
   (*c*) P(drawing a yellow marble)
   (*d*) P(drawing a green marble)

2. What is the sum of the probabilities obtained in Question 1?

3. What is the probability of drawing *either* a yellow *or* a green marble?

4. State the probability of getting a marble that is not red.

D *Example 1*

One letter is selected from the letters of the word NANAIMO.
(*a*) List the possible outcomes of this experiment.
(*b*) Find the probability of choosing each letter.

Solution

(*a*) The possible outcomes are N, A, I, M, O.
(*b*) ∵ There are 7 equally likely ways of choosing a letter and 2 of these result in the choice of an N

$\therefore \quad P(N) = \frac{2}{7}$

Similarly, $P(A) = \frac{2}{7}$

∵ The letters I, M, and O occur only once,

$P(I) = \frac{1}{7},\ P(M) = \frac{1}{7},\ P(O) = \frac{1}{7}$

Note that $P(N) + P(A) + P(I) + P(M) + P(O)$

$= \frac{2}{7} + \frac{2}{7} + \frac{1}{7} + \frac{1}{7} + \frac{1}{7}$

$= \frac{7}{7}$

$= 1$

Example 2

Two-thirds of a class of 36 students are boys. What is the probability of choosing a girl when one student is chosen *at random*?

Each student has the same chance of being chosen.

Solution

$\because \frac{2}{3}$ of the class are boys, there are $\frac{2}{3} \times 36$ or 24 boys.

$\therefore$ There are $36 - 24 = 12$ girls.

A girl may be chosen in 12 equally likely ways from the 36 possible choices.

$$\therefore \text{P(girl)} = \frac{12}{36} = \frac{1}{3}$$

Exercise 25.2

Discussion

1. Ian Flayshun's piggy bank contains nickels, dimes, and quarters. One coin is drawn at random.
   (*a*) List the possible outcomes.
   (*b*) If there are 7 quarters, 5 dimes, and 3 nickels, state the probability of drawing each type of coin.

2. Betty Bridge holds a hand of 13 playing cards containing 4 spades, 4 clubs, 3 hearts, and 2 diamonds. She draws one card at random from her hand.
   (*a*) List the possible outcomes.
   (*b*) State the probability of drawing a club.
   (*c*) State the probability of drawing a red card.
   (*d*) State the probability of choosing a spade *or* a diamond.

3. From a jar containing black and white marbles only, what is the probability of drawing a red marble? What would have to be true for the probability of drawing a black marble to be equal to that of drawing a white marble?

4. Peter Probable chooses one letter at random from the letters of SASKATOON.
   (*a*) What is the probability that the letter is a vowel? A consonant?
   (*b*) What is the probability that the letter is between B and M in the alphabet? After N?

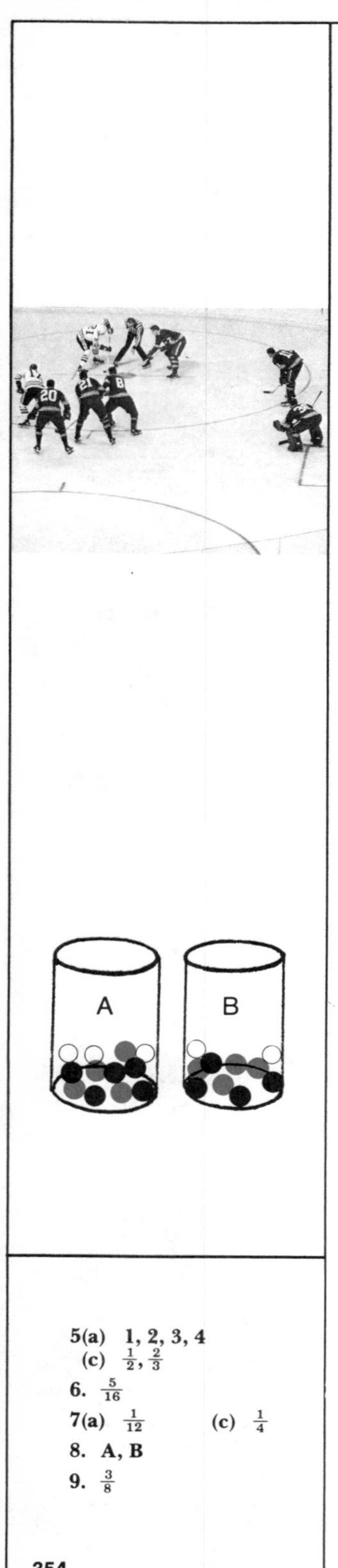

Written Solutions

5. The faces on a die are numbered 1, 1, 2, 3, 4, 4.
   (*a*) List the possible outcomes when the die is thrown.
   (*b*) Find the probability of throwing a 1, a 2.
   (*c*) Find the probability of throwing an even number, a perfect square.

6. The hockey record of the Vancouver Canucks in games with the Toronto Maple Leafs is 8 wins, 5 losses, and 3 ties. Judging strictly by their past performance, what is the probability of a Toronto win?

7. A class of Grade 9 students has the following age and sex distribution.

	Age			
	12	13	14	15
Male	0	3	10	6
Female	0	5	9	3

   In choosing one student at random, find the probability of choosing
   (*a*) a 13-year-old boy,
   (*b*) a 14-year-old girl,
   (*c*) a 15-year-old boy or girl,
   (*d*) a 12-year-old boy or girl.

8. Jar A contains 5 black marbles, 3 white marbles, and 4 colored marbles. Jar B contains 4 black marbles, 2 white marbles, and 4 colored marbles. If you are to draw one marble at random from one of the jars, from which jar are you more likely to draw a black marble? A colored marble?

9. An automotive repair shop collects the following information concerning the time at which a brake job was necessary on a certain type of car.

Distance covered (km)	0–30 000	30 000 –45 000	45 000 –60 000	60 000 –75 000	75 000 –100 000
Number of cars repaired	3	10	12	8	7

   Using this data, state the probability of a car with this type of brakes covering at least 60 000 km before requiring repair.

5(a) 1, 2, 3, 4
(c) $\frac{1}{2}, \frac{2}{3}$
6. $\frac{5}{16}$
7(a) $\frac{1}{12}$ **(c)** $\frac{1}{4}$
8. A, B
9. $\frac{3}{8}$

25.3 Compound Experiments

A Since you normally throw a *pair* of dice in a game, listing the possible outcomes may be rather complicated. Throwing 2 dice is an example of a *compound experiment*, in which more than one simple experiment is involved. To assist you in listing the outcomes, you may use *tree diagrams*.

Example 1

Use a tree diagram to list the possible combinations of girls and/or boys in a family of 2 children. Find the probability of there being 1 boy and 1 girl.

Solution

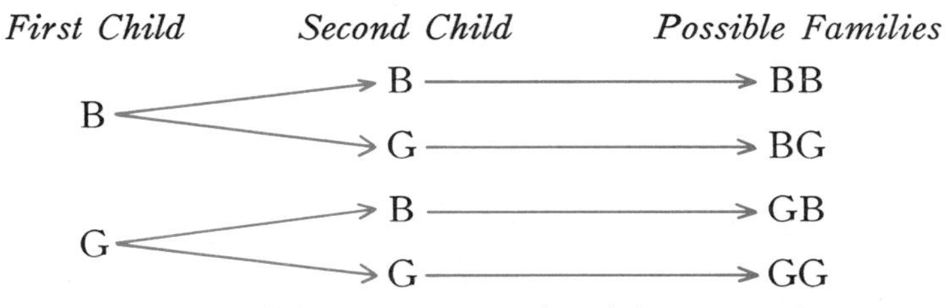

Follow the "branches" to form the outcomes.
CANADA
1975

There are 4 possible outcomes, of which 2 contain 1 boy and 1 girl. $\therefore$ P(1 boy and 1 girl) $= \frac{2}{4}$

$= \frac{1}{2}$

Example 2

In flipping 3 coins, what is the probability of getting exactly 2 heads?

Solution

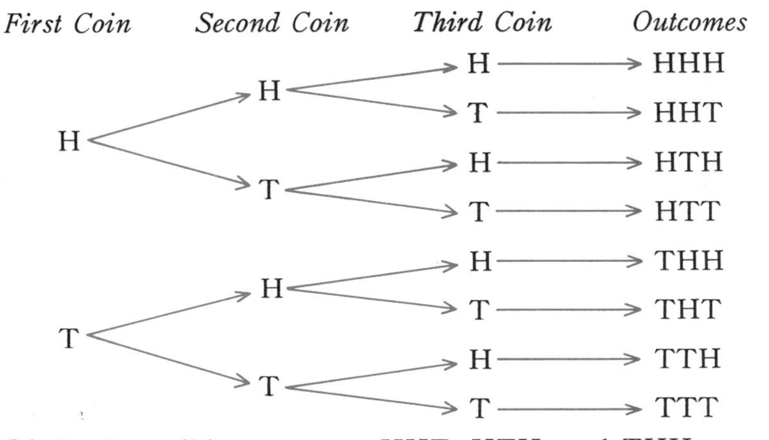

Of the 8 possible outcomes, HHT, HTH, and THH contain exactly 2 heads. $\therefore$ P(exactly 2 heads) $= \frac{3}{8}$

B Here is the beginning of a tree diagram illustrating the set of outcomes for throwing 2 dice.

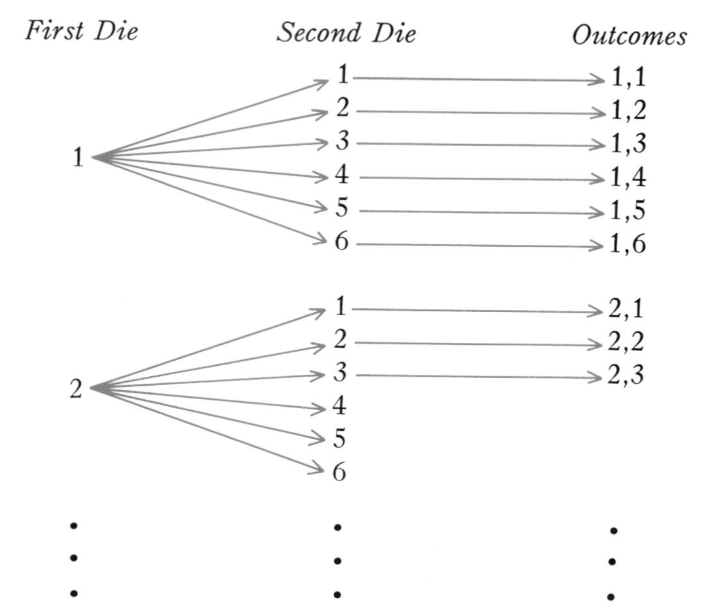

1. Copy this tree diagram (or use a chart) and complete it in your notebook. Use it to find the probability of getting a sum of 3, of 7, of 10 on the 2 dice.

2. Compare your answers to the results you found in throwing 2 dice 60 times in Section 25.1.

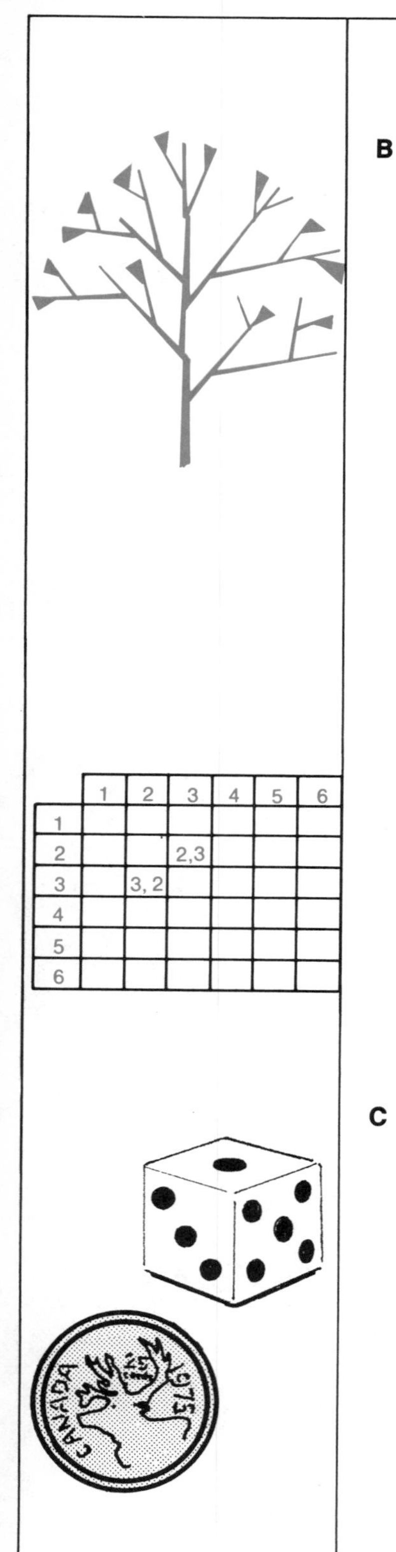

C Tree diagrams can be used in a wide variety of situations.

1. Laura, Steve, Jeff, Karen, and Tim want to pick 1 girl and 1 boy to represent their group. Use a tree diagram to list all the possible pairs.

2. A compound experiment requires you to roll a die and flip a coin. List the outcomes using a tree diagram.

3. There are 3 possible conclusions for a football game — a win (W), a tie (T), or a loss (L). For a 3-game series, find the possible outcomes for a given team using a tree diagram.

4. Black, white, and red chips are in a container. Three chips are drawn, one at a time, with each chip drawn being replaced before the next is drawn. Construct a tree diagram that gives the 27 possible outcomes.

Exercise 25.3

Discussion

1. Using the following tree diagrams, state the possible outcomes.

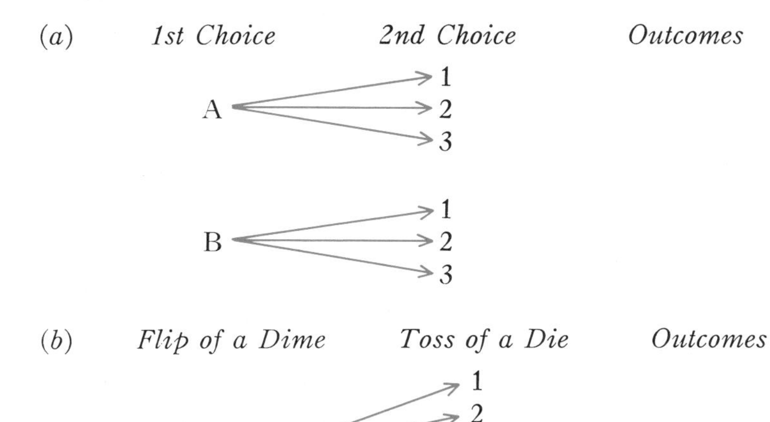

(*b*) *Flip of a Dime* *Toss of a Die* *Outcomes*

H → 1, 2, 3, 4, 5, 6

T → 1, 2, 3, 4, 5, 6

2. In a compound experiment, the first stage has 2 possibilities and the second stage has 3. How many outcomes are there for the complete experiment?

3. A 3-child family represents a 3-stage situation with 2 possible outcomes at each stage. How many different outcomes are possible?

4. How many outcomes are possible when you throw 2 dice? How many of these produce "doubles"? State the probability of throwing doubles.

5. If you rolled 3 dice, how would you determine the number of outcomes without actually constructing a tree diagram?

Written Solutions

6. Orville Outcome flips a nickel, a dime, and a quarter. He gets heads on each flip. Use a tree diagram to determine the probability of this outcome.

7. For the experiment in which a coin is flipped and a die is tossed, find the probability of an even number with a head.

8. Rebecca Random has her house key, her car key, and an office key loose in her purse. She removes 2 keys. By means of a tree diagram, find the probability that Rebecca selected the house and car keys.

9. Using a tree diagram, find the most likely combination of boys and girls in a family of 4 children.

10. Using your tree diagram for the 36 outcomes of throwing 2 dice, find the probability of obtaining a sum
    (*a*) of 7, of 11.
    (*b*) greater than 9.
    (*c*) less than 6.

11. A committee of 1 Cub, 1 Scout, and 1 Rover is to be selected from a Cub pack of 20 Cubs, a Scout troop of 10 Scouts, and a group of 5 Rovers. Without actually drawing the tree diagram, calculate the number of possible committees.

12. On a multiple-choice test of 3 questions, each having 5 possible answers, how many different sets of answers may be given? State the probability of a student's guessing and getting all correct.

6. $\frac{1}{8}$
7. $\frac{1}{4}$
8. $\frac{1}{3}$
9. **2 girls and 2 boys**
10(a) $\frac{1}{6}, \frac{1}{18}$
(c) $\frac{5}{18}$
11. **1000**
12. **125,** $\frac{1}{125}$

25.4 Odds

At the time of a championship boxing match, the playing of the Grey Cup, or the Stanley Cup finals, you hear phrases like,

"The odds in the Lions' favor are 5 to 2."
"The odds are heavily weighted against the Canadiens."

You can understand these phrases with only a basic grasp of probability.

To find the *odds in favor* of an event, you divide the probability that the event will occur by the probability that it will *not* occur. In short,

$$\text{odds in favor of E} = \frac{P(E)}{P(\textit{not } E)}$$

Example 1

Find the odds in favor of choosing an ace when drawing a single card from a deck of 52 playing cards.

Solution

There are 4 aces in a deck of 52 cards.

∴ An ace may be drawn in 4 of the 52 different cards possible.

$$\therefore \quad P(\text{ace}) = \tfrac{4}{52}$$
$$= \tfrac{1}{13}$$
$$\therefore \quad P(\textit{not}\ \text{ace}) = \tfrac{12}{13}$$

P(ace) + P(*not* ace) = 1

∴ Odds in favor of drawing an ace are

$$\frac{\frac{1}{13}}{\frac{12}{13}} = \frac{1}{\cancel{13}} \times \frac{\cancel{13}}{12}$$
$$= \frac{1}{12}$$

Example 2

The odds in favor of a "long shot" in a horse race are 1 to 40. What is the probability of a win for this horse?

∵ The 2 outcomes are a win and a loss,

∴ P(W) + P(L) = 1

∴ P(L) = 1 − P(W)

Recall equivalent ratios

Solution

Let the probability of a win be x.

∴ The probability of a loss is $1 - x$.

But the odds in favor of a win are $\frac{1}{40}$

and the odds in favor of a win are $\frac{x}{1 - x}$

$$\therefore \quad \frac{x}{1-x} = \frac{1}{40}$$

$$\text{then} \quad 40x = 1(1 - x)$$

$$\text{or} \quad 40x = 1 - x$$

$$\text{then} \quad 41x = 1$$

$$\therefore \quad x = \frac{1}{41}$$

∴ The probability of a win is $\frac{1}{41}$.

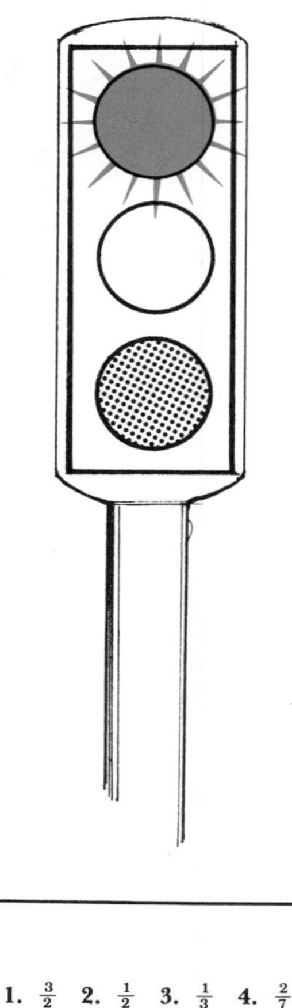

Exercise 25.4

Written Solutions

1. If the probability of Hank's Hammers defeating Joe's Jousters is 0.6, find the odds in favor of the Hammers.

2. Doris Designer knows from experience that on 1 out of every 3 trips home from work she meets a red light at the corner of Ottawa and King Streets. What are the odds in favor of her meeting a red light?

3. A meteorologist reports that there is a 75% chance of rain over the next 24 h. What are the odds in favor of *no* rain?

4. The odds favoring a win for the Calgary Stampeders are quoted as 2 to 5. Find their probability of winning.

5. For a "long shot," the odds at a race track are usually quoted as being *against* the horse. A 50-to-1 "long shot" means the odds against a win are $\frac{50}{1}$.
   (*a*) What are the odds in favor of a win?
   (*b*) Find the probability of a loss.

1. $\frac{3}{2}$ **2.** $\frac{1}{2}$ **3.** $\frac{1}{3}$ **4.** $\frac{2}{7}$
5(a) **1 to 50**

Now try a mixture of probability problems!

6. There are 6 white discs, 4 colored discs, and 5 black discs in a container. Find the probability that a black disc is *not* drawn.

7. For drawing 1 card at random from a deck of 52 cards, find the probability of getting a King or an ace.

8. For throwing 2 dice, find the probability that the 2 numbers differ by exactly 4.

9. At the track, the odds in favor of Daddy Longlegs are 3 to 5 and those in favor of Tillie Trotter are 1 to 4. Which horse is favored to win?

10. Is the probability of selecting a vowel from the letters of the word MANITOBA greater than that of choosing a consonant from the letters of SASKATCHEWAN?

11. "For a group of 30 people, the probability that at least 2 of them will have the same birthday is better than 0.7."

    Do you believe this statement? Survey the members of your math class to determine whether the statement is realistic.

6. $\frac{2}{3}$ **7.** $\frac{2}{13}$ **8.** $\frac{1}{9}$

Maintaining Basic Skills

Exercise 6

1. Add the following terms.

   (*a*) $0.031 + 0.005 + 1.326$
   (*b*) $0.75 + 0.875 + 0.5$
   (*c*) $1\frac{3}{10} + 2\frac{4}{5}$
   (*d*) $-3\frac{1}{5} + 2\frac{3}{7}$
   (*e*) $3xy + 2x + (-4xy) + 7x$
   (*f*) $\frac{2}{3} + \frac{5}{6} + 1\frac{4}{5}$

2. Find the difference.

   (*a*) $2 - (-4)$
   (*b*) $0.035 - 0.020$
   (*c*) $(\frac{55}{-11}) - (\frac{-24}{6})$
   (*d*) $2\frac{7}{12} - 1\frac{3}{8}$
   (*e*) $(\frac{-5}{7}) - 1\frac{2}{3}$
   (*f*) $4xy - xy$

3. Find the products.

   (*a*) 36.8×1.075
   (*b*) $(-15)(-43)$
   (*c*) $\frac{2}{3} \times (-\frac{6}{7})$
   (*d*) $1\frac{5}{16} \times \frac{4}{7}$
   (*e*) $(3x^2)(x^5)$
   (*f*) $(-2a^4)(-5a^2)$
   (*g*) $(5a^2)(4b^3)$
   (*h*) $(-3.2)(0.875)(-1.5)$

4. Find the quotients.

   (*a*) $14.68 \div 8.32$
   (*b*) $-16 \div (-4)$
   (*c*) $5\frac{3}{4} \div 9\frac{1}{5}$
   (*d*) $15b^4 \div (-3b)$
   (*e*) $-24xy \div 16x$
   (*f*) $1.035 \div 0.005$

5. Find the value.

   (*a*) $\sqrt{121}$ (*b*) $\sqrt{324}$ (*c*) $\sqrt{20}$ (*d*) $\sqrt{75.6}$

6. Write in standard notation.

   (*a*) 155 (*b*) 14.2 (*c*) 0.364 (*d*) 0.005 10

7. Simplify.

   (*a*) $(3.8 \times 10^2) \times (5.7 \times 10^5)$
   (*b*) $(4.1 \times 10^{-3}) \times (8.7 \times 10^2)$
   (*c*) $(6.8 \times 10^{-1}) \times (4.7 \times 10^{-4})$
   (*d*) $(3.2 \times 10^5) \div (1.8 \times 10^2)$
   (*e*) $(5.8 \times 10^{-1}) \div (4.1 \times 10^{-2})$

8. Convert to decimal form.

   (*a*) $\frac{3}{8}$ (*b*) $\frac{2}{3}$ (*c*) $\frac{7}{16}$ (*d*) $\frac{3}{40}$ (*e*) 75% (*f*) 2.5% (*g*) 250% (*h*) 62.5% (*i*) 8.75% (*j*) 0.1%

9. Convert to fraction form.

   (*a*) 20% (*b*) 68% (*c*) 5.5% (*d*) 4.75% (*e*) 0.625 (*f*) 0.95 (*g*) 0.0375 (*h*) 0.005

1(a) 1.362 **(b)** 2.125 **(d)** $-\frac{27}{35}$ **(f)** $3\frac{3}{10}$
2(a) 6 **(b)** 0.015 **(c)** -1 **(d)** $1\frac{5}{24}$
3(a) 39.56 **(b)** 645 **(c)** $-\frac{4}{7}$ **(d)** $\frac{3}{4}$ **(e)** $3x^7$ **(f)** $10a^6$ **(g)** $20a^2b^3$ **(h)** 4.2
4(a) 1.76 **(c)** $\frac{5}{8}$ **(e)** $-\frac{3}{2}y$ **(f)** 207
5(c) 4.47 **(d)** 8.69
6(a) 1.55×10^2 **(d)** 5.10×10^{-3}
7(a) 2.166×10^8 **(b)** 3.567×10^0 **(c)** 3.196×10^{-4} **(d)** 1.7×10^3 **(e)** 1.41×10^1
8(a) 0.375 **(b)** 0.6 **(c)** 0.4375 **(d)** 0.075 **(e)** 0.75 **(g)** 2.5 **(h)** 0.625
9(a) $\frac{1}{5}$ **(b)** $\frac{17}{25}$ **(d)** $\frac{19}{400}$ **(e)** $\frac{5}{8}$ **(f)** $\frac{19}{20}$ **(h)** $\frac{1}{200}$

10. Convert to a percent.

(*a*) $\frac{2}{5}$ (*b*) $\frac{3}{8}$ (*c*) 0.875 (*d*) 0.075 (*e*) 1.25 (*f*) 2.4 (*g*) 0.005 (*h*) $\frac{1}{500}$

11. Expand.

(*a*) $3(x + y)$ (*b*) $-5(a - b)$ (*c*) $2(x + 3y)$ (*d*) $x(x - 3)$ (*e*) $(x + 2)(x + 3)$ (*f*) $(a - 5)(a - 7)$ (*g*) $(c + 9)(c - 4)$ (*h*) $(t - 6)(t + 2)$ (*i*) $(s + 6)(s - 3)$

12. Expand.

(*a*) $(2t + 1)(3t + 1)$ (*b*) $(4x - 3)(2x - 1)$ (*c*) $(4x + 5)(4x - 5)$ (*d*) $(3b - 2)(3b + 2)$ (*e*) $(a - b)^2$ (*f*) $(5p - 3q)^2$

13. Factor.

(*a*) $2a + 2b$ (*b*) $3x + 6y$ (*c*) $3r - 3s$ (*d*) $5c - 15d$ (*e*) $x^2 + 5x$ (*f*) $y^2 - 3y$

14. Factor.

(*a*) $a^2 + 3a + 2$ (*b*) $y^2 - 5y + 6$ (*c*) $r^2 - 7r + 10$ (*d*) $a^2 + 2a - 15$ (*e*) $t^2 - t - 12$ (*f*) $x^2 + 10x + 25$ (*g*) $y^2 - 9$ (*h*) $25p^2 - 16$

15. Find the value of the expressions.

(*a*) $x^2,\ x = 5$ (*b*) $-2x^3,\ x = -3$ (*c*) $a - b,\ a = 4, b = -1$ (*d*) $r^2 - 5r,\ r = -3$ (*e*) $p^2 - q^2,\ p = -2, q = 3$ (*f*) $\frac{x}{5} - \frac{y}{3},\ x = 10, y = -6$ (*g*) $(x + 5)(x - 2),\ x = -2$ (*h*) $6r - 3s,\ r = -1, s = 4$

16. Graph the following sets of ordered pairs.

(*a*) $\{(-3, -1), (0, 0), (3, 1), (6, 2)\}$

(*b*) $\{(-1, 6), (0, 5), (3, 2), (5, 0)\}$

(*c*) $\{(-3, 9), (-2, 4), (-1, 1), (0, 0), (1, 1), (2, 4), (3, 9)\}$

17. Find ordered pairs and graph the following equations.

(*a*) $y = x + 2$ (*b*) $y = 3x - 4$ (*c*) $y = x^2$ (*d*) $y = 2x$ (*e*) $3x + y = 1$ (*f*) $x + 3y = 4$

18. Solve the following equations.

(*a*) $3x + 5 = x - 7$ (*b*) $4 + 5y = 17 - 8y$ (*c*) $2(a - 3) = 5a + 4$ (*d*) $0.5r + 6 = r - 0.75$ (*e*) $\frac{1}{5}(x + 1) = \frac{1}{6}(2x - 3)$ (*f*) $0.5n - 1.6 = 2.8 - 1.3n$

10(a) 40% **(b)** 37.5% **(c)** 87.5% **(g)** 0.5%
11(a) $3x + 3y$ **(e)** $x^2 + 5x + 6$ **(f)** $a^2 - 12a + 35$
12(a) $6t^2 + 5t + 1$ **(c)** $16x^2 - 25$ **(e)** $a^2 - 2ab + b^2$
14(a) $(a + 2)(a + 1)$ **(e)** $(t - 4)(t + 3)$
15(a) 25 **(c)** 5 **(g)** −12 **(h)** −18
18(a) $x = -6$ **(c)** $a = -\frac{10}{3}$ **(e)** $x = \frac{21}{4}$

Summary of Units 19 to 25

	Do you understand...?	Can you...?
Unit 19 **Perimeter and Area of Plane Figures**		
19.1 Perimeter and Linear Measure	perimeter plane figure linear units semicircle circumference arc slant height of a cone rectangular solid	find the perimeter of a plane figure by substituting values in the formula
19.2 Areas and Square Measure	cylinder, sphere surface area square pyramid lateral surface area	determine the surface area of a figure or object using the proper formula
Unit 20 **Volume of Solid Figures**		
20.1 Volume	volume, capacity	determine the volume of a 3-dimensional object using the proper formula
20.2 Measurement Problems		solve problems involving perimeter, area, and volume
Unit 21 **Graphs, Part 1**		
21.1 Ordered Pairs and Their Graphs	table of values ordered pairs horizontal axis, vertical axis origin	construct a table of values from a formula graph the ordered pairs represented by the table of values
21.2 Solving Problems by Graphs	steepness of a graph	"read" a graph; that is, obtain information from the graph of an equation

	Do you understand . . . ?	*Can you . . . ?*
Unit 22 **Graphs, Part 2**		
22.1 Graphing Points in a Plane	coordinates of a point quadrant	graph points in a plane in each of the 4 quadrants
22.2 Graphs of Linear Equations	linear equation	set up a table of values and graph a linear equation
22.3 Graphs of Non-Linear Equations	non-linear equation	set up a table of values and graph a non-linear equation
Unit 23 **Basic Geometric Constructions**		
Common Geometric Terms	point, line segment, ray, line, plane, angle, collinear points polygon, triangle, quadrilateral, pentagon, hexagon, octagon, decagon, square, rectangle, parallelogram	
23.1 The Six Basic Ruler-and-Compasses Constructions	bisector right bisector perpendicular parallel	draw the right bisector of a line segment bisect an angle draw a perpendicular to a line at a point in the line and from a point outside the line draw a line parallel to a line construct an angle equal to a given angle
23.2 Parallel Lines	parallel lines transversal corresponding, alternate, and interior angles	use the "F", "Z", and "C" rules
23.3 Special Angle Constructions		using ruler and compasses, construct angles related to 90° and 60°

	Do you understand...?	*Can you...?*
23.4 Construction of Triangles	scalene, isosceles, and equilateral triangles acute-, obtuse-, and right-angled triangles	accurately construct a triangle, given its measurements
Unit 24 **Similar Triangles**		
24.1 Basic Properties of Similar Triangles	similar triangles corresponding sides and angles	given a ratio of corresponding sides in a pair of similar triangles, calculate the length of unknown sides
24.2 Problems Involving Similar Triangles		solve problems involving similar triangles
Unit 25 **Probability**		
25.1 Experiments with Chance Events	chance probability	determine, by experiment, the probability of an event
25.2 Finding Probabilities	probability of an event impossible event certain event equally likely events choosing at random	list the outcomes of an experiment select the outcomes satisfying a given condition calculate the probability of an event
25.3 Compound Experiments	tree diagrams	construct a tree diagram to list the outcomes of an experiment
25.4 Odds	odds in favor of an event	find the odds in favor of an event, given the probability find the probability of an event, given the odds in favor

Review Exercise, Units 19 to 25

Use $\pi = \frac{22}{7}$ *unless otherwise noted.*

1. Determine the perimeter of the following figures.

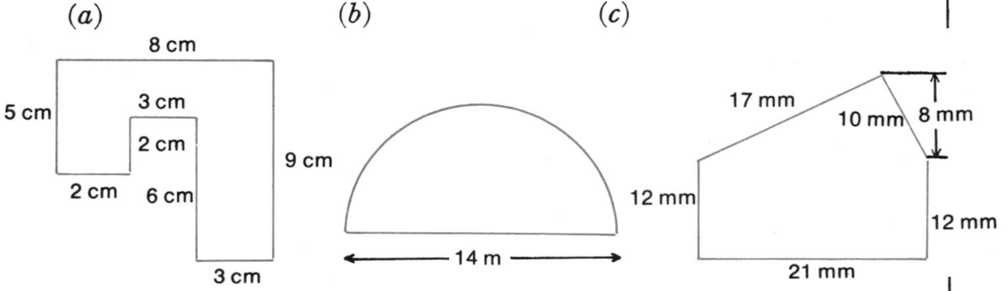

2. Calculate the area of each figure in Question 1.

3. Find the length of strapping required to support the heating pipe shown.

4. The distance travelled by an object is given by the formula $d = ut + \frac{1}{2}at^2$. Find the distance travelled when $u = 40$, $t = 2$, and $a = 32$.

5. A record 35 cm in diameter is pulled halfway out of its jacket. Calculate the total surface covered when it is laid on a counter top.

6. Determine the area of a football playing field measuring 100 m by 55 m.

7. Determine the area of the largest triangle that can be cut from a 1.2 m by 2.4 m sheet of plywood.

8. A book measuring 20 cm by 24 cm by 2.5 cm thick lies flat on a desk. Calculate the surface area of contact between the book and the desk.

9. A hat is to be made by cutting a circular piece of material 42 cm in diameter into 4 equal parts, and then sewing them together in a particular way. Calculate the area of one of the equal parts.

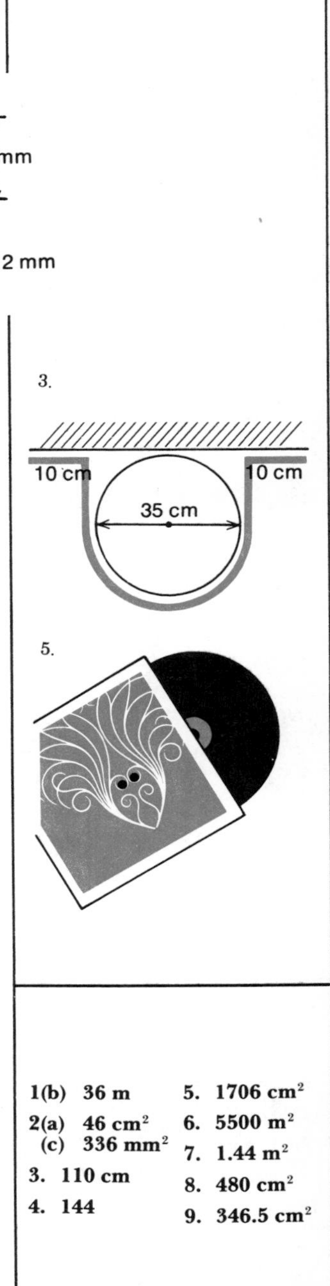

1(b) 36 m
2(a) 46 cm²
(c) 336 mm²
3. 110 cm
4. 144
5. 1706 cm²
6. 5500 m²
7. 1.44 m²
8. 480 cm²
9. 346.5 cm²

See page 290 for formulas.

10. M.A.D. Hatter, a milliner, has made a "pillbox" hat 21 cm in diameter and 12 cm high. Determine the total exposed surface area of the hat as it sits on a customer's head.

11. Calculate the surface area of a beach ball with radius 35 cm.

12. The roof of a small cottage is in the shape of a square pyramid whose base measures 4 m by 4 m and whose slant height is 2 m. Find the number of square metres of shingles required to cover the roof.

13. The nose cone of an experimental rocket is 21 cm in diameter and has a slant height of 75 cm. Calculate the surface area of the nose cone exposed to air friction during the rocket's flight.

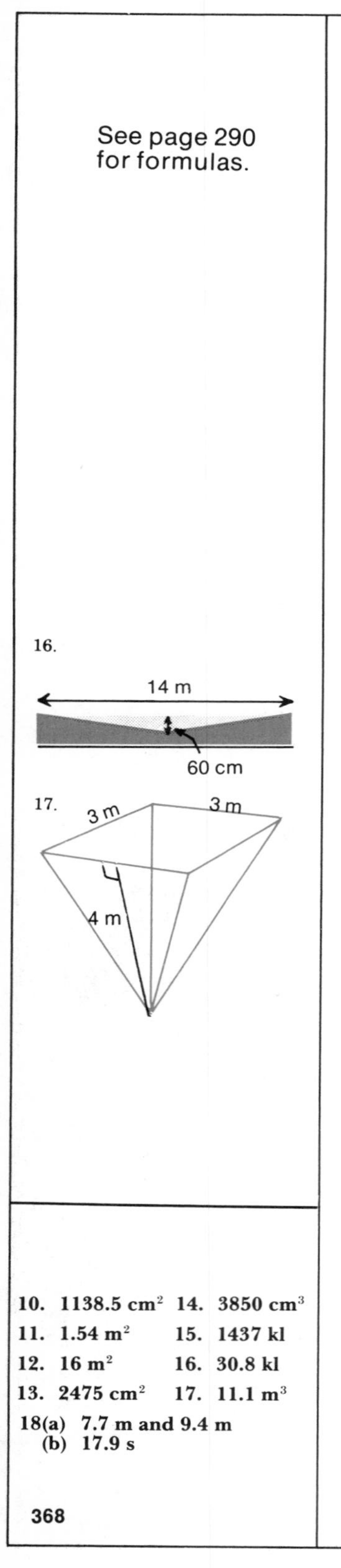

14. Determine the volume of a tin can 14 cm in diameter and 25 cm high.

15. How much air is required to fill a spherical weather balloon whose radius is 7 m?

16. A park wading pool is in the shape of a shallow cone 14 m in diameter and 60 cm deep at the center. Find the volume of water in the pool when it is full.

17. Calculate the volume of a hopper in the shape of an inverted pyramid, if the base is 3 m square and the slant height is 4 m.

18. An elevator starts at ground level and rises 1.4 m each second. Draw a graph showing "height above ground level" on the vertical axis, and "time" on the horizontal axis, for times of 1 s, 2 s, 3 s, . . ., 10 s. Draw a straight line through the points of your graph, and use it to determine
    (*a*) the height of the elevator after 5.5 s and 6.7 s;
    (*b*) the time at which the elevator was 25 m above ground level.

19. (*a*) Find a set of ordered pairs (x, y) for the formula $y = 3x - 2$ for $x = -2, -1, 0, 1, 2, 3, 4$.
    (*b*) Graph the set of ordered pairs from part (*a*) and join them with a straight line.

10. 1138.5 cm^2 14. 3850 cm^3
11. 1.54 m^2 15. 1437 kl
12. 16 m^2 16. 30.8 kl
13. 2475 cm^2 17. 11.1 m^3
18(a) 7.7 m and 9.4 m
(b) 17.9 s

20. Two cars slow to a stop from 50 km/h.
   (*a*) How long does it take each car to stop?
   (*b*) Which car slows at the faster rate?
   (*c*) At what time is car A travelling at 25 km/h?
   (*d*) What is the speed of car B after 13 s?

21. The graph shows the speeds of 2 cars at various times.
   (*a*) At what time do the cars have the same speed?
   (*b*) For how long does car A travel at a fixed speed?
   (*c*) What is the total time during which car A is slowing down?
   (*d*) How fast is car B travelling 2 s after car A stops?

22. Find ordered pairs and graph each of the following equations.
   (*a*) $y = 2x - 4$ (*b*) $5x + y = 7$ (*c*) $y = 3x^2$

Use ruler and compasses only for these constructions.

23. Draw the right bisector of line segment PQ, and check by measurement.

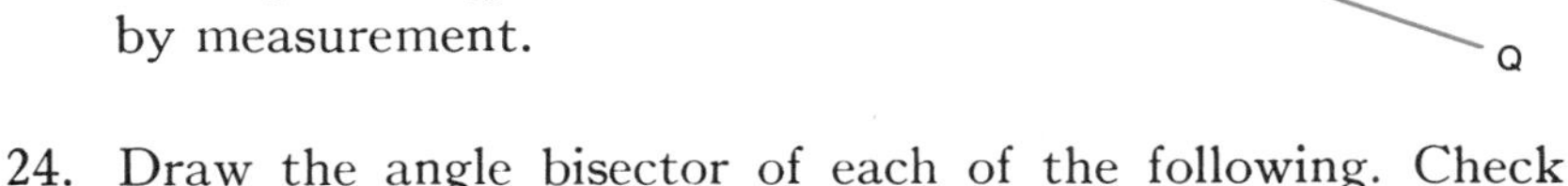

24. Draw the angle bisector of each of the following. Check using a protractor.

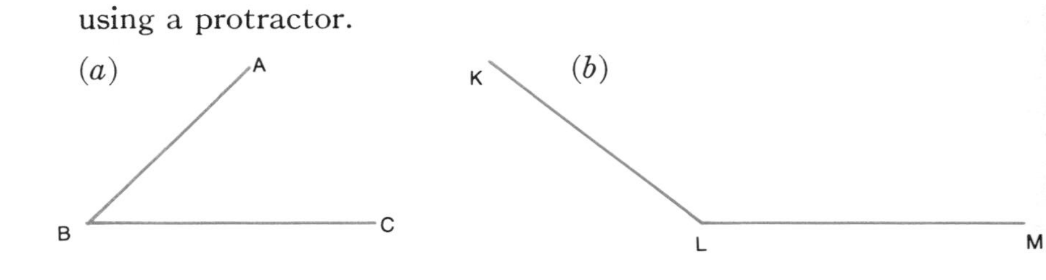

25. Draw a line segment PQ that is at right angles to the given line segment.

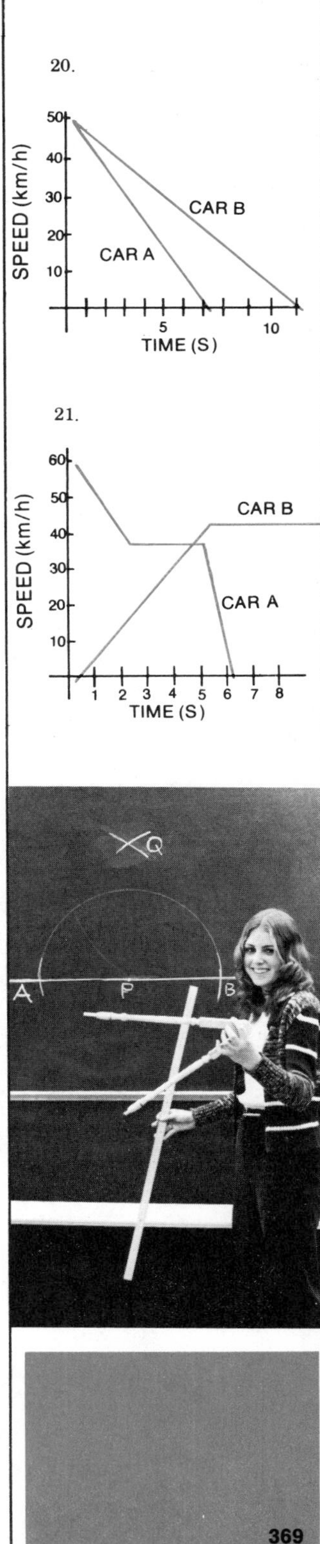

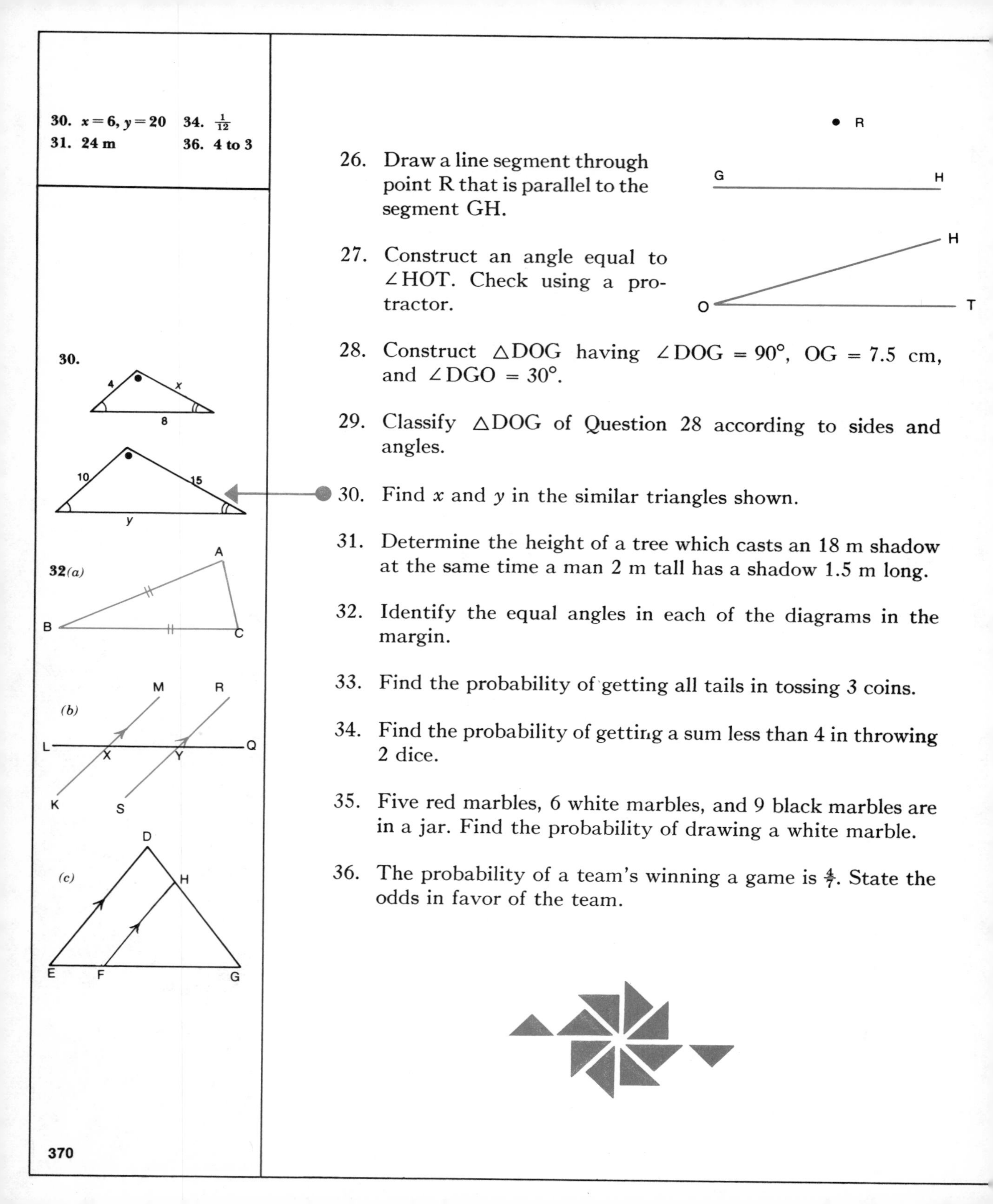

30. $x = 6, y = 20$
31. 24 m
34. $\frac{1}{12}$
36. 4 to 3

26. Draw a line segment through point R that is parallel to the segment GH.

27. Construct an angle equal to $\angle HOT$. Check using a protractor.

28. Construct $\triangle DOG$ having $\angle DOG = 90°$, $OG = 7.5$ cm, and $\angle DGO = 30°$.

29. Classify $\triangle DOG$ of Question 28 according to sides and angles.

30. Find x and y in the similar triangles shown.

31. Determine the height of a tree which casts an 18 m shadow at the same time a man 2 m tall has a shadow 1.5 m long.

32. Identify the equal angles in each of the diagrams in the margin.

33. Find the probability of getting all tails in tossing 3 coins.

34. Find the probability of getting a sum less than 4 in throwing 2 dice.

35. Five red marbles, 6 white marbles, and 9 black marbles are in a jar. Find the probability of drawing a white marble.

36. The probability of a team's winning a game is $\frac{4}{7}$. State the odds in favor of the team.

Square Root Table

n	$\sqrt{n}$	n	$\sqrt{n}$	n	$\sqrt{n}$	n	$\sqrt{n}$	n	$\sqrt{n}$
1	1.00	51	7.14	101	10.05	151	12.29	201	14.18
2	1.41	52	7.21	102	10.10	152	12.33	202	14.21
3	1.73	53	7.28	103	10.15	153	12.37	203	14.25
4	2.00	54	7.35	104	10.20	154	12.41	204	14.28
5	2.24	55	7.42	105	10.25	155	12.45	205	14.32
6	2.45	56	7.48	106	10.30	156	12.49	206	14.35
7	2.65	57	7.55	107	10.34	157	12.53	207	14.39
8	2.83	58	7.62	108	10.39	158	12.57	208	14.42
9	3.00	59	7.68	109	10.44	159	12.61	209	14.46
10	3.16	60	7.75	110	10.49	160	12.65	210	14.49
11	3.32	61	7.81	111	10.54	161	12.69	211	14.53
12	3.46	62	7.87	112	10.58	162	12.73	212	14.56
13	3.61	63	7.94	113	10.63	163	12.77	213	14.59
14	3.74	64	8.00	114	10.68	164	12.81	214	14.63
15	3.87	65	8.06	115	10.72	165	12.85	215	14.66
16	4.00	66	8.12	116	10.77	166	12.88	216	14.70
17	4.12	67	8.19	117	10.82	167	12.92	217	14.73
18	4.24	68	8.25	118	10.86	168	12.96	218	14.76
19	4.36	69	8.31	119	10.91	169	13.00	219	14.80
20	4.47	70	8.37	120	10.95	170	13.04	220	14.83
21	4.58	71	8.43	121	11.00	171	13.08	221	14.87
22	4.69	72	8.49	122	11.05	172	13.11	222	14.90
23	4.80	73	8.54	123	11.09	173	13.15	223	14.93
24	4.90	74	8.60	124	11.14	174	13.19	224	14.97
25	5.00	75	8.66	125	11.18	175	13.23	225	15.00
26	5.10	76	8.72	126	11.22	176	13.27	226	15.03
27	5.20	77	8.77	127	11.27	177	13.30	227	15.07
28	5.29	78	8.83	128	11.31	178	13.34	228	15.10
29	5.39	79	8.89	129	11.36	179	13.38	229	15.13
30	5.48	80	8.94	130	11.40	180	13.42	230	15.17
31	5.57	81	9.00	131	11.45	181	13.45	231	15.20
32	5.66	82	9.06	132	11.49	182	13.49	232	15.23
33	5.74	83	9.11	133	11.53	183	13.53	233	15.26
34	5.83	84	9.17	134	11.58	184	13.56	234	15.30
35	5.92	85	9.22	135	11.62	185	13.60	235	15.33
36	6.00	86	9.27	136	11.66	186	13.64	236	15.36
37	6.08	87	9.33	137	11.70	187	13.67	237	15.39
38	6.16	88	9.38	138	11.75	188	13.71	238	15.43
39	6.24	89	9.43	139	11.79	189	13.75	239	15.46
40	6.32	90	9.49	140	11.83	190	13.78	240	15.49
41	6.40	91	9.54	141	11.87	191	13.82	241	15.52
42	6.48	92	9.59	142	11.92	192	13.86	242	15.56
43	6.56	93	9.64	143	11.96	193	13.89	243	15.59
44	6.63	94	9.70	144	12.00	194	13.93	244	15.62
45	6.71	95	9.75	145	12.04	195	13.96	245	15.65
46	6.78	96	9.80	146	12.08	196	14.00	246	15.68
47	6.86	97	9.85	147	12.12	197	14.04	247	15.72
48	6.93	98	9.90	148	12.17	198	14.07	248	15.75
49	7.00	99	9.95	149	12.21	199	14.11	249	15.78
50	7.07	100	10.00	150	12.25	200	14.14	250	15.81

Square Root Table

n	$\sqrt{n}$	n	$\sqrt{n}$	n	$\sqrt{n}$	n	$\sqrt{n}$	n	$\sqrt{n}$
251	15.84	301	17.35	351	18.73	401	20.02	451	21.24
252	15.87	302	17.38	352	18.76	402	20.05	452	21.26
253	15.91	303	17.41	353	18.79	403	20.07	453	21.28
254	15.94	304	17.44	354	18.81	404	20.10	454	21.31
255	15.97	305	17.46	355	18.84	405	20.12	455	21.33
256	16.00	306	17.49	356	18.87	406	20.15	456	21.35
257	16.03	307	17.52	357	18.89	407	20.17	457	21.38
258	16.06	308	17.55	358	18.92	408	20.20	458	21.40
259	16.09	309	17.58	359	18.95	409	20.22	459	21.42
260	16.12	310	17.61	360	18.97	410	20.25	460	21.45
261	16.16	311	17.64	361	19.00	411	20.27	461	21.47
262	16.19	312	17.66	362	19.03	412	20.30	462	21.49
263	16.22	313	17.69	363	19.05	413	20.32	463	21.52
264	16.25	314	17.72	364	19.08	414	20.35	464	21.54
265	16.28	315	17.75	365	19.10	415	20.37	465	21.56
266	16.31	316	17.78	366	19.13	416	20.40	466	21.59
267	16.34	317	17.80	367	19.16	417	20.42	467	21.61
268	16.37	318	17.83	368	19.18	418	20.45	468	21.63
269	16.40	319	17.86	369	19.21	419	20.47	469	21.66
270	16.43	320	17.89	370	19.24	420	20.49	470	21.68
271	16.46	321	17.92	371	19.26	421	20.52	471	21.70
272	16.49	322	17.94	372	19.29	422	20.54	472	21.73
273	16.52	323	17.97	373	19.31	423	20.57	473	21.75
274	16.55	324	18.00	374	19.34	424	20.59	474	21.77
275	16.58	325	18.03	375	19.36	425	20.62	475	21.79
276	16.61	326	18.06	376	19.39	426	20.64	476	21.82
277	16.64	327	18.08	377	19.42	427	20.66	477	21.84
278	16.67	328	18.11	378	19.44	428	20.69	478	21.86
279	16.70	329	18.14	379	19.47	429	20.71	479	21.89
280	16.73	330	18.17	380	19.49	430	20.74	480	21.91
281	16.76	331	18.19	381	19.52	431	20.76	481	21.93
282	16.79	332	18.22	382	19.54	432	20.78	482	21.95
283	16.82	333	18.25	383	19.57	433	20.81	483	21.98
284	16.85	334	18.28	384	19.60	434	20.83	484	22.00
285	16.88	335	18.30	385	19.62	435	20.86	485	22.02
286	16.91	336	18.33	386	19.65	436	20.88	486	22.05
287	16.94	337	18.36	387	19.67	437	20.90	487	22.07
288	16.97	338	18.38	388	19.70	438	20.93	488	22.09
289	17.00	339	18.41	389	19.72	439	20.95	489	22.11
290	17.03	340	18.44	390	19.75	440	20.98	490	22.14
291	17.06	341	18.47	391	19.77	441	21.00	491	22.16
292	17.09	342	18.49	392	19.80	442	21.02	492	22.18
293	17.12	343	18.52	393	19.82	443	21.05	493	22.20
294	17.15	344	18.55	394	19.85	444	21.07	494	22.23
295	17.18	345	18.57	395	19.87	445	21.10	495	22.25
296	17.20	346	18.60	396	19.90	446	21.12	496	22.27
297	17.23	347	18.63	397	19.92	447	21.14	497	22.29
298	17.26	348	18.65	398	19.95	448	21.17	498	22.32
299	17.29	349	18.68	399	19.97	449	21.19	499	22.34
300	17.32	350	18.71	400	20.00	450	21.21	500	22.36

Index

10 cm

The water that fills a 1 ℓ box has a mass of 1 kg.

10 cm

1 litre

10 cm × 10 cm × 10 cm = 1000 cm^3

or

1000 ml (millilitres)

1 cubic centimetre = 1 cm^3 or 1 ml

1 ml of water has a mass of 1 g

10 cm

EVERYDAY METRIC UNITS

Length		*Area*		*Volume*		*Mass*	
millimetre	mm	square centimetre	cm^2	cubic centimetre	cm^3 (or ml)	gram	g
centimetre	cm	square metre	m^2	litre (1000 cm^3)	litre or ℓ	kilogram	kg
metre	m	hectare (10 000 m^2)	ha	kilolitre	kl	tonne	t
kilometre	km	square kilometre	km^2				